New Edition

MATHEMATICS

Structure and Method

Course 2

Mary P. Dolciani
Robert H. Sorgenfrey
John A. Graham

Editorial Advisers

Richard G. Brown
Robert B. Kane

HOUGHTON MIFFLIN COMPANY · Boston
Atlanta Dallas Geneva, Ill. Hopewell, N.J. Palo Alto Toronto

AUTHORS

Mary P. Dolciani Professor of Mathematical Sciences, Hunter College of the City University of New York

Robert H. Sorgenfrey Professor of Mathematics, University of California, Los Angeles

John A. Graham Mathematics Teacher, Buckingham Browne and Nichols School, Cambridge, Massachusetts

Editorial Advisers

Richard G. Brown Mathematics Teacher, The Phillips Exeter Academy, Exeter, New Hampshire

Robert B. Kane Director of Teacher Education and Head of the Department of Education, Purdue University

Teacher Consultants

Jimmie B. Jenkins Mathematics and Science Teacher, Conyers Middle School, Conyers, Georgia

Steven P. Meiring State Mathematics Consultant, Ohio Department of Education

Sharon A. Sandhu Mathematics Teacher and Department Chairman, El Dorado Middle Intermediate School, Concord, California

Acknowledgment
The authors wish to thank Joan MacDonald, Mathematics Teacher and Department Chairman, Milton Academy, Milton, Massachusetts, for her valuable contribution to this edition.

Printed in U.S.A.

ISBN: 0-395-33267-2

ABCDEFGHIJ-VH-93210/8987654

Contents

Reading Mathematics

This page shows many of the metric measures and symbols that are used in this book. Use this page as a reference when you read the book.

Symbols

Symbol	Meaning	Page
$\cdot$	times	3
$\dots$	and so on	9
$<$	is less than	12
$>$	is greater than	12
$\approx$	is approximately equal to	48
$^{-}4$	negative 4	72
$\|n\|$	absolute value of *n*	72
$-n$	opposite of *n*	84
$0.6\overline{81}$	81 repeats without end	131
$\overleftrightarrow{PQ}$	line *PQ*	182
$\overline{FG}$	segment *FG*	182
$\overrightarrow{BA}$	ray *BA*	182
FG	length of $\overline{FG}$	182
π	pi	188
$\angle A$	angle *A*	191
$m\angle A$	measure of angle *A*	191
$60°$	sixty degrees	191
$\cong$	is congruent to	192
⅂	is a right angle	195
$\perp$	is perpendicular to	195
$\parallel$	is parallel to	200
$\triangle ABC$	triangle *ABC*	204
1:5	1 to 5	230
(6, 8)	ordered pair 6, 8	272
$\sqrt{n}$	positive square root of *n*	356
$\sim$	is similar to	368
4!	4 factorial	396
$P(A)$	probability of *A*	404

Metric Measures

Prefixes

Prefix	kilo	centi	milli
Factor	1000	0.01	0.001
Symbol	k	c	m

Base Units

Length: **meter** (m)
Mass: **kilogram** (kg)
Capacity: **liter** (L)

Temperature **Degree Celsius** (° C)

Length	1 mm = 0.001 m 1 m = 1000 mm	1 cm = 0.01 m 1 m = 100 cm	1 km = 1000 m 1 cm = 10 mm
Mass	1 kg = 1000 g	1 mg = 0.001 g	1 g = 0.001 kg
Capacity	1 mL = 0.001 L	1 L = 1000 mL	1 L = 1000 cm^3
Time	60 s = 1 min	60 min = 1 h	3600 s = 1 h

Examples of compound units: kilometers per hour: km/h; square centimeters: cm^2; cubic meters: m^3

Diagnostic Test of Decimal Skills

This test reviews the skills of addition, subtraction, multiplication, and division necessary to begin Chapter 1. More practice of these skills can be found on pages 470–473.

Addition

Add.

1. 5.246 + 6.38	**2.** 16.439 + 28.32	**3.** 9.85 + 3.7647	**4.** 34.62 + 17.9903	**5.** 218.951 + 0.006
6. 35.046 + 17.923	**7.** 3.84 2.07 + 9.39	**8.** 72.8 6.349 + 0.76	**9.** 67.4 2.0051 6.28 + 7.3	**10.** 0.16 54.3 119.057 + 2.0918

11. 18.7 + 5.394

12. 0.06 + 19.803

13. 254.81 + 93

14. 126 + 9.4078

15. 11.882 + 6.49 + 0.083

16. 583.117 + 72.5 + 3.76824

17. 26.5 + 180.1 + 0.39 + 5.18

18. 0.05 + 11.026 + 9.38 + 4.7829

19. 35.402 + 17.6 + 5.28 + 0.314

20. 3.4289 + 5.005 + 3.1 + 8.57

Subtraction

Subtract.

1. 6.75 − 3.81	**2.** 14.90 − 7.88	**3.** 675.01 − 25.312	**4.** 31.801 − 6.03	**5.** 22.008 − 5.911
6. 388.6 − 97.86	**7.** 2008.11 − 487.8	**8.** 705.56 − 314.6	**9.** 0.615 − 0.038	**10.** 0.986 − 0.097

11. 12.6 − 3.9

12. 9.5 − 4.8

13. 567 − 199.1

14. 379 − 65.7

15. 46.71 − 22.52

16. 853.7 − 139.8

17. 0.551 − 0.493

18. 0.877 − 0.098

19. 0.039 − 0.0271

20. 0.8743 − 0.33591

21. 4.00682 − 2.01985

22. 5.04876 − 2.29

Multiplication

Multiply.

1. $\begin{array}{r} 473 \\ \times\ 0.3 \\ \hline \end{array}$	**2.** $\begin{array}{r} 846 \\ \times\ 2.5 \\ \hline \end{array}$	**3.** $\begin{array}{r} 127.3 \\ \times\ 6.6 \\ \hline \end{array}$	**4.** $\begin{array}{r} 885.1 \\ \times\ 4.5 \\ \hline \end{array}$
5. $\begin{array}{r} 0.061 \\ \times\ 0.02 \\ \hline \end{array}$	**6.** $\begin{array}{r} 3.08 \\ \times\ 0.007 \\ \hline \end{array}$	**7.** $\begin{array}{r} 0.681 \\ \times\ 14.7 \\ \hline \end{array}$	**8.** $\begin{array}{r} 0.263 \\ \times\ 8.08 \\ \hline \end{array}$
9. $\begin{array}{r} 288.86 \\ \times\ 31.3 \\ \hline \end{array}$	**10.** $\begin{array}{r} 810.95 \\ \times\ 1.35 \\ \hline \end{array}$	**11.** $\begin{array}{r} 67.05 \\ \times\ 2.39 \\ \hline \end{array}$	**12.** $\begin{array}{r} 99.7 \\ \times\ 10.06 \\ \hline \end{array}$

13. 621.82×4.3	**14.** 63.71×2.5	**15.** 18.7×16
16. 46×86.91	**17.** 0.08×58.6	**18.** 0.75×0.69
19. 27.9×33.3	**20.** 10.29×4.79	**21.** 17.003×0.301
22. 0.473×86.11	**23.** 6.0810×148.3	**24.** 5.62×83.109

Division

Divide.

1. $5\overline{)37.60}$	**2.** $81\overline{)108.54}$	**3.** $5.4\overline{)3348}$	**4.** $0.8\overline{)168}$
5. $4.1\overline{)37.761}$	**6.** $1.6\overline{)99.68}$	**7.** $2.9\overline{)279.27}$	**8.** $8.3\overline{)5.6025}$
9. $38.4\overline{)0.192}$	**10.** $36.1\overline{)0.722}$	**11.** $2.86\overline{)247.39}$	**12.** $1.13\overline{)1006.83}$

Divide. Round to the nearest tenth.

13. $798.06 \div 98.7$	**14.** $486.09 \div 17.3$	**15.** $0.851 \div 0.33$
16. $0.268 \div 0.59$	**17.** $0.909 \div 1.35$	**18.** $0.284 \div 7.31$
19. $486 \div 0.391$	**20.** $276 \div 0.106$	**21.** $81.69 \div 73.12$
22. $5.005 \div 0.095$	**23.** $37.076 \div 55.619$	**24.** $43.761 \div 27.515$

1

Introduction to Algebra

All of the many pieces of information handled by computers are stored and processed by means of tiny microchips, such as the one shown at the right. Each microchip is about 2 mm square and is made up of thin layers of silicon crystals. Each layer is treated chemically and etched photographically with different patterns containing tens of thousands of microscopic switches. Information on the microchip is represented by a code made up of a series of "on" or "off" switches.

Although we use words and numbers to communicate with a computer, the machine does not work directly with those words and numbers. A program within the computer automatically translates the information that we use into the special code that the machine understands. In a similar way, when we work with algebra, we translate our words and ideas into the language of mathematics. In this chapter, you will learn many of the symbols that we use to express mathematical ideas.

Career Note

Consider how intricate the design of a single microchip is. Electrical engineers are involved in designing and testing new electrical equipment such as the microchip. Electrical engineers must therefore be qualified in both mathematics and science. Most, in fact, specialize in a major field such as communications, industrial equipment, or computers.

1-1 Mathematical Expressions

A **numerical expression** is simply a name for a number. For example,

$4 + 6$ is a numerical expression for the number 10.

Since $4 + 6$ and 10 name the same number, we can use the equals sign, $=$, and write

$$4 + 6 = 10.$$

We **simplify the numerical expression** $4 + 6$ when we replace it with its simplest name, 10.

EXAMPLE 1 Simplify each numerical expression.

a. 400×4 **b.** $37 - 19$ **c.** $5.1 \div 3$

Solution **a.** $400 \times 4 = 1600$ **b.** $37 - 19 = 18$ **c.** $5.1 \div 3 = 1.7$

If a computer can do 100 million arithmetic computations in one second, the table below shows how many million computations the computer can do in two, three, and four seconds.

Number of Seconds	Millions of Computations
1	100×1
2	100×2
3	100×3
4	100×4

Each of the numerical expressions 100×1, 100×2, 100×3, and 100×4 fits the pattern

$$100 \times n$$

where n stands for 1, 2, 3, or 4. A letter, such as n, that is used to represent one or more numbers is called a **variable.** The numbers are called the **values of the variable.**

An expression, such as $100 \times n$, that contains a variable is called a **variable expression.** When we write a product that contains a variable, we usually omit the multiplication sign.

$100 \times n$ may be written $100n$.

$x \times y$ may be written xy.

In a numerical expression for a product, such as 100×4, we must use a multiplication sign to avoid confusion.

A raised dot is also a multiplication sign.

100×4 may be written $100 \cdot 4$.

When we replace each variable in a variable expression by one of its values and simplify the resulting numerical expression, we say that we are **evaluating the expression** or **finding the value of the expression.**

When the value of n is 4, the value of $100n$ is 400.

EXAMPLE 2 Evaluate each expression when $a = 6$ and $b = 2$.

a. $9 + a$ **b.** $a \div b$ **c.** $3ab$

Solution

a. Substitute 6 for a. $9 + a = 9 + 6 = 15$

b. Substitute 6 for a and 2 for b. $a \div b = 6 \div 2 = 3$

c. Substitute 6 for a and 2 for b. $3ab = 3 \times 6 \times 2 = 36$

In the expression $9 + a$, 9 and a are called the **terms** of the expression because they are the parts that are separated by the +. In an expression such as $3ab$, the number 3 is called the **numerical coefficient** of ab.

Reading Mathematics: ***Vocabulary***

Look back at this first lesson. Notice the words in heavier type throughout the text. They are important new words and ideas, such as the following:

numerical expression	simplify a numerical expression
variable	value of a variable
variable expression	evaluate a variable expression
terms	numerical coefficient

When you see a word in heavier type, look near it for an explanation or example to help you understand the new word. For an unusual new word, look up the definition in the glossary to help you understand and remember it.

Class Exercises

Simplify the numerical expression.

1. $24 + 18 + 32$ **2.** $125 \div 5$ **3.** $3.6 + 5.1$ **4.** 0.25×10

Evaluate the variable expression when $x = 4$.

5. $x + 7$ **6.** $5x$ **7.** $28 \div x$ **8.** $13 - x$

9. What is another way to write $17 \times x$?

10. In the variable expression $12a$, the numerical coefficient is __?__ and the variable is __?__.

Written Exercises

Simplify the numerical expression.

A **1.** $16 \cdot 3$ **2.** $37 + 12$ **3.** $114 - 9$ **4.** $918 \div 6$

5. $1.65 + 12.5$ **6.** $1.05 + 9.7$ **7.** 0.5×9 **8.** $2.53 \div 11$

Evaluate the expression when $y = 2$.

9. $y + 23$ **10.** $6y$ **11.** $8 \div y$ **12.** $4 + y + 7$

Evaluate the expression when $q = 3$.

13. $36 \div q$ **14.** $q \div 3$ **15.** $q \times 9$ **16.** $q - q$

Evaluate the expression when $a = 5$.

17. $a - 3$ **18.** $a \times a$ **19.** $42 + a$ **20.** $a + a$

Evaluate the expression when $m = 8$.

21. $6 + 9 + 3 + m$ **22.** $m \times 3$ **23.** $m \times m \times m$ **24.** $m \div m$

Evaluate the expression when $x = 8$ and $y = 1$.

B **25.** $x + y$ **26.** $x - y - 2$ **27.** $3x$ **28.** $x \div y$

Evaluate the expression when $c = 7.5$ and $d = 3$.

29. $c \div d$ **30.** $c + d + 20$ **31.** $c \times 15$ **32.** $4cd$

Evaluate the expression when $s = 12.3$ and $t = 6.15$.

33. $9st$ **34.** $s \div t$ **35.** $s - t - 3$ **36.** $73.8 \div s$

C **37.** Find the value of a for which the expressions $2a$ and $2 + a$ have the same value.

38. Find a value of x for which $x \div 7$ and $7 \div x$ are equal.

Review Exercises

Perform the indicated operation.

1. $43.8 + 8.07$ **2.** 51×3.4 **3.** $80.47 - 34.54$ **4.** $6.29 + 0.124$

5. $11.61 \div 43$ **6.** 6.328×0.729 **7.** $32.004 \div 5.08$ **8.** $2403 - 976.8$

1-2 Order of Operations

The expression

$$2 + (6 \times 3)$$

involves both addition and multiplication. The parentheses indicate that the multiplication is to be done first.

$$2 + (6 \times 3) = 2 + 18 = 20$$

For the expression

$$(2 + 6) \times 3$$

the parentheses indicate that the addition is to be done first.

$$(2 + 6) \times 3 = 8 \times 3 = 24$$

Parentheses used to indicate the order of the arithmetic operations are called **grouping symbols.** Operations within grouping symbols are to be done first.

We usually write a product such as $4 \times (3 + 5)$ without the multiplication symbol as $4(3 + 5)$. We may also use parentheses in any one of the following ways to indicate a product such as 4×8:

$$4(8) \qquad \text{or} \qquad (4)8 \qquad \text{or} \qquad (4)(8).$$

A fraction bar is both a division symbol and a grouping symbol. Recall that $18 \div 2$ may be written as $\frac{18}{2}$. When operation symbols appear above or below the fraction bar, those operations are to be done before the division. For example, to simplify

$$\frac{6 + 15}{3},$$

we add first:

$$\frac{6 + 15}{3} = \frac{21}{3} = 7.$$

EXAMPLE 1 Evaluate each expression when $n = 8$.

a. $4(n - 3)$ **b.** $\dfrac{45 - 15}{n + 7}$

Solution Substitute 8 for n in each expression.

a. $4(n - 3) = 4(8 - 3) = 4(5) = 20$

b. $\dfrac{45 - 15}{n + 7} = \dfrac{45 - 15}{8 + 7} = \dfrac{30}{15} = 2$

If there are no grouping symbols in an expression, we agree to perform the operations in the following order.

Rule for Order of Operations

When there are no grouping symbols:

1. Perform all multiplications and divisions in order from left to right.
2. Perform all additions and subtractions in order from left to right.

EXAMPLE 2 Simplify $392 + 637 \div 49$.

Solution

$$392 + \underbrace{637 \div 49}$$
$$\underbrace{392 + \quad 13}$$
$$405$$

When a product of two numbers or of a number and a variable is written without a multiplication symbol, as in 5(7) or $4n$, we perform the multiplication before the other operations.

EXAMPLE 3 Evaluate the expression when $x = 6$.

a. $27 \div 2x$ **b.** $\frac{3x - 2}{4}$

Solution Substitute 6 for x in each expression.

a. $27 \div 2x = 27 \div 2(6) = 27 \div 12 = 2.25$

b. $\frac{3x - 2}{4} = \frac{3(6) - 2}{4} = \frac{18 - 2}{4} = \frac{16}{4} = 4$

Class Exercises

Tell in which order the operations should be performed to simplify the expression.

1. $6 + 14 \times 3$ **2.** $(6 + 14)3$ **3.** $18 - 12 \div 3 + 1$

4. $18 - 12 \div (3 + 1)$ **5.** $23 - 9 \div 5 + 2$ **6.** $(9 + 16) \div (4 + 1)$

Evaluate the expression when $m = 4$.

7. $(m + 6)2$ **8.** $5m + 8$ **9.** $3(m - 1)$

10. $8 \div m + 7$ **11.** $m(2 + m)$ **12.** $\frac{3m}{18 - 6}$

Written Exercises

Simplify the expression.

A **1.** $35 - 14 \div 2 + 64$ **2.** $54 \div 6 + 18 \times 2$ **3.** $44 + 17 - 5 \times 2$

4. $(45 - 19)(8 + 7)$ **5.** $(12 + 18) \div (19 - 4)$ **6.** $\frac{9 + (4 \times 3)}{7}$

Evaluate the expression when $n = 7$.

7. $(14 + n)6$ **8.** $36 \div (n - 3)$ **9.** $(n + 28) \div 5$

10. $(27 - n)3$ **11.** $12(n - 4)$ **12.** $\frac{94 - 38}{n}$

Evaluate the expression when $t = 10$.

13. $5t \div (14 - 9)$ **14.** $\frac{25 - t}{10 - 5}$ **15.** $(t + 6 - 9)t$

16. $2(t + 5) - t$ **17.** $(t - 4)(t - 4)$ **18.** $50 \div (t + 15) + t$

Evaluate the expression when $s = 16$.

19. $7(s + 12)$ **20.** $5(s - 4)$ **21.** $(s + 32) \div s$

22. $(3s - 6) \div 7$ **23.** $18(6s - 12)$ **24.** $4s \div (s - 8)$

Evaluate the expression when $b = 6$ and $c = 7$.

B **25.** $(b + c)c$ **26.** $3c \div (b - 4)$ **27.** $2bc \div (c - b)$

Evaluate the expression when $m = 4$ and $n = 9$.

28. $5n \div (m + 5)$ **29.** $(n + m) \div (35 - n)$ **30.** $m(n - m) \div 8$

Evaluate the expression when $a = 3.6$ and $b = 8.2$.

31. $ab \div 2a$ **32.** $(b - a)(3a + 6)$ **33.** $7ab(3b + a)$

Evaluate the expression when $e = 5$, $f = 8$, and $g = 13$.

34. $(e + f)(g + e)$ **35.** $f \div (g - f) + g$ **36.** $f(e + g) - e$

Copy the expression as shown. Add grouping symbols so that the value of the expression is 24 when $x = 3$, $y = 7$, and $z = 21$.

C **37.** $2x \times y - 4 + 2x$ **38.** $y + z \div 4 \times x + x$ **39.** $x \times y + z \div 3 + 1 - z$

Review Exercises

Simplify in your head if you can. Write down the answer.

1. 2.4×10 **2.** 3.1×5 **3.** 2.2×6 **4.** 5.4×20 **5.** 6.8×300

6. $8.4 \div 10$ **7.** $6.5 \div 5$ **8.** $14.21 \div 7$ **9.** $18.9 \div 30$ **10.** $25.2 \div 400$

Calculator Key-In

To use your calculator to simplify an expression with more than one operation, you must keep in mind the order in which you want the operations to be performed. Try to simplify $2(6 + 4)$ by entering the following on your calculator exactly as it is shown.

[2] [×] [6] [+] [4] [=]

Although the correct answer is 20, your calculator will perform the operations in the order in which you entered them and will display 16 for the answer.

To obtain the correct answer, you must enter the expressions in the order in which you want them to be performed. Enter the following exactly as it is shown.

[6] [+] [4] [=] [×] [2] [=]

Now your calculator should display the correct answer, 20. By entering = after entering the expression in parentheses, you complete the operation inside the parentheses before doing the next operation. Some calculators will complete the operation for you even if you do not enter = between operations. Check to see if your calculator will.

Use your calculator to simplify the expression.

1. $12(15 + 9)$ **2.** $57 \div (36 - 17)$ **3.** $(437 + 322) \div 46$

4. $(108 + 63) \div (9 - 6)$ **5.** $(55 + 8) \times (2 + 94)$ **6.** $(56 - 32) \div (4 + 16) \times 5$

1-3 Equations

A **number sentence** indicates a relationship between two mathematical expressions. A sentence, such as the one below, that indicates that two expressions name the same number is called an **equation.**

$$4 \times 3 = 12$$

The expressions to the left and to the right of the equals sign are called the **sides** of the equation. In the example above, 4×3 is the left side of the equation, and 12 is the right side of the equation.

A number sentence may be *true* or *false*. For example, $3 + 9 = 12$ is a true equation, but $3 + 9 = 13$ is a false equation.

A number sentence that contains one or more variables is called an **open number sentence,** or simply an **open sentence.** Frequently a set of intended values, called the **replacement set,** for a variable is specified. An open sentence may be true or false when each variable is replaced by one of the values in its replacement set.

When a value of the variable makes an open sentence a true statement, we say that the value is a **solution** of, or **satisfies,** the sentence. We can **solve** an open sentence in one variable by finding all the solutions of the sentence. An open sentence may have one solution, several solutions, or no solutions.

EXAMPLE 1 The replacement set for x is $\{5, 6, 7\}$. Find all solutions of

$$x + 6 = 13.$$

Solution Substitute each value in the replacement set for the variable x.

$5 + 6 = 13$	$6 + 6 = 13$	$7 + 6 = 13$
$11 = 13$	$12 = 13$	$13 = 13$
false	false	true

The solution of the equation is 7.

EXAMPLE 2 The replacement set for q is the set of whole numbers. Find all solutions of

$$2q = 9.$$

Solution The replacement set for q is $\{0, 1, 2, 3, \ldots\}$, so $2q$ must be one of the numbers $2 \times 0, 2 \times 1, 2 \times 2, 2 \times 3, \ldots$, or $0, 2, 4, 6, \ldots$. Because 9 is not one of these numbers, the equation $2q = 9$ has no solution in the given replacement set.

Notice that in the solution to Example 2, we used three dots, read *and so on,* to indicate that the list of numbers continues without end.

Class Exercises

Tell whether the equation is true or false for the given value of the variable.

1. $20 - y = 17;\ y = 3$

2. $n \times 7 = 42;\ n = 8$

3. $144 \div r = 46;\ r = 3$

4. $18x = 90;\ x = 5$

5. $156 + q = 179;\ q = 23$

6. $t + 5 = 20;\ t = 5$

State the solution or solutions of the equation for the given replacement set.

7. $x + 7 = 12;\ \{4, 5, 6\}$

8. $7y = 56;\ \{8, 9, 10\}$

9. $m + 6 = 72;\ \{50, 60, 70, 80\}$

10. $x \div 12 = 7;\ \{81, 82, 83, 84\}$

11. $r - 23 = 19;\ \{40, 41, 42, 43\}$

12. $b \times 8 = 64;\ \{2, 4, 6, 8\}$

Written Exercises

Tell whether the equation is true or false for the given value of the variable.

A **1.** $x + 9 = 35;\ x = 26$

2. $r - 15 = 40;\ r = 55$

3. $10m = 130;\ m = 10$

4. $9 + y = 100;\ y = 91$

5. $44 - q = 11;\ q = 55$

6. $t \times 7 = 84;\ t = 91$

7. $n \div 8 = 104;\ n = 832$

8. $26 \div d = 2;\ d = 52$

9. $p \times 15 = 255;\ p = 13$

10. $32a = 448;\ a = 14$

Find the solution or solutions of the equation for the given replacement set.

11. $r + 8 = 14;\ \{6, 7, 8\}$

12. $12a = 84;\ \{5, 6, 7\}$

13. $m - 26 = 59;\ \{80, 85, 90\}$

14. $g + 113 = 789;\ \{900, 901, 902\}$

15. $5d = 145;\ \{29, 30, 31\}$

16. $t - 53 = 67;\ \{13, 14, 15\}$

17. $b \times 14 = 112;\ \{6, 8, 10\}$

18. $c \div 12 = 228;\ \{17, 19, 21\}$

19. $98 - h = 21;\ \{75, 80, 85\}$

20. $38f = 912;\ \{24, 25, 26\}$

21. $e \div 19 = 152;\ \{8, 18, 28\}$

22. $46 + n = 99;\ \{50, 52, 54\}$

23. $q \div 23 = 66$; $\{1516, 1517, 1518\}$

24. $b \div 41 = 7$; $\{287, 288, 289\}$

25. $106 + a = 123$; $\{16, 17, 18\}$

26. $75 - r = 43$; $\{30, 31, 32\}$

B 27. $4n + 7 = 51$; $\{10, 11, 12\}$

28. $58 - 3a = 10$; $\{16, 17, 18\}$

29. $6x - 12 = 294$; $\{50, 51, 52\}$

30. $8r + 24 = 208$; $\{21, 22, 23\}$

31. $4(b - 5) = 28$; $\{10, 11, 12\}$

32. $17(k + 4) = 170$; $\{4, 6, 8\}$

33. $(t + 18) \div 3 = 9$; $\{9, 10, 11\}$

34. $56 \div (d + 8) = 4$; $\{5, 6, 7\}$

35. $5(2c - 4) = 0$; $\{0, 1, 2\}$

36. $(3f + 7) \div 4 = 4$; $\{3, 4, 5\}$

Find the solution or solutions of the equation. The replacement set is all even whole numbers.

37. $x + 1 = 10$

38. $5x = 35$

39. $4x = 16$

40. $x - 1 = 20$

Write an equation with the given solution if the replacement set is all whole numbers.

C 41. 10

42. 15

43. 100

44. Write an equation with no solution if the replacement set is all whole numbers.

Replace $\underline{\ ?\ }$ with $+$, $-$, $\times$, or $\div$ so the equation has the given solution.

45. $x \underline{\ ?\ } 17 \underline{\ ?\ } 13 = 24$; $\{20\}$

46. $n \underline{\ ?\ } 12 \underline{\ ?\ } 8 = 11$; $\{36\}$

47. $14 \underline{\ ?\ } r \underline{\ ?\ } 9 = 17$; $\{27\}$

48. $y \underline{\ ?\ } 12 \underline{\ ?\ } 6 = 10$; $\{8\}$

49. $d \underline{\ ?\ } (16 \underline{\ ?\ } 4) \underline{\ ?\ } 8 = 8$; $\{12\}$

50. $27 \underline{\ ?\ } (q \underline{\ ?\ } 9) \underline{\ ?\ } 15 = 45$; $\{18\}$

51. $21 \underline{\ ?\ } (19 \underline{\ ?\ } 8) \underline{\ ?\ } b = 12$; $\{3\}$

52. $11 \underline{\ ?\ } (16 \underline{\ ?\ } a) \underline{\ ?\ } 4 = 59$; $\{11\}$

Review Exercises

Simplify.

1. $14(11 + 31)$

2. $(36 - 5)8$

3. $(15 + 17) \div 4$

4. $4 \times 11 - 56 \div 8$

5. $116 \times 4 \div 16 + 31$

6. $100 - 39 \div 3 \times 4$

7. $(21 + 14 + 8)(22 - 18)$

8. $(136 - 82) \div (115 - 106)$

1-4 Inequalities

The sentences below are called **inequalities.**

$8 > 6$ — Eight *is greater than* six.

$6 < 8$ — Six *is less than* eight.

The sentences illustrate how we use the inequality symbols $>$ and $<$ to compare numbers or mathematical expressions. To avoid confusing these symbols, think of them as arrowheads whose small ends point toward the smaller numbers.

A good way to picture numbers is to use a number line. The **graph** of a number is the point paired with the number on the number line. The number paired with a point is called the **coordinate** of the point. The graphs of the whole numbers 0 through 8 are shown on the number line below. The coordinates of the points shown are 0, 1, 2, 3, 4, 5, 6, 7, and 8.

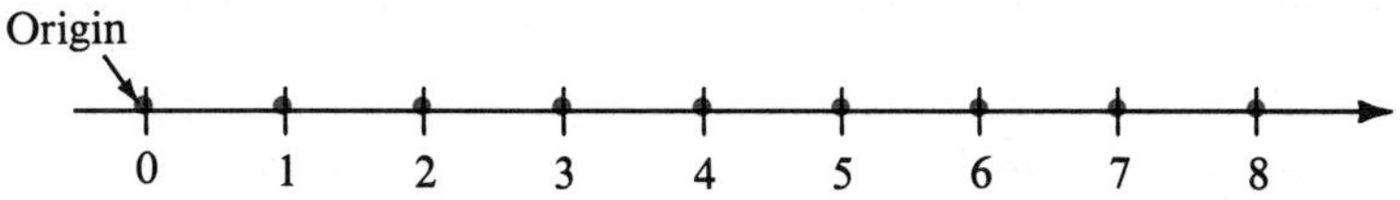

Starting with the graph of 0, which is called the **origin,** the graphs of the whole numbers are equally spaced. The greater a number is, the farther to the right its graph is.

We can indicate that one number is between two others by combining two inequalities. We know that $5 < 6$ and $6 < 8$; thus we can write

$$5 < 6 < 8 \qquad \text{or} \qquad 8 > 6 > 5.$$

Other inequality symbols that we use are shown below with their meanings.

$\neq$	*is not equal to*
$\geq$	*is greater than or equal to*
$\leq$	*is less than or equal to*

We can use inequality symbols to write open sentences. The open sentence $n \leq 6$ means $n < 6$ *or* $n = 6$.

Sometimes it is helpful to draw a graph to find the solutions of an open sentence with an inequality symbol. Example 1 shows how a graph is used to find the solutions of an inequality.

EXAMPLE 1 Find the solutions of $t \leq 7$. The replacement set is the set of all whole numbers.

Solution First, draw a number line showing the replacement set of whole numbers, $\{0, 1, 2, 3, 4, 5, 6, 7, 8, 9, 10, \ldots\}$. Then graph all the whole numbers that are less than 7 or equal to 7.

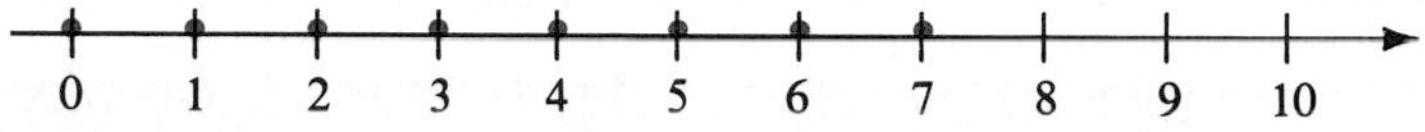

The graph shows that there are only eight numbers in the replacement set that are less than or equal to 7. The solutions are 0, 1, 2, 3, 4, 5, 6, and 7.

EXAMPLE 2 Find the solutions of $r + 8 \geq 15$. The replacement set for r is $\{5, 7, 9\}$.

Solution Substitute each value of the replacement set for r.

$5 + 8 \geq 15$	$7 + 8 \geq 15$	$9 + 8 \geq 15$
$13 \geq 15$	$15 \geq 15$	$17 \geq 15$
false	true	true

The solutions are 7 and 9.

Class Exercises

Read each sentence.

1. $5 < 7$ **2.** $n \geq 9$ **3.** $24 > 12 > 8$ **4.** $y \leq 15$

True or false?

5. $7 > 7$ **6.** $18 \leq 20$ **7.** $15 > 5$

8. $14 > 6 > 2$ **9.** $20 < 18 < 16$ **10.** $33 \geq 24 \geq 11$

The replacement set for x is $\{1, 2, 3, 4, 5\}$. Find the solutions.

11. $x < 9$ **12.** $7 - x > 3$ **13.** $2x \geq 4$

Written Exercises

For each exercise, draw a number line and graph the given numbers.

A **1.** 0, 2, 5, 7, 8 **2.** 0, 1, 3, 4, 6 **3.** 7, 11, 13, 19, 15

4. 12, 2, 7, 5, 14 **5.** 9, 14, 4, 0, 3 **6.** 6, 1, 12, 2, 17

Replace __?__ with =, >, or < to make a true statement.

7. 21 __?__ 14
8. 18 __?__ 35
9. 76 __?__ 67
10. 104 __?__ 104
11. 265 __?__ 256
12. 390 __?__ 309
13. $17 + 82$ __?__ 93
14. $47 - 31$ __?__ 61
15. $25 \div 5$ __?__ 10
16. 26×4 __?__ 52
17. 19×11 __?__ 208
18. $84 \div 3$ __?__ 24

Use > or < to write a true statement with the given numbers.

19. 18, 46, 32
20. 29, 5, 31
21. 103, 130, 310
22. 256, 652, 526
23. 986, 689, 698
24. 717, 177, 771

Graph the solutions of the inequality on the number line. The replacement set for b is {1, 2, 3, 4, 5, 6, 7, 8, 9, 10}.

25. $b < 11$
26. $b > 6$
27. $b \geq 5$
28. $b \leq 8$
29. $b + 4 < 9$
30. $20 - b > 16$
31. $2b \leq b$
32. $12 + b \geq 15$
33. $19 + b > 24$
34. $5b < 20$
35. $b - 1 \geq 9$
36. $18 - b \leq 13$

Find the solutions of the inequality. The replacement set for x is the set of whole numbers.

EXAMPLE **a.** $7 < x$ **b.** $10 > x > 5$

Solution **a.** The solutions are 8, 9, 10, and so on.
b. The solutions are 6, 7, 8, and 9.

37. $12 > x$
38. $x \geq 15$
39. $6 \leq x$
40. $x < 11$
41. $24 < x$
42. $35 \leq x$
43. $x \geq 66$
44. $x > 14$

B

45. $10 < x < 19$
46. $16 > x > 6$
47. $28 \geq x \geq 22$
48. $35 \leq x \leq 42$
49. $104 \leq x \leq 117$
50. $200 < x < 209$

Find the solutions of the inequality for the given replacement set.

51. $3x + 5 \leq 35$; {5, 10, 15}
52. $6r - 9 > 20$; {5, 6, 7}
53. $12y - 18 > 126$; {10, 11, 12}
54. $2t + 2 < 30$; {10, 20, 30}
55. $6(w + 5) \geq 165$; {21, 22, 23}
56. $3(14 - q) \leq 6$; {12, 13, 14}

57. $(m + 14) \div 6 < 5$; $\{4, 10, 16\}$

58. $24 \div (b + 2) \geq 4$; $\{2, 4, 6\}$

59. $(a - 7)4 < 32$; $\{14, 15, 16\}$

60. $(f - 8) \div 6 \geq 41$; $\{253, 254, 255\}$

61. $(n - 9) \div 5 > 11$; $\{60, 62, 64\}$

62. $5(x + 3) < 25$; $\{0, 1, 2\}$

Find the solutions of the inequality. The replacement set is {1, 2, 3, 4, 5, 6, 7, 8, 9, 10}.

EXAMPLE $4 < y + 1 < 9$.

Solution The inequality has two parts:

$$4 < y + 1 \qquad \text{and} \qquad y + 1 < 9$$

Find the solutions of each part.

4, 5, 6, 7, 8, 9, 10   1, 2, 3, 4, 5, 6, 7

Those numbers that occur in the solutions of *both* parts are the solutions of the inequality. The solutions of the inequality $4 < y + 1 < 9$ are 4, 5, 6, and 7.

C 63. $12 > y + 2 > 6$

64. $4 \leq y - 1 \leq 8$

65. $20 \geq 2y \geq 10$

66. $9 < 3y < 27$

67. $5 < 2y + 1 < 15$

68. $15 > 2y - 1 > 5$

Review Exercises

Simplify.

1. $16.5 + 5.4$
2. $21.9 - 5.4$
3. $8.07 - 1.9$
4. $6.17 + 1.9$
5. 18.3×5
6. $91.5 \div 18.3$
7. $21.6 \div 24$
8. 0.9×24
9. 0.07×0.092

Challenge

Each letter in each exercise stands for a digit from 0 through 9. Find the value of each letter to make the computation correct. (There may be more than one correct answer.)

1. $$\begin{array}{r} \text{HOW} \\ +\ \text{ARE} \\ \hline \text{YOU} \end{array}$$

2. $$\begin{array}{r} \text{TIME} \\ +\ \text{SURE} \\ \hline \text{FLIES} \end{array}$$

3. $$\begin{array}{r} \text{MATH} \\ -\ \quad \text{IS} \\ \hline \text{FUN} \end{array}$$

1-5 Inverse Operations

Addition and subtraction are related operations, as shown by the following facts.

$$5 + 6 = 11$$
$$5 = 11 - 6$$

We say that adding a number and subtracting the same number are **inverse operations.**

The relationship between addition and subtraction holds when we work with variables, as well. Thus we can write the following related equations.

$$n + 6 = 11$$
$$n = 11 - 6$$

We can use this relationship to solve equations that involve addition or subtraction. Throughout the rest of the chapter if no replacement set is given for an open sentence, assume that the solution can be any number.

EXAMPLE 1 Use the inverse operation to write a related equation and solve for the variable.

a. $x + 9 = 35$ **b.** $y - 12 = 18$

Solution

a. $x = 35 - 9$
$x = 26$
The solution is 26.

b. $y = 18 + 12$
$y = 30$
The solution is 30.

To check each solution, substitute the value of the variable in the original equation.

a. $x + 9 = 35$
$26 + 9 = 35$ ✓

b. $y - 12 = 18$
$30 - 12 = 18$ ✓

Multiplying by a number and dividing by the same number are inverse operations.

$$4 \times 6 = 24$$
$$6 = 24 \div 4$$

We can use this relationship to help solve equations that involve multiplication and division.

EXAMPLE 2 Use the inverse operation to write a related equation and solve for the variable.

a. $6r = 30$ **b.** $x \div 7 = 12$

Solution

a. Recall that $6r$ means $6 \times r$.

$$6 \times r = 30$$
$$r = 30 \div 6$$
$$r = 5$$

The solution is 5.

Check: $6 \times 5 = 30$ ✓

b. $x \div 7 = 12$

$$x = 12 \times 7$$
$$x = 84$$

The solution is 84.

Check: $84 \div 7 = 12$ ✓

We can use inverse operations to solve equations that contain two operations.

EXAMPLE 3 Use inverse operations to solve the equation

$$3n + 25 = 61.$$

Solution First write the related subtraction equation that will give the value of $3n$.

$$3n = 61 - 25$$
$$3n = 36$$

Then write the related division equation that will give the value of n.

$$n = 36 \div 3$$
$$n = 12$$

The solution is 12.

Check:
$$3n + 25 = 61$$
$$3(12) + 25 = 61$$
$$36 + 25 = 61 \ ✓$$

We can also use inverse operations to solve inequalities that involve addition, subtraction, multiplication, or division.

EXAMPLE 4 Use the inverse operation to write a related inequality and solve for the variable.

a. $y + 6 > 10$

b. $5t \leq 25$

Solution

a.
$$y > 10 - 6$$
$$y > 4$$

The solutions are all numbers greater than 4.

Check: $4 + 6 = 10$, so any number greater than 4 will be a solution. ✓

b.
$$t \leq 25 \div 5$$
$$t \leq 5$$

The solutions are all numbers less than or equal to 5.

Check: $5 \times 5 = 25$, so any number less than or equal to 5 will be a solution. ✓

Class Exercises

Use the inverse operation to state a related equation or inequality and solve for *t*.

1. $t + 6 = 15$ **2.** $t - 4 = 7$ **3.** $6t = 48$ **4.** $t \div 8 = 7$

5. $t + 7 > 18$ **6.** $4t \leq 32$ **7.** $t + 24 = 60$ **8.** $13t = 78$

9. $t - 26 = 59$ **10.** $t - 38 < 79$ **11.** $t \div 32 = 8$ **12.** $t \div 15 \geq 90$

Written Exercises

Use the inverse operation to write a related equation and solve for the variable.

A **1.** $x + 8 = 15$ **2.** $a + 6 = 11$ **3.** $f + 38 = 74$ **4.** $t + 46 = 91$

5. $y - 9 = 14$ **6.** $n - 7 = 9$ **7.** $b - 25 = 32$ **8.** $r - 55 = 87$

9. $3c = 27$ **10.** $5g = 45$ **11.** $9m = 108$ **12.** $4d = 88$

13. $n \div 6 = 9$ **14.** $s \div 8 = 4$ **15.** $g \div 16 = 7$ **16.** $w \div 9 = 14$

17. $a + 17 = 17$ **18.** $j - 54 = 61$ **19.** $14n = 42$ **20.** $e + 26 = 61$

21. $h \div 11 = 297$ **22.** $b + 45 = 256$ **23.** $d - 87 = 110$ **24.** $18b = 18$

25. $31q = 465$ **26.** $k \div 17 = 527$ **27.** $p + 208 = 358$ **28.** $f - 11 = 523$

29. $c + 511 = 536$ **30.** $18r = 414$ **31.** $g - 19 = 401$ **32.** $m \div 4 = 216$

Use the inverse operation to write a related inequality and solve for the variable.

33. $r + 8 > 12$ **34.** $x - 9 < 18$ **35.** $4p \geq 36$

36. $m \div 11 \leq 99$ **37.** $q - 24 \leq 59$ **38.** $13d > 182$

39. $a \div 17 < 340$ **40.** $x + 21 \geq 50$ **41.** $c + 113 \leq 177$

42. $f \div 27 < 162$ **43.** $t - 55 \geq 9$ **44.** $39n > 273$

45. $y \div 80 < 20$ **46.** $a - 109 \leq 214$ **47.** $43x > 86$

Use inverse operations to solve.

B **48.** $3q + 9 = 27$ **49.** $4a + 19 = 39$ **50.** $7d - 12 = 37$

51. $5b - 16 = 39$ **52.** $3r + 24 = 63$ **53.** $2s - 30 = 62$

54. $9x - 84 = 69$ **55.** $6w + 81 = 486$ **56.** $(z \div 3) + 22 = 30$

57. $(t \div 7) - 4 = 4$

58. $(c \div 5) - 13 = 11$

59. $(y \div 3) + 15 = 36$

C 60. $3n + 10 > 40$

61. $5b - 12 \leq 42$

62. $6m - 17 \geq 49$

63. $4d + 21 \geq 53$

64. $(y \div 14) - 32 \leq 38$

65. $(x \div 8) + 15 < 19$

Self-Test A

Simplify the numerical expression.

1. 4.3×6 2. $4.15 + 1.6$ 3. $8.16 - 5.7$ 4. $68.4 \div 9$ **[1-1]**

Evaluate the expression when $k = 4$ and $m = 6$.

5. $184 \div k$ 6. $8 + m + 1$ 7. $7km$

Simplify the expression.

8. $8 + 3 \times 14$ 9. $48 \div (6 \times 2 - 4)$ 10. $\dfrac{7 + (9 \times 3) - 2}{(5 \times 4) - (2 \times 2)}$ **[1-2]**

Evaluate the expression when $s = 12$ and $t = 18$.

11. $\frac{s}{4} + 6$ 12. $(t + 2) \div 5$ 13. $2s - t$

Find the solution or solutions for the given replacement set.

14. $72 - m = 43$; $\{19, 29, 31\}$ 15. $6r = 48$; $\{6, 7, 8\}$ **[1-3]**

16. $t \div 12 = 11$; $\{23, 24, 25\}$ 17. $4d + 16 = 28$; $\{3, 4, 5\}$

Replace __?__ with $=$, $>$, or $<$ to make a true statement.

18. 430 __?__ 403 19. $52 \div 17$ __?__ 19 20. 225 __?__ 9×25 **[1-4]**

Find the solutions of the inequality. The replacement set for x is the set of whole numbers.

21. $x < 5$ 22. $x \geq 85$ 23. $19 \leq x \leq 27$

Use inverse operations to solve.

24. $g - 32 = 12$ 25. $7d < 112$ 26. $5a + 4 = 49$ **[1-5]**

Self-Test answers and Extra Practice are at the back of the book.

1-6 Writing Expressions for Word Phrases

In mathematics we often use symbols to translate word phrases into mathematical expressions. The same mathematical expression can be used to translate many different word expressions. Consider the phrases below.

Three more than a number n The sum of three and a number n

Written as a variable expression, each of the phrases becomes

$$3 + n.$$

Notice that both the phrase *more than* and the phrase *the sum of* indicate addition.

The following are some of the word phrases that we associate with each of the four operations.

+	−	×	÷
add	subtract	multiply	divide
sum	difference	product	quotient
plus	minus	times	
total	remainder		
more than	less than		
increased by	decreased by		

EXAMPLE 1 Write a variable expression for the word phrase.

a. A number t increased by nine **b.** Sixteen less than a number q

c. A number x decreased by twelve, divided by forty

d. The product of sixteen and the sum of five and a number r

Solution

a. In this expression, the phrase *increased by* indicates that the operation is addition. $t + 9$

b. In this expression, the phrase *less than* indicates that the operation is subtraction. $q - 16$

c. In this expression, the phrases *decreased by* and *divided by* indicate that two operations, subtraction and division, are involved. $(x - 12) \div 40$

d. In this expression, the words *product* and *sum* indicate that multiplication and addition are involved.
$16 \times (5 + r)$, or $16(5 + r)$

Reading Mathematics: ***Attention to Order***

Often a word expression contains more than one phrase that indicates an operation. Notice in Example 1 parts (c) and (d), on page 20, how parentheses were needed to represent the word phrase accurately. When translating from words to symbols, be sure to include grouping symbols if they are needed to make the meaning of an expression clear.

Many words that we use in everyday speech indicate operations or relationships between numbers. *Twice* and *doubled,* for example, indicate multiplication by 2. *Consecutive* whole numbers are whole numbers that differ by 1. The *preceding* whole number is the whole number *before* a particular number, and the *next* whole number is the whole number *after* a particular number.

EXAMPLE 2 If twice n is a whole number, represent (a) the preceding whole number and (b) the next four consecutive whole numbers. Represent the whole number by $2n$.

Solution

a. The preceding whole number is 1 less than $2n$, or $2n - 1$.

b. Each of the next whole numbers is 1 more than the whole number before.

$$2n + 1, 2n + 2, 2n + 3, 2n + 4$$

Class Exercises

Match.

1. A number x multiplied by fourteen

2. The quotient of fourteen divided by a number x

3. Fourteen less than a number x

4. Seven increased by a number x

5. A number x subtracted from fourteen

6. Fourteen more than a number x

7. Seven more than the product of fourteen and a number x

8. Twice the sum of a number x and seven

9. The product of seven and the sum of fourteen and a number x

10. Fourteen divided by the difference when a number x is subtracted from seven

A. $14 - x$

B. $2(x + 7)$

C. $14 \div (7 - x)$

D. $7 + 14x$

E. $14 \div x$

F. $7(14 + x)$

G. $x - 14$

H. $7 + x$

I. $14x$

J. $x + 14$

Written Exercises

Write a variable expression for the word phrase.

A **1.** The product of eight and a number b

2. A number q divided by sixteen

3. A number d subtracted from fifty-three

4. Four less than a number f

5. Thirty increased by a number t

6. Five times a number c

7. The sum of a number g and nine

8. A number k minus twenty-seven

9. Seventy-eight decreased by a number m

10. A number y added to ninety

11. Nineteen more than a number n

12. Sixty-two plus a number h

13. The quotient when a number d is divided by eleven

14. The difference when a number a is subtracted from a number b

15. The remainder when a number z is subtracted from twelve

16. The total of a number x, a number y, and thirteen

17. Fifteen more than the product of a number t and eleven

18. The quotient when a number b is divided by nine, decreased by seven

19. The sum of a number m and a number n, multiplied by ninety-one

20. Forty-one times the difference when six is subtracted from a number a

21. A number r divided by the remainder of eighty-three minus ten

22. The total of a number p and twelve, divided by eighteen

23. The product of a number c and three more than the sum of nine and twelve

24. The sum of a number y and ten, divided by the difference when a number x is decreased by five

25. The total of sixty, forty, and ten, divided by a number d

26. The product of eighteen less than a number b and the sum of twenty-two and forty-five

B 27. The greatest of four consecutive whole numbers, the smallest of which is b

28. The smallest of three consecutive whole numbers, the greatest of which is q

29. The greatest of three consecutive even numbers following the even number x

30. The greatest of three consecutive odd numbers following the odd number y

31. The value in cents of q quarters

32. The number of inches in f feet

33. The number of hours in x minutes

34. The number of dollars in y cents

C 35. The difference between two numbers is ten. The greater number is x. Write a variable expression for the smaller number.

36. One number is six times another. The greater number is a. Write a variable expression for the smaller number.

Review Exercises

Use the inverse operation to solve for the variable.

1. $x + 32 = 59$	**2.** $2y = 68$	**3.** $a \div 8 = 72$	**4.** $q - 14 = 23$
5. $m - 27 > 45$	**6.** $f \div 6 < 8$	**7.** $n + 12 \leq 26$	**8.** $6d \geq 132$

Challenge

In the set of whole numbers, there are two different values for a for which this equation is true.

$$a + a = a \times a$$

What are they?

1-7 Equations and Inequalities for Word Sentences

We can use what we know about translating word phrases into variable expressions to translate word sentences into equations and inequalities.

EXAMPLE 1 Write an equation or inequality for the word sentence.

a. Twice a number x is less than or equal to 14.
b. Thirty-five is sixteen more than a number t.
c. The product of five and the difference when ten is subtracted from a number r is greater than forty.

Solution

a. First, write the word phrase *twice a number x* as the variable expression $2x$. Use the symbol $\leq$ to translate the phrase *is less than or equal to.*

$$2x \leq 14$$

b. Use the equals sign to translate *is.* Write *sixteen more than a number t* as $t + 16$.

$$35 = t + 16$$

c. Write *the product of five and the difference when ten is subtracted from a number r* as $5(r - 10)$. Use the symbol $>$ to express *is greater than.*

$$5(r - 10) > 40$$

A word sentence may involve an unknown number without specifying a variable. When translating such a sentence into an equation or inequality, we may use any letter to represent the unknown number.

EXAMPLE 2 Write an equation or inequality for the word sentence.

a. The sum of a number and seven is less than thirteen.
b. A number increased by six is equal to three times the number.

Solution

a. Let n stand for the unknown number. $n + 7 < 13$

b. Let x stand for the unknown number. $x + 6 = 3x$

Both sides of an equation or inequality may be variable expressions, as illustrated in Example 2, part (b).

Class Exercises

Tell how you would translate each word sentence into an equation or an inequality.

1. The sum of six and a number m is greater than fifteen.

2. A number p subtracted from forty-eight is seventeen.

3. Fourteen times a number r is less than or equal to two hundred.

4. Twice the sum of eleven and nine is four times a number b.

Write an equation or inequality for the word sentence.

5. Eighty-two is less than three times a number q.

6. Eighty-three is fifteen less than a number g.

7. Six times a number z is greater than or equal to z plus two.

8. A number divided by eleven is twelve.

9. The product of a number and five is less than the number minus three.

Written Exercises

Write an equation or inequality for the word sentence.

A 1. Five times a number d is greater than twenty.

2. A number t increased by thirty-five is sixty.

3. Seven less than the product of a number w and three equals eight.

4. The difference when a number z is subtracted from sixteen is two.

5. Five divided by the product of six and a number r is less than forty-two.

6. The sum of a number and seven is greater than or equal to nine.

7. A number decreased by one is less than five.

8. Twelve is greater than a number divided by four.

9. Twice a number, divided by three, is fifteen.

10. The product of a number and eight, decreased by three, is less than or equal to nine.

B 11. The quotient when the sum of four and x is divided by two is thirty-four.

12. The sum of n and twenty-two, multiplied by three, is seventy-eight.

13. The product of a and the difference of six minus one is equal to a.

14. The sum of z and seventeen is less than or equal to the difference of twenty-one minus z.

Write an equation or inequality for the word sentence.

15. Fifty-nine minus x is greater than the sum of twice x and three.

16. Two increased by eight times a number is equal to the number divided by five.

17. The product when the sum of y and twelve is multiplied by five is one hundred.

18. The difference when the product of m and nine is subtracted from sixty-six is zero.

19. The sum when the quotient of b divided by eight is added to nine is less than thirty.

20. The quotient when a number is divided by five is greater than the sum of the product of the number and two added to eleven.

21. Twice a number is equal to the product when the sum of the number and four is multiplied by eight.

22. The sum when the quotient of a number divided by three is added to thirteen is greater than or equal to the difference when the product of the number multiplied by five is subtracted from ten.

For each exercise, (a) write an equation or inequality for the word sentence and (b) solve the equation or inequality for the given replacement set.

23. Twice a number x is equal to thirty-two. $\{14, 15, 16\}$

24. A number z decreased by nine is less than fifteen. $\{23, 24, 25\}$

C 25. The product of y and ten, decreased by six, is greater than or equal to twenty-five. $\{3, 4, 5\}$

26. The difference when the product of a number and three is subtracted from thirty is greater than or equal to the number increased by ten. $\{0, 5, 10, 15\}$

Review Exercises

Simplify the expression.

1. $13 - 9 \div 3 + 12$ **2.** $40 \div 8 + 21 \times 3$ **3.** $16(2 + 5) - 4$

4. $6(94 - 72) + 18$ **5.** $(8 + 11 - 3) \div 8$ **6.** $(19 + 2)(81 - 54)$

7. $(14 + 9) \div (10 - 3)$ **8.** $13.11 - (3.8 + 5.2) \div 3$ **9.** $4(8.15 - 2.11) + 9.50$

1-8 A Plan for Solving Problems

What we know about mathematics enables us to solve many problems. Problems, however, are not usually as neatly organized as the information in the expressions with which we have been working. We must sort out and organize the facts of a problem before we begin to solve. A plan such as the one below can be useful in solving many kinds of problems.

Plan for Solving Word Problems

1. Read the problem carefully. Make sure that you understand what it says. You may need to read it more than once.
2. Use questions like these in planning the solution:
   What is asked for?
   What facts are given?
   Are enough facts given? If not, what else is needed?
   Are unnecessary facts given? If so, what are they?
   Will a sketch or diagram help?
3. Determine which operation or operations can be used to solve the problem.
4. Carry out the operations carefully.
5. Check your results with the facts given in the problem. Give the answer.

EXAMPLE 1 On Saturday, the Nizel family drove 17 mi from Topsfield to Newton and 22.5 mi from Newton to Harbor Bluffs. The trip took 50 min. On the way back, the Nizels took the same route, but they stopped for lunch after driving 9.5 mi. If they continue on the same route after lunch, how much farther will they have to drive to return to Topsfield?

Solution

- The problem asks for the number of miles to return to Topsfield.
- The following facts are given in the problem:
  17 mi from Topsfield to Newton
  22.5 mi from Newton to Harbor Bluffs
  drove 9.5 mi back toward Topsfield

(*The solution is continued on the next page.*)

- We have enough facts to solve the problem since we know the distance between the cities and the distance driven toward Topsfield.
- We do not need to know that the trip took 50 min.

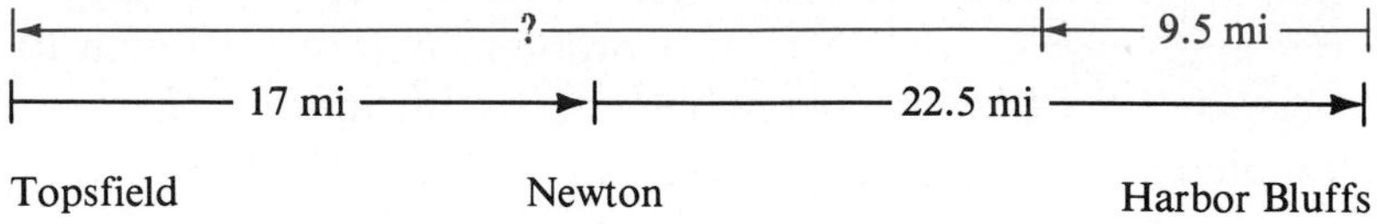

- The sketch shows that we subtract the distance driven back toward Topsfield from the distance between Topsfield and Harbor Bluffs.

$$(17 + 22.5) - 9.5 = 30$$

- Check: If they drive 9.5 mi and 30 mi farther, will the Nizels have driven the distance from Harbor Bluffs to Topsfield?

$$9.5 + 30 = 17 + 22.5 \ \checkmark$$

The Nizels must drive 30 mi to return to Topsfield.

EXAMPLE 2 Records at the Howard City Weather Bureau show that it rained on a total of 17 days during the months of July through September and on twice as many days during the months of October through December. During October through December, how many days did not have rain?

Solution

- The problem asks for the number of days without rain during October, November, and December.
- Given facts: 17 days of rain in July through September
  twice as many days of rain in October through December
- We need to supply these facts:
  31 days in October, 30 days in November, 31 days in December
- To find the number of days without rain, subtract the number of days that did have rain from the total number of days.

$$(31 + 30 + 31) - (2 \times 17) = 92 - 34 = 58$$

- Check: Are 34 days twice as many as 17? $34 \div 2 = 17$ ✓
  Do 58 days without rain and 34 days with rain total the number of days in the three months?
  $58 + 34 = 31 + 30 + 31$ ✓

During October through December, 58 days did not have rain.

Class Exercises

For each problem, answer the following questions.
a. What number or numbers does the problem ask for?
b. Are enough facts given? If not, what else is needed?
c. Are unneeded facts given? If so, what are they?
d. What operation or operations would you use to find the answer?

1. Kevin completed the bicycle race in 2 h 24 min, Lori completed the race in 2 h 13 min, and Helen completed the race in 2 h 54 min. How much faster than Kevin's time was Lori's time?

2. Steve bought 1 lb of Swiss cheese, 12 oz of mild cheddar cheese, and 6 oz of sharp cheddar cheese. How much cheese did he buy in all?

3. Elise bought a record for $5.69, another record for $4.88, and a record cleaning kit for $12.75. How much more than the cost of the records was the cost of the kit?

4. The eighth-grade classes are holding a hobbies and crafts fair on Saturday. Maurice plans to help out at the stamp-collecting booth from 9 A.M. to 11 A.M. and at the model-airplane booth from 2 P.M. to 5 P.M. How many hours does he plan to spend helping?

Problems

Solve, using the five-step plan.

A **1.** Mimi is buying weather-stripping tape for some windows. How much should she buy for a window that needs 4.85 m, a window that needs 4.25 m, and a window that needs 2.55 m?

2. A package of 2 paintbrushes is on sale for $2.40. How much will 3 packages cost?

3. Irene Lanata pays $235.40 each month to repay her automobile loan. How much will she pay in one year?

4. On its fifth orbit, the space shuttle *Freedom* was as close as 110 mi from Earth and as far away as 180 mi from Earth. By how many miles do these distances differ?

5. Hill School plans to buy 4 computers for each of 12 classrooms. The cost of each computer is $865. What will the total cost be?

6. An 8 mm camera shoots 24 frames of film each second. How many frames will it shoot in 5 min?

Solve, using the five-step plan.

7. There are 38 rows with 2 dozen seats each in the Little Theater. An additional 24 people are allowed to stand during a performance. What is the total number of people that can attend a performance?

8. Yesterday it took Jeff Holland 1 h to get to work. This morning, Jeff drove to the train station in 20 min, waited for the train for 7 min, rode the train for 12 min, and then walked for 15 min to get to work. How long did it take Jeff to get to work this morning?

9. Roy paid $81.88 for a new jacket and sweater. He then exchanged the sweater, which cost $23.00, for another sweater that cost $19.99. What was the final cost for Roy's jacket and sweater?

10. The information on a bag of High-Pro dog food states that a dog weighing 50 pounds should eat 3 cups of food each day and a dog weighing 20 pounds should eat 1.5 cups each day. How much food should 3 dogs, each weighing 50 pounds, eat in one day?

B 11. Tickets for the drama club's performance last weekend cost $2.50 for adults and $2.00 for students. Four hundred twenty adults attended the performance, and 273 students attended. What was the total amount of money collected from tickets for the performance last weekend?

12. On September 1, City Auto had an inventory of 220 Firefly station wagons and 317 Firefly sedans. On October 1, the inventory was 108 Firefly station wagons and 192 Firefly sedans. How many more sedans than station wagons were sold?

13. First-class tickets on flight 107 to Los Angeles cost $482, tourist-class tickets cost $324, and economy-class tickets cost $212. Today 41 economy-class passengers, 237 tourist-class passengers, and 8 first-class passengers were on the flight. What was the total cost of the tickets for passengers on the flight?

14. Sarah Holness had her car tuned up for $60 and she purchased 4 new tires for $37 each. She gave the cashier 11 twenty-dollar bills. How much change did Sarah receive?

15. Gregory ordered the following items from the Huntington Gardens catalog: a watering can for $15.80, a trowel for $4.49, and 6 packages of seeds for $.75 each. He must add $2.50 for shipping charges. He has 2 coupons, each allowing him to deduct $2.00 from his order. How much will Gregory pay for the order?

C 16. Joy and David Kramer had $30 to spend on dinner, a movie, and parking. Dinner cost $15.50 and parking cost $4. The Kramers had $2 left after paying for everything. What was the cost of one movie ticket?

17. The museum charges $4.50 per person for a 2 h tour with fewer than 20 people. If 20 or more people take the tour, the charge is $3.75 per person. Of the 23 people in today's tour, 17 had paid $4.50 in advance. How much money will the museum return as a refund?

Self-Test B

Write a variable expression for the word phrase.

1. Twelve divided by a number y **[1-6]**
2. Five less than a number x
3. The difference when twenty-one is subtracted from the product of nine and a number g

Write an equation or inequality for the word sentence.

4. Fifteen is the sum of nine and twice a number x. **[1-7]**
5. Twenty-five times the sum of a number b and 7 is greater than eleven divided by four.
6. When the product of four and a number is subtracted from twenty-four, the result is less than or equal to twelve.

Solve, using the five-step plan.

7. Laura bought a hammer for $12.95, 5 lb of nails for $5.20, and 8 sheets of plywood for $12 each. What was her total bill? **[1-8]**
8. Between the hours of 6 A.M. and 9 P.M., 8 buses that were filled to capacity left the terminal. Since the capacity of each bus is the same and 392 tickets were sold, how many passengers were on each bus?

Self-Test answers and Extra Practice are at the back of the book.

ENRICHMENT

The Development of Computers

The development of the modern computer began in 1946 with the completion of the ENIAC computer. It weighed 30 tons, contained 18,000 vacuum tubes and 6000 switches, and filled a room 30 feet by 50 feet. Since that time computers have become steadily more compact, powerful, and inexpensive.

Today's large computer systems, called **mainframes,** can process large amounts of data at very fast speeds. **Minicomputers** are smaller and somewhat slower, meeting the needs of colleges and small businesses at lower cost. The smallest of today's computers, such as the computer shown in the photo above, are the **microcomputers.** These computers are often called personal computers because they are inexpensive enough and small enough to go into classrooms and homes. The processing unit of these small computers is the **microprocessor,** a one-quarter-inch-square integrated circuit chip. This tiny chip is more powerful than the ENIAC with its 18,000 vacuum tubes.

The microprocessor controls the microcomputer and performs arithmetic operations. But other parts are needed to make the computer a useful tool. The computer has two kinds of **memory. ROM** (read only memory) permanently stores information needed for the computer to work properly. It cannot be changed by the user. **RAM** (random access memory) is available to the user and can store the user's programs and data. Memory size is measured in **bytes** or K. One K is about 1000 bytes. Each byte can store one character (letter or digit), so an 8K memory can store about 8000 typed characters.

The **keyboard** is used to input programs and data, and the **CRT** screen displays input, results, and graphics. A **disk drive** can be used to read programs and data into the computer from a disk, or to save programs on disk. A **printer** will save output in printed form. A **modem** can connect you to a network of other computers over your telephone line.

As computers have evolved, people have invented programming languages to help users program the computer to solve problems. Some of the more common languages are **BASIC,** which is available on almost all microcomputers, **FORTRAN,** often used for scientific problem solving, and **COBOL,** a business-oriented language. **Pascal** and **Logo** are two languages finding increasing application in education.

The development of computers has opened many new careers. Systems analysts use computers to analyze and solve problems for business and government. Programmers write the programs, or software, that help users apply the computer to their needs. Installation and maintenance of a computer's physical components, or hardware, are done by field engineers.

1. The fastest modern computers can do 100 million arithmetic operations in a second. Estimate how long it would take you to do this many additions. Suppose you are adding two four-digit numbers each time.

2. Each byte of memory will hold one typed character. About how many K of memory would it take to store these two pages? A disk for a microcomputer holds 160 K. About how many pages of this book could you store on one disk?

3. Ask your librarian to help you find out about the Mark I, IBM 360, and UNIVAC 1 computers. Find out about the size of each computer, the number of its components, its purpose, its inventors.

4. The computer language ADA was named after Ada Byron Lovelace (1815–1852). See what you can find out about Ada Lovelace and the computer language.

Career Activity

Look in the Help Wanted section of a newspaper and make a list of the job openings for systems analysts and programmers. Include in your list education requirements, what computers or computer languages the candidate should be familiar with, and the salary range.

Chapter Review

Match.

1. 22×8 **2.** $52.6 - 9.95$ **A.** 32 **B.** 176 [1–1]

3. $9 \times (3 + 1) - 4$ **4.** $\frac{4 + (6 \times 2 \times 3)}{(14 - 12)5}$ **C.** 4 **D.** 42.65 [1–2]

Is the equation or inequality true or false for the given value of the variable?

5. $9y = 108;\ y = 12$ **6.** $k \div 4 = 28;\ k = 7$ **7.** $6g + 2 = 20;\ g = 3$ [1–3]

8. $a \geq 18;\ a = 14$ **9.** $5x > 15;\ x = 5$ **10.** $r - 24 \leq 12;\ r = 30$ [1–4]

True or false?

11. If $k + 5 = 140$, $k = 140 - 5$. **12.** If $p \div 21 < 14$, $p < 21 - 14$. [1–5]

13. If $9b = 162$, $b = 162 \div 9$. **14.** If $t - 87 \leq 87$, $t \leq 87 - 87$.

Match.

15. Six more than a number x **A.** $\frac{x}{6} - 9$ [1–6]

16. The difference when nine is subtracted from the quotient of a number x divided by six **B.** $x + 6$

C. $9(x + 6) < 2 \times 6$

17. Nine less than the product of six and a number x is twice the number x. **D.** $6x - 9 = 2x$ [1–7]

18. The product of nine and the sum of a number x plus six is less than the product of two and six.

Write the letter of the correct answer.

19. Julia Carmona hired 3 people to landscape her yard. They each received the same hourly rate and it took them 5 h to do the job. If her bill was \$60, how much did each person earn an hour? [1–8]

a. \$6 **b.** \$12 **c.** \$3 **d.** \$4

20. The ski resort has 5 beginners' trails. Two of them are 1.1 km long, 2 others are 2.8 km long, and 1 trail is 4.5 km long. How many kilometers of trails are available for beginners?

a. 12.1 km **b.** 11.2 km **c.** 12.3 km **d.** 9.5 km

Chapter Test

Evaluate the expression when $a = 4$ and $b = 12$.

1. $91 + a$ 2. $27 - b - a$ 3. $5b$ 4. $36 \div a \div b$ **[1-1]**

Evaluate the expression when $m = 14$ and $n = 16$.

5. $n - 4 \times 3$ 6. $3 \times \frac{m}{7}$ 7. $2mn - 9$ 8. $(m + n) \div 3$ **[1-2]**

Find the solution or solutions for the given replacement set.

9. $d - 9 = 27$; $\{3, 18, 35\}$ 10. $14r = 70$; $\{3, 4, 5\}$ **[1-3]**

11. $9(x + 4) = 63$; $\{1, 2, 3\}$ 12. $3k + 1 = 13$; $\{4, 5, 6\}$

Find the solutions of the inequality. The replacement set for *t* is the set of whole numbers.

13. $t \leq 9$ 14. $7 < t$ 15. $3 \leq t \leq 8$ 16. $12 > t$ **[1-4]**

Use the inverse operation to write a related equation or inequality and solve for the variable.

17. $6g = 72$ 18. $b \div 9 \geq 44$ 19. $3f - 1 = 53$ **[1-5[**

Write a variable expression for the word phrase.

20. The quotient of a number divided by seven   **[1-6]**

21. Twenty added to the product of a number and ten

Write an equation or inequality for the word sentence.

22. The sum of fourteen and a number *l* is greater than thirty.   **[1-7]**

23. Two less than the product of a number *k* and three equals four.

Solve, using the five-step plan.

24. The tickets for the theater cost $7.50 each. Miles bought 4 of them and gave the cashier a fifty dollar bill. What was the cost of the tickets?   **[1-8]**

25. There are 120 students in each of the freshman and junior classes. There are 20 more sophomores than juniors and 15 fewer seniors than sophomores. What is the total number of students in the four classes?

Cumulative Review

Exercises

Simplify.

1. $28 + 781$ **2.** $630 - 52.1$ **3.** $65.1 \div 21$

4. 1.2×3.64 **5.** $48 + 303.9$ **6.** 0.042×0.8

7. $3(14 - 5)$ **8.** $(6 + 3) \div 9$ **9.** $4 \times 5 + 5$

10. $16 - 2 \times 3 - 1$ **11.** $(8 + 2) \div (12 - 7)$ **12.** $(14 + 36) \times (54 - 8)$

Evaluate the expression when $p = 7$ and $q = 8$.

13. $4q + 23$ **14.** $3q - 6$ **15.** $p + q \div 5$

16. $pq - 6$ **17.** $28 \div (q - p)$ **18.** $p(13 - 9)q$

Find the solution or solutions of the equation for the given replacement set.

19. $k + 16 = 23$; $\{5, 6, 7\}$ **20.** $58 - d = 31$; $\{39, 38, 37\}$

21. $7x - 1 = 20$; $\{1, 2, 3\}$ **22.** $8(y - 3) = 32$; $\{7, 8, 9\}$

23. $5a = 2a + 57$; $\{19, 20, 21\}$ **24.** $(c + 6) \div 6 = 1$; $\{0, 1, 2\}$

Find the solution of the inequality. The replacement set for x is the set of whole numbers.

25. $x > 12$ **26.** $2 \geq x$ **27.** $x < 9$

28. $3 < x < 5$ **29.** $12 \geq x \geq 8$ **30.** $15 \leq x \leq 20$

Use inverse operations to solve.

31. $18 + g = 20$ **32.** $a \div 9 = 18$ **33.** $5z < 65$

34. $20d + 8 = 68$ **35.** $7f - 1 \leq 13$ **36.** $3h + 2 \geq 26$

Write a variable expression for the word phrase.

37. A number t decreased by thirty-one

38. The quotient when a number m is divided by eighty-three

39. Four more than the product of two and a number k

40. The product of twelve and the sum of a number b and six

Write an equation or inequality for the word sentence.

41. Fifteen less than a number is twenty-four.

42. Twenty increased by the product of a number y and eight is sixty.

43. The difference when three is subtracted from the product of a number and two is nine.

44. Forty-five more than a number is less than fifty-one.

Problems

Problem Solving Reminders
Here are some reminders that may help you solve some of the problems on this page.
- Determine which facts are necessary to solve the problem.
- Supply additional information if needed.
- Consider whether drawing a sketch will help.

1. Jeanne can type 45 words each minute and Brian can type 68 words each minute. What is the combined number of words they can type in 1 h?

2. Martin bought 0.8 kg of bananas at $.55 a kilogram, 1.5 kg of tomatoes at $1.54 a kilogram, and 18 oranges for $1.77. How much did he spend?

3. Nine crew teams will attend the annual regatta. Each team consists of eight members and a coxswain. If each person on a team is to receive a certificate, how many certificates need to be ordered?

4. A car can go 600 km on 1 tank of gas. How many kilometers can it go on 2.5 tanks of gas?

5. In an opinion survey concerning breakfast drinks, 398 people preferred orange juice, 275 people preferred grapefruit juice, and 88 people liked both juices equally. How many of the people interviewed liked at least one kind of juice?

6. A chemist has 558 mL of a solution and needs to prepare samples of it. If each sample must contain 23.25 mL, how many samples can be prepared?

7. A swimming pool is 24 m by 18 m. If you swim its length 3 times, how far will you swim?

2

The Decimal System

Astronomers and some other scientists deal with extremely large or small numbers. Their work is greatly simplified by the use of exponents, which you will learn about in this chapter.

Using radio telescopes like the one pictured, astronomers can "see" far beyond the distances possible with optical telescopes. Radio waves can go through interstellar dust clouds that light cannot. Many objects in space give off radio waves. Quasars, for example, look like ordinary stars but are very strong radio sources. They are actually much brighter than stars and very far away. One quasar may be ten billion light years away and ten thousand times as bright as all the stars in our galaxy put together.

Career Note

Astronomers are scientists who study objects in space. To become an astronomer, you need a strong background in advanced mathematics as well as training in the sciences. Astronomy is a difficult but rewarding field of research, in which you often read reports of new discoveries and may sometimes present your own. Some astronomers combine teaching with their careers in research.

2-1 Exponents

When two or more numbers are multiplied, these numbers are called **factors** of the product. For example,

$$\underbrace{5 \times 8}_{\text{factors}} = 40 \quad \text{and} \quad \underbrace{3 \times 7}_{\text{factors}} = 21.$$

When one factor is used a number of times, we may use an *exponent* to simplify the notation, as shown in the following example.

$$125 = \underbrace{5 \times 5 \times 5}_{\text{equal factors}} = 5^3$$

The expression 5^3 is read *5 cubed,* or *5 to the third power,* where 5 is the **base** and 3 is the **exponent.**

Since 125 is the product of three factors of 5, we say that 125 is *the third power of 5.* Examples of other bases and exponents are listed below.

$15 = 15^1$	*15 to the first power*
$36 = 6 \times 6 = 6^2$	*6 squared,* or *6 to the second power*
$64 = 4 \times 4 \times 4 = 4^3$	*4 cubed,* or *4 to the third power*
$16 = 2 \times 2 \times 2 \times 2 = 2^4$	*2 to the fourth power*

EXAMPLE 1 Express 81 as a power of 3.

Solution

$$81 = 3 \times 3 \times 3 \times 3$$
$$= 3^4$$

EXAMPLE 2 Simplify the expression $2^3 \times 5^2$.

Solution

$$2^3 = 2 \times 2 \times 2 = 8 \qquad 5^2 = 5 \times 5 = 25$$
$$2^3 \times 5^2 = 8 \times 25 = 200$$

Can we give an expression such as 7^0 a meaning? When the powers of any base are listed in order, we may recognize a pattern. Study the example at the top of the next page.

$$7^4 = 7 \times 7 \times 7 \times 7 = 2401$$

$$7^3 = 7 \times 7 \times 7 = 343$$

$$7^2 = 7 \times 7 = 49$$

$$7^1 = 7$$

Notice that in increasing order each power of 7 is seven times the preceding power. Conversely, in decreasing order, each power of 7 is the quotient of the preceding power divided by a factor of 7. That is, $7^3 = 7^4 \div 7$, $7^2 = 7^3 \div 7$, and so on. This decreasing pattern suggests that 7^0 (read *7 to the zero power*) is $7^1 \div 7$. Study the example below to verify that the expression $7^0 = 1$.

$$7^0 = 7^1 \div 7 = 7 \div 7 = 1$$

In general,

Definition

For every number a $(a \neq 0)$, $a^0 = 1$.

If an expression contains powers of the same base, the expression may be written as a single power of that base. For example, $13^2 \times 13^3$ can be written as a single power of 13.

$$13^2 \times 13^3 = (13 \times 13) \times (13 \times 13 \times 13)$$
$$= 13 \times 13 \times 13 \times 13 \times 13$$
$$= 13^5$$

Notice that the exponent in the product is the sum of the exponents in the factors, that is, $2 + 3 = 5$.

In general,

Rule

For every number a $(a \neq 0)$ and all whole numbers m and n,

$$a^m \times a^n = a^{m+n}$$

Notice that the bases must be the same.

EXAMPLE 3 Write $15^3 \times 15^4$ as a single power of 15.

Solution $15^3 \times 15^4 = 15^{3+4} = 15^7$

EXAMPLE 4 Evaluate the expression if $n = 3$.

a. n^2 **b.** $4n^2$ **c.** $(4n)^2$ **d.** $n^2 \times n^2$

Solution Replace n with 3 in each expression and simplify.

a. $n^2 = 3^2 = 3 \times 3 = 9$

b. $4n^2 = 4(3^2) = 4 \times 9 = 36$

c. $(4n)^2 = (4 \times 3)^2 = 12^2 = 12 \times 12 = 144$

d. $n^2 \times n^2 = n^{2+2} = n^4 = 3^4 = 3 \times 3 \times 3 \times 3 = 81$

Notice in parts (b) and (c) of Example 4 how grouping symbols change the values of expressions that have the same numbers.

Reading Mathematics: *Study Helps*
Look back at this lesson. Notice that the information in the blue boxes on page 41 summarizes important ideas from the lesson. The first box gives a definition and the second box states a rule. Both are applied in the examples. Throughout the book, boxes are used to help you identify important definitions, rules, properties, facts, and formulas. Use them as reminders when you do the exercises and when you review the lesson.

Class Exercises

Read each expression.

1. 4^5 **2.** 9^1 **3.** 15^2 **4.** 3^7 **5.** 10^3 **6.** 2^8

Write using exponents.

7. 9 to the third power **8.** 15 cubed **9.** 4 squared

10. 6 to the fifth power **11.** 216 is the third power of 6.

Express the number as a power of 3.

12. 9 **13.** 27 **14.** 3 **15.** 243 **16.** 1

Simplify the expression.

17. 8^2 **18.** 2^3 **19.** 1^{11} **20.** 18^0 **21.** 83^1

Written Exercises

Simplify the expression.

A **1.** 2^6 **2.** 5^4 **3.** 10^2 **4.** 6^3 **5.** 14^1

6. $3^2 + 5^2$ **7.** $(3 \times 5)^2$ **8.** $2^4 + 3^2$ **9.** $(5 + 12)^0$ **10.** $(5 + 12)^1$

Which is greater?

11. 2^3 or 3^2 **12.** 5^2 or 2^5 **13.** 9×2 or 9^2

14. 3×10 or 10^3 **15.** $(16 \times 4)^2$ or $2 \times 16 \times 4$ **16.** $(10 + 2)^0$ or $10 + 2$

Write as a single power of the given base.

17. $2^3 \times 2^4$ **18.** $3^2 \times 3^5$ **19.** 10×10^4 **20.** $5^5 \times 5^6$ **21.** $n^3 \times n^8$

Evaluate the expression if $m = 5$, $n = 3$, and $p = 2$.

22. p^2 **23.** $4m^2$ **24.** $(9n)^2$ **25.** $9n^2$ **26.** n^0

27. $(8n)^2$ **28.** np^0 **29.** $(mn)^0$ **30.** $m^3 - n^3$ **31.** $5m^3n$

B **32.** $(7n)^n$ **33.** $(3m)^p$ **34.** $6^m \times 6^n$ **35.** $(8 + m)^{n-3}$ **36.** $(15^n)^{p-1}$

37. $p^n m^n$ **38.** $(7 + n^m)^n$ **39.** np^m **40.** $(p^m p^n) + 4$ **41.** $m^p + n^n$

42. $(m^p)^n$ **43.** $(m - n)^p$ **44.** $\frac{m^n}{m^p}$ **45.** $\frac{3p^n}{6p^m}$ **46.** $\frac{(m - 1)^{n+1}}{p}$

C **47.** Find a value of n such that $(5 + 2)^n = 5^n + 2^n$.

48. Is the equation true?

a. $4^4 \div 4^3 = 4^1$ **b.** $5^3 \div 5^1 = 5^2$ **c.** $2^7 \div 2^4 = 2^3$

d. Using your answers from parts (a)–(c), state a general rule to describe what appears to be true for division of powers of the same base.

Review Exercises

Replace __?__ with > or < to make a true statement.

1. 19 __?__ 24 __?__ 31 **2.** 84 __?__ 79 __?__ 66

3. 56 __?__ 49 __?__ 41 **4.** 20 __?__ 40 __?__ 50

5. 81 __?__ 46 __?__ 17 **6.** 37 __?__ 33 __?__ 30

7. 28 __?__ 67 __?__ 82 **8.** 44 __?__ 91 __?__ 99

2-2 The Decimal System

Our number system uses the powers of 10 to express all numbers. This system is called the **decimal system** (from the Latin word *decem,* meaning *ten*). Using the digits 0, 1, 2, . . . , 9, we can write any number. The **value** of each digit depends on the position of the digit in the number. For example, the 2 in 312 means 2 ones, but the 2 in 298 means 2 hundreds. The decimal system is a system with **place value.**

The chart below shows place values for some of the digits of a **decimal number,** or **decimal.**

Place-value Chart

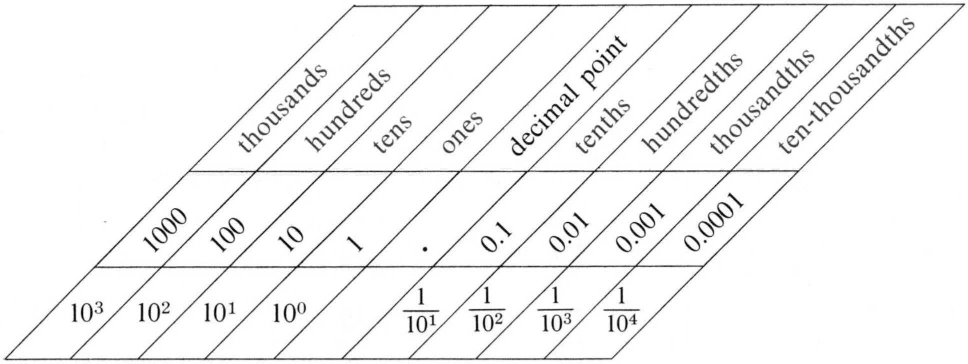

Moving left to right, place values decrease. As illustrated in the examples below, each place value is one tenth, or 0.1, of the place value to its left.

$1000 \times 0.1 = 100$ $\qquad$ $10 \times 0.1 = 1$ $\qquad$ $0.01 \times 0.1 = 0.001$

We can see from the place-value chart that values to the left of the decimal point are greater than or equal to 1, while values to the right are less than 1.

When a decimal number is written, the value of the number is the sum of the values of the digits. To illustrate this, we can write decimal numbers in **expanded form,** that is, as a sum of products of each digit and its place value.

EXAMPLE 1 Write the decimal in expanded form.

a. 3053 $\qquad$ **b.** 16.9 $\qquad$ **c.** 0.074

Solution

a. $3053 = (3 \times 1000) + (5 \times 10) + 3$

b. $16.9 = (1 \times 10) + 6 + (9 \times 0.1)$

c. $0.074 = (7 \times 0.01) + (4 \times 0.001)$

Recall that zeros can be added at the right of a decimal in the following manner without changing the value of the number.

$$1.039 = 1.0390 = 1.03900$$

We will need to use this fact when we compare decimals.

When comparing two decimals, we compare their place values. For example, 382 is greater than 97.5 because its first digit is in the hundreds' place and the first digit of 97.5 is in the tens' place.

382
97.5

When we compare 6.5142 and 6.5187, the first place from the left in which the numbers differ is the thousandths' place. Because the value of 4 thousandths is less than the value of 8 thousandths, 6.5142 is less than 6.5187.

6.5142
6.5187

EXAMPLE 2 Replace _?_ with $>$ or $<$ to make a true statement.

a. 97,486 _?_ 305,472 **b.** 130 _?_ 7.42 **c.** 0.59 _?_ 0.592

Solution

a. Reading from left to right, the first digit in 305,472 is in the hundred-thousands' place, while the first digit in 97,486 is in the ten-thousands' place. Thus $97,486 < 305,472$.

b. The first digit in 130 is in the hundreds' place, while the first digit in 7.42 is in the ones' place. Thus $130 > 7.42$.

c. We write 0.59 as 0.590 and see that the first place in which the digits differ is the thousandths' place. Zero is less than 2, so $0.59 < 0.592$.

EXAMPLE 3 Use the symbol $<$ to order the numbers from least to greatest.

1.038, 1.036, 1.0045

Solution Using place value to order the numbers from least to greatest, we have the following.

$$1.0045 < 1.036 < 1.038$$

Class Exercises

Read the number.

1. 5496 **2.** 0.51 **3.** 28.7 **4.** 0.0317 **5.** 8.026

Name the value of the digit 6 in the number.

6. 657.3 **7.** 0.062 **8.** 8.1416 **9.** 6.023 **10.** 408.6

Write as a decimal.

11. 255 thousandths **12.** 4 and 11 hundredths **13.** 307 ten-thousandths

Replace $\underline{\ ?\ }$ with $>$ or $<$ to make a true statement.

14. $0.255 \underline{\ ?\ } 0.619$ **15.** $4.11 \underline{\ ?\ } 0.0307$ **16.** $194{,}763 \underline{\ ?\ } 78{,}241$

Written Exercises

Write the decimal in expanded form.

A **1.** 38 **2.** 256 **3.** 8091 **4.** 5 **5.** 0.47

6. 28.4 **7.** 0.063 **8.** 9.070 **9.** 0.187 **10.** 5.5

Write as a decimal.

11. $(5 \times 10) + 4 + (5 \times 0.1) + (7 \times 0.01)$

12. $(4 \times 100) + (7 \times 0.01) + (3 \times 0.001) + (2 \times 0.0001)$

13. $(9 \times 1000) + 2 + (1 \times 0.1) + (4 \times 0.01) + (6 \times 0.001)$

14. $(1 \times 100) + (9 \times 10) + 3 + (2 \times 0.01) + (3 \times 0.001)$

Write as a decimal.

15. 7 and 43 hundredths **16.** 11 and 4 tenths

17. 19 and 5 thousandths **18.** 37 ten-thousandths

19. 48 ten-thousandths **20.** 5 and 6 hundredths

21. 6 and 25 thousandths **22.** 94 and 7 ten-thousandths

Replace $\underline{\ ?\ }$ with $=$, $>$, or $<$ to make a true statement.

23. $32.41 \underline{\ ?\ } 324.1$ **24.** $65.7 \underline{\ ?\ } 6.57$ **25.** $0.086 \underline{\ ?\ } 0.0798$

26. $6.308 \underline{\ ?\ } 6.312$ **27.** $87.06 \underline{\ ?\ } 87.009$ **28.** $0.0208 \underline{\ ?\ } 0.208$

29. $92.077 \underline{\ ?\ } 92.07$ **30.** $0.002 \underline{\ ?\ } 0.01$ **31.** $0.135 \underline{\ ?\ } 1.035$

32. $43 \underline{\ ?\ } 17 + 28$ **33.** $0.06 \underline{\ ?\ } 0.038 + 0.052$

34. $3.62 - 2.91 \underline{\ ?\ } 0.71$ **35.** $59.81 - 42.65 \underline{\ ?\ } 16.16$

36. $2.14 \times 0.8 \underline{\ ?\ } 2$ **37.** $43.472 \underline{\ ?\ } 8.36 \times 5.2$

38. $81.9 \div 9 \underline{\ ?\ } 9$ **39.** $2.68 \underline{\ ?\ } 13.4 \div 5$

B **40.** $57.4 + 32.8 \underline{\ ?\ } 108.64 - 18.44$

41. $94.76 - 51.36 \underline{\ ?\ } 83.97 - 65.14$

42. $176 \div 5 \underline{\ ?\ } 85.49 - 63.24$

43. $6.13 \times 0.2 \underline{\ ?\ } 6.13 \div 5$

Use < to order the numbers from least to greatest.

44. 1.28, 1.09, 1.42

45. 3.97, 3.16, 3.08

46. 62.08, 62.1, 62.9

47. 0.07, 0.2, 0.08

48. 0.188, 0.029, 0.04

49. 7.028, 7.11, 7.0862

50. 3×1.65, 3×2.1, 3×1.2806

51. $0.27 + 0.81$, $0.406 + 0.215$, $1.62 + 0.09$

52. 2×0.86, 5×1.24, 10×0.09

Write in expanded form using exponents by writing each number as a sum of multiples of powers of 10.

1000	100	10	1	.	0.1	0.01	0.001
10^3	10^2	10^1	10^0	and	$\frac{1}{10} = \frac{1}{10^1}$	$\frac{1}{100} = \frac{1}{10^2}$	$\frac{1}{1000} = \frac{1}{10^3}$

EXAMPLE 367.04

Solution $(3 \times 10^2) + (6 \times 10^1) + (7 \times 10^0) + \left(0 \times \frac{1}{10^1}\right) + \left(4 \times \frac{1}{10^2}\right)$

53. 5280

54. 64.7

55. 183.08

56. 0.043

57. 0.091

58. 12.931

59. 7.482

60. 0.806

61. 204.5

62. 0.306

63. 38.003

64. 10.009

Review Exercises

Simplify in your head. Write down the answer.

1. $30 + 20 + 40$

2. 80×30

3. $150 \div 30$

4. $70 - 10 - 30$

5. $110 + 30 + 70 + 40$

6. $15 \times 10 \div 30$

7. $420 \div 60 + 20$

8. $40 \times 8 + 50$

9. $100 \div 50 \div 10$

2-3 Rounding

When we use an *approximation* for a number, we say that we are **rounding** the number. For example, suppose that a distance is 6.7 km. We know that 6.7 is between 6 and 7. If we round 6.7 to the nearest whole number, we say that the distance is about 7 km.

We can see that 6.7 is closer to 7 than to 6 by graphing 6.7 on the number line. First we divide the portion of the number line between 6 and 7 into ten equal parts. Then we graph 6.7 on the number line as shown.

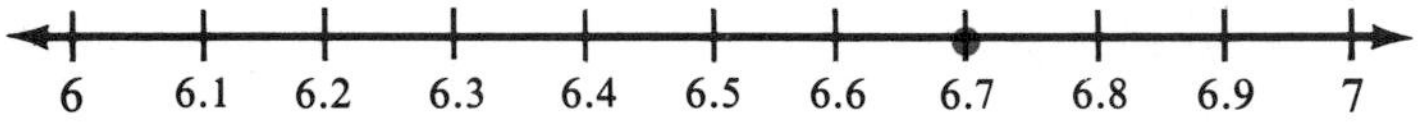

Since 6.7 rounded to the nearest whole number is 7, we can write $6.7 \approx 7$. The symbol $\approx$ means *is approximately equal to.*

The rule for rounding decimal numbers can be stated as follows:

> **1.** Find the decimal place to which you wish to round, and mark it with a caret ($_\wedge$). Look at the digit to the right.
>
> **2.** If the digit to the right is 5 or greater, add 1 to the marked digit. If the digit to the right is less than 5, leave the marked digit unchanged.
>
> **3.** If the marked digit is to the left of the decimal point, replace each digit to the right of the marked place with "0," and drop all digits to the right of the decimal point.
> If the marked digit is to the right of the decimal point, drop all digits to the right of the marked place.

EXAMPLE 1 Round 16.0973 to the nearest

a. ten **b.** tenth **c.** hundredth

Solution

a. $\underset{\wedge}{1}6.0973$
20
$16.0973 \approx 20$

b. $16.\underset{\wedge}{0}973$
16.1
$16.0973 \approx 16.1$

c. $16.0\underset{\wedge}{9}73$
16.10
$16.0973 \approx 16.10$

Rounding is often used as a quick check on calculations. In general, we **estimate** by rounding to the highest place value of the smaller number for all operations. As a result, our estimated answer should be reasonably close to the exact answer.

EXAMPLE 2 Find an estimated answer for each operation.

a. $\begin{array}{r} 386 \\ +\ 54 \\ \hline \end{array}$ **b.** $\begin{array}{r} 2.849 \\ -\ 0.154 \\ \hline \end{array}$ **c.** $\begin{array}{r} 32.9 \\ \times\ 8.7 \\ \hline \end{array}$ **d.** $12\overline{)253}$

Solution **a.** $\begin{array}{r} 386 \\ +\ 54 \\ \hline \end{array} \longrightarrow \begin{array}{r} 390 \\ +\ 50 \\ \hline 440 \end{array}$ **b.** $\begin{array}{r} 2.849 \\ -\ 0.154 \\ \hline \end{array} \longrightarrow \begin{array}{r} 2.8 \\ -\ 0.2 \\ \hline 2.6 \end{array}$

c. $\begin{array}{r} 32.9 \\ \times\ 8.7 \\ \hline \end{array} \longrightarrow \begin{array}{r} 33 \\ \times\ 9 \\ \hline 297 \end{array}$ **d.** $12\overline{)253} \longrightarrow \begin{array}{r} 25 \\ 10\overline{)250} \end{array}$

Class Exercises

Round to the place underlined.

1. $8.0\underline{3}9$ **2.** $2\underline{9}4.65$ **3.** $7\underline{5},452$ **4.** $1\underline{0}.988$

5. $0.9\underline{9}6$ **6.** $1.35\underline{4}7$ **7.** $\underline{3}19.84$ **8.** $0.\underline{3}828$

Round to the highest place value.

9. 43 **10.** 127.14 **11.** 0.036 **12.** 0.8981

13. 1986 **14.** 532.3 **15.** 0.073 **16.** 0.0249

Written Exercises

Round to the nearest ten.

A **1.** 27.5149 **2.** 82.604 **3.** 293.4 **4.** 70.76

5. 648.01 **6.** 108.3 **7.** 159.62344 **8.** 97.23

Round to the nearest hundredth.

9. 72.459 **10.** 26.804 **11.** 0.0643 **12.** 12.395

13. 0.0103 **14.** 8.142 **15.** 18.1657 **16.** 0.70605

Round to the nearest thousandth.

17. 0.0006 **18.** 12.3568 **19.** 401.0904 **20.** 30.0317

21. 250.3407 **22.** 7.0063 **23.** 8.0995 **24.** 0.9996

Select the most reasonable estimated answer.

B	**25.** $89.6 + 13.5$	**a.** 90	**b.** 100	**c.** 70
	26. $35 + 12 + 26 + 11$	**a.** 70	**b.** 110	**c.** 90
	27. $65.43 - 8.92$	**a.** 56	**b.** 60	**c.** 90
	28. $2196 - 924$	**a.** 1300	**b.** 1000	**c.** 3100
	29. 6.82×4.7	**a.** 24	**b.** 35	**c.** 28
	30. $54 \div 2.5$	**a.** 30	**b.** 20	**c.** 18
	31. $36\overline{)283}$	**a.** 10	**b.** 3	**c.** 7
	32. $4.7 \times 1.8 + 3.7$	**a.** 7	**b.** 14	**c.** 32

Self-Test A

Simplify the expression.

1. 2^4 **2.** 8^3 **3.** 9^1 **4.** $5^2 \times 5^3$ **5.** $a^6 \times a^5$ **[2-1]**

Replace __?__ with > or < to make a true statement.

6. 30.694 __?__ 27.35 **7.** 0.024 __?__ 0.017 **8.** 0.87 __?__ 1.22 **[2-2]**

Round to the place specified.

9. tens: 84.307 **10.** hundredths: 3.176 **11.** hundreds: 293.84 **[2-3]**

Self-Test answers and Extra Practice are at the back of the book.

Calculator Key-In

Use a calculator to simplify the expressions.

1. $15^2 - 13^2$ and $(15 + 13)(15 - 13)$

2. $47^2 - 21^2$ and $(47 + 21)(47 - 21)$

3. $82^2 - 59^2$ and $(82 + 59)(82 - 59)$

4. $104^2 - 76^2$ and $(104 + 76)(104 - 76)$

Do you recognize a pattern?
Write two expressions that will result in the same pattern.

2-4 Basic Properties

When we work with decimals, we see that the properties of whole numbers apply to decimals as well.

Changing the order of the addends in a sum or the factors in a product does not change the sum or product. For example,

$9.2 + 4.7 = 4.7 + 9.2$ $\qquad$ $3.5 \times 8.4 = 8.4 \times 3.5$

Commutative Property

For all numbers a and b,

$a + b = b + a$ and $a \times b = b \times a$

Changing the grouping of addends in a sum or of factors in a product does not change the sum or product. For example,

$5.6 + 0.8 + 11.2$
$(5.6 + 0.8) + 11.2 = 17.6$
$5.6 + (0.8 + 11.2) = 17.6$

$4.1 \times 2.3 \times 7.2$
$(4.1 \times 2.3) \times 7.2 = 67.896$
$4.1 \times (2.3 \times 7.2) = 67.896$

Associative Property

For all numbers a, b, and c,

$(a + b) + c = a + (b + c)$

and $(a \times b) \times c = a \times (b \times c)$

We can use these properties to find the easiest way to add or multiply a long list of numbers.

EXAMPLE 1 Use the properties to simplify the expression.

a. $4.8 + 1.1 + 0.2 + 3.9 + 7$ **b.** $2 \times 6 \times 5 \times 3$

Solution One possible way to rearrange the numbers is shown.

a. $4.8 + 1.1 + 0.2 + 3.9 + 7$
$(4.8 + 0.2) + (1.1 + 3.9) + 7$
$5 + 5 + 7$
$10 + 7$
17

b. $2 \times 6 \times 5 \times 3$
$(2 \times 5) \times (6 \times 3)$
10×18
180

The numbers 0 and 1 are called the **identity elements** for addition and multiplication respectively. The word *identity* comes from the Latin word *idem,* which means *the same.* The result of adding 0 to a number or subtracting 0 from a number is the same as the original number. The result of multiplying a number by 1 or dividing a number by 1 is the same as the original number. Study the following examples.

$$4.53 + 0 = 4.53 \qquad 29.7 \times 1 = 29.7$$

$$4.53 - 0 = 4.53 \qquad 29.7 \div 1 = 29.7$$

Addition and Subtraction Properties of Zero

For every number a, $\quad a + 0 = a \quad a - 0 = a$

$0 + a = a \quad a - a = 0$

Multiplication and Division Properties of One

For every number a, $\quad a \times 1 = a \quad a \div 1 = a$

$1 \times a = a \quad a \div a = 1$

The product of any number and 0 is 0. Similarly, 0 divided by any number is 0.

$$3.784 \times 0 = 0 \qquad 0 \div 3.784 = 0$$

Can we divide by 0? Recall that multiplication and division are inverse operations. Thus, if we were to divide 3.784 by 0, we would have the following.

$$3.784 \div 0 = x \qquad 3.784 = x \times 0$$

We cannot accept the equation at the right because any number times 0 is 0. So it makes no sense to divide by 0.

Multiplication and Division Properties of Zero

For every number a,

$$a \times 0 = 0 \quad \text{and} \quad 0 \times a = 0$$

For every number a, $a \neq 0$,

$$0 \div a = 0$$

The distributive property is different from the other properties because it involves two operations. The example below illustrates how we may distribute a multiplier over each term in an addition expression.

$7 \times (8.2 + 1.8)$	$(7 \times 8.2) + (7 \times 1.8)$
7×10	$57.4 + 12.6$
70	70

Therefore $7 \times (8.2 + 1.8) = (7 \times 8.2) + (7 \times 1.8)$.

We may also distribute a multiplier over each term in a subtraction expression.

Distributive Property

For all numbers a, b, and c,

$$a \times (b + c) = (a \times b) + (a \times c)$$

$$a \times (b - c) = (a \times b) - (a \times c)$$

EXAMPLE 2 Use the distributive property to simplify the expression.

a. $(4 + 6.2)5$ **b.** $(13 \times 2.7) - (13 \times 1.3)$

Solution

a. $(4 + 6.2)5 = (4 \times 5) + (6.2 \times 5) = 20 + 31 = 51$

b. $(13 \times 2.7) - (13 \times 1.3) = 13(2.7 - 1.3) = 13(1.4) = 18.2$

EXAMPLE 3 What value of the variable makes the statement true?

a. $6 + 5 = 5 + m$ **b.** $3.7 \times 4 = 4t$ **c.** $3(14 + 20) = 42 + b$

Solution

a. $6 + 5 = 5 + m$
$6 + 5 = 5 + 6$, so $m = 6$

b. $3.7 \times 4 = 4t$
$3.7 \times 4 = 4 \times 3.7$, so $t = 3.7$

c. $3(14 + 20) = 42 + b$
$3(14 + 20) = (3 \times 14) + (3 \times 20) = 42 + 60$, so $b = 60$

Class Exercises

Name the property illustrated.

1. $7.6 + 0 = 0 + 7.6$

2. $(19 \times 3)6.2 = 19(3 \times 6.2)$

3. $11.9 \times 1 = 11.9$

4. $5(9 + 8.2) = (5 \times 9) + (5 \times 8.2)$

5. $138.6 \times 7.4 = 7.4 \times 138.6$

6. $6(1.2 + 0.8) = (1.2 + 0.8)6$

Use the properties of addition and multiplication to simplify the expression. Name the property or properties used.

7. 0.4×0 **8.** $3.02 \times 5 \times 2$ **9.** 1×12.87

10. $2.4 + 13 + 2.6$ **11.** $(8 \times 13) + (8 \times 7)$ **12.** 5.93×0

What value of the variable makes the statement true?

13. $25 + 37 = m + 25$ **14.** $(7 \times 6) + (5 \times 6) = (7 + 5)q$

15. $(17 + 12) + 8 = b + (12 + 8)$ **16.** $9(w - 20) = (9 \times 35) - (9 \times 20)$

Written Exercises

Use the properties to simplify the expression. Name the property or properties used.

A **1.** $2.6 + 11.5 + 0.5$ **2.** 0×23.15

3. $4(2.5 + 1.06)$ **4.** $8(40 - 12)$

5. $7.24 + 8.97 + 2.76$ **6.** $(22 \times 8) + (22 \times 2)$

7. $0.5 \times 2.1 \times 0.2$ **8.** $4 \times 32 \times 5.25$

9. $15.3 \times 317 \times 0$ **10.** $11.5 + 2.6 + 0.5 + 0.4$

11. $(15.7 \times 6) - (3.7 \times 6)$ **12.** $(6 \times 1.3) + (6 \times 1.7)$

True or false?

13. $7.386 + 0 = 0$ **14.** $(3 + 12)6 = (3 \times 6) + (12 \times 6)$

15. $(19.7 + 36 + 41.5)0 = 0$ **16.** $15(2 + 7.4) = (15 + 2) \times (15 + 7.4)$

17. $3.84 + 6.73 + 3.77 + 2.1 = 3.84 + 10.5 + 21$

18. $9(15.1 - 6.3) = (9 \times 15.1) + (9 \times 6.3)$

What value of the variable makes the statement true?

19. $6 + n = 6$ **20.** $7.02 \times 23 = t \times 7.02$

21. $6.4 + t = 3.2 + 6.4$ **22.** $3r = 3$

23. $5w = w$ **24.** $(6 + 4.03) + 0.97 = 6 + (x + 0.97)$

25. $9(8 + 5) = (c \times 8) + (c \times 5)$ **26.** $2.43 \times 0 = f$

27. $(15.9 \times 3)4.2 = g(3 \times 4.2)$ **28.** $(13 - 11.7)8 = (13 \times 8) - (r \times 8)$

29. $(2 + 4.8)3 = (2n) + (4.8n)$

30. $(3.02 + 4.9)1 = b$

31. $5(11.7 + 313) = 58.5 + d$

32. $(7 \times 1.2) + (7 \times 3.8) = 7m$

33. $(8.31 + 2.73)t = t$

34. $2.59 + 7.03 + 18.61 + 3.97 = u + 11$

Use the properties to simplify the expression.

B 35. $116 \times 3.7 \times 0 \times 4.93 \times 1.47 + 3.88$

36. $(78 \times 1) + (1.36 \times 0) + (92 + 0)$

37. $(18 + 46) + (12 + 4) + (8 \times 17) + (23 \times 8)$

38. $(12 \times 7) + (56 \div 8) + (13 \times 12)$

39. $5(81 \div 3) + 5(63 \div 1) + 450$

40. $(18 + 9)4 + (12 + 11)4$

Find values for *a*, *b*, and *c* that show that the equation is not true for all numbers.

C 41. $(a \times b) + (b \times c) = b(a \times c)$

42. $(a + b)(b + c) = b(a + c)$

43. $(b + c)(a + c) = c(b \times a)$

Review Exercises

Evaluate the expression when $a = 7$ and $m = 9$.

1. $3 + a + 12 + m$

2. $(63 \div a) + m$

3. $(27 - a) + 6m$

4. $95 - (am) + 12 - a$

5. $(11m + 12a - 14) \div 13$

6. $(am + 4m) \div 11m$

7. $35 + (6a \div 21) + (m \div 3)$

8. $m(a + 2a + 3a)$

Challenge

Start with your age in years.

1. Multiply by 4.

2. Add 2.

3. Divide by 2.

4. Subtract your age.

Your answer is your age one year from now! Can you explain?

2-5 Simplifying Expressions

We have already seen how parentheses are used as grouping symbols in a mathematical expression. We may also use brackets, [ ], as grouping symbols. When more than one pair of grouping symbols are used, we perform the operation in the innermost pair of grouping symbols first. Then we work outward until the whole expression is simplified.

When an expression contains exponents, we simplify the terms containing the exponents before proceeding with the other operations.

EXAMPLE 1 Simplify the expression.

a. $[(5 - 3.2) \div (7.3 + 2.7) + 4]7$ **b.** $\dfrac{(4^2 - 15)3^2}{3^3 - (2 \times 12)}$

Solution

a.
$$\begin{aligned}[(5 - 3.2) \div (7.3 + 2.7) + 4]7 &= [1.8 \div 10 + 4]7\\ &= [0.18 + 4]7\\ &= [4.18]7 = 29.26\end{aligned}$$

b.
$$\frac{(4^2 - 15)3^2}{3^3 - (2 \times 12)} = \frac{(16 - 15)9}{27 - 24} = \frac{(1)9}{3} = \frac{9}{3} = 3$$

In a variable expression such as

$$3a + 11 + 4a,$$

the terms $3a$ and $4a$ are called **like terms** because they differ only in their numerical coefficients. We can use the properties of addition and multiplication to simplify expressions with like terms. To simplify $3a + 11 + 4a$, we use the commutative and distributive properties.

$$\begin{aligned}3a + 11 + 4a &= (3a + 4a) + 11\\ &= (3 + 4)a + 11\\ &= 7a + 11\end{aligned}$$

The terms $7a$ and 11 cannot be combined because they are *unlike terms*. When an expression is in simplest form, it contains no like terms.

EXAMPLE 2 Simplify the expression.

a. $[(37 + 51)a + 5 + 7a]3$ **b.** $7m + 6(2 + 4m)$

Solution

a.
$$\begin{aligned}[(37 + 51)a + 5 + 7a]3 &= [88a + 5 + 7a]3\\ &= [(88a + 7a) + 5]3\\ &= [(88 + 7)a + 5]3\\ &= [95a + 5]3\\ &= (95a \times 3) + (5 \times 3)\\ &= 285a + 15\end{aligned}$$

b. $7m + 6(2 + 4m) = 7m + (6 \times 2) + (6 \times 4m)$
$= 7m + 12 + 24m$
$= (7m + 24m) + 12$
$= (7 + 24)m + 12 = 31m + 12$

Class Exercises

Name the order of the operations to use in simplifying the expression.

1. $(2.8 + 0.36)0.2 - 4$
2. $310 \div 5 + 7$
3. $[(0.42 \div 7) + 0.94]8$
4. $6 \times 7 - 4 + 8 \div 2$
5. $260 + 8^2 \times 6$
6. $15 + (6 \div 2) + 4$

Has the expression on the left side of the equation been simplified correctly? If not, give the correct answer.

7. $14.7 + 0.8 \times 2.1 = 16.38$
8. $14 + 8 + 26 \div 2 = 24$
9. $8 + 12 \div 4 + 4 = 24$
10. $5.4 \div 9 + 3.8 \div 8 = 1$

Written Exercises

Simplify the expression.

A

1. $5 + 7^2$
2. $(9^2 \div 3)6$
3. $2^2 \times 5 \times 2^3 + 17$
4. $(3.8 + 2)5$
5. $9 \times 2^3 + 7 \times 5^2$
6. $8.7 + 1.5 \div 3$
7. $(1.3 + 0.9) \div 4$
8. $(6.4 \div 2^3)7$
9. $5^2 + 6(72 \div 3^2)$
10. $(56x^2)(0.4x^2)$
11. $(18m^2)(3m^4) + 7$
12. $(a^2)(a^3)(a^4)7$
13. $\left[\frac{7.6 + 16.4 \times 0.5}{(24.7 - 16.7) \div 4}\right] + (2 \times 11)$
14. $\frac{(2.4 - 1.8)3 + 6.2}{[0.5(11.7 - 4.9)] + 4.6}$
15. $14x + 8y + 3x + 6y$
16. $0.56 + 8.3n + 1.6 + 2.1n$
17. $6[(4.5 - 3.6)d + 5.1d]$
18. $[7(p + 5) + p] + 6p$
19. $[(2 + 3)m + 5(4 + 6m)]8$
20. $5a^2(a + 3) + (4 + 8a)6$

Evaluate the expression when $a = 3.04$, $b = 0.8$, and $c = 4$.

21. $6a + b^3$
22. $3b^2c^3$
23. $(abc)^0$
24. $(a + b)^2$
25. $a + 5(c^2 \div b)$
26. $a(2c + 3) - 5b$
27. $8c + (10b + c^2)4$
28. $(3c - 5)(3c)^2$
29. $[9a - 2(c - a)]c$

Place grouping symbols so that the expression will have the given value.

EXAMPLE $10 \times 6^2 \div 2 - 3 \div 3 = 50$

Solution

$$\begin{aligned} 10 \times 6^2 \div 2 - 3 \div 3 &= 10[(6^2 \div 2 - 3) \div 3] \\ &= 10[(36 \div 2 - 3) \div 3] \\ &= 10[(18 - 3) \div 3] \\ &= 10[15 \div 3] = 10 \times 5 = 50 \end{aligned}$$

B **30.** $4^2 - 3 \times 5 - 2 = 3$

31. $4^2 - 3 \times 5 - 2 = 63$

32. $6 \times 7 - 2^3 \div 2^2 = 30$

33. $12 - 10 \div 2 + 3 \times 8 = 31$

34. $4.9 - 0.7 \times 2.5 + 11 = 14.15$

35. $4.2 + 3 \times 3.6 \div 0.4 + 9.6 = 60$

Review Exercises

Round to the highest place value.

1. 0.00614 **2.** 18.59 **3.** 240.003 **4.** 0.9817

5. 5.53002 **6.** 7481.99 **7.** 34.956 **8.** 0.08024

Computer Byte

This program will round a decimal to any desired place value.

```
10  PRINT "INPUT NUMBER TO BE ROUNDED";
20  INPUT N
30  PRINT "ROUND TO THE NEAREST ";
40  INPUT T
50  LET A = T * INT (N / T + .5)
60  PRINT A
70  END
```

Use the program to round each number to the place value specified.

1. 785 to the nearest 100

2. 785 to the nearest 10

3. 6898 to the nearest 1000

4. 6898 to the nearest 10

5. 17.49 to the nearest 1

6. 15.057 to the nearest 0.01

7. 0.004 to the nearest 0.1

8. 3.999731 to the nearest 0.001

Now try these.

9. Round 76 to the nearest 5.

10. Round $37,487.15 to the nearest $500.

2-6 Solving and Checking Problems

You can now apply what you have learned about decimal numbers to solving problems. Recall the steps in the plan for solving word problems that you learned in Chapter 1. Remember that some problems may require more than one operation to reach their answers. When you have reached an answer, it is important not only to check your result with the facts given in the problem, but also to reread the question to be sure that you have answered with the information requested.

EXAMPLE 1 Alice Grego is recruiting volunteers for the Blood Drive. On Monday morning 15 people signed up. That afternoon an additional 17 people volunteered. The next day twice as many people signed up as on Monday. How many people were recruited each day?

Solution

- The problem asks for the number of people recruited on each day.
- Given facts: 15 volunteers on Monday morning
  17 volunteers on Monday afternoon
  twice as many people on Tuesday as on Monday
- First we add to find the total number of people recruited on Monday.

$$15 + 17 = 32$$

The total number of volunteers recruited on Monday is 32.

The problem asks for the number of people recruited on *each* day, so we must also find the number of volunteers recruited on Tuesday. Multiply the first answer, the total number recruited on Monday, by 2.

$$2 \times 32 = 64$$

- Alice recruited 32 volunteers on Monday and 64 on Tuesday.

Check: Are 32 people 17 more than 15 people? $32 - 17 = 15$ ✓
Are 64 people twice as many as 32 people?
$64 \div 2 = 32$ ✓

Was the question answered? Yes, the answer includes the number recruited on each day.

When planning your solution to a problem, you may find that there is more than one way to proceed. When there is more than one method for solving a problem, you may find it helpful to use one method to obtain an answer and to use the other method to check your results. Study the example on the following page.

EXAMPLE 2 The Treble Clef celebrated Heritage Day with a two-week sale on the Flexwood turntables. Twelve turntables were sold during the first week of the sale and 17 were sold during the second week of the sale. The sale price for each turntable was \$74.90. How much money did the Treble Clef receive for the turntables sold during the sale?

Solution

- The problem asks for the amount of money received from the sale of the turntables.
- Given facts: 12 turntables sold the first week
  17 more sold the second week
  \$74.90 received for each turntable
- There are two ways to solve this problem.

  Method 1
  First multiply the sale price by the number sold each week to find the amount of money received each week.

  $12 \times 74.90 = 898.80 \qquad 17 \times 74.90 = 1273.30$

  Then add the amounts of money received to find the total amount of money received from the sale of the turntables.

  $$898.80 + 1273.30 = 2172.10$$

  Method 2
  First add to find the total number of turntables sold during the sale.

  $$12 + 17 = 29$$

  Then multiply the sale price by the total number sold to find the amount of money received from the sale of the turntables.

  $$29 \times 74.90 = 2172.10$$

- By either method, the Treble Clef received \$2172.10 from the sale of the turntables.

Another way to check an answer is to use rounding to find an estimated answer. If the answer and the estimate are close, then the estimate leads us to accept our answer.

EXAMPLE 3 Last summer Elka and David drove from Los Angeles to Boston. Along the way they stopped in Albuquerque, Kansas City, Atlanta, and Washington, D.C. They recorded the distance they traveled, as shown on the next page.

Los Angeles–Albuquerque	806 mi
Albuquerque–Kansas City	790 mi
Kansas City–Atlanta	810 mi
Atlanta–Washington, D.C.	630 mi
Washington, D.C.–Boston	437 mi

How many miles did Elka and David travel?

Solution

- The problem asks for the total distance traveled.
- Given facts: traveled 806 mi, 790 mi, 810 mi, 630 mi, 437 mi
- To find the total distance traveled, we add.

$$806 + 790 + 810 + 630 + 437 = 3473$$

- Elka and David traveled 3473 miles on their trip.

To check the answer, we round the distances and add. In this case, round to the nearest hundred miles.

$$800 + 800 + 800 + 600 + 400 = 3400$$

The estimate, 3400 mi, and the answer, 3473 mi, are quite close, so the actual answer seems reasonable.

Class Exercises

State the operations you would use to solve the problem and the order in which you would use them.

1. The Dreyer Trucking Company moved 453 cartons one day, and then 485 the next day. On the third day they moved twice as many as on the first two days. What is the total number of cartons moved during those three days?

State two methods that you could use to solve the problem.

2. Three friends went out to dinner. The bill was $41.10, and they left a $6.15 tip. If they divided the total three ways, how much did each person pay?

Estimate the answer to the problem.

3. Frank is in the check-out line at the grocery store. He has a gallon of milk ($1.83), a bag of flour ($2.15), a box of oatmeal ($1.15), a package of cheese ($1.57), and a dozen eggs ($1.05). How much is the bill?

Problems

Solve. Check to be sure you have answered the question.

A **1.** The August electric bill for $75.80 was twice as much as the July bill. What was the total cost of electricity for July and August?

2. Alvin has $1863.50 in his savings account. His sister Alvis has $756 more in her account. Geoffrey borrowed $257 from each person. How much money do Alvin and Alvis have left in each of their accounts after making the loans?

Solve. Check by using an alternate method.

3. Each member of the Best Buy Book Club receives 2 bonus points for every book ordered through the club. So far Chris has ordered 3 books in March, 2 in April, and 6 in May. How many bonus points has Chris accumulated so far?

4. The admission ticket to Tyler Amusement Park is $1.25 per person. A total of 815 tickets were sold on Saturday. The attendance decreased by 96 on Sunday. How much money did the park receive from ticket sales in all?

Solve. Check by estimating the answer to the problem.

5. During one game at a bowling tournament the five-member Bright Team scored the following points: 169, 152, 187, 174, and 193. What is the difference between the highest and the lowest scores?

6. Jackie is taking an inventory of the furniture going on sale next week.

sofas, 128	platform beds, 250
love seats, 105	stereo cabinets, 83
lamps, 216	bookcases, 45

How many items are going on sale?

Solve.

B **7.** The Hillview School Band held a car wash on Friday and Saturday. The charge was $2.25 per car on Friday and $2.50 per car on Saturday. On Friday, 87 cars were washed. On Saturday, 117 cars were washed. What was the total amount of money collected?

8. A photograph is enlarged so that its new dimensions are four times its original dimensions. If the new dimensions are 19.2 cm by 25.6 cm, what were the original dimensions?

9. Today the firm of Beckman and Beckman bought three types of stocks: 4780 shares of utility stocks, 1389 shares of commodity stocks, and 3542 shares of energy-related stocks. This is exactly three times the number of shares the firm bought yesterday. How many shares of stock did the firm buy in the past two days?

10. Yukio bought traveler's checks in the following denominations: five \$50 checks, thirty \$20 checks, five \$10 checks, and twenty \$5 checks. What is the total value of the checks bought?

11. Katelyn had 3 twenty-dollar bills to buy school clothes. She picked out a pair of jeans for \$15.90, two pairs of socks at \$2.35 each, and three blouses at \$12.50 each. How much change did she receive?

12. A direct dial call from Boston to Australia costs \$3.17 for the first minute and \$1.19 for each additional minute. A station-to-station operator-assisted call costs \$9.45 for the first 3 minutes and \$1.19 for each additional minute. How much money would you save by dialing direct for a 5-minute call?

Self-Test B

Use the properties of addition and multiplication to simplify.

1. $12(15 - 8) + 6 \times 3$ **2.** $(31 \times 4) + (15 \times 4) - 91$ [2-4]

3. $7(56 \div 8) - 7(24 \div 6)$ **4.** $9(0.36 \times 4) + 55$

5. $[(128 \div 4) \div 8)]9$ **6.** $(12 + 9)5 + (17 - 3)6$

Simplify the expression.

7. $(6a + 7)2 + 4a$ **8.** $(1.26 + 3.74)^2 \div 4$ [2-5]

9. $[(12 + 6) \div 6] + [(25 + 5) \div 3]$ **10.** $(7b + 3)5 + (11 + 4b)2$

Solve.

11. Jeremy and his roommate share the monthly utility bills evenly. For November the cost of electricity was \$87.90, gas was \$24.35, heating fuel was \$215.80, and water was \$36.43. How much did each person pay that month? [2-6]

Self-Test answers and Extra Practice are at the back of the book.

BASIC, A Computer Language

Computers are very powerful tools, but issuing an order such as "Do problem 12 on page 46 of my math book" will produce no results at all. There are many things computers can do more quickly and efficiently than people, but we need to communicate with computers in a special way to get them to work for us.

To tell a computer what to do, we write a set of instructions, called a *program,* using a *programming language.* Since most microcomputers use some version of BASIC (with slight differences), that is the language that we will use in this book. A BASIC program is made up of a set of *numbered lines* that provide step-by-step instructions for the computer. We can use any numbers from 1 to 99999 for line numbers, but we often use numbers in intervals of 10 so that we can insert other lines later if we need to.

A *statement* that tells the computer what to do follows each line number in a program. In the BASIC language, we use the symbols shown below to tell the computer to perform arithmetic operations.

+	addition	−	subtraction
*	multiplication	/	division

The symbol ↑ (or some similar symbol) is used to indicate exponentiation. Thus 3 ↑ 6 means 3^6. When a statement contains more than one operation, the computer will perform all operations in parentheses first and will follow the order of operations that you learned in Chapters 1 and 2.

We use a **PRINT** statement to tell the computer to perform the operations listed in a statement and to print the result. We use an **END** statement to tell the computer that the program is over. The program shown below tells the computer to simplify the numerical expression and print the answer.

```
10  PRINT 5↑3 * (16 - 8 / 2)
20  END
```

After you have typed in this program (press RETURN or ENTER after each line), you type the *command* **RUN** to tell the computer to run (or *execute*) the program. The result, or *output*, is 1500.

A computer handles variables much as we do. We can ask it, for example, to give us the value of a variable expression when we give it a value of the variable in it. One way of doing this is to use an **INPUT** statement. This causes the computer to print a question mark and wait for the value to be typed in. Here is a simple program with a RUN shown at the right below.

```
10  INPUT X                      RUN
20  PRINT X↑2 + 2 * X + 4        ?10
30  END                           124
```

As you can see, we need some statement to tell the person using this program what is expected after the question mark. We do this by enclosing a descriptive expression in quotation marks in a PRINT statement, as in line 5 below. The semicolon at the end of line 5 will cause the question mark from line 10 to be printed right after the quoted expression. We have also inserted lines 12 and 15. After typing lines 5, 12, and 15, we can type the command **LIST** to see the revised program. A RUN is shown at the right below.

```
5  PRINT "WHAT IS YOUR VALUE OF X";
10  INPUT X                      RUN
12  PRINT "FOR X = ";X           WHAT IS YOUR VALUE OF X?10
15  PRINT "X↑2 + 2X + 4 = ";     FOR X = 10
20  PRINT X↑2 + 2 * X + 4        X↑2 + 2X + 4 = 124
30  END
```

1. Change lines 15 and 20 in the program above to evaluate another variable expression, with x as the variable, that involves the operation or operations listed.

a. subtraction
b. multiplication
c. division
d. multiplication and addition
e. division and subtraction

2. Change the program above to evaluate a variable expression using m as the variable.

Chapter Review

Complete. Use =, >, or < to make a true statement.

1. 2^3 ___?___ 2×4 **2.** $14 \div 7$ ___?___ 19^0 **3.** $(4 + 3)^1$ ___?___ 4×3 [2-1]

4. 7.1 ___?___ $7 + 0.01$ **5.** $4.2 \div 2$ ___?___ 0.7×3 [2-2]

6. $7.23 \div 5$ ___?___ 1.44 **7.** $82.03 - 5.4$ ___?___ 87.43

True or false?

8. 21.09 to the nearest whole number is 20. [2-3]

9. 124.4 to the nearest hundred is 100.

10. 83.415 to the nearest hundredth is 83.42.

11. 0.959 to the nearest tenth is 1.0.

12. $(17.2 + 1.8)4 = (1.8 + 17.2)4$ illustrates the commutative property. [2-4]

13. $(8 + 7.9)2.3 = (8 \times 2.3) + (7.9 \times 2.3)$ illustrates the distributive property of multiplication with respect to subtraction.

14. $1.3(7 + 4) = (7 + 4)1.3$ illustrates the associative property.

Match.

15. $5 + (4^2 \div 2)^2$ **16.** $4 \times 5 + 6^2 \div 9$ **A.** 0.512 **B.** 69 [2-5]

17. $6 + 5a + 3a + 4^2$ **18.** $[0.2 \times (3 + 1)]^3$ **C.** $8a + 22$ **D.** 17

19. $4 + 2a(5 + 6) + 4$ **20.** $\dfrac{1.5 + 3.5 \times 2}{3.6 \div 18 + 0.3}$ **E.** $22a + 8$ **F.** 24

Write the letter of the correct answer.

21. There were 27,240 books at the library at the start of the day on Friday. During the day the following transactions occurred: 21 people borrowed 2 books each, 12 people borrowed 3 books each, 8 people borrowed a single book each, and 46 books were returned. How many books were in the library at the close of the day? [2-6]

a. 27,154 **b.** 27,200 **c.** 27,280 **d.** 27,240

22. To raise money for a local charity, the 26 students of the eighth-grade class participated in a bike-a-thon. Each of the sponsors agreed to pay the students $.35 for each mile they rode their bicycles. If 20 students ride 20 mi each and the rest of the students ride 30 mi each, for how many miles will the students be paid?

a. $203 **b.** 50 mi **c.** $17.50 **d.** 580 mi

Chapter Test

Which is greater?

1. 3^3 or 2^4 **2.** $(2 + 3)^2$ or 4^3 **3.** 10^3 or $(4 \times 6)^2$ **[2–1]**

Write as a single power of the given base.

4. $3^4 \times 3^2$ **5.** $6^5 \times 6^7$ **6.** $a \times a^3$

Evaluate the expression if $m = 6$, $n = 4$, and $p = 8$.

7. p^2 **8.** $5m - p$ **9.** $(2n)^3$ **10.** $(m + n)^p$

Write the decimal in expanded form.

11. 121 **12.** 80.08 **13.** 1.401 **14.** 5.2 **[2–2]**

Use the symbol < to order the numbers from least to greatest.

15. 4.003, 4.01, 4.023 **16.** 0.297, 0.035, 0.03

Round to the place specified.

17. tenths: 7.49 **18.** tens: 423.6 **19.** hundredths: 4.283 **[2–3]**

What value of the variable makes the statement true?

20. $2.4 + (r + 9.5) = 2.4 + (9.5 + 7.8)$ **21.** $19.2k = k$ **[2–4]**

22. $62d - 19d = (62 - 19)4$ **23.** $1(3.4 + 1.3) = a$

Simplify the expression.

24. $114.5 - (6.3 + 2.7)^2$ **25.** $[6^2 \div (8 + 1)] + 5$ **[2–5]**

26. $12x + 14 + 2x + 8 + 3y$ **27.** $5p(p + 4) + 3p$

Solve and check your answer.

28. For the trip, Kari bought 3 stocking caps for $6.75 each and 3 scarfs for $8.50 each. How much money did she spend? **[2–6]**

29. Dean commutes 17 km to work and Bob commutes 8 km more than Dean. If Becky commutes 3 times as far as Bob, how far does she commute?

30. Mickey Dayton purchased 5 cases of packages of flour. If each package was 2.2 kg and each case contained 20 packages, how many kilograms of flour were purchased?

Cumulative Review (Chapters 1 and 2)

Exercises

Evaluate the expression using the given values of the variables.

1. xy; $x = 3, y = 2.5$

2. $3a - b$; $a = 4.2, b = 6$

3. $\frac{m}{n} + 3$; $m = 8, n = 0.4$

4. $f + \frac{g}{6}$; $f = 10, g = 18$

5. $x^2 + 3xy$; $x = 8, y = 2.5$

6. $a \div b$; $a = 12.3, b = 3$

7. $4d + 7c^3$; $d = 0.3, c = 2$

8. $6m - 8n$; $m = 10.5, n = 0.5$

9. $\frac{p}{q} - 2p$; $p = 15, q = 0.5$

Evaluate the expression when $a = 4.2$, $b = 9.5$, and $c = 3.2$.

10. $2a + 3(a - c)$

11. $ab - c$

12. $bc + a$

13. $(a + c)(a + b)$

14. $4ab(b + c)$

15. $6c + (b - a)$

16. $a \div (c - 2.8)$

17. $(b + 0.5) \div (5.2 - c)$

18. $(30 - a) \div (a + 3.8)$

Use $>$ or $<$ to write a true statement with the given numbers.

19. 15, 48, 26

20. 83, 93, 43, 53

21. 125, 115, 225

22. $4^2, 2^3, 3^2$

23. $3^5, 5^3, 2^2$

24. $6^2, 2^6, 3^2$

Select the most reasonable estimated answer.

25. $43.6 - 2.79$ **a.** 41 **b.** 20 **c.** 45

26. 9.6×53.66 **a.** 500 **b.** 450 **c.** 540

27. $22.7 + 18.9 + 7.38$ **a.** 49 **b.** 37 **c.** 110

28. $165.7 + 38.21 + 6.44$ **a.** 1300 **b.** 210 **c.** 246

True or false?

29. $46.7 \times 1.0 = 46.7$

30. $87.91 \times 0 = 87.91$

31. $4(8 + 2) = 4 \times 8 + 4 \times 2$

32. $16 \div 8 + 2 = 16 \div (8 + 2)$

33. $99.5 - (6 + 7) = (99.5 - 6) + 7$

34. $(43 \times 0) + (43 \times 1) = 0$

35. $11.89 + (426 \div 2) = (11.89 + 426) \div 2$

36. $(68 - 7) = (7 - 68)$

37. $(658 + 15)7 = (7 \times 658) + (7 \times 15)$

Problems

Problem Solving Reminders
Here are some reminders that may help you solve some of the problems on this page.

- Determine which facts are necessary to solve the problem.
- Supply additional information if needed.
- Check by using rounding to find an estimated answer.
- If more than one method can be used to solve a problem, use one method to solve and the other to check.

Solve.

1. Merry and Sandy rented an apartment for $645 each month and shared the rent equally. After 4 months, Tess moved in and the rent was divided three ways. How much was Merry's rent for the year?

2. Hungarian paprika costs $1.30 for 2 oz, $4.00 for $\frac{1}{2}$ lb, and $6.00 for a pound. What is the cost of each ounce if you buy a pound? How much do you save per ounce if you buy a pound?

3. Mal ordered a set of 6 steak knives for $35.00. Additional costs included $4.95 for shipping, $1.25 for a gift box, and $1.75 for tax. What was the total cost of the order?

4. "I can save $19.50 if I buy a half dozen glasses on sale," said Ellis. How much is saved on each glass? If Ellis pays $30.00 for 6 glasses on sale, what was the original price of each glass?

5. House numerals that are 4 in. high cost $4.00 each. Numerals that are 7 in. high cost $10.00 each. How much will it cost to buy numerals that are 4 in. high for your house if your address is 16332 Long Meadow Road?

6. In 1918, a sheet of 100 airmail stamps was mistakenly printed with an airplane upside down. A stamp collector bought the sheet for $.24 per stamp and later sold the sheet for $15,000. How much did the collector make on his lucky buy?

7. A membership to the Science Center costs $53 per year and includes a subscription to a monthly magazine. If the magazine costs $3 per issue, what are the annual dues for membership alone?

8. Dale took advantage of the gas company's offer to make average monthly payments. The payments were based on the average of the two highest and the two lowest bills for the past 12 months. If these bills were $135.50, $142.71, $68.29, and $56.30, what is Dale's average monthly payment?

3

Positive and Negative Numbers

Geysers are underground springs that spout extremely hot water and steam. They occur in regions where volcanic forces heat the underground terrain. Geysers may spout a few meters or a few hundred meters and at short or long intervals. Old Faithful, a geyser at Yellowstone National Park, earned its name by spouting regularly at intervals of approximately 65 min.

Cloud formations, such as those in the photograph, are produced by the extreme differences in the temperatures of the hot steam and the cold winter air. As air temperatures drop, steam from the geyser condenses on plants and flowers, forming a frosty coating. When air temperatures fall below 0°C, the ice crystals begin to form beautiful patterns. In this chapter, you will learn to work with the numbers that we use to represent values that are below 0.

Career Note

State and national parks provide facilities for many forms of outdoor recreation. Park rangers help maintain park areas by enforcing rules and regulations, providing information for visitors, and protecting the area's wildlife and natural resources. A college degree with courses in earth science and animal care is essential for park ranger candidates. Courses in behavioral sciences that stress skills needed for dealing with people are also desirable.

3-1 The Integers

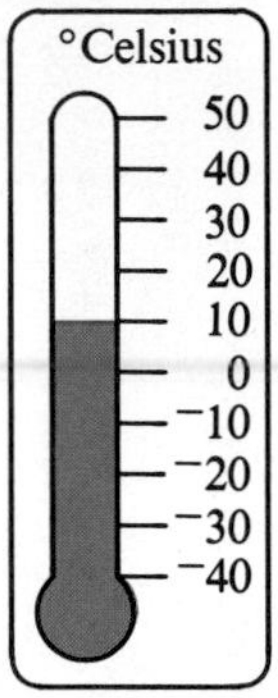

When we measure temperature, we use a scale that has 0 as a reference point. We use *positive numbers* to indicate temperatures above 0°, and we use *negative numbers* to indicate temperatures below 0°.

We often have occasion to measure quantities on different sides of a zero reference point, such as distances above and below sea level, time before and after a rocket launch, increases and decreases in stock prices, and deposits and withdrawals in a bank account. Positive and negative numbers help us to measure these quantities.

We may graph both positive and negative numbers on a horizontal number line by extending the number line to the *left* of the origin as shown below. Like the positive whole numbers, the negative whole numbers are equally spaced, but they are positioned to the left of 0.

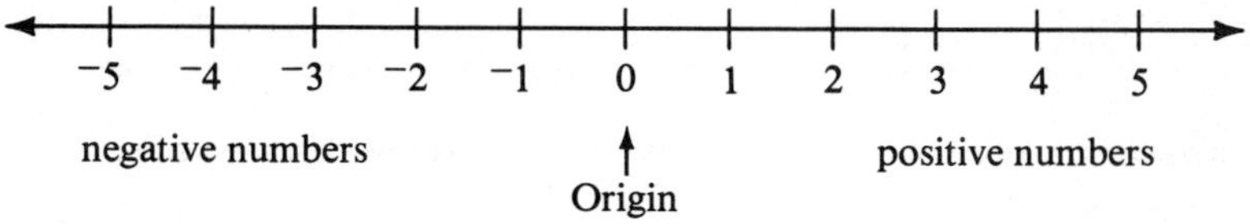

We read $^-1$ as *negative one.* We may read 1 as *positive one,* or simply *one.* For emphasis, we may use the symbol $^+1$ for positive one.

Any pair of numbers, such as 3 and $^-3$, that are the same distance from the origin but in opposite directions are called **opposites.** The opposite of 3 is $^-3$ and the opposite of $^-3$ is 3. The opposite of 0 is 0.

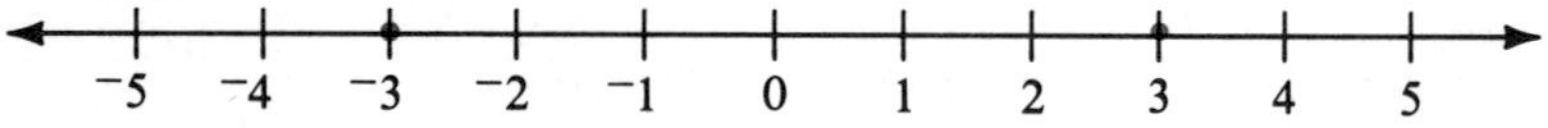

We use the symbol $|^-3|$, read *the absolute value of* $^-3$, to represent the distance between $^-3$ and 0. Because $^-3$ is 3 units from the origin, $|^-3| = 3$. In general, $|n|$ (read *the absolute value of n*) represents the distance between the number n and the origin.

The whole numbers, 0, 1, 2, 3, . . . , together with their opposites, 0, $^-1$, $^-2$, $^-3$, . . . , form the set of numbers called the **integers:**

$$\ldots, {}^-3, {}^-2, {}^-1, 0, 1, 2, 3, \ldots.$$

The **positive integers** are the numbers 1, 2, 3, . . . , and the **negative integers** are the numbers $^-1$, $^-2$, $^-3$, ... Although 0 is an integer, it is neither positive nor negative.

EXAMPLE 1 Express as an integer.

a. $|^-5|$ **b.** $|0|$

Solution **a.** $|^{-}5|$ represents the distance between 0 and the number $^{-}5$. Thus $|^{-}5| = 5$.

b. $|0|$ represents the distance between 0 and 0. Thus $|0| = 0$.

EXAMPLE 2 Arrange $^{-}3$, 1, $^{-}4$, 0, $^{-}1$ in order from least to greatest.

Solution We can graph the numbers on a number line, with 1 at the right of 0.

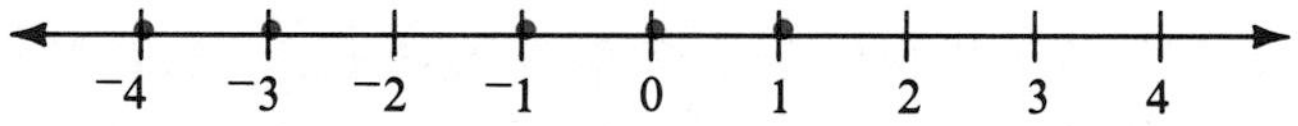

Reading the coordinates of the points from left to right will order the numbers from least to greatest. $^{-}4, ^{-}3, ^{-}1, 0, 1$

Class Exercises

Name an integer that represents each of the following.

1. 15 s before blastoff of a rocket
2. A gain of 6 yd in a football play
3. A withdrawal of 90 dollars from a bank account
4. An elevation of 350 ft below sea level
5. The opposite of 80
6. The opposite of $^{-}2$
7. The absolute value of $^{-}14$
8. The absolute value of 27
9. Name two integers, each of which is 12 units from 0.
10. If $|n| = 15$, then $n = \underline{\ ?\ }$ or $n = \underline{\ ?\ }$.

Replace ? with > or < to make a true statement.

11. a. $^{-}6 \underline{\ ?\ } ^{-}2$ **b.** $|^{-}6| \underline{\ ?\ } |^{-}2|$ **12. a.** $4 \underline{\ ?\ } ^{-}5$ **b.** $|4| \underline{\ ?\ } |^{-}5|$

Written Exercises

Graph the integers in each exercise on the same number line.

A **1.** 0, 1, $^{-}1$, 3, $^{-}3$ **2.** 0, 2, $^{-}2$, 5, $^{-}5$ **3.** 6, 0, $^{-}4$, $^{-}9$, 7 **4.** $^{-}1$, 3, $^{-}8$, 4, $^{-}6$

Graph the number and its opposite on the same number line.

5. 3 **6.** 10 **7.** $^{-}7$ **8.** $^{-}2$ **9.** 0 **10.** $^{-}4$

Replace _?_ with > or < to make a true statement.

11. $^-3$ _?_ $^-4$ **12.** $^-2$ _?_ 1 **13.** 7 _?_ $^-8$

14. 0 _?_ $^-2$ **15.** $^-11$ _?_ 0 **16.** $^-7$ _?_ 10

Express as an integer.

17. $|^-3|$ **18.** $|^-6|$ **19.** $|0|$ **20.** $|12|$ **21.** $|9|$ **22.** $|^-7|$ **23.** $|^-8|$ **24.** $|^-1|$

Write the integers in order from least to greatest.

25. 6, $^-15$, 0, $^-2$

26. $^-3$, 1, 0, $^-7$

27. $^-12$, 7, $^-8$, 1, $^-1$

28. 0, 2, $^-5$, $^-9$, 10

29. $^-10$, 4, 14, $^-14$, 8

30. 3, 9, $^-13$, 11, $^-15$

For Exercises 31-42, (a) list the integers that can replace *n* to make the statement true, and (b) graph the integers on the number line.

B **31.** $|n| = 6$ **32.** $|n| = 3$ **33.** $|n| = 4$

34. $|n| = 5$ **35.** $|n| = 0$ **36.** $|n| = 14$

37. $|n| < 2$ **38.** $|n| < 5$ **39.** $|n| \leq 4$

40. $|n| \leq 7$ **41.** $2 < |n| < 8$ **42.** $0 < |n| < 3$

Complete with the word *positive* or *negative*.

C **43.** If an integer is equal to its absolute value, then the integer must be a __?__ integer or 0.

44. If an integer is equal to the opposite of its absolute value, then the integer must be a __?__ integer or 0.

45. Explain why there is no number that can replace *n* to make the equation $|n| = {}^-3$ true.

Review Exercises

Replace _?_ with the symbols < or > to make a true statement.

1. 43.8 _?_ 4.38 **2.** 27.35 _?_ 273.5 **3.** 0.064 _?_ 0.0597

4. 0.003 _?_ 0.02 **5.** 0.182 _?_ 1.082 **6.** 5.407 _?_ 5.413

7. 98.04 _?_ 09.007 **8.** 48.066 _?_ 46.06 **9.** 0.0705 _?_ 0.705

3-2 Decimals on the Number Line

The graphs of the *positive decimal* 2.5 and its opposite, the *negative decimal* $^{-}2.5$, are shown on the number line below. We graph 2.5 by locating the point that is 2.5 units to the *right* of 0, and we graph $^{-}2.5$ by locating the point that is 2.5 units to the *left* of 0.

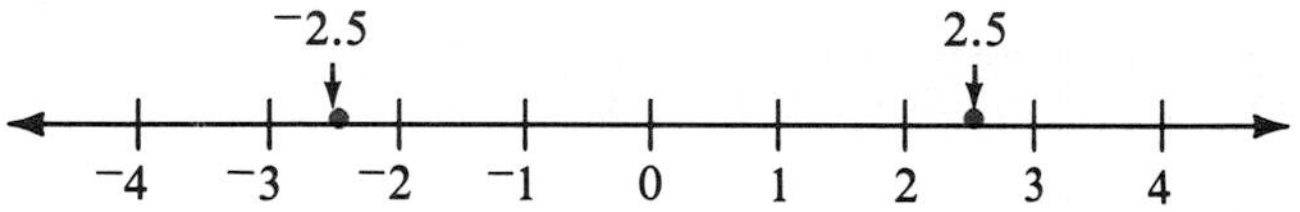

The positive decimals together with the negative decimals and 0 form the set of *decimal numbers.* The set of decimal numbers includes all of the whole numbers and all of the integers.

EXAMPLE 1 Write the following numbers in order from least to greatest.

$^{-}2$, 4.1, 0.2, $^{-}2.6$, $^{-}1.34$

Solution We can graph the given numbers on a number line.

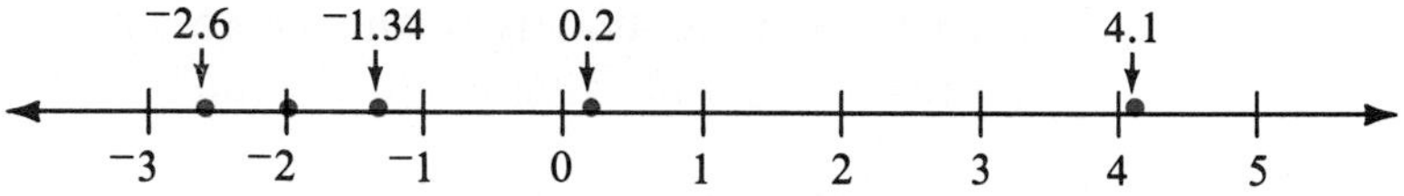

Reading the coordinates from left to right will give the numbers in order from least to greatest.

$^{-}2.6$, $^{-}2$, $^{-}1.34$, 0.2, 4.1

We have been representing decimals by their graphs, that is, by dots on a number line. We can also use directed line segments or arrows to illustrate decimals. Arrows that point to the *left* (the negative direction) represent negative numbers. Arrows that point to the *right* (the positive direction) represent positive numbers.

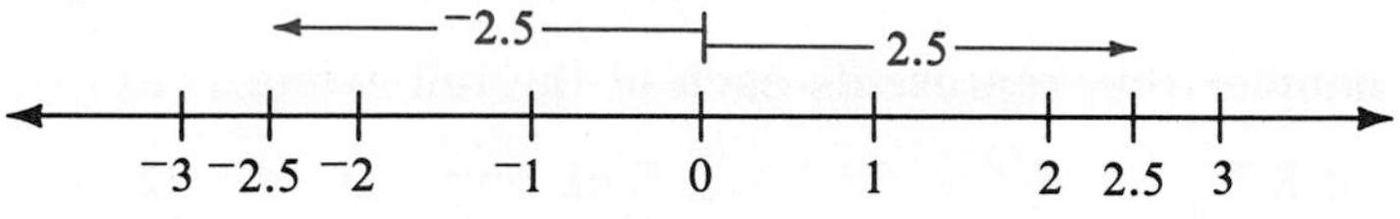

Notice in the diagram above that both the arrow representing $^{-}2.5$ and the arrow representing 2.5 have length 2.5.

An arrow representing a number may have any point on the number line as its starting point, as long as it has length and direction indicated by that number. The length of the arrow is the absolute value of the number that the arrow represents. The direction of the arrow is determined by the sign of the number.

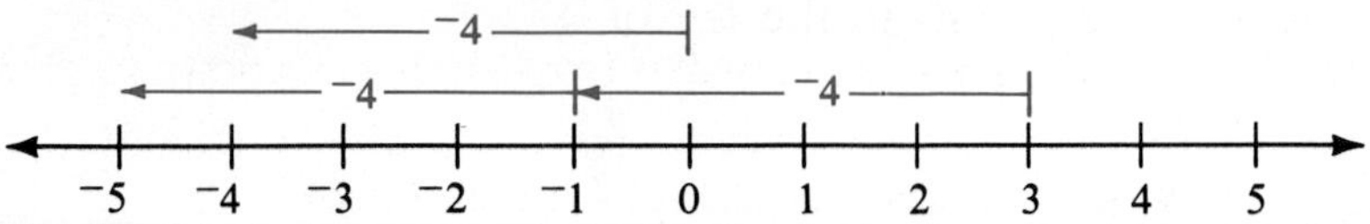

On the number line above, each arrow represents the decimal number $^{-}4$, for each has length 4 and points to the left.

EXAMPLE 2 What number is represented by the arrow above the number line below?

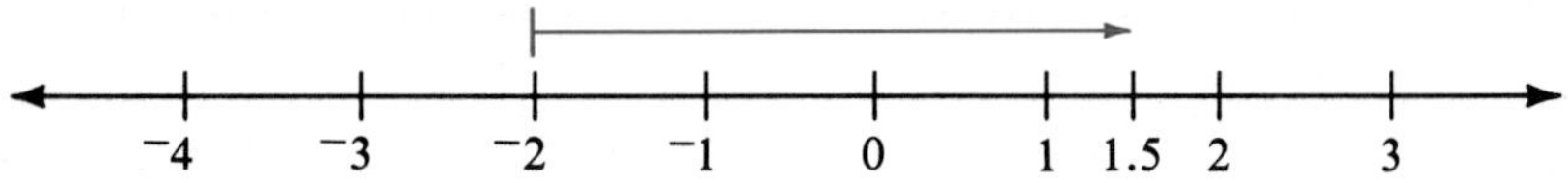

Solution The starting point of the arrow is $^{-}2$ and the endpoint is 1.5. The arrow points to the right and is 3.5 units long. Thus, the arrow represents the positive decimal number 3.5.

EXAMPLE 3 An arrow representing the number $^{-}7$ has starting point 3. What is its endpoint?

Solution Draw a number line. Starting at 3, draw an arrow 7 units long in the negative direction (left). The endpoint of the arrow is $^{-}4$.

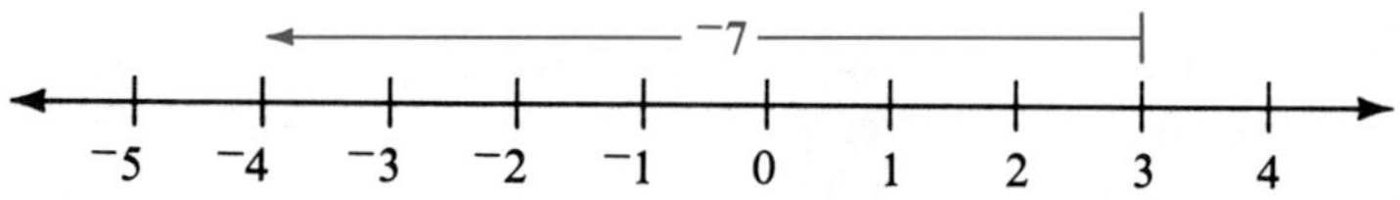

Class Exercises

Name a decimal number that represents each of the following.

1. The opposite of 8.71

2. The opposite of $^{-}10.16$

3. A discount of fifty-nine cents

4. A rise in body temperature of 0.6°C

5. The absolute value of $^{-}67.5$

6. The absolute value of 9.07

7. Name the letter written above the graph of the given number.

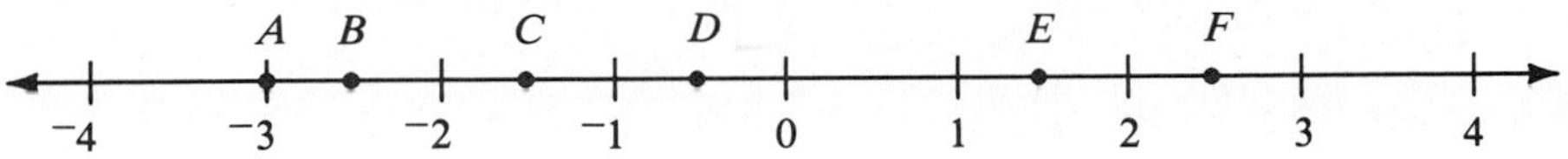

a. $^{-}0.5$ **b.** $^{-}1.5$ **c.** 1.5 **d.** $^{-}2.5$

8. State the numbers in Exercise 7 in order from least to greatest.

Name the number represented by each arrow described below.

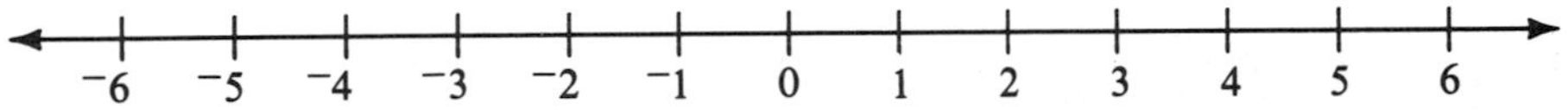

9. Starting point at 0, endpoint at $^{-}2.5$

10. Starting point at $^{-}1$, endpoint at 3

11. Starting point at 2, endpoint at $^{-}4$

12. Starting point at $^{-}0.5$, endpoint at 5

Written Exercises

Graph the numbers in each exercise on the same number line.

A **1.** $^{-}2$, $^{-}3.5$, 0 **2.** 3.2, $^{-}4$, $^{-}3.2$ **3.** $^{-}1.5$, $^{-}7$, $^{-}3.25$ **4.** $^{-}0.9$, $^{-}1$, $^{-}4.1$

Graph the number and its opposite on the same number line.

5. 2.25 **6.** 1.9 **7.** $^{-}0.5$ **8.** $^{-}3.1$

9. $^{-}4.2$ **10.** 0.75 **11.** 0.3 **12.** 5.5

Write the decimal number that is equal to each of the following.

13. $|^{-}2.36|$ **14.** $|1.921|$ **15.** $|^{-}16|$ **16.** $|^{-}100|$ **17.** $|3.03|$ **18.** $|^{-}0.2|$

Replace _?_ with < or > to make a true statement.

19. $^{-}2.93$ _?_ 1.1 **20.** 4 _?_ $^{-}0.5$ **21.** $^{-}8.1$ _?_ 2.3

22. $^{-}1.95$ _?_ $^{-}1.96$ **23.** $^{-}5.01$ _?_ $^{-}4.99$ **24.** $^{-}2.99$ _?_ $^{-}2.98$

25. 0.1 _?_ $^{-}18.25$ **26.** 12.2 _?_ $^{-}13.3$ **27.** $^{-}3.7$ _?_ 3.07

Write the numbers in order from least to greatest.

28. $^{-}2.72$, $^{-}3$, 0.03, $^{-}3.5$, 0.2

29. 6.3, $^{-}8$, $^{-}7.6$, $^{-}1.75$, 6.03

30. 0, 2.99, $^{-}10$, $^{-}0.1$, $^{-}0.01$

31. $^{-}100.5$, $^{-}2$, 3.11, $^{-}2.1$, $^{-}46.8$

32. $^{-}0.5$, $^{-}0.05$, $^{-}5$, $^{-}50$, 500

33. $^{-}0.3$, 30.3, $^{-}0.33$, $^{-}3.3$, 33

Draw an arrow to represent each decimal number described below.

34. The number 3, with starting point $^{-}1$

35. The number 2.5, with starting point $^{-}0.5$

36. The number $^{-}5$, with starting point 1.5

37. The number $^{-}3$, with starting point $^{-}0.5$

38. The number 5.5, with starting point $^{-}3$

39. The number $^{-}4$, with endpoint $^{-}2$

40. The number $^{-}2$, with endpoint 5

List the decimal numbers that can replace x to make the statement true.

B **41.** $|x| = 4.1$ **42.** $|x| = 0.001$ **43.** $|x| = 26.3$

44. $|x| = 0$ **45.** $|x| = |^{-}1.19|$ **46.** $|x| = |^{-}2.2|$

Copy and complete the chart so that the two arrows represent the same decimal number.

	Arrow 1		Arrow 2	
	Starting Point	**Endpoint**	**Starting Point**	**Endpoint**
47.	$^{-}2.5$	$^{-}7$	0	?
48.	?	4	1.5	$^{-}1.5$
49.	$^{-}0.5$	8.5	?	$^{-}3$
50.	4	$^{-}6.25$	?	$^{-}2$

For Exercises 51–54, (a) list the *integers* that can replace n to make the statement true, and (b) show their graphs on a number line.

51. $|n| < 4.3$ **52.** $|n| < 2.99$ **53.** $|n| \leq 5.001$ **54.** $|n| \leq 0.08$

Review Exercises

Use the properties to simplify the expression. Name the property or properties used.

1. $2(4.5 + 1.07)$ **2.** $3.7 + 12.5 + 0.5$ **3.** 1×27.18

4. $8.69 + 4.78 + 2.31$ **5.** $7(30 - 11.1)$ **6.** $(44 \times 0.3) + (44 \times 0.7)$

7. $6.25 \times 43 \times 4$ **8.** $0.2 \times 3.7 \times 0.5$ **9.** $17.6 \times 283 \times 0$

3-3 Adding Positive and Negative Numbers

We can use arrows on the number line, as shown below, to add two positive numbers or to add two negative numbers. We draw a solid arrow with starting point 0 to represent the first addend. We draw another solid arrow with *starting point at the endpoint of the first arrow* to represent the second addend. To represent the sum, we draw a dashed arrow from the starting point of the first arrow to the endpoint of the second arrow.

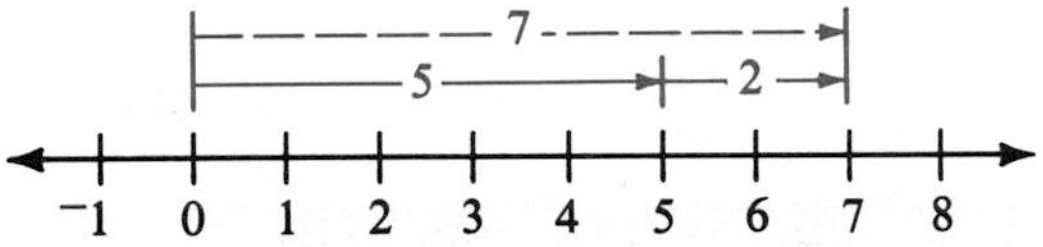

$5 + 2 = 7$

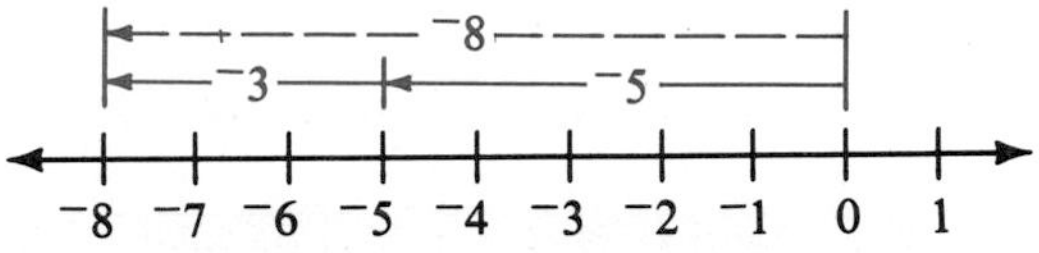

$^-5 + {}^-3 = {}^-8$

In each case, if we add the absolute values of the addends, we obtain the absolute value of the sum. The sum has the same sign as the addends.

Rules

The sum of two positive numbers is positive.

The sum of two negative numbers is negative.

EXAMPLE 1 Find the sum. **a.** $2.5 + 4.3$ **b.** $^-7 + {}^-1.5$

Solution **a.** Since the addends are positive, the sum is positive.

$$2.5 + 4.3 = 6.8$$

b. Since the addends are negative, the sum is negative.

$$^-7 + {}^-1.5 = {}^-8.5$$

We can also use arrows on the number line to add a positive and a negative number. The sum of a positive and a negative number may be positive, negative, or zero, as shown in the following illustrations.

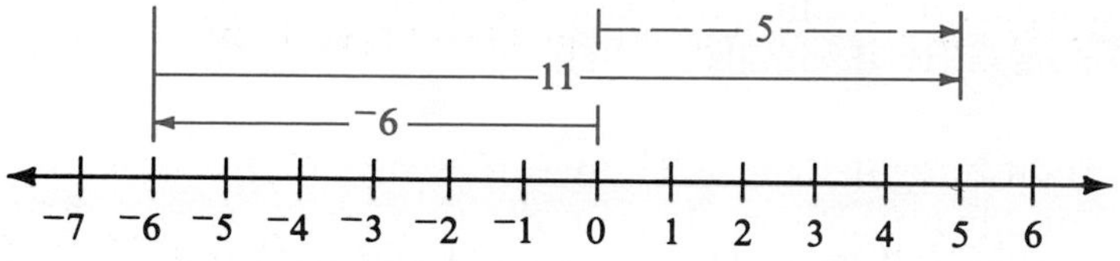

$^-6 + 11 = 5$

The positive number 11 has greater absolute value than the negative number $^-6$. Thus the sum is positive.

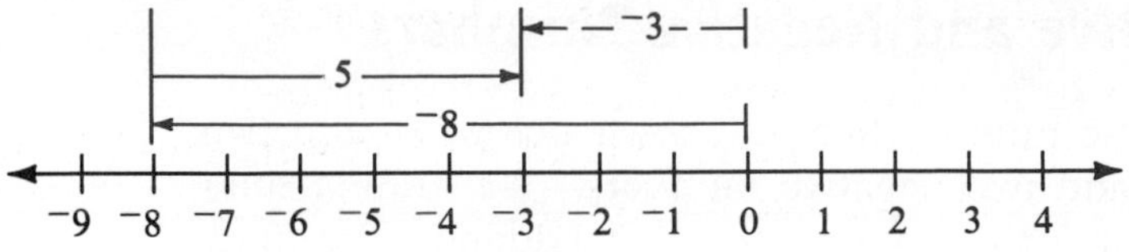

$^{-}8 + 5 = {}^{-}3$

The negative number $^{-}8$ has greater absolute value than the positive number 5. Thus the sum is negative.

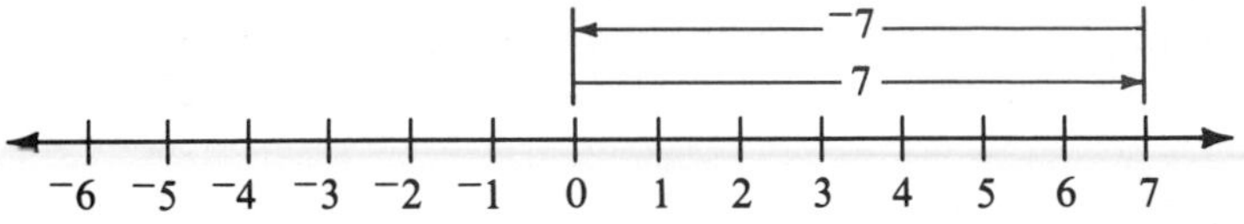

$7 + {}^{-}7 = 0$

The positive number 7 and the negative number $^{-}7$ are opposites and thus have the same absolute value. The sum is zero.

Notice that, in each case, the absolute value of the sum is the *difference* of the absolute values of the addends. The sum has the same sign as the addend with the greater absolute value.

Rules

The sum of a positive number and a negative number is

1. positive if the positive number has the greater absolute value.
2. negative if the negative number has the greater absolute value.
3. zero if the numbers have the same absolute value.

EXAMPLE 2 Find the sum.

a. $3.5 + {}^{-}10.5$ **b.** $^{-}7.6 + 12.2$ **c.** $^{-}4.8 + 0$

Solution

a. The negative addend has the greater absolute value, so the sum is negative. $3.5 + {}^{-}10.5 = {}^{-}7$

b. The positive addend has the greater absolute value, so the sum is positive. $^{-}7.6 + 12.2 = 4.6$

c. Think of adding 0 as *moving no units* on the number line. Thus, $^{-}4.8 + 0 = {}^{-}4.8$.

As shown in Example 2, part (c), the addition property of zero holds for the positive and negative decimals. All of the properties for positive decimals hold for negative decimals as well.

EXAMPLE 3 Sally Wright bought some stock in ABC Computer Company. The stock went down \$2.50 per share in the first week, went up \$3.00 in the second week, and went down \$1.25 in the third week. If Sally paid \$30.50 per share for the stock, did she gain or lose money?

Solution

- The question asks if Sally gained or lost money.
- Given information: Sally paid \$30.50 per share
  price went down \$2.50, went up \$3.00, went down \$1.25
- First, find the new price per share. Express the given information as a sum of positive and negative decimals.

$$30.50 + {}^{-}2.50 + 3 + {}^{-}1.25 = (30.50 + 3) + ({}^{-}2.50 + {}^{-}1.25)$$
$$= 33.50 + {}^{-}3.75$$
$$= 29.75$$

  To find whether Sally gained or lost money, compare the new price per share to the price paid per share.

$$29.75 < 30.50$$

- Because the new price per share is less than the price paid per share, Sally lost money.

Problem Solving Reminder
Many problems involve *more than one step,* but the steps may not always involve operations. In Example 3, we used addition in the first step, but in the second step we compared the answer to the first step with an amount given in the problem.

Class Exercises

State the addition fact illustrated by the diagram.

1.
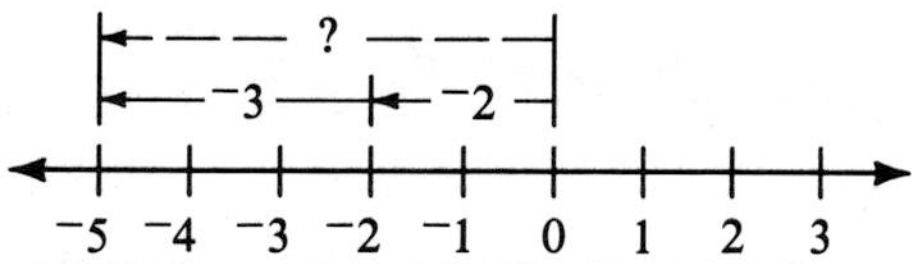

2.
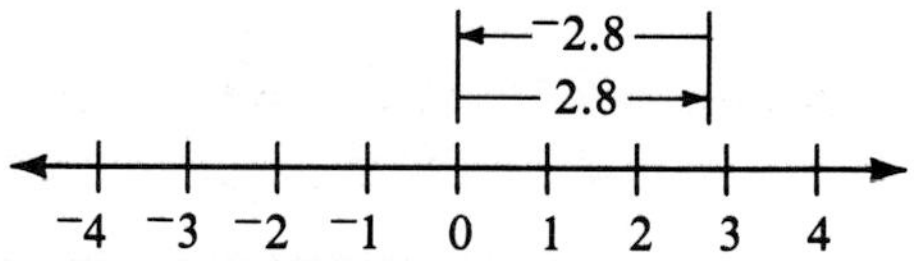

3.
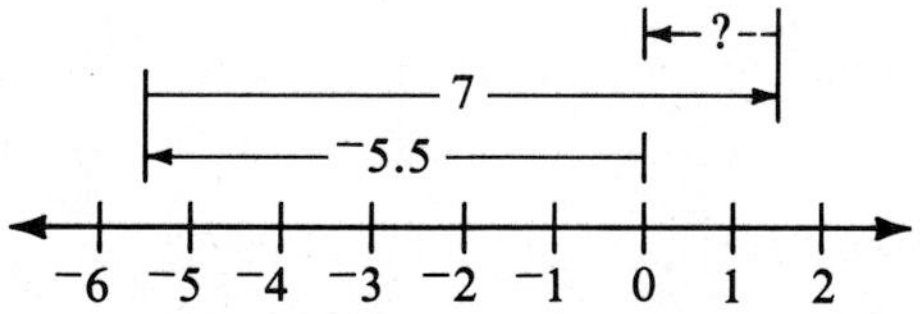

4.
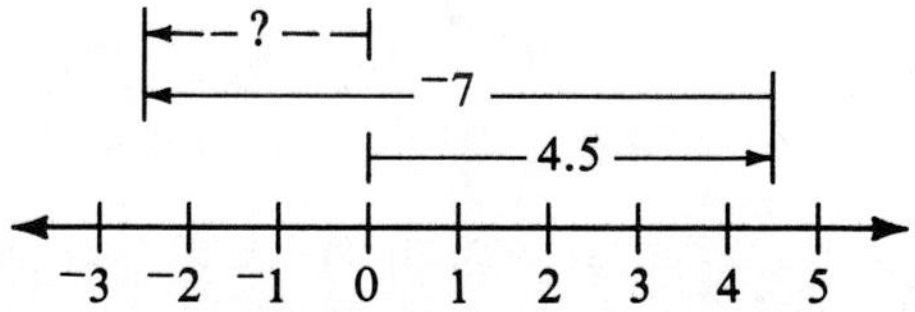

Without computing the exact sum, state whether the sum is positive, negative, or 0.

5. ${}^{-}3.4 + {}^{-}2.6$

6. $25.7 + {}^{-}8.6 + {}^{-}25.7$

7. $2.37 + {}^{-}9.99$

8. ${}^{-}6.8 + 11.5$

9. $36.3 + 0.14 + {}^{-}36.3$

10. ${}^{-}15.4 + 0 + {}^{-}3.2$

Written Exercises

Find the sum by using arrows on a number line.

A **1.** $^{-}3 + {}^{-}8$ **2.** $10.7 + {}^{-}10.7$ **3.** $^{-}12.5 + 22$ **4.** $2.9 + {}^{-}6.9$

Find the sum.

5. $^{-}2 + {}^{-}17$ **6.** $^{-}8 + {}^{-}9$ **7.** $8.3 + {}^{-}21.3$ **8.** $^{-}4.6 + 38.6$

9. $^{-}0.1 + {}^{-}0.2$ **10.** $^{-}1.82 + {}^{-}3.68$ **11.** $16.5 + {}^{-}16.5$ **12.** $^{-}8.7 + 3.4$

13. $16.9 + {}^{-}0.7$ **14.** $^{-}51.3 + 51.3$ **15.** $12.37 + {}^{-}8.2$ **16.** $^{-}85 + {}^{-}41$

17. $^{-}16 + {}^{-}68$ **18.** $4.1 + {}^{-}13$ **19.** $26.4 + {}^{-}15.9$ **20.** $9.65 + {}^{-}10.1$

21. $^{-}13.12 + {}^{-}5.6$ **22.** $^{-}26.01 + 26.0$ **23.** $2.9 + {}^{-}29$ **24.** $7 + {}^{-}13.2$

25. $81.9 + {}^{-}81.9$ **26.** $32.8 + {}^{-}36$ **27.** $0 + {}^{-}0.12$ **28.** $^{-}7.9 + 0$

29. $^{-}4.2 + {}^{-}6.5 + 17$ **30.** $7.1 + {}^{-}9 + 2.3$ **31.** $5 + {}^{-}16.9 + 1.1$

32. $^{-}8.6 + {}^{-}17.1 + {}^{-}4.3$ **33.** $^{-}3.3 + {}^{-}7.25 + 3.3$ **34.** $0.98 + {}^{-}13.4 + {}^{-}0.98$

What value of the variable makes the statement true?

35. $^{-}8 + x = 4$ **36.** $x + 4 = {}^{-}9$ **37.** $^{-}41 + x = {}^{-}53$

38. $^{-}19 + x = 0$ **39.** $18.5 + x = 0$ **40.** $^{-}6 + x = {}^{-}1$

B **41.** $^{-}4.3 + x = {}^{-}6.7$ **42.** $x + {}^{-}5.6 = {}^{-}37$ **43.** $x + 18.6 = {}^{-}1.2$

44. $^{-}0.66 + x = 0.10$ **45.** $12.9 + x = {}^{-}13$ **46.** $x + 20.2 = {}^{-}5.1$

47. **a.** $9 + 6.7 + x = 9$
b. $9 + 6.7 + x = 6.7$

48. **a.** $^{-}6.3 + {}^{-}8.1 + x = {}^{-}6.3$
b. $^{-}6.3 + {}^{-}8.1 + x = {}^{-}8.1$

Replace _?_ with =, >, or < to make a true statement.

49. $(^{-}25.3 + {}^{-}8.8)$ _?_ $(^{-}12.4 + {}^{-}19.7)$ **50.** $(6.24 + {}^{-}15.9)$ _?_ $(^{-}6.24 + 15.9)$

51. $(^{-}34.9 + 27.5)$ _?_ $(9.7 + {}^{-}18.4)$ **52.** $(14.4 + {}^{-}18.6)$ _?_ $(^{-}3.2 + {}^{-}0.98)$

C **53.** **a.** $|{}^{-}3 + {}^{-}19|$ _?_ $|{}^{-}3| + |{}^{-}19|$ **b.** $|{}^{-}4.6 + 4.6|$ _?_ $|{}^{-}4.6| + |4.6|$

c. $|{}^{-}8.7 + 12.6|$ _?_ $|{}^{-}8.7| + |12.6|$ **d.** $|{}^{-}18.6 + 4.9|$ _?_ $|{}^{-}18.6| + |4.9|$

e. $|53.5 + 3.7|$ _?_ $|53.5| + |3.7|$ **f.** $|{}^{-}4 + 13.75|$ _?_ $|{}^{-}4| + |13.75|$

g. On the basis of your answers to parts (a)–(f), write a general rule for $|x + y|$ _?_ $|x| + |y|$ that holds for all numbers x and y. Explain why this rule is true.

Problems

Solve each problem by first expressing the given data as a sum of positive and negative numbers. Then, compute the sum of the numbers and answer the questions.

A **1.** The temperature in Lynn at 7:00 A.M. was $^{-}7$°C. By 12:00 noon, the temperature had increased by 13°C, but it then decreased by 3°C between noon and 5:00 P.M. What was the temperature reading at 5:00 P.M.?

2. From the Andersons' farm, Bonnie drove 20.4 km due east to Fairvale. From Fairvale, she drove 33.7 km due west to Ward City. How far was she then from the farm and in what direction?

3. The Tigers football team gains 3.5 yd on a first down, loses 11 yd on the second down, and gains 2 yd on the third down. Do the Tigers gain or lose total yardage in these three plays? What is the total number of yards gained or lost?

B **4.** For a summer job, Tom plans to clean the Wilsons' house. He estimates that each week he will spend \$1.25 and \$3.80 on cleaning supplies. How much should he charge the Wilsons if he wishes to make a profit of \$6.50 each week?

5. Carl purchased stock in the Dependable Equipment Company. The price per share of the stock fell by \$4.30 in the first month, rose by \$2.50 in the second month, and rose by \$2.60 in the third month. Carl sold the stock for \$22.00 per share at the end of the third month. Did he gain or lose money?

Review Exercises

Evaluate the expression when $s = 2.7$ and $t = 8.4$.

1. $(25 - s)7$	**2.** $102 \div (t + 12)$	**3.** $11(7s - 13)$
4. $(t + 6 - 4.4)t$	**5.** $(s + 4)(s + 4)$	**6.** $10st \div (t - 4.2)$
7. $st \div 2s$	**8.** $(s + t) \div (t + 13.8)$	**9.** $(t - s)(5t + 8)$

3-4 Subtracting Positive and Negative Numbers

You know that $7.5 - 3 = 4.5$. In the preceding lesson, you learned that $7.5 + {}^{-}3 = 4.5$. Thus, $7.5 - 3 = 7.5 + {}^{-}3$. This example suggests the following general rule.

Rule

For any numbers a and b,

$$a - b = a + (\text{the opposite of } b)$$

or

$$a - b = a + (-b)$$

Note the lowered position of the minus sign in the expression $(-b)$, above. We use an *unraised* minus sign to mean *the opposite of.* For example,

$-3 = {}^{-}3$, read *the opposite of three equals negative three*

$-({}^{-}5) = 5$, read *the opposite of negative five equals five*

Because the numerals -3 and ${}^{-}3$ name the same number, one may be used in place of the other. From now on, we will use an unraised minus sign to denote subtraction, a negative number, and the opposite of a number.

EXAMPLE 1 Find the difference.

a. $5 - 13$ **b.** $12.4 - (-8)$

c. $-4.6 - 1.5$ **d.** $-10.9 - (-3.4)$

Solution

a. $5 - 13 = 5 + (-13) = -8$

b. $12.4 - (-8) = 12.4 + 8 = 20.4$

c. $-4.6 - 1.5 = -4.6 + (-1.5) = -6.1$

d. $-10.9 - (-3.4) = -10.9 + 3.4 = -7.5$

It is important to read a variable expression such as $-n$ as *the opposite of n* because n may denote a negative number, a positive number, or 0.

EXAMPLE 2 Evaluate the expression when $m = -5.2$.

a. $m - 14$ **b.** $-m - 14$

Solution a. $m - 14 = -5.2 - 14 = -5.2 + (-14) = -19.2$

b. $-m - 14 = -(-5.2) - 14 = 5.2 - 14 = 5.2 + (-14) = -8.8$

Reading Mathematics: ***Using Examples***

The worked-out examples in each lesson show you how the general statements in the lesson can be applied to specific situations. If you need help as you work on the exercises, look back at the examples for models to follow or for ideas on how to begin your solutions.

Class Exercises

Complete.

1. $6 - 12 = 6 + \underline{\ ?\ }$

2. $-10 - 8 = -10 + \underline{\ ?\ }$

3. $6.7 - (-1.5) = 6.7 + \underline{\ ?\ }$

4. $-26.01 - (-8.2) = -26.01 + \underline{\ ?\ }$

Without computing the exact difference, state whether the difference is positive, negative, or 0.

5. $-4.2 - 4.2$

6. $4.2 - (-4.2)$

7. $4.2 - 4.2$

8. $-4.2 - (-4.2)$

Find the difference.

9. $3 - (-6)$

10. $-2 - (-3.5)$

11. $-1.8 - 5.8$

12. $2.25 - 4$

Written Exercises

Write the difference as a sum.

A **1.** $7 - 19$

2. $-21 - 42$

3. $6.2 - (-8.3)$

4. $-2.9 - (-11.6)$

5–8. Find each difference in Exercises 1–4 above.

Find the difference.

9. $4 - 10$

10. $25 - 34$

11. $-3 - 24$

12. $-12 - 5$

13. $9 - (-33)$

14. $14 - (-46)$

15. $-2 - (-17)$

16. $-6 - (-5)$

17. $0 - 43$

18. $0 - 101$

19. $0 - (-20)$

20. $0 - (-14)$

21. $44 - 0$

22. $-16 - 0$

23. $6.9 - 8$

24. $12 - 20.5$

25. $4.3 - 2.1$

26. $23.4 - 6.8$

27. $-16.1 - 8.5$

28. $-0.4 - 8.9$

29. $-19 - 5.6$

30. $-41.1 - 2.9$

31. $0 - (-3.37)$

32. $0 - 12.8$

Find the difference.

33. $12.4 - (-12.4)$ **34.** $-18.1 - (-25)$ **35.** $-52.9 - (-11.6)$

36. $(6 - 9.7) - 8.8$ **37.** $(-2.5 - 8.1) - (-12.4)$ **38.** $(0 - 8.3) - (-24.1)$

39. $[0 - (-0.2)] - 6.1$ **40.** $0 - [3.6 - (-2.1)]$ **41.** $5.3 - (8 - 10.7)$

Evaluate the expression when $a = -4.5$ and $b = -6.2$.

42. $-a$ **43.** $-b$ **44.** $-|b|$ **45.** $-|a|$

46. $a - b$ **47.** $b - a$ **48.** $-a - b$ **49.** $-b - a$

50. $a - (-b)$ **51.** $b - (-a)$ **52.** $-b - (-a)$ **53.** $-a - (-b)$

What value of the variable makes the statement true?

B **54.** $2 - d = -6$ **55.** $d - 5 = -13$ **56.** $-3 - d = -11$

57. $8 - d = 13$ **58.** $-7 - d = 12$ **59.** $d - (-6) = -7$

60. $-d - 4 = 14$ **61.** $-d - 5 = -9$ **62.** $7 - (-d) = 14$

63. $d - (-8) = 17$ **64.** $-8 - (-d) = -16$ **65.** $-4 - (-d) = 10$

C **66.** Replace _?_ with $=$, $>$, or $<$ to make a true statement.

a. $|13.6 - 8.9|$ _?_ $|13.6| - |8.9|$ **b.** $|-8.9 - (-13.6)|$ _?_ $|-8.9| - |-13.6|$

c. $|8.9 - 13.6|$ _?_ $|8.9| - |13.6|$ **d.** $|-8.9 - 13.6|$ _?_ $|-8.9| - |13.6|$

e. Based on your answers to parts (a)–(d), write a general rule for $|x - y|$ _?_ $|x| - |y|$, where x and y are any decimal numbers.

Problems

Solve Problems 1–6 by first expressing the given data as a difference of positive and negative numbers. Then, compute the difference of the numbers and answer the question.

A **1.** On a winter day, the temperature dropped from $-3°C$ to $-11°C$. Find the change in temperature.

2. Find the difference in the ages of two people if one was born in 27 B.C. and the other was born in 16 A.D.

3. The elevation of the highest point in a region is 1226 m above sea level. If the difference between the highest point and lowest point in the region is 1455 m, find the elevation of the lowest point.

4. Two stages of a rocket burn for a total of 114.5 s. If the first stage burns for 86.8 s, how long does the second stage burn?

5. A parachutist jumped from an airplane flying at an altitude of 1100 m, dropped 200 m in the first 25 s, and then dropped 350 m in the next 35 s. What was the altitude of the parachutist 60 s after jumping?

6. In Summit City, 78 cm of snow fell on Sunday. The snow melted approximately 5.8 cm on Monday, approximately 7.5 cm on Tuesday, and approximately 12 cm on Wednesday. Approximately how much snow remained?

B 7. Donna receives an allowance every 2 weeks that includes \$20 for school lunches. During the past 4 weeks, she spent \$7.50, \$8.25, \$5.25, and \$8.75 on lunches. How much did Donna have left from the money allowed for lunches for the 4 weeks?

8. Eric Chung had \$65.10 in his checking account on June 1. He wrote two checks in June, one for \$42.99. Eric forgot to write down the amount of the other check. At the end of the month, he received a notice that his account was overdrawn by \$22.11. What was the amount of Eric's second check?

Self-Test A

Replace $\underline{\ ?\ }$ with =, >, or < to make a true statement.

1. $^{-}4 \underline{\ ?\ } {}^{-}5$ **2.** $0 \underline{\ ?\ } {}^{-}3$ **3.** $^{-}8 \underline{\ ?\ } 9$ **4.** $|^{-}7| \underline{\ ?\ } 7$ **5.** $|0| \underline{\ ?\ } 0$ **[3-1]**

Write the numbers in order from least to greatest.

6. 0, 5.4, $^{-}4.52$, $^{-}0.25$, $^{-}54$ **7.** $^{-}3.79$, 37, $^{-}7.3$, $^{-}0.37$, $^{-}0.09$ **[3-2]**

Find the sum or difference.

8. $^{-}9.3 + 42.3$ **9.** $17.8 + {}^{-}17.8$ **10.** $8.76 + {}^{-}10.2$ **[3-3]**

11. $8 - (-27)$ **12.** $-5.1 - (-5.1)$ **13.** $0 - 36$ **[3-4]**

Evaluate the expression when $a = -6.4$ and $b = -5.2$.

14. $-b - a$ **15.** $a - (-b)$ **16.** $b - |a|$

Self-Test answers and Extra Practice are at the back of the book.

3-5 Multiplying Positive and Negative Numbers

To find a product such as $5(-2)$, we can think of the product as the sum of five identical addends.

$$5(-2) = -2 + (-2) + (-2) + (-2) + (-2)$$

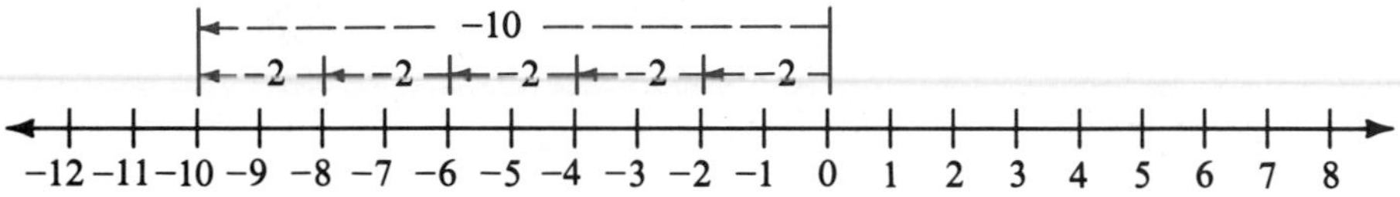

The diagram shows that $-2 + (-2) + (-2) + (-2) + (-2) = -10$. Thus $5(-2) = -10$.

To find the product $-7(2)$, we may use the commutative property of multiplication to write

$$-7(2) = 2(-7).$$

We know that $2(-7) = -7 + (-7) = -14$, so $-7(2) = -14$.

Notice that in the two examples above, the product is the opposite of the product of the absolute values of the numbers. The examples suggest the following rule.

Rule

The product of a positive number and a negative number is a negative number.

We may use other properties that we have learned for addition and multiplication of positive decimals to determine what a product of negative numbers, such as $-5(-3)$, must be. The multiplication property of zero states that the product of any number and 0 is 0. Thus,

$$-5(0) = 0.$$

Since we know that $3 + (-3) = 0$, we may write

$$-5[3 + (-3)] = 0.$$

By the distributive property, we may write the following.

$$-5(3) + (-5)(-3) = 0$$

$$-15 + (-5)(-3) = 0$$

But we know that $-15 + 15 = 0$, so $-5(-3)$ must equal 15.

Notice that the product of $-5(-3)$ is the product of the absolute values of the factors. The example suggests the following rule.

> ***Rule***
>
> The product of two negative numbers is a positive number.

EXAMPLE 1 Find the product.

a. $-4.5(8.6)$ **b.** $5.32(-1)$ **c.** $-1(-14.7)$ **d.** $-9.2(-3.1)$

Solution

a. One number is negative and one number is positive, so the product is negative.

$$-4.5(8.6) = -38.7$$

b. One number is positive and one number is negative, so the product is negative.

$$5.32(-1) = -5.32$$

c. Both numbers are negative, so the product is positive.

$$-1(-14.7) = 14.7$$

d. Both numbers are negative, so the product is positive.

$$-9.2(-3.1) = 28.52$$

Notice in Example 1, parts (b) and (c), that when one of the factors is -1, the product is the opposite of the other factor.

> ***Rule***
>
> The product of -1 and any number equals the opposite of that number.

We may use the rules for products of positive and negative numbers to multiply any number of positive and negative numbers.

EXAMPLE 2 Find the product.

a. $-3.7(2.5)(-4.8)$ **b.** $-11.1(-7)(6.5)(-3.2)$

Solution

a. $-3.7(2.5)(-4.8) = [-3.7(2.5)](-4.8) = (-9.25)(-4.8) = 44.4$

b. $-11.1(-7)(6.5)(-3.2) = [-11.1(-7)][(6.5)(-3.2)]$
$= 77.7(-20.8) = -1616.16$

Example 2, on the preceding page, illustrates the following rules.

Rules

For a product with no zero factors:

1. if the number of negative factors is odd, the product is negative.

2. if the number of negative factors is even, the product is positive.

We can use the properties of addition and multiplication to simplify variable expressions that involve positive and negative numbers.

EXAMPLE 3 Simplify.

a. $15 - 8a - 6 + 4a$ **b.** $8x - 2(x - 1)$

Solution

a. $15 - 8a - 6 + 4a = 15 + (-8a) + (-6) + 4a$
$= 15 + (-6) + (-8a) + 4a$
$= 9 + (-4a) = 9 - 4a$

b. $8x - 2(x - 1) = 8x + (-2)(x - 1) = 8x + (-2x + 2)$
$= 8x + (-2x) + 2 = 6x + 2$

Class Exercises

Without computing the exact product, state whether the product is positive, negative, or 0.

1. $-3(-4.2)$ **2.** $2.1(-0.8)$ **3.** $-5(1.6)(-7)$ **4.** $-4.5(3.7)(0)$

Find the product.

5. $3(-16)$ **6.** $-7(-12)$ **7.** $13(-1)(-5)$ **8.** $-2(-8)(-5)(0)$

Written Exercises

Find the product.

A **1.** $-3(-9)$ **2.** $4(-6)$ **3.** $-8(7)$ **4.** $-7(-11)$

5. $2(-8)(-6)$ **6.** $-3(5)(-6)$ **7.** $-2(0)(-12)$ **8.** $14(-1)(0)$

9. $-1.5(8)$ **10.** $0.6(-9)$ **11.** $-3.4(-1.5)$ **12.** $-0.4(-0.7)$

13. $2.9(-1)$ 14. $-1(7.84)$ 15. $-8.8(-1.75)$ 16. $-1.11(70)$

17. $-20(0.25)$ 18. $12(-1.2)$ 19. $-15(-30.6)$ 20. $0.24(-100)$

21. $3.9(-17.1)$ 22. $-5.6(80.1)$ 23. $-13.7(0)$ 24. $16.7(0)$

25. $-1.8(-1.9)$ 26. $-0.125(-8.1)$ 27. $-5.4(20.6)$ 28. $-8.9(30.9)$

29. $10.1(3.75)$ 30. $4.25(20.4)$ 31. $-3.72(-16.5)$ 32. $0.78(-42)$

33. $-1.7(-0.2)(-3.1)$ 34. $-9(-2.7)(-80)$ 35. $3.25(-17)(0)$

36. $-1.21(0)(-1.1)$ 37. $9.4(-3.5)(-11)$ 38. $18(-5.75)(6.2)$

Simplify the expression.

B 39. $(-1.2 - 6.5)(-1.2 + 6.5)$

40. $18 + 3 - (-12 - 7)$

41. $(-7)(2.4)(0)(-9.3)(-1) + (-8.2)$

42. $(14.4 - 200)(14.4 + 200)$

43. $(-8.1 - 0.02)(-8.1 - 0.03)$

44. $[6.2 - (-9.7)][6.2 - (-9.7)]$

45. $-4[27 - (-9)] + (-4)(-2 - 9)$

46. $(-20 + 12)7 + (-2 + 20)7$

47. $6m - 11 + 3m$

48. $-19 + 5r - 12$

49. $2q - 9 - 2q + 11$

50. $-3n + 7 + 2n - 8$

51. $-a[9 + (-3)] + a$

52. $3x + 12 - x(2 + 5)$

53. $[4 + (-3)]b - b(-6 + 2)$

54. $y(-8 + 11) + y(-9 - 5)$

Find the integer *n* that will make the statement true.

55. $-3(n) = 6$ 56. $4(n) = -28$ 57. $-9(-n) = -18$

58. $3(n) = 6(-3)$ 59. $-n(-7) = -14(0)$ 60. $-5(n) = 25(2)$

C 61. $-3(-1.5)(-n) = -18(-1)(-0.5)$

62. $-1.2(30)(-n) = -9(-0.4)(-100)$

63. $-1.5(n)(-0.8) = -12(-1.5)(-2)$

64. $-0.6(-n)(-1.9) = -18(-1.3)(0)$

65. $n(-3.7 + 61.4) = 0$

66. $-n(-1.1 - 30.6) = 0$

Review Exercises

Use the inverse operation to solve for the variable.

1. $f + 27 = 83$ 2. $n - 13 = 54$ 3. $g + 364 = 518$ 4. $w - 216 = 435$

5. $6c = 78$ 6. $x \div 17 = 6$ 7. $14j = 364$ 8. $y \div 37 = 142$

3-6 Dividing Positive and Negative Numbers

Recall that multiplication and division are inverse operations for positive numbers. For example, because we know that $4 \times 8 = 32$, we also know that $8 = 32 \div 4$. We can use the relationship between multiplication and division to find quotients of positive and negative numbers. Consider the following examples.

$4 \times (-8) = -32$	$-8 = -32 \div 4$
$-4 \times 8 = -32$	$8 = -32 \div -4$
$-4 \times (-8) = 32$	$-8 = 32 \div -4$

Notice that in the examples above, the quotient of two numbers with differing signs is the opposite of the quotient of the absolute values of the numbers. The quotient of two numbers with the same sign is the quotient of the absolute values of the numbers.

The examples suggest the following rules for dividing positive and negative numbers.

Rules

The quotient of two positive or two negative numbers is positive.

The quotient of a positive number and a negative number is negative.

By the multiplication property of zero, we know that $-4 \times 0 = 0$ and thus $0 = 0 \div (-4)$. Remember that we cannot divide by 0.

EXAMPLE Find the quotient.

a. $-3.06 \div 0.9$ **b.** $36.8 \div (-2.3)$ **c.** $-4.046 \div (-1.7)$

Solution

a. Since -3.06 is negative and 0.9 is positive, the quotient will be negative.

$$-3.06 \div 0.9 = -3.4$$

b. Since 36.8 is positive and -2.3 is negative, the quotient will be negative.

$$36.8 \div -2.3 = -16$$

c. Since -4.046 and -1.7 are both negative, the quotient will be positive.

$$-4.046 \div (-1.7) = 2.38$$

Class Exercises

Without computing the exact quotient, state whether the quotient is positive, negative, or 0.

1. $-3.6 \div (-40)$ **2.** $-0.216 \div 400$ **3.** $0 \div (-17.5)$ **4.** $850 \div (-0.05)$

Find the quotient.

5. $-28 \div 7$ **6.** $33 \div (-1)$ **7.** $0 \div -50$

8. $-51 \div (-3)$ **9.** $-22 \div 4$ **10.** $-75 \div 15$

Written Exercises

Find the quotient.

A **1.** $-18 \div 3$ **2.** $25 \div (-5)$ **3.** $-21 \div (-7)$

4. $-54 \div (-18)$ **5.** $0 \div (-7)$ **6.** $0 \div (-24)$

7. $144 \div (-12)$ **8.** $-100 \div 25$ **9.** $22.5 \div (-3)$

10. $-42 \div 4$ **11.** $-3.6 \div (-1)$ **12.** $-1.01 \div (-1)$

13. $-1.75 \div 0.05$ **14.** $-69.3 \div 3.3$ **15.** $-32.86 \div 6.2$

16. $-17.05 \div (-1.1)$ **17.** $-0.48 \div (-0.06)$ **18.** $0.06 \div (-0.3)$

19. $0 \div (-14.7)$ **20.** $0 \div (-0.25)$ **21.** $-0.9 \div 1.8$

22. $-0.042 \div (-0.6)$ **23.** $-38 \div 4$ **24.** $-45 \div (-6)$

25. $9.9 \div (-4.5)$ **26.** $46.2 \div (-6)$ **27.** $-13.8 \div (-1)$

28. $0.003 \div (-1)$ **29.** $-9.27 \div (-60)$ **30.** $0.25 \div (-40)$

31. $13.23 \div (-2.1)$ **32.** $-2.6 \div 0.52$ **33.** $-14.57 \div (-3.1)$

34. $-0.53 \div (-0.1)$ **35.** $-18.5 \div 10$ **36.** $3.84 \div (-9.6)$

Evaluate the expression when $a = -8$ and $b = 2.5$.

37. $a \div b$ **38.** $b \div a$ **39.** $2b \div (-a)$ **40.** $-3a \div b$

41. $(a - b) \div b$ **42.** $2ab \div a$ **43.** $-9a \div 3ab$ **44.** $-5b \div (-2a)$

Use inverse operations to solve for the variable.

B **45.** $-3n = 6$ **46.** $d \div 5 = -7$ **47.** $b \div (-8) = 9$

48. $-15x = -30$ **49.** $-2y - 8 = 8$ **50.** $4c + 12 = -36$

C **51.** Explain why $\left|\frac{x}{y}\right| = \frac{|x|}{|y|}$ for all decimal numbers for which it is possible to find the quotient $\frac{x}{y}$.

52. Replace $\underline{\ ?\ }$ with $=$, $>$, or $<$ to make a true statement.

a. $0.10 \underline{\ ?\ } 2.5$

$\frac{0.10}{0.5} \underline{\ ?\ } \frac{2.5}{0.5}$

$\frac{0.10}{-0.5} \underline{\ ?\ } \frac{2.5}{-0.5}$

b. $-0.21 \underline{\ ?\ } 0$

$\frac{-0.21}{70} \underline{\ ?\ } \frac{0}{70}$

$\frac{-0.21}{-70} \underline{\ ?\ } \frac{0}{-70}$

c. $-3.6 \underline{\ ?\ } -1.5$

$\frac{-3.6}{3} \underline{\ ?\ } \frac{-1.5}{3}$

$\frac{-3.6}{-3} \underline{\ ?\ } \frac{-1.5}{-3}$

Use your answers to parts (a)–(c) to answer parts (d) and (e).

d. If $x < y$ and if k is a positive number, then $\frac{x}{k} \underline{\ ?\ } \frac{y}{k}$.

e. If $x < y$ and if j is a negative number, then $\frac{x}{j} \underline{\ ?\ } \frac{y}{j}$.

Write examples similar to those in parts (a)–(c) to answer parts (f) and (g).

f. If $x > y$ and if k is a positive number, then $\frac{x}{k} \underline{\ ?\ } \frac{y}{k}$.

g. If $x > y$ and if j is a negative number, then $\frac{x}{j} \underline{\ ?\ } \frac{y}{j}$.

Review Exercises

Evaluate the expression if $x = 3$, $y = 7$, and $z = 4$.

1. y^2 **2.** $5x^2$ **3.** $(7z)^2$ **4.** z^0 **5.** $7z^2$

6. $(6x)^2$ **7.** $(yz)^0$ **8.** xy^0 **9.** $z^3 - x^3$ **10.** $8x^3y$

Calculator Key-In

Does your calculator have a change-sign key? The key may look like this: $\boxed{+/-}$. If you press this key after entering a number or doing a calculation, the sign of the number displayed on your calculator will change. For example, if you enter 116 $\boxed{+/-}$, your calculator will change 116 to -116.

Solve with a calculator that has a change-sign key, if possible.

1. $20.7 + (-19.6)$ **2.** $-55.59 + 438.2$ **3.** $-0.86 + (-27.341)$

4. $-426.38 - (-25.004)$ **5.** $-83.5(-61.09)$ **6.** $6.8(-4.17)(-1.61)$

3-7 Negative Integers as Exponents

You know by the rule of exponents that you learned for multiplying powers of the same base that

$$10^1 \times 10^2 = 10^{1+2} = 10^3.$$

Since we want to apply the same rule to negative exponents, we must have

$$10^1 \times 10^{-1} = 10^{1+(-1)} = 10^0 = 1$$

$$10^2 \times 10^{-2} = 10^{2+(-2)} = 10^0 = 1$$

and so on. We know that

$$10^1 \times \frac{1}{10} = 10 \times 0.1 = 1 \text{ and } 10^2 \times \frac{1}{10^2} = 100 \times 0.01 = 1,$$

so 10^{-1} should equal $\frac{1}{10}$ and 10^{-2} should equal $\frac{1}{10^2}$. This example suggests the following general rule.

> ***Rule***
>
> For all numbers $a (a \neq 0)$, m, and n,
>
> $$a^{-m} = \frac{1}{a^m}$$

EXAMPLE Write the expression without exponents.

a. 5^{-2} **b.** $(-3)^{-2}$ **c.** $(-4)^{-1}(-4)^{-2}$

Solution

a. $5^{-2} = \frac{1}{5^2} = \frac{1}{5 \times 5} = \frac{1}{25}$

b. $(-3)^{-2} = \frac{1}{(-3)^2} = \frac{1}{(-3)(-3)} = \frac{1}{9}$

c. $(-4)^{-1} \times (-4)^{-2} = (-4)^{-1+(-2)} = (-4)^{-3}$

$$= \frac{1}{(-4)^3} = \frac{1}{(-4)(-4)(-4)} = \frac{1}{-64}$$

Class Exercises

Use the rules for exponents to state the expression without exponents.

1. 3^{-4} **2.** $(-6)^{-2}$ **3.** $10^4 \times 10^{-4}$ **4.** $3^5 \times 3^{-7}$ **5.** $(-2)^3(-2)^{-1}$

Use exponents to state as a power of 2.

6. 8 **7.** $\frac{1}{8}$ **8.** 64 **9.** $\frac{1}{64}$ **10.** $\frac{1}{512}$

Written Exercises

Write the expression without exponents.

A **1.** $(-2)^{-5}$ **2.** 3^{-3} **3.** 10^{-3} **4.** $(-3)^{-5}$ **5.** 1^{-4}

6. $(-1)^{-6}$ **7.** $(-5)^{-2}$ **8.** 4^{-5} **9.** 2^{-6} **10.** $(-4)^{-2}$

11. $7^4 \times 7^{-6}$ **12.** $10^3 \times 10^{-2}$ **13.** $5^{10} \times 5^{-10}$

14. $6^{-23} \times 6^{23}$ **15.** $3^{-3} \times 3^0$ **16.** $2^{-3} \times 2^{-4}$

17. $(-4)^{-2} \times (-4)^{-2}$ **18.** $(-7)^{-1} \times (-7)^{-1}$ **19.** $(-2)^{-6} \times (-2)^3$

20. $(-8)^{-2} \times (-8)^0$ **21.** $6^{-1} \times 6^3 \times 6^{-2}$ **22.** $9^{-5} \times 9^{-1} \times 9^7$

What value of the variable makes the statement true?

23. $5^n = \frac{1}{125}$ **24.** $4^{-n} = \frac{1}{256}$ **25.** $3^{-n} = \frac{1}{243}$

26. $4^2 \times 4^{-2} = 4^n$ **27.** $7^3 \times 7^{-5} = 7^n$ **28.** $9^{-4} \times 9^3 = \frac{1}{9^n}$

B **29.** $3^7 \times 3^n = 3^5$ **30.** $2^{-3} \times 2^n = 2^{-11}$

31. $(-2)^{-5} \times (-2)^n = 8$ **32.** $(-10)^3 \times (-10)^{-n} = -10$

33. $144 \times 12^{-2} = 12^n$ **34.** $5^{-3} \times 25 = 5^{-n}$

35. $4^n \times 4^{-3} = \frac{1}{16}$ **36.** $6^{-n} \times 6^3 = \frac{1}{216}$

37. $9^{-7} \times 9^{-n} = \frac{1}{729}$ **38.** $8^{-4} \times 8^{-n} = \frac{1}{64}$

39. $(-5)^{-n} \times (-5)^{-3} = 1$ **40.** $(-3)^{-n} \times (-3)^{-8} = \frac{1}{-243}$

Simplify. Write the expression with non-negative exponents.

41. x^{-5} **42.** n^{-9} **43.** $a^{-3} \times a^{-2}$

44. $b^7 \times b^{-7}$ **45.** $w^{-10} \times w^3 \times w^{-1}$ **46.** $v^4 \times v^{-12} \times v^3$

C **47.** Explain why $a^m = (-a)^m$ if m is any even integer.

48. Explain why $(-a)^n = -1(a)^n$ if n is any odd integer.

Self-Test B

Find the product.

1. $4.2(-11.3)$ **2.** $-6.7(20.4)$ **3.** $7.5(-4.2)(-12)$ **[3-5]**

Find the quotient.

4. $121 \div (-11)$ **5.** $-68.2 \div 2.2$ **6.** $-0.56 \div (-0.07)$ **[3-6]**

Write the expression without exponents.

7. 4^{-2} **8.** $(-6)^{-3}$ **9.** $7^5 \times 7^{-8}$ **10.** $(-9)^{-2} \times (-9)^0$ **[3-7]**

Self-Test answers and Extra Practice are at the back of the book.

Challenge

We use the symbol $[x]$ (read *the greatest integer in x*) to represent the greatest integer less than or equal to x.

EXAMPLE **a.** $[5.4]$ **b.** $[^{-}3.2]$

Solution **a.** There is no integer equal to 5.4, so we must find the greatest integer that is less than 5.4.

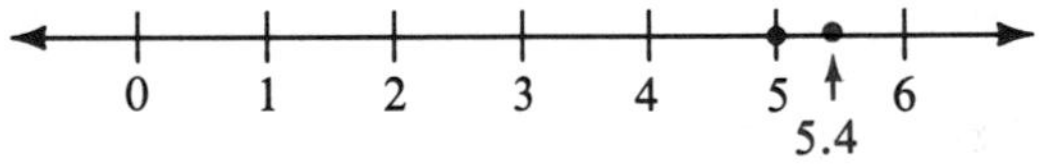

As shown on the number line, the greatest integer that is less than 5.4 is 5. Thus *the greatest integer in 5.4* is 5.

b. There is no integer equal to $^{-}3.2$, so we must find the greatest integer that is less than $^{-}3.2$.

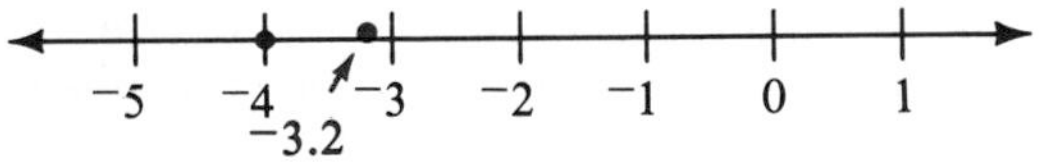

As shown on the number line, the greatest integer that is less than $^{-}3.2$ is $^{-}4$. Thus the *greatest integer in* $^{-}3.2$ is $^{-}4$.

Find the value of each of the following.

1. $[6.2]$ **2.** $[1.23]$ **3.** $[3]$ **4.** $[45]$

5. $[^{-}12]$ **6.** $[^{-}1]$ **7.** $[^{-}4.89]$ **8.** $[^{-}0.36]$

Scientific Notation

Scientists frequently deal with data that range from very small to very large magnitudes. For example, when Saturn is closest to Earth, it is about 1,630,000,000 km away. The diameter of a hydrogen atom is approximately $\frac{1}{100,000,000}$ cm. To cope with numbers such as these, a method for writing numbers, called **scientific notation,** has been adopted.

Scientific notation makes use of positive exponents to write large numbers and negative exponents to write small numbers. For example,

$$4800 = 4.8 \times 1000 = 4.8 \times 10^3$$

$$0.000507 = 5.07 \times \frac{1}{10,000} = 5.07 \times 10^{-4}$$

> ***Rule***
>
> To express any positive number in scientific notation, write it as the product of a power of ten and a number between 1 and 10.

In addition to being a convenient method for expressing very large or very small numbers, scientific notation provides an exact gauge of the precision of a measurement, based on the smallest unit of calibration on the measuring instrument. Each digit in a number that specifies the degree of precision of measurement is called a **significant digit.**

Zeros that appear to the right of nonzero digits, and to the right of the decimal point, are significant. For example,

$$0.50 \text{ has two significant digits,}$$

$$40{,}521 \text{ has five significant digits.}$$

The zeros in a measurement such as 41,500 km, however, may be misleading since it is unclear whether the number is rounded to the nearest hundred or is an exact measurement. Scientific notation provides a means of avoiding this confusion. For example, when we write 40,500 as 4.05×10^4, it means that the measurement is precise to three significant digits. When we write 40,500 as 4.050×10^4, it means that the measurement is precise to four significant digits.

In general, to write a number in scientific notation, shift the decimal point to just after the first nonzero digit. Then multiply by 10^n, when n is the number of places the decimal point was shifted. As an example,

$$3165 = 3.165 \times 10^3.$$

Note that 7.46 is written as 7.46 since $10^0 = 1$. Also, 1,000,000 is usually written simply as 10^6 rather than 1×10^6.

Write the number in scientific notation.

1. 5798 **2.** 30,090 **3.** 8,915,673 **4.** 2,175,000,000

5. 1.75 **6.** 0.003 **7.** 0.0501 **8.** 0.0333

Write the number in decimal form.

9. 3.79×10^3 **10.** 4.86×10^4 **11.** 3.01×10^5 **12.** 6×10^9

13. 5.6×10^{-2} **14.** 7.09×10^{-3} **15.** 3.99×10^{-8} **16.** 2.0111×10^{-6}

17. The diameter of a red blood cell is about 0.00074 cm. Write this number in scientific notation with two significant digits.

18. An atom of gold is about 0.0000000025 m in diameter. Write this number in scientific notation with two significant digits.

19. The radius of Earth's orbit is 150,000,000,000 m. Write this number in scientific notation with two significant digits.

20. A communications satellite was orbited at an altitude of 625,000 m. Write this number in scientific notation with three significant digits.

Chapter Review

Complete. Use =, >, or < to make a true statement.

1. $^{-}2$ ___?___ 3 **2.** $^{-}6$ ___?___ $^{-}7$ **3.** 3 ___?___ $^{-}4$ [3–1]

4. 0 ___?___ $^{-}1$ **5.** $|^{-}9|$ ___?___ 9 **6.** $|2|$ ___?___ $^{-}2$

7. $^{-}8.7$ ___?___ $^{-}0.87$ **8.** $^{-}42$ ___?___ 2.4 **9.** 3.05 ___?___ -3.55 [3–2]

10. 0.4 ___?___ $^{-}4.3$ **11.** $|^{-}5.6|$ ___?___ $^{-}5.6$ **12.** $|4.93|$ ___?___ $|^{-}4.93|$

True or false?

13. $0 + {}^{-}14.2 = 0$

14. $16.8 + {}^{-}16.8 = 33.6$ [3–3]

15. $^{-}13.2 + {}^{-}7.8 = {}^{-}21$

16. $7.6 + {}^{-}10.5 = 2.9$

17. $^{-}33 + 20.2 = {}^{-}12.8$

18. $19.5 + {}^{-}14.3 = {}^{-}5.2$

19. $37.2 - (-9.6) = 25.6$

20. $-5.8 - (-5.8) = 11.6$ [3–4]

21. $-12.2 - 13.1 = -25.3$

22. $0 - (-0.5) = -0.05$

23. If $a = -7$, $-a = -7$.

24. If $b = -2.4$, $-|b| = -2.4$.

25. $-40(0.33) = -1.42$

26. $1.2(-6.2) = -7.4$ [3–5]

27. $-17(-24.2) = 411.4$

28. $7(-8.3)0 = -58.1$

29. $-5(2.8)(-20) = 280$

30. $-12(-1)(-8.6) = 103.2$

31. $75.5 \div (-5) = -15.1$

32. $-0.006 \div (-1) = 0.006$ [3–6]

33. $-115.2 \div (-2.4) = 48$

34. $-5.04 \div 3.6 = 1.4$

35. $0 \div (-19.8) = 0$

36. $-6.21 \div (-0.23) = -27$

What value of the variable makes the statement true? Write the letter of the correct answer.

37. $3^n = \frac{1}{81}$ **a.** 4 **b.** 81 **c.** -4 **d.** 9 [3–7]

38. $4^{-n} = \frac{1}{64}$ **a.** 16 **b.** -16 **c.** 4 **d.** 3

39. $7^{-6} \times 7^6 = 7^n$ **a.** -36 **b.** 0 **c.** 12 **d.** -12

40. $(-2)^{-3} \times (-2)^n = \frac{1}{-32}$ **a.** 2 **b.** -5 **c.** -2 **d.** -7

Chapter Test

Replace __?__ with =, >, or < to make a true statement.

1. $^-7$ __?__ 8 **2.** 4 __?__ $^-5$ **3.** 0 __?__ $^-6$ **4.** $^-2$ __?__ $^-3$ **[3-1]**

Express as an integer.

5. $|^-3|$ **6.** $|7|$ **7.** $|^-12|$ **8.** $|0|$

Write the numbers in order from least to greatest.

9. $^-6.5$, $^-56$, 6.05, $^-556$, $^-0.6$ **10.** 3.02, $^-3.2$, $^-23$, 0.32, $^-333$ **[3-2]**

Find the sum.

11. $^-8.4 + 36.8$ **12.** $^-6.3 + {}^-0.12$ **13.** $13.2 + {}^-13.2$ **[3-3]**

14. $14.6 + 23.1$ **15.** $0 + {}^-11.5$ **16.** $0.89 + {}^-16.1 + {}^-0.94$

Find the difference.

17. $26.5 - 8.3$ **18.** $-4.3 - 20.6$ **19.** $0 - 13.6$ **[3-4]**

20. $-14.2 - (-9.5)$ **21.** $41 - (-11.67)$ **22.** $-6.4 - (-6.4)$

Evaluate the expression when $a = -5$ and $b = -3.6$.

23. $-a - b$ **24.** $-a - (-b)$ **25.** $-|b|$

Find the product.

26. $12(-6.37)$ **27.** $-30(0.45)$ **28.** $-0.37(-20.8)$ **[3-5]**

29. $-1(-14.27)$ **30.** $5.4(-8.2)(-3)$ **31.** $-6.11(-9)(-5.5)$

Find the quotient.

32. $69.3 \div (-3)$ **33.** $-18 \div (-2.5)$ **34.** $-19.2 \div 10$ **[3-6]**

35. $-0.004 \div (-1)$ **36.** $0 \div (-15)$ **37.** $-0.08 \div (-0.2)$

Write the expression without exponents.

38. 6^{-2} **39.** $(-5)^{-3}$ **40.** $8^{-9} \times 8^7$ **41.** $(-3) \times (-3)^{-2}$ **[3-7]**

Cumulative Review (Chapters 1–3)

Exercises

Use inverse operations to solve.

1. $9x = 54$ **2.** $17 + a > 20$ **3.** $a \div 6 < 30$ **4.** $35 - b = 7$

5. $15z = 45$ **6.** $w \div 12 < 96$ **7.** $18 + p = 35$ **8.** $n - 5 \geq 19$

Write a variable expression for the word phrase.

9. The sum of a number p and forty-two

10. The quotient when a number x is divided by three tenths

11. A number w raised to the third power plus seventeen

12. The difference of sixty-eight and a number q

13. The product of a number y cubed and fifty-nine

Write an equation or inequality for the word sentence.

14. Twenty-nine is greater than twice the sum of x and nine.

15. Three times a number m is thirty-three.

16. The sum of x and negative four and three tenths is eleven.

17. The difference when seventy-seven is subtracted from x is less than or equal to the sum when x is added to five.

18. The quotient when a number is divided by twelve is equal to the number multiplied by five.

Round to the place specified.

19. tenths: 68.461 **20.** thousandths: 4.00891 **21.** tens: 188.72

22. hundreds: 7740.68 **23.** hundredths: 37.5505 **24.** tenths: 909.09

Simplify the expression.

25. $75.8 + (6.7 + 3.3)^2$ **26.** $100.6 + (3^3 \div 9)$ **27.** $(4^3 - 6) \times (81 - 5^2)$

28. $3x + 4 - 2x + y$ **29.** $5n - 5m + 12n$ **30.** $3(a^2)(a^3)$

31. $2a^2 \times 4a^3 \times b^2$ **32.** $[6(4 - r) + r] - 12r$ **33.** $4w^5 + (w^2 \times 3w)$

Express as an integer.

34. $|-2|$ **35.** $|6|$ **36.** $|0|$ **37.** $|-100|$ **38.** $|-15|$

Write the integers in order from least to greatest.

39. 12, 15, 0, −7, 6, −20 **40.** 0, −5, 6, −6, 5 **41.** 7, 9, −3, −5, 0, 1

Problems

Problem Solving Reminders
Here are some reminders that may help you solve some of the problems on this page.
- Determine which facts are necessary to solve the problem.
- Determine which operations are needed to solve the problem.
- Supply additional information if necessary.

Solve.

1. At Angler's Supply Company, deluxe waders cost \$69.95 a pair. A similar product can be purchased for \$10.49 less at Go Fish Discount. What is the price at Go Fish Discount?

2. Alice's Mountain Goat Cheese is currently being promoted through supermarket taste demonstrations. An average of 200 samples are distributed between 11:00 A.M. and 5:00 P.M. each day. To the nearest whole number, find the average number of samples given out each hour. If the daily cost of samples averages \$50, what is the average cost per sample?

3. Cabin Fever Ski Area runs a mountain slide ride during the summer months. A single ride costs \$3.75 and a day's pass costs \$14.00. How many times would you have to ride the slide to make it less expensive to buy a day's pass?

4. Approximately 3.3 Calories are burned per hour per kilogram of body mass by walking. If a student with mass 58 kg takes 20 min to walk to school, how many Calories are burned?

5. The Gourmet Luncheonette is giving out coupons that let customers buy one large roast beef sandwich at the regular price of \$2.45 and receive one free. Deli Delights is giving out coupons that let customers deduct \$.75 from the regular price of \$1.95 for every large roast beef sandwich. Is it less expensive to buy two large roast beef sandwiches at The Gourmet Luncheonette or at Deli Delights?

6. Because of a grain shortage, the price of a loaf of bread increased by 2 cents. When grain again became plentiful, the price decreased by 4 cents, but later it again rose by 5 cents because of inflation. If the original price was 86 cents per loaf, what was the final price?

4

Rational Numbers

Hummingbirds, like the Violet-Capped Woodnymph Hummingbird shown at the right, can fly forward, vertically, and even backward. Perhaps their most unusual feat is their ability to hover apparently motionless in the air while sipping nectar from a flower. This ability comes from their specialized wing structure and its unique movement. The hummingbird pictured lives in the forests of Brazil. It is only $4\frac{1}{2}$ in. long and has a wing beat of 33 beats per second. To photograph the hummingbird so that its wings appear motionless, an electronic flash time of about $\frac{1}{1000}$ of a second was used. Exposure times of $\frac{1}{100{,}000}$ of a second have been used to study the precise motion of some hummingbird's wings and to learn exactly how the wings enable hummingbirds to remain at a fixed point with great ease. In this chapter on rational numbers, you will learn about fractions and decimals and their relationship to each other.

Career Note

Understanding the relationship between animals and their environments is the job of the ecologist. Ecologists study the influence that factors such as temperature, humidity, rainfall, and altitude have on the environment. They monitor levels of pollutants and predict their long term effects on the life cycles of plants and animals.

4-1 Positive and Negative Fractions

In any fraction the number above the fraction bar is called the **numerator** and the number below the bar is called the **denominator.** Since the fraction bar indicates division,

$$\frac{3}{5} \text{ means } 3 \div 5.$$

A study of fractions on a number line shows some important properties of fractions.

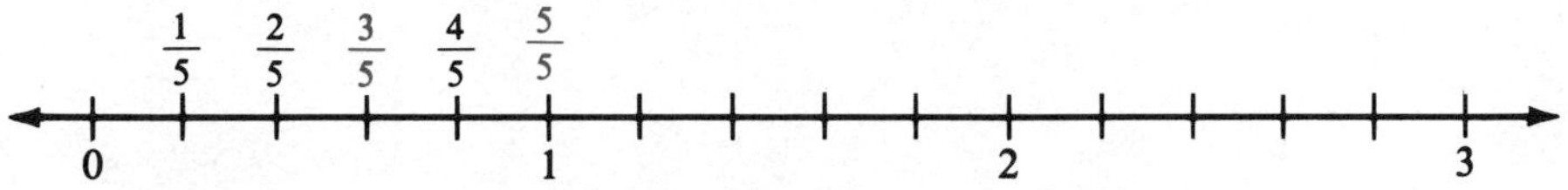

$$\underbrace{\frac{1}{5} + \frac{1}{5} + \frac{1}{5} + \frac{1}{5} + \frac{1}{5}}_{5 \text{ addends}} = \frac{5}{5} = 1 \qquad \underbrace{\frac{1}{5} + \frac{1}{5} + \frac{1}{5}}_{3 \text{ addends}} = \frac{3}{5}$$

$$5 \times \frac{1}{5} = 1 \qquad 3 \times \frac{1}{5} = \frac{3}{5}$$

We can state these properties in general terms that apply to all positive fractions.

Properties

For all whole numbers a and b ($a > 0$, $b > 0$),

$$\underbrace{\frac{1}{b} + \frac{1}{b} + \cdots + \frac{1}{b}}_{b \text{ addends}} = \frac{b}{b} = 1 \qquad \underbrace{\frac{1}{b} + \frac{1}{b} + \cdots + \frac{1}{b}}_{a \text{ addends}} = \frac{a}{b}$$

$$b \times \frac{1}{b} = 1 \qquad a \times \frac{1}{b} = \frac{a}{b}$$

$$1 \div b = \frac{1}{b} \qquad a \div b = \frac{a}{b}$$

Just as the negative integers are the opposites of the positive integers, the negative fractions are the opposites of the positive fractions. For every fraction $\frac{a}{b}$ there is a fraction denoted by $-\frac{a}{b}$ that is said to be the **opposite** of $\frac{a}{b}$. On the number line the graphs of $\frac{a}{b}$ and $-\frac{a}{b}$ are on opposite sides of 0 and at equal distances from 0. For example, $\frac{3}{5}$ and $-\frac{3}{5}$ are opposites. They are shown on the number line below.

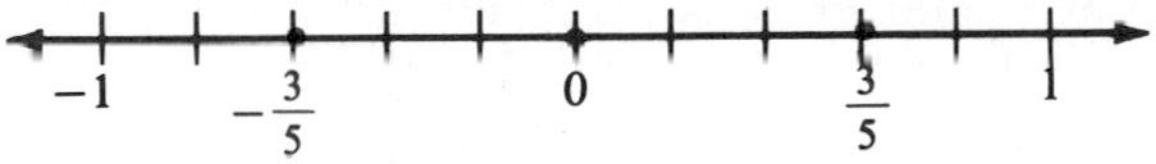

Properties similar to those for positive fractions apply to negative fractions.

$$\underbrace{-\tfrac{1}{5} + \left(-\tfrac{1}{5}\right) + \left(-\tfrac{1}{5}\right) + \left(-\tfrac{1}{5}\right) + \left(-\tfrac{1}{5}\right)}_{\text{5 addends}} = -1 \qquad \underbrace{-\tfrac{1}{5} + \left(-\tfrac{1}{5}\right) + \left(-\tfrac{1}{5}\right)}_{\text{3 addends}} = -\tfrac{3}{5}$$

$$5 \times \left(-\tfrac{1}{5}\right) = -1 \qquad 3 \times \left(-\tfrac{1}{5}\right) = -\tfrac{3}{5}$$

In an earlier section you learned that the quotient of two numbers of opposite sign is negative. Using this rule we can write the following:

$$1 \div (-4) = \frac{1}{-4} = -\frac{1}{4} \qquad (-1) \div 4 = \frac{-1}{4} = -\frac{1}{4}$$

Therefore, we can write the opposite of $\frac{1}{4}$ as $-\frac{1}{4}$, or as $\frac{-1}{4}$, or as $\frac{1}{-4}$. In general, for $b \neq 0$, $-\frac{a}{b} = \frac{-a}{b} = \frac{a}{-b}$.

EXAMPLE 1 Express $-\frac{3}{8}$ in two other ways.

Solution $-\frac{3}{8} = \frac{-3}{8} = \frac{3}{-8}$

EXAMPLE 2 Complete.

a. $\left(-\frac{1}{3}\right) + \left(-\frac{1}{3}\right) + \left(-\frac{1}{3}\right) = \underline{\ ?\ }$

b. $3 \times \underline{\ ?\ } = -1$

c. $2 \times \left(-\frac{1}{5}\right) = \underline{\ ?\ }$

d. $-\frac{2}{5} = \underline{\ ?\ } \div 5$

Solution

a. $\left(-\frac{1}{3}\right) + \left(-\frac{1}{3}\right) + \left(-\frac{1}{3}\right) = -1$

b. $3 \times \left(-\frac{1}{3}\right) = -1$

c. $2 \times \left(-\frac{1}{5}\right) = -\frac{2}{5}$

d. $-\frac{2}{5} = \frac{-2}{5} = -2 \div 5$

When we work with fractions having numerators and denominators that are integers, we are working with a new set of numbers called *rational numbers.* Any number that can be represented by a fraction $\frac{a}{b}$, where a and b are integers and b is not 0, is a **rational number.** Notice that the integers themselves are rational numbers. For example, -9 can be written as $\frac{-9}{1}$, 0 as $\frac{0}{1}$, and 26 as $\frac{26}{1}$.

Class Exercises

Name the rational numbers whose graphs are shown.

1.
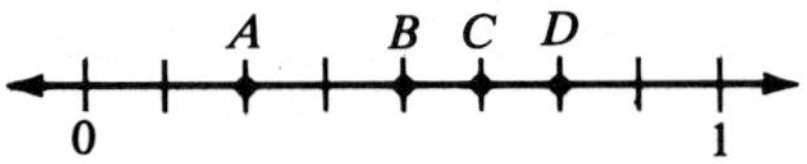

2.
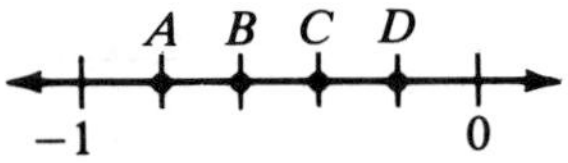

3.
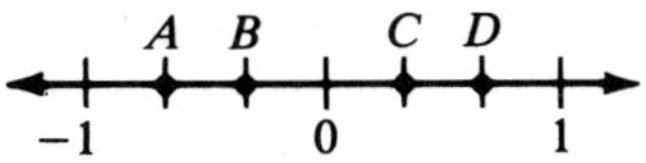

4.
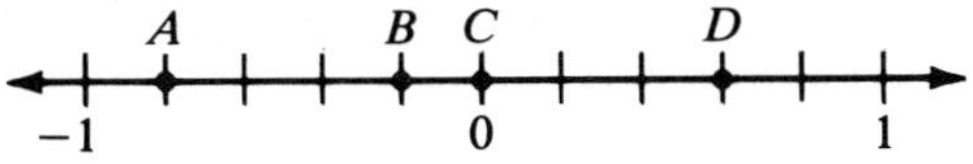

Complete.

5. $\frac{1}{7} + \frac{1}{7} = \underline{\ ?\ }$ **6.** $2 \times \frac{1}{7} = \underline{\ ?\ }$ **7.** $2 \div 7 = \underline{\ ?\ }$

8. $\left(-\frac{1}{8}\right) + \left(-\frac{1}{8}\right) + \left(-\frac{1}{8}\right) = \underline{\ ?\ }$ **9.** $3 \times \left(-\frac{1}{8}\right) = \underline{\ ?\ }$ **10.** $3 \div (-8) = \underline{\ ?\ }$

11. $4 \times \underline{\ ?\ } = -1$ **12.** $5 \times \underline{\ ?\ } = -\frac{5}{8}$ **13.** $\frac{2}{9} = 2 \div \underline{\ ?\ }$

Written Exercises

Graph each set of rational numbers on a number line.

A **1.** $-1, -\frac{1}{3}, 0, \frac{1}{3}, 1$ **2.** $-1, -\frac{1}{4}, 0, \frac{1}{4}, 1$ **3.** $0, \frac{1}{5}, \frac{5}{5}, \frac{6}{5}$

4. $-\frac{4}{3}, -\frac{3}{3}, -\frac{2}{3}, 0$ **5.** $-\frac{5}{4}, -\frac{3}{4}, \frac{3}{4}, \frac{5}{4}$ **6.** $-\frac{5}{3}, -\frac{4}{3}, \frac{4}{3}, \frac{5}{3}$

Express in two other ways.

7. $-\frac{1}{2}$ **8.** $\frac{-1}{3}$ **9.** $\frac{-1}{11}$ **10.** $\frac{-1}{6}$ **11.** $\frac{2}{-9}$

12. $\frac{-9}{10}$ **13.** $-\frac{13}{6}$ **14.** $\frac{5}{-8}$ **15.** $-\frac{3}{4}$ **16.** $\frac{5}{-9}$

Complete.

17. $\underline{\ ?\ } \times \left(-\frac{1}{6}\right) = -1$

18. $4 \times \underline{\ ?\ } = \frac{4}{7}$

19. $3 \times \underline{\ ?\ } = \frac{3}{4}$

20. $5 \div 6 = \underline{\ ?\ }$

21. $2 \div \underline{\ ?\ } = \frac{2}{3}$

22. $4 \times \underline{\ ?\ } = -\frac{4}{9}$

Evaluate the expression when $a = 4$, $b = -3$, and $c = 5$.

B **23.** $\frac{a + c}{b}$ **24.** $\frac{a - c}{a}$ **25.** $\frac{2b - 1}{8}$ **26.** $\frac{2c - b}{a}$ **27.** $\frac{a^2 - c^2}{a + c}$

What value of the variable makes the statement true?

28. $x \times \frac{1}{5} = 1$

29. $3y = -1$

30. $\frac{1}{b} = -\frac{1}{8}$

31. $-\frac{3}{4} = \frac{c}{4}$

32. $-\frac{3}{5} = d \div 5$

33. $\frac{-5}{9} = \frac{5}{m}$

Write the expression as a positive or a negative fraction.

EXAMPLE **a.** $3(7)^{-1}$ **b.** $(-5)^{-1}$

Solution **a.** $3(7)^{-1} = 3 \times \frac{1}{7} = \frac{3}{7}$ **b.** $(-5)^{-1} = \frac{1}{-5} = -\frac{1}{5}$

C **34.** $2(3)^{-1}$ **35.** $7(6)^{-1}$ **36.** $5^{-1} + 5^{-1}$ **37.** $7^{-1} + 7^{-1} + 7^{-1}$

38. $(-2)^{-1}$ **39.** $(-9)^{-1}$ **40.** $3(-5)^{-1}$ **41.** $2(-7)^{-1}$

42. $(-3)^{-1} + (-3)^{-1}$ **43.** $(-8)^{-1} + (-8)^{-1} + (-8)^{-1}$

Review Exercises

Complete.

1. Factors of 72: 1, 2, $\underline{\ ?\ }$, $\underline{\ ?\ }$, 6, $\underline{\ ?\ }$, 9, 12, $\underline{\ ?\ }$, 24, $\underline{\ ?\ }$, 72

2. What is the prime factorization of 72?

3. Factors of 90: $\underline{\ ?\ }$, 2, 3, $\underline{\ ?\ }$, $\underline{\ ?\ }$, 9, $\underline{\ ?\ }$, $\underline{\ ?\ }$, 18, $\underline{\ ?\ }$, $\underline{\ ?\ }$, 90

4. What is the prime factorization of 90?

5. $18x^2y = 3 \times \underline{\ ?\ } \times x \times \underline{\ ?\ } \times y$

6. $24ab^3 = 4 \times \underline{\ ?\ } \times \underline{\ ?\ } \times \underline{\ ?\ } \times b \times b$

4-2 Equivalent Fractions

The number line shows the graphs of several fractions.

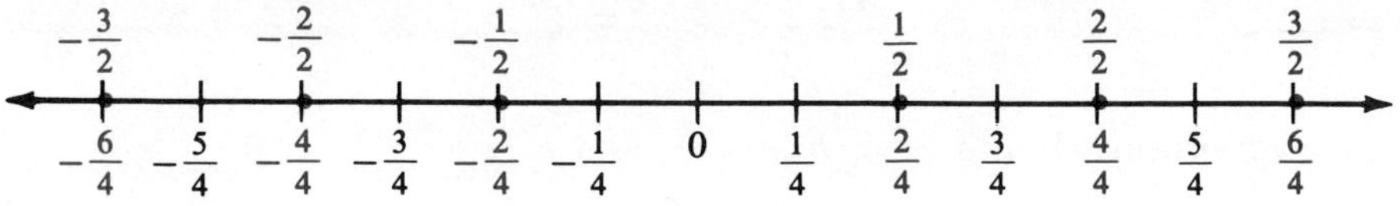

Since $-\frac{1}{2}$ and $-\frac{2}{4}$ have the same graph, they are two names for the same number. Fractions that represent the same number are called **equivalent** fractions. Thus,

$$-\frac{3}{2} \text{ is equivalent to } -\frac{6}{4};$$

$$\frac{3}{2} \text{ is equivalent to } \frac{6}{4}.$$

Notice that $\frac{3}{2} = \frac{3 \times 2}{2 \times 2} = \frac{6}{4}$ and $\frac{6}{4} = \frac{6 \div 2}{4 \div 2} = \frac{3}{2}$.

We may state the following general rule.

Rule

For all numbers a, b, and c ($b \neq 0$, $c \neq 0$),

$$\frac{a}{b} = \frac{a \times c}{b \times c} \quad \text{and} \quad \frac{a}{b} = \frac{a \div c}{b \div c}$$

EXAMPLE 1 Write as an equivalent fraction with a denominator of 12.

a. $\frac{5}{6}$ **b.** $-\frac{32}{48}$

Solution

a. Since $6 \times 2 = 12$, we write $\frac{5}{6} = \frac{5 \times 2}{6 \times 2} = \frac{10}{12}$.

b. *Method 1*
Since $48 \div 4 = 12$, we write

$$-\frac{32}{48} = \frac{-32}{48} = \frac{-32 \div 4}{48 \div 4} = \frac{-8}{12}, \text{ or } -\frac{8}{12}.$$

Method 2

$$-\frac{32}{48} = -\frac{32 \div 4}{48 \div 4} = -\frac{8}{12}$$

Sometimes we simply show the results of dividing a numerator and denominator by the same number. In Example 1, we can think of dividing by 4 as we write

$$-\frac{\overset{8}{\cancel{32}}}{\underset{12}{\cancel{48}}} = -\frac{8}{12}.$$

A fraction is in **lowest terms** when the numerator and denominator have no common factor other than 1. To write a fraction in lowest terms, we can divide numerator and denominator by a common factor as many times as needed until they have no common factor other than 1.

$$\frac{45}{75} = \frac{45 \div 5}{75 \div 5} = \frac{9 \div 3}{15 \div 3} = \frac{3}{5}$$

Sometimes it is easier to use the *prime factorization method* shown below. Recall that a **prime number** is a whole number greater than 1 whose only factors are the number itself and 1. Every whole number can be written as a product of prime factors in exactly one way except for the order of the factors.

EXAMPLE 2 Write $\frac{84}{120}$ as an equivalent fraction in lowest terms.

Solution Prime factorization of 84: $2 \times 2 \times 3 \times 7$
Prime factorization of 120: $2 \times 2 \times 2 \times 3 \times 5$

$$\frac{84}{120} = \frac{\overset{1}{\cancel{2}} \times \overset{1}{\cancel{2}} \times \overset{1}{\cancel{3}} \times 7}{2 \times \underset{1}{\cancel{2}} \times \underset{1}{\cancel{2}} \times \underset{1}{\cancel{3}} \times 5} = \frac{7}{2 \times 5} = \frac{7}{10}$$

When two whole numbers have no common factor other than 1, they are called **relatively prime.** For example, 7 and 10, as just discovered, are relatively prime. A fraction is in lowest terms when its numerator and denominator are relatively prime.

A **proper fraction** is a positive fraction whose numerator is less than its denominator, or the opposite of such a fraction, for example $\frac{3}{8}$ or $-\frac{7}{9}$. A fraction that is not a proper fraction, such as $\frac{9}{4}$ or $-\frac{9}{4}$, is called an **improper fraction.** A number, such as $1\frac{1}{4}$, consisting of a whole number plus a fraction is called a **mixed number.** Mixed numbers may be written as improper fractions, and improper fractions may be written as mixed numbers. A mixed number is in **simple form** if the fractional part is in lowest terms.

$$7\frac{15}{27} \text{ in simple form is } 7\frac{5}{9}.$$

EXAMPLE 3 Write as a mixed number in simple form.

a. $\frac{12}{8}$ **b.** $-\frac{12}{8}$

Solution **a.** $\frac{12}{8} = 12 \div 8$, which gives 1 R4.

Therefore $\frac{12}{8} = 1\frac{4}{8} = 1\frac{1}{2}$.

b. $-\frac{12}{8}$ is *the opposite of* $\frac{12}{8}$, so $-\frac{12}{8} = -1\frac{1}{2}$.

EXAMPLE 4 Write $7\frac{2}{5}$ as an improper fraction.

Solution $7\frac{2}{5} = \frac{7}{1} + \frac{2}{5} = \frac{7 \times 5}{1 \times 5} + \frac{2}{5} = \frac{(7 \times 5) + 2}{5} = \frac{37}{5}$

Class Exercises

Complete.

1. $\frac{4}{7} = \frac{?}{21}$ **2.** $-\frac{4}{18} = -\frac{?}{9}$ **3.** $\frac{3}{5} = \frac{?}{15}$ **4.** $\frac{-6}{8} = \frac{?}{4}$ **5.** $\frac{16}{28} = \frac{?}{7}$

For each fraction, state the GCF of the numerator and denominator. Then state an equivalent fraction in lowest terms.

6. $\frac{4}{24}$ **7.** $\frac{5}{20}$ **8.** $\frac{-12}{16}$ **9.** $-\frac{8}{12}$ **10.** $\frac{-9}{12}$

State an equivalent improper fraction.

11. $3\frac{2}{5}$ **12.** $-4\frac{1}{8}$ **13.** $-7\frac{2}{3}$ **14.** $9\frac{3}{4}$ **15.** $-5\frac{1}{6}$

State an equivalent mixed number in simple form.

16. $\frac{13}{5}$ **17.** $-\frac{14}{4}$ **18.** $\frac{-24}{5}$ **19.** $\frac{19}{3}$ **20.** $\frac{-32}{10}$

Written Exercises

Complete.

A **1.** $\frac{2}{3} = \frac{?}{6}$ **2.** $\frac{5}{7} = \frac{?}{21}$ **3.** $1 = \frac{5}{?}$ **4.** $4 = \frac{?}{2}$ **5.** $-\frac{14}{32} = -\frac{?}{16}$

6. $\frac{42}{-54} = \frac{?}{-9}$ **7.** $\frac{18}{27} = \frac{2}{?}$ **8.** $-7 = -\frac{?}{3}$ **9.** $\frac{-7}{25} = \frac{-35}{?}$ **10.** $-\frac{3}{4} = -\frac{?}{16}$

Write as a proper fraction in lowest terms or as a mixed number in simple form.

11. $\frac{21}{35}$ 12. $\frac{24}{40}$ 13. $\frac{11}{4}$ 14. $\frac{25}{7}$ 15. $-\frac{9}{81}$

16. $\frac{54}{81}$ 17. $-\frac{17}{3}$ 18. $-\frac{56}{72}$ 19. $\frac{-34}{85}$ 20. $-\frac{29}{5}$

21. $\frac{125}{12}$ 22. $\frac{49}{63}$ 23. $-\frac{79}{13}$ 24. $\frac{32}{10}$ 25. $\frac{-300}{7}$

26. $\frac{560}{490}$ 27. $\frac{1440}{960}$ 28. $-\frac{84}{144}$ 29. $\frac{461}{15}$ 30. $\frac{-462}{12}$

Write as an improper fraction.

31. $3\frac{1}{4}$ 32. $2\frac{1}{8}$ 33. $5\frac{3}{7}$ 34. $6\frac{3}{16}$ 35. $5\frac{3}{8}$

36. $-4\frac{3}{8}$ 37. $-3\frac{7}{8}$ 38. $-16\frac{1}{3}$ 39. $-7\frac{2}{9}$ 40. $-8\frac{3}{10}$

What value of the variable makes the statement true?

B 41. $\frac{b}{4} = \frac{6}{12}$ 42. $\frac{x}{16} = \frac{9}{48}$ 43. $\frac{a}{6} = \frac{10}{60}$ 44. $\frac{d}{5} = \frac{-3}{15}$

45. $\frac{1}{x} = \frac{4}{16}$ 46. $\frac{0}{6} = \frac{n}{12}$ 47. $\frac{5}{-1} = \frac{20}{n}$ 48. $\frac{1}{3} = \frac{8}{n}$

Simplify by writing an equivalent fraction in which the numerator and denominator have no common factors.

EXAMPLE $\frac{15x^2y}{20xy^2} = \frac{3 \times \overset{1}{\cancel{5}} \times \overset{1}{\cancel{x}} \times x \times \overset{1}{\cancel{y}}}{4 \times \underset{1}{\cancel{5}} \times \underset{1}{\cancel{x}} \times \underset{1}{\cancel{y}} \times y} = \frac{3x}{4y}$

49. $\frac{2a}{6a}$ 50. $\frac{4b}{20}$ 51. $\frac{c}{c^2}$ 52. $\frac{d^2e}{de^2}$

53. $\frac{3x}{15y}$ 54. $\frac{6n^2}{18n}$ 55. $\frac{4h}{6hk}$ 56. $\frac{uv^2}{3u^2v}$

Problems

Solve. Write fractional answers in lowest terms.

A 1. Of the 24 apartments in the building, 16 have been newly painted. What fraction of the apartments have not been newly painted?

2. John has one half dollar, one quarter, and two dimes. Express the total value as a fraction of a dollar.

3. Gene Cornell pays five cents of every dollar he earns to the government for taxes. Jim Watanabe pays $\frac{1}{20}$ of his earnings for taxes. Do they pay equivalent fractions of their earnings for taxes?

4. One day Bob worked 8 h. Janet said she worked a third of the day. Did they spend equivalent portions of the day working?

B 5. In an eighth-grade class of 30 students, there are 15 students who can speak both Spanish and English. There are 12 others who can speak both French and English. The rest speak only English.
a. What fraction of the class can speak Spanish?
b. What fraction of the class can speak French?
c. What fraction of the class can speak English?
d. What fraction of the class can speak a second language?

6. Lisa Washington, a radio reporter, is allowed exactly 90 s to relate a story. What part of a broadcast that is 30 min long is this?

7. A bulb importer advertised six varieties of tulips in a collection of 72 bulbs, with an equal number of each variety. Colors of the varieties were red, pink, maroon, yellow, white, and blue. Pearl Wang bought the collection.
a. What part of the bulbs were yellow?
b. Pearl planted the red, white, and blue bulbs in one flower bed. What fraction of the total collection is planted in that flower bed?

8. In a flock of 75 sheep, there are 3 sets of twins. What fraction of the sheep in the flock do not have a twin?

C 9. The results of a survey of 100 families showed that 75 families used the town swimming pool, 20 families used the town tennis courts, and 15 families used both the pool and the courts. What fraction of the families surveyed used neither the pool nor the courts?

Review Exercises

Simplify.

1. 7^2	**2.** 11^3	**3.** 6^4	**4.** 2^8	**5.** 1^5
6. $5^2 \times 3^2$	**7.** $4^3 \times 9^2$	**8.** $2^7 \times 6^2$	**9.** $3^3 \times 3^2$	**10.** $8^2 \times 2^4$

4-3 Least Common Denominator

In calculations and comparisons, we work with more than one fraction. It is sometimes necessary to replace fractions with equivalent fractions so that all have the same denominator, called a *common denominator.* For example, in the addition $\frac{1}{6} + \frac{3}{4}$ we may write $\frac{1}{6}$ as $\frac{2}{12}$ and $\frac{3}{4}$ as $\frac{9}{12}$, using 12 as a common denominator. We may also use 24, 36, 48, or any other multiple of both denominators as a common denominator.

The **least common denominator** (LCD) of two or more fractions is the *least common multiple* (LCM) of their denominators. The LCD of $\frac{1}{6}$ and $\frac{3}{4}$ is 12, since 12 is the LCM of 6 and 4.

EXAMPLE 1 Write equivalent fractions with the LCD: $\frac{1}{24}, \frac{5}{48}, \frac{11}{120}$.

Solution The LCD is the least common multiple of 24, 48, and 120. Use prime factorization to find the LCM.

Prime factorization of 24: $2 \times 2 \times 2 \times 3$, or $2^3 \times 3$
Prime factorization of 48: $2 \times 2 \times 2 \times 2 \times 3$, or $2^4 \times 3$
Prime factorization of 120: $2 \times 2 \times 2 \times 3 \times 5$, or $2^3 \times 3 \times 5$

The LCM is the product of the highest powers of each factor. The LCM $= 2^4 \times 3 \times 5 = 240$, so the LCD $= 240$.

$$\frac{1}{24} = \frac{1 \times 10}{24 \times 10} = \frac{10}{240} \qquad \frac{5}{48} = \frac{5 \times 5}{48 \times 5} = \frac{25}{240} \qquad \frac{11}{120} = \frac{11 \times 2}{120 \times 2} = \frac{22}{240}$$

EXAMPLE 2 Replace __?__ with $<$, $>$, or $=$ to make a true statement.

a. $\frac{5}{6}$ __?__ $\frac{6}{7}$ **b.** $-\frac{5}{8}$ __?__ $-\frac{9}{14}$

Solution First rewrite each pair of fractions as equivalent fractions with the LCD. Then compare the fractions.

a. The LCD is the LCM of 6 and 7, or 42.

$$\frac{5}{6} = \frac{5 \times 7}{6 \times 7} = \frac{35}{42} \qquad \frac{6}{7} = \frac{6 \times 6}{7 \times 6} = \frac{36}{42}$$

$$\frac{35}{42} < \frac{36}{42}, \text{ so } \frac{5}{6} < \frac{6}{7}.$$

b. The LCD is the LCM of 8 and 14, or 56.

$$-\frac{5}{8} = -\frac{5 \times 7}{8 \times 7} = -\frac{35}{56} \qquad -\frac{9}{14} = -\frac{9 \times 4}{14 \times 4} = -\frac{36}{56}$$

$$-\frac{35}{56} > -\frac{36}{56}, \text{ so } -\frac{5}{8} > -\frac{9}{14}.$$

When fractions have variables in their denominators, we may obtain a common denominator by finding a common multiple of the denominators.

EXAMPLE 3 Write equivalent fractions with a common denominator: $\frac{2}{a}, \frac{3}{b}$.

Solution $\frac{2}{a} = \frac{2 \times b}{a \times b} = \frac{2b}{ab}$ $\quad$ $\frac{3}{b} = \frac{3 \times a}{b \times a} = \frac{3a}{ab}$

Class Exercises

State the LCM of the pair of numbers.

1. 6, 18 **2.** 11, 4 **3.** 10, 8 **4.** 15, 12 **5.** 32, 48

State the LCD of the pair of fractions.

6. $\frac{1}{2}, \frac{3}{4}$ **7.** $\frac{5}{6}, \frac{1}{2}$ **8.** $\frac{3}{4}, -\frac{1}{3}$ **9.** $-\frac{2}{9}, \frac{1}{6}$ **10.** $\frac{1}{16}, \frac{5}{12}$

Written Exercises

Write the fractions as equivalent fractions with the least common denominator (LCD).

A **1.** $\frac{1}{3}, \frac{1}{12}$ **2.** $\frac{1}{4}, \frac{1}{12}$ **3.** $\frac{3}{4}, \frac{5}{8}$ **4.** $\frac{3}{8}, \frac{3}{16}$

5. $\frac{2}{9}, -\frac{1}{27}$ **6.** $-\frac{1}{7}, \frac{1}{49}$ **7.** $\frac{10}{21}, \frac{2}{49}$ **8.** $\frac{7}{18}, \frac{5}{36}$

9. $-\frac{2}{3}, \frac{7}{30}$ **10.** $\frac{5}{12}, -\frac{6}{11}$ **11.** $\frac{4}{75}, \frac{7}{100}$ **12.** $\frac{9}{56}, \frac{4}{63}$

13. $-\frac{3}{7}, -\frac{7}{112}$ **14.** $-\frac{4}{17}, -\frac{9}{16}$ **15.** $\frac{5}{42}, \frac{5}{49}$ **16.** $\frac{5}{84}, \frac{7}{12}$

B **17.** $\frac{7}{8}, \frac{5}{16}, \frac{21}{40}$ **18.** $\frac{1}{4}, \frac{1}{9}, \frac{1}{5}$ **19.** $\frac{3}{7}, \frac{7}{4}, \frac{4}{9}$ **20.** $\frac{11}{18}, \frac{1}{54}, \frac{2}{27}$

21. $\frac{1}{65}, \frac{3}{5}, \frac{9}{26}$ **22.** $-\frac{7}{8}, \frac{9}{28}, \frac{2}{49}$ **23.** $-\frac{5}{6}, \frac{2}{9}, -\frac{7}{8}$ **24.** $\frac{11}{12}, \frac{1}{72}, -\frac{7}{8}$

25. $\frac{a}{3}, \frac{b}{6}$ **26.** $\frac{m}{25}, \frac{n}{15}$ **27.** $\frac{h}{25}, \frac{h}{100}, \frac{h}{125}$ **28.** $\frac{a}{2}, \frac{b}{3}, \frac{c}{4}$

Write the fractions as equivalent fractions with a common denominator.

29. $\frac{1}{c}, \frac{2}{3c}$ **30.** $\frac{1}{x}, \frac{1}{y}$ **31.** $\frac{3}{x}, \frac{1}{y}, \frac{5}{z}$ **32.** $\frac{-1}{r}, \frac{2}{rs}, \frac{r}{s}$

Replace _?_ with <, >, or = to make a true statement.

33. $\frac{1}{3}$ _?_ $\frac{3}{6}$

34. $\frac{3}{4}$ _?_ $\frac{5}{8}$

35. $-\frac{2}{3}$ _?_ $-\frac{7}{12}$

36. $-\frac{5}{8}$ _?_ $-\frac{5}{16}$

37. $-\frac{3}{5}$ _?_ $-\frac{5}{7}$

38. $-\frac{2}{4}$ _?_ $-\frac{3}{5}$

39. $\frac{7}{21}$ _?_ $\frac{9}{27}$

40. $\frac{7}{15}$ _?_ $\frac{11}{20}$

41. $\frac{8}{45}$ _?_ $\frac{13}{75}$

42. $\frac{5}{24}$ _?_ $\frac{8}{21}$

43. $-\frac{3}{34}$ _?_ $-\frac{5}{39}$

44. $\frac{27}{36}$ _?_ $\frac{6}{8}$

C **45.** Let $\frac{a}{b}$ and $\frac{c}{d}$ be fractions with $b > 0$ and $d > 0$. Write $\frac{a}{b}$ and $\frac{c}{d}$ as equivalent fractions with a common denominator. How do $\frac{a}{b}$ and $\frac{c}{d}$ compare when $ad < bc$? when $ad = bc$? when $ad > bc$? Give two examples to illustrate each of your conclusions.

Review Exercises

1. $17.06 + 8.7$

2. $8.73 + (-11.2)$

3. $-4.16 + 9.03$

4. $-5.8 + (-3.24)$

5. $-9.2 - 2.6$

6. $6.4 - 11.2$

7. $23 - (-0.4)$

8. $-5.4 - (-1.82)$

9. $-16.5 - (-31)$

Calculator Key-In

You can use your calculator to compare fractions. Simply carry out the division of each fraction to express each as a decimal. Then compare the decimals.

EXAMPLE Which is greater, $\frac{11}{40}$ or $\frac{5}{8}$?

Solution $\frac{11}{40} = 11 \div 40 = 0.275$ $\quad$ $\frac{5}{8} = 5 \div 8 = 0.625$

$$0.275 < 0.625$$

$\frac{5}{8}$ is greater.

Use your calculator to compare these fractions. Replace the _?_ with >, <, or = to make a true statement.

1. $\frac{3}{16}$ _?_ $\frac{1}{5}$

2. $\frac{6}{25}$ _?_ $\frac{3}{8}$

3. $\frac{5}{32}$ _?_ $\frac{3}{20}$

4. $\frac{25}{64}$ _?_ $\frac{37}{80}$

4-4 Adding and Subtracting Fractions

You have added fractions having a common denominator by adding the numerators and writing the result over the denominator. We can illustrate the reasoning for this rule by looking at the sum $\frac{2}{13} + \frac{5}{13}$. The reason for each statement in the column on the left below is given on the same line in the column on the right. For example, the second statement means that $(2 \times \frac{1}{13}) + (5 \times \frac{1}{13}) = (2 + 5) \times \frac{1}{13}$ because of the distributive property. All the properties that you have learned for addition, subtraction, multiplication, and division of positive and negative decimals hold true for the rational numbers.

$\frac{2}{13} + \frac{5}{13} = \left(2 \times \frac{1}{13}\right) + \left(5 \times \frac{1}{13}\right)$	By the rule: $\frac{a}{b} = a \times \frac{1}{b}$
$= (2 + 5) \times \frac{1}{13}$	By the distributive property
$= (7) \times \frac{1}{13}$	Substitution of 7 for 2 + 5
$= \frac{7}{13}$	By the rule: $a \times \frac{1}{b} = \frac{a}{b}$

The methods you learned for adding and subtracting positive fractions apply as well to adding and subtracting negative fractions.

Rules

For all numbers a, b, and c ($c \neq 0$),

$$\frac{a}{c} + \frac{b}{c} = \frac{a+b}{c} \quad \text{and} \quad \frac{a}{c} - \frac{b}{c} = \frac{a-b}{c}$$

EXAMPLE 1 Add or subtract. Write the answer to part (a) in lowest terms.

a. $-\frac{3}{8} + \frac{1}{8}$

b. $\frac{1}{a} - \frac{2}{a}$

Solution

a. $-\frac{3}{8} + \frac{1}{8} = \frac{-3}{8} + \frac{1}{8}$

$= \frac{-3 + 1}{8}$

$= \frac{-2}{8} = \frac{-1}{4}$, or $-\frac{1}{4}$

b. $\frac{1}{a} - \frac{2}{a} = \frac{1-2}{a}$

$= \frac{-1}{a}$, or $-\frac{1}{a}$

When two fractions have different denominators, we may need to write the fractions as equivalent fractions with a common denominator before adding or subtracting.

The rules for adding and subtracting fractions also apply to mixed numbers.

EXAMPLE 2 Subtract. Write the answer in lowest terms.

a. $5\frac{1}{4} - 2\frac{1}{3}$ b. $2\frac{3}{8} - \left(-1\frac{5}{6}\right)$

Solution

a.
$$\begin{array}{rcrcr} 5\frac{1}{4} & = & 5\frac{3}{12} & = & 4\frac{15}{12} \\ -\,2\frac{1}{3} & = & -\,2\frac{4}{12} & = & -\,2\frac{4}{12} \\ \hline & & & & 2\frac{11}{12} \end{array}$$

b.
$$\begin{array}{rcr} 2\frac{3}{8} & = & 2\frac{9}{24} \\ -\left(-1\frac{5}{6}\right) & = & +\,1\frac{20}{24} \\ \hline & & 3\frac{29}{24} = 4\frac{5}{24} \end{array}$$

Class Exercises

Add or subtract.

1. $\frac{3}{16} + \frac{8}{16}$ **2.** $\frac{3}{10} + \frac{6}{10}$ **3.** $\frac{5}{8} - \frac{2}{8}$ **4.** $\frac{17}{6} - \frac{4}{6}$

5. $-\frac{3}{4} + \frac{1}{4}$ **6.** $-\frac{5}{6} - \frac{5}{6}$ **7.** $2\frac{7}{8} - 1\frac{5}{8}$ **8.** $7\frac{3}{4} - 6\frac{1}{4}$

9. $1\frac{4}{8} - \frac{1}{8}$ **10.** $-1\frac{3}{7} - \left(-\frac{3}{7}\right)$ **11.** $-3\frac{4}{8} - \left(-2\frac{1}{8}\right)$ **12.** $-\frac{6}{n} - \frac{2}{n}$

Written Exercises

Add or subtract. Write the answer as a proper fraction in lowest terms or as a mixed number in simple form.

A **1.** $\frac{3}{4} + \frac{3}{4}$ **2.** $\frac{9}{4} - \frac{8}{4}$ **3.** $\frac{2}{3} - \frac{2}{3}$ **4.** $\frac{2}{3} + \frac{4}{3}$

5. $\frac{3}{4} - \frac{3}{8}$ **6.** $-\frac{3}{4} + \frac{5}{16}$ **7.** $-\frac{2}{3} - \frac{1}{4}$ **8.** $\frac{1}{6} - \frac{1}{3}$

9. $\frac{11}{12} + \frac{13}{13}$ **10.** $\frac{5}{6} + \frac{3}{20}$ **11.** $-\frac{5}{8} + \frac{1}{18}$ **12.** $-\frac{2}{15} - \frac{6}{21}$

13. $3\frac{1}{4} + \frac{1}{8}$ **14.** $5 - \frac{3}{4}$ **15.** $1\frac{1}{12} - \frac{5}{6}$ **16.** $-2\frac{5}{6} + 2\frac{3}{5}$

17. $-1\frac{5}{6} + 2\frac{3}{8}$ **18.** $-\frac{3}{4} + \left(-\frac{5}{12}\right)$ **19.** $\frac{3}{4} - \left(-\frac{5}{12}\right)$ **20.** $8\frac{1}{8} - \left(-2\frac{1}{2}\right)$

21. $-3\frac{1}{4} - \left(-1\frac{1}{6}\right)$ **22.** $7 + \left(-3\frac{1}{5}\right)$ **23.** $-16\frac{1}{2} - \frac{1}{21}$ **24.** $13\frac{1}{3} - 5\frac{1}{6}$

B **25.** $\frac{1}{4} + \frac{1}{5} + \frac{1}{2}$ **26.** $\frac{1}{6} + \frac{1}{8} + \frac{1}{12}$ **27.** $\frac{3}{2} + \frac{7}{4} + \left(-\frac{5}{3}\right)$

Add or subtract. Simplify the answer.

28. $2\frac{7}{12} + 1\frac{3}{7} - \frac{1}{8}$ **29.** $-2\frac{1}{3} + \frac{2}{3} - 5$ **30.** $7 - 1\frac{1}{4} - \frac{1}{2}$

31. $38\frac{7}{8} + 22\frac{1}{4} - 13\frac{2}{3}$ **32.** $101\frac{1}{4} - 98\frac{3}{40} - 10\frac{1}{8}$ **33.** $11\frac{1}{6} - 19\frac{3}{4} + 1\frac{1}{10}$

34. $\frac{13}{a} - \frac{8}{a}$ **35.** $\frac{b}{6} + \frac{5}{6}$ **36.** $\frac{2}{c} + \frac{3}{d}$ **37.** $\frac{5}{g} - \frac{3}{g}$

38. $8 - \frac{1}{a}$ **39.** $3b + \frac{1}{2}$ **40.** $\frac{2c}{3} - 1$ **41.** $-5 - \frac{3}{a}$

C **42.** $\frac{a}{6} + \frac{5a}{6}$ **43.** $\frac{7t}{4} - \frac{t}{4}$ **44.** $\frac{7e}{b} - \frac{3e}{b}$ **45.** $\frac{n}{2r} - \frac{5n}{2r}$

46. $\frac{7d}{5} + \frac{d}{10}$ **47.** $\frac{5y}{2} - \frac{3y}{4}$ **48.** $\frac{c}{2} + 4c$ **49.** $\frac{2x}{3} + x$

50. Show that $\frac{a}{c} + \frac{b}{c} = \frac{a+b}{c}$ $(c \neq 0)$ by supplying the rule or property that justifies each statement.

$\frac{a}{c} + \frac{b}{c} = \left(a \times \frac{1}{c}\right) + \left(b \times \frac{1}{c}\right)$ Why?

$= (a + b) \times \frac{1}{c}$ Why?

$= \frac{a+b}{c}$ Why?

51. As in Exercise 50, show that $\frac{a}{c} - \frac{b}{c} = \frac{a-b}{c}$ $(c \neq 0)$.

Problems

Solve. Write the answer as a proper fraction in lowest terms or as a mixed number in simple form.

A **1.** Jess is using three recipes. One requires $\frac{2}{3}$ cup of flour, another requires $\frac{7}{8}$ cup of flour, and the third requires $\frac{3}{4}$ cup of flour. How much flour will Jess use?

2. The Meyers family drove $1\frac{1}{2}$ h to a ball game. The trip home by another route took $1\frac{2}{3}$ h. What was the total travel time?

3. Joan Kent bought $15\frac{3}{4}$ yd of drapery material for \$63 at a sale. If she used all except $1\frac{1}{16}$ yd, how much material did she actually use?

4. Carl is 4 ft tall. If he grew $1\frac{1}{8}$ in. during the past year, and $\frac{3}{4}$ in. the year before, how tall was he one year ago?

5. On Monday, Kim jogged $1\frac{1}{2}$ mi in $\frac{1}{4}$ h. On Wednesday she jogged $2\frac{1}{3}$ mi in $\frac{1}{3}$ h. How much farther did Kim jog on Wednesday than on Monday?

B 6. Last year, total rainfall for April and May was $7\frac{1}{4}$ in. This year 3 in. of rain fell in April and $2\frac{5}{8}$ in. fell in May. How much less rain fell this year than last year during April and May?

C 7. A 512-page book has pages 7 in. wide by 9 in. high. The printed area measures $5\frac{3}{8}$ in. by $7\frac{3}{4}$ in. The left margin is $\frac{5}{16}$ in. and the top margin is $\frac{9}{16}$ in. How wide are the margins at the right and the bottom of each page?

Self-Test A

Complete.

1. $5 \times \underline{\ ?\ } = \frac{5}{8}$ 2. $3 \times \underline{\ ?\ } = -1$ [4-1]

3. $7 \div 9 = \underline{\ ?\ }$ 4. $-\frac{2}{3} = \frac{-2}{3} = \underline{\ ?\ }$

Write as a proper fraction in lowest terms or as a mixed number in simple form.

5. $\frac{16}{64}$ 6. $-\frac{72}{30}$ 7. $\frac{32}{42}$ 8. $\frac{-71}{48}$ 9. $\frac{68}{16}$ [4-2]

Write as an improper fraction.

10. $2\frac{1}{5}$ 11. $-3\frac{2}{3}$ 12. $6\frac{4}{15}$ 13. $1\frac{7}{12}$ 14. $-8\frac{5}{8}$

Write as equivalent fractions with the least common denominator.

15. $\frac{7}{9}, \frac{7}{8}$ 16. $-\frac{10}{49}, \frac{2}{21}$ 17. $\frac{3}{50}, \frac{6}{225}$ 18. $-\frac{8}{15}, -\frac{1}{30}$ [4-3]

Add or subtract. Write the answer as a proper fraction in lowest terms or as a mixed number in simple form.

19. $\frac{1}{3} + \frac{1}{4}$ 20. $\frac{1}{5} - \frac{1}{3}$ 21. $\frac{2}{15} + \left(-\frac{5}{6}\right)$ [4-4]

22. $16\frac{5}{8} - \frac{3}{4}$ 23. $17\frac{1}{3} + 5\frac{1}{9}$ 24. $-6\frac{3}{8} + 2\frac{1}{6}$

Self-Test answers and Extra Practice are at the back of the book.

4-5 Multiplying Fractions

To develop a method for multiplying fractions, we begin by showing that $\frac{7}{3} \times 3 = 7$.

$\frac{7}{3} \times 3 = \left(7 \times \frac{1}{3}\right) \times 3$	By the rule: $\frac{a}{b} = a \times \frac{1}{b}$
$= 7 \times \left(\frac{1}{3} \times 3\right)$	By the associative property
$= 7 \times \left(3 \times \frac{1}{3}\right)$	By the commutative property
$= 7 \times 1$	By the rule: $b \times \frac{1}{b} = 1$
$= 7$	By the multiplication property of one

In a similar way, it can be shown that $-\frac{7}{3} \times 3 = -7$. It is possible to prove the following general rule for all fractions.

Rule

For all numbers a and b $(b \neq 0)$,

$$\frac{a}{b} \times b = a$$

The rule tells us how to find the product of a fraction and a whole number. Using the rule on page 106, we can arrive at another rule for finding the product of two fractions such as $\frac{1}{5} \times \frac{1}{2}$. We begin by showing that $10 \times (\frac{1}{5} \times \frac{1}{2}) = 1$.

$10 \times \left(\frac{1}{5} \times \frac{1}{2}\right) = (2 \times 5) \times \left(\frac{1}{5} \times \frac{1}{2}\right)$	Substitution of 2×5 for 10
$= \left(2 \times \frac{1}{2}\right) \times \left(5 \times \frac{1}{5}\right)$	By the associative and commutative properties
$= 1 \times 1$	By the rule: $b \times \frac{1}{b} = 1$
$= 1$	By the multiplication property of one

We have shown that $10 \times (\frac{1}{5} \times \frac{1}{2}) = 1$ and we know that $10 \times \frac{1}{10} = 1$, so we conclude that $\frac{1}{5} \times \frac{1}{2} = \frac{1}{10}$. Similarly, we may prove the following general rule.

Rule

For all numbers a and b ($a \neq 0, b \neq 0$),

$$\frac{1}{a} \times \frac{1}{b} = \frac{1}{ab}$$

EXAMPLE 1 Multiply $\frac{1}{-3} \times \frac{1}{4}$.

Solution

$$\frac{1}{-3} \times \frac{1}{4} = \frac{1}{-3 \times 4} = \frac{1}{-12}, \text{ or } -\frac{1}{12}$$

In Exercise 44 you will have an opportunity to prove the following rule for multiplying any two fractions.

Rule

For all numbers a, b, c, and d ($b \neq 0, d \neq 0$),

$$\frac{a}{b} \times \frac{c}{d} = \frac{ac}{bd}$$

EXAMPLE 2 Multiply. Write the answers to parts (a) and (b) as proper fractions in lowest terms or as mixed numbers in simple form.

a. $\frac{5}{6} \times \frac{7}{3}$ **b.** $\frac{3}{2} \times \left(-\frac{5}{7}\right)$ **c.** $-\frac{7}{a} \times \left(-\frac{4}{b}\right)$

Solution

a. $\frac{5}{6} \times \frac{7}{3} = \frac{5 \times 7}{6 \times 3} = \frac{35}{18}$, or $1\frac{17}{18}$

b. $\frac{3}{2} \times \left(-\frac{5}{7}\right) = \frac{3}{2} \times \frac{-5}{7} = \frac{3 \times (-5)}{2 \times 7} = \frac{-15}{14}$, or $-1\frac{1}{14}$

c. $-\frac{7}{a} \times \left(-\frac{4}{b}\right) = \frac{-7}{a} \times \frac{-4}{b} = \frac{-7 \times (-4)}{a \times b} = \frac{28}{ab}$

Sometimes it is easier to divide by common factors of the numerator and denominator before multiplying.

EXAMPLE 3 $\frac{-3}{5} \times \frac{15}{16} \times \frac{-2}{3}$

Solution

$$\frac{-3}{5} \times \frac{15}{16} \times \frac{-2}{3} = \frac{\overset{-1}{\cancel{-3}}}{\underset{1}{\cancel{5}}} \times \frac{\overset{3}{\cancel{15}}}{\underset{8}{\cancel{16}}} \times \frac{\overset{-1}{\cancel{-2}}}{\underset{1}{\cancel{3}}} = \frac{-1 \times 3 \times (-1)}{1 \times 8 \times 1} = \frac{3}{8}$$

Reading Mathematics: ***Reading Fractions***

Usually you read across a line from left to right, and you read a page from top to bottom. You have learned many special ways to read things in mathematics. For example, you read a fraction from top to bottom. You read first the numerator and then the denominator of each fraction before continuing to the next word or symbol.

To multiply mixed numbers, first write each mixed number as an improper fraction.

EXAMPLE 4 Multiply. Write the answer as a proper fraction in lowest terms or as a mixed number in simple form.

a. $3\frac{1}{2} \times \left(-\frac{1}{4}\right)$ **b.** $5\frac{1}{4} \times 1\frac{3}{7}$

Solution

a. $3\frac{1}{2} \times \left(-\frac{1}{4}\right) = \frac{7}{2} \times \frac{-1}{4} = \frac{-7}{8}$, or $-\frac{7}{8}$

b. $5\frac{1}{4} \times 1\frac{3}{7} = \frac{\overset{3}{\cancel{21}}}{\underset{2}{\cancel{4}}} \times \frac{\overset{5}{\cancel{10}}}{\underset{1}{\cancel{7}}} = \frac{15}{2}$, or $7\frac{1}{2}$

Class Exercises

Multiply.

1. $\frac{5}{6} \times 6$ **2.** $-\frac{3}{5} \times (-5)$ **3.** $-4 \times \frac{7}{4}$ **4.** $9 \times \left(-\frac{8}{9}\right)$

5. $\frac{1}{8} \times \frac{1}{3}$ **6.** $-\frac{1}{4} \times \frac{1}{5}$ **7.** $\frac{1}{15} \times \left(-\frac{1}{2}\right)$ **8.** $-\frac{1}{10} \times \left(-\frac{1}{10}\right)$

9. $\frac{5}{8} \times \frac{3}{11}$ **10.** $\frac{2}{5} \times \left(-\frac{3}{7}\right)$ **11.** $1\frac{1}{2} \times 2$ **12.** $-3 \times 1\frac{1}{5}$

Written Exercises

Multiply. Write the answer as a proper fraction in lowest terms or as a mixed number in simple form.

A **1.** $\frac{7}{12} \times 12$ **2.** $-6 \times \frac{3}{6}$ **3.** $3 \times \left(-\frac{2}{3}\right)$ **4.** $-14 \times \left(-\frac{5}{14}\right)$

5. $-\frac{1}{4} \times \left(-\frac{1}{7}\right)$ **6.** $\frac{1}{8} \times \left(-\frac{1}{20}\right)$ **7.** $-\frac{1}{10} \times \frac{1}{6}$ **8.** $-\frac{1}{15} \times \frac{1}{2}$

9. $\frac{2}{3} \times \frac{5}{9}$ **10.** $\frac{6}{7} \times \frac{2}{5}$ **11.** $\frac{3}{8} \times \left(-\frac{2}{3}\right)$ **12.** $\frac{5}{6} \times \left(-\frac{2}{5}\right)$

13. $-\frac{1}{3} \times \frac{2}{9}$ **14.** $-\frac{3}{8} \times \frac{2}{9}$ **15.** $\frac{-5}{8} \times (-1)$ **16.** $\frac{-2}{5} \times \left(-\frac{15}{16}\right)$

17. $-\frac{1}{4} \times 0$ 18. $-\frac{3}{4} \times 0$ 19. $\frac{5}{16} \times \frac{30}{40}$ 20. $\frac{9}{8} \times \frac{24}{27}$

B 21. $3\frac{1}{4} \times \frac{4}{13}$ 22. $5\frac{2}{5} \times \frac{5}{9}$ 23. $4\frac{1}{4} \times 10\frac{1}{3}$ 24. $10\frac{1}{2} \times 2\frac{3}{4}$

25. $-4\frac{2}{7} \times 5\frac{1}{6}$ 26. $3\frac{1}{8} \times \left(-4\frac{1}{5}\right)$ 27. $-2\frac{1}{3} \times \left(-1\frac{4}{9}\right)$ 28. $-6\frac{1}{4} \times \left(-5\frac{2}{5}\right)$

29. $\frac{1}{4} \times \frac{1}{3} \times \frac{1}{2}$ 30. $\frac{5}{16} \times \frac{1}{2} \times \frac{1}{5}$ 31. $\frac{3}{4} \times \frac{1}{6} \times \frac{1}{9}$

32. $-\frac{5}{8} \times \left(-\frac{3}{25}\right) \times \left(-\frac{1}{9}\right)$ 33. $-2\frac{1}{4} \times 6\frac{1}{2} \times \frac{12}{39}$ 34. $-5\frac{1}{8} \times \frac{24}{25} \times 10\frac{1}{2}$

Multiply. Simplify the answer.

EXAMPLE $\frac{3}{5} \times 15a = \frac{3}{\cancel{5}_{1}} \times \frac{\cancel{15a}^{3a}}{1} = \frac{3 \times 3a}{1 \times 1} = 9a$

35. $\frac{2}{3} \times 9n$ 36. $5 \times \frac{3x}{10}$ 37. $-3 \times \frac{y}{6}$ 38. $-5 \times \left(\frac{-7a}{10}\right)$

39. $\frac{2r}{5} \times \frac{1}{r}$ 40. $\frac{-6}{s} \times \frac{s}{2}$ 41. $\frac{3c}{5} \times \frac{5}{c}$ 42. $\frac{2m}{7} \times \frac{14}{m}$

C 43. Let $\frac{a}{b}$ be any fraction ($b \neq 0$). Show that $\frac{a}{b} \times b = a$ by supplying the rule or property that justifies each statement.

$\frac{a}{b} \times b = \left(a \times \frac{1}{b}\right) \times b$ Why?

$= a \times \left(\frac{1}{b} \times b\right)$ Why?

$= a \times \left(b \times \frac{1}{b}\right)$ Why?

$= a \times 1$ Why?

$= a$ Why?

44. Let $\frac{a}{b}$ and $\frac{c}{d}$ represent any two fractions ($b \neq 0, d \neq 0$). Show as in Exercise 43 that $\frac{a}{b} \times \frac{c}{d} = \frac{ac}{bd}$.

Review Exercises

Evaluate the expression when $x = -8$ and $y = 12$.

1. $5 \times y$ 2. $7x \div 4$ 3. $3x - y$ 4. $x + 8y$

5. $2(x + y)$ 6. $x \div (y - 6)$ 7. $(2y + 4) \div (x - 1)$ 8. $(x \div 4) \times (y \div 3)$

4-6 Dividing Fractions

To develop a method for dividing fractions, recall that multiplication and division are inverse operations. If $2 \times n = 10$, then $n = 10 \div 2$. Similarly, if $\frac{7}{5} \times x = \frac{2}{3}$, then $x = \frac{2}{3} \div \frac{7}{5}$. We can show by substitution that the multiplication equation is true when the value of x is $(\frac{2}{3} \times \frac{5}{7})$.

$$\frac{7}{5} \times \left(\frac{2}{3} \times \frac{5}{7}\right) = \frac{\overset{1}{\cancel{7}} \times 2 \times \overset{1}{\cancel{5}}}{\underset{1}{\cancel{5}} \times 3 \times \underset{1}{\cancel{7}}} = \frac{2}{3}$$

Therefore, the related division equation must also be true when the value of x is $(\frac{2}{3} \times \frac{5}{7})$. That is,

$$\frac{2}{3} \times \frac{5}{7} = \frac{2}{3} \div \frac{7}{5}.$$

Two numbers, like $\frac{5}{7}$ and $\frac{7}{5}$, whose product is 1 are called **reciprocals.** The reciprocal of $\frac{c}{d}$ is $\frac{d}{c}$ because $\frac{c}{d} \times \frac{d}{c} = 1$. Every nonzero rational number has exactly one reciprocal.

We may state the following general rule.

> ***Rule***
>
> For all numbers a, b, c, and d ($b \neq 0, c \neq 0, d \neq 0$),
>
> $$\frac{a}{b} \div \frac{c}{d} = \frac{a}{b} \times \frac{d}{c}$$
>
> To divide by a fraction, multiply by its reciprocal.

EXAMPLE 1 Name the reciprocal, if any.

a. $\frac{2}{3}$ **b.** $-\frac{5}{8}$ **c.** 2 **d.** 0

Solution

a. The reciprocal of $\frac{2}{3}$ is $\frac{3}{2}$ since $\frac{2}{3} \times \frac{3}{2} = 1$.

b. The reciprocal of $-\frac{5}{8}$ is $-\frac{8}{5}$ since $-\frac{5}{8} \times \left(-\frac{8}{5}\right) = 1$.

c. The reciprocal of 2 is $\frac{1}{2}$ since $2 \times \frac{1}{2} = 1$.

d. The equation $0 \times n = 1$ has no solution since 0 times any number is 0. Therefore, 0 has no reciprocal.

EXAMPLE 2 Divide. Write the answer as a proper fraction in lowest terms or as a mixed number in simple form.

a. $\frac{5}{6} \div \frac{3}{2}$ **b.** $-\frac{4}{3} \div \frac{5}{8}$ **c.** $2\frac{1}{3} \div 1\frac{3}{8}$ **d.** $\frac{\frac{2}{5}}{\frac{1}{4}}$

Solution **a.** $\frac{5}{6} \div \frac{3}{2} = \frac{5}{\cancel{6}_3} \times \frac{\cancel{2}^1}{3} = \frac{5}{9}$

b. $-\frac{4}{3} \div \frac{5}{8} = -\frac{4}{3} \times \frac{8}{5} = -\frac{32}{15}$, or $-2\frac{2}{15}$

c. $2\frac{1}{3} \div 1\frac{3}{8} = \frac{7}{3} \div \frac{11}{8} = \frac{7}{3} \times \frac{8}{11} = \frac{56}{33}$, or $1\frac{23}{33}$

d. $\frac{\frac{2}{5}}{\frac{1}{4}} = \frac{2}{5} \div \frac{1}{4} = \frac{2}{5} \times \frac{4}{1} = \frac{8}{5}$, or $1\frac{3}{5}$

EXAMPLE 3 Ann bought 2 packages of ground beef. One package was $2\frac{1}{2}$ lb, and the other package was $3\frac{1}{8}$ lb. Ann divided the total amount of beef into 5 equal packages for the freezer. How many pounds were in each package?

Solution

- The problem asks for the number of pounds in each of the 5 packages.
- Given facts: $2\frac{1}{2}$ lb and $3\frac{1}{8}$ lb of beef
  total divided into 5 equal packages
- To solve, first add to find the total amount of beef, and then divide to find the amount in each package.

$$2\frac{1}{2} + 3\frac{1}{8} = 2\frac{4}{8} + 3\frac{1}{8} = 5\frac{5}{8}$$

$$5\frac{5}{8} \div 5 = \frac{\cancel{45}^9}{8} \times \frac{1}{\cancel{5}_1} = \frac{9 \times 1}{8 \times 1} = \frac{9}{8}, \text{ or } 1\frac{1}{8}$$

Each package contained $1\frac{1}{8}$ lb of beef.

Problem Solving Reminder

When solving a problem, *review the problem solving strategies and tips* that you have learned. As you work through the problems in the lesson, remember that you may need to supply additional information, eliminate extra information, or plan more than one step. Remember to reread the problem to be sure your answer is complete.

Class Exercises

State the reciprocal.

1. 4 **2.** -5 **3.** $\frac{3}{4}$ **4.** $-\frac{5}{8}$ **5.** $\frac{2}{7}$ **6.** $\frac{11}{3}$

7. $-\frac{2}{3}$ **8.** $-\frac{6}{5}$ **9.** $\frac{11}{12}$ **10.** $\frac{3}{16}$ **11.** $-\frac{4}{7}$ **12.** $\frac{14}{5}$

Complete.

13. $\frac{2}{3} \div 5 = \frac{2}{3} \times \underline{\ ?\ }$ **14.** $\frac{2}{3} \div \frac{1}{5} = \frac{2}{3} \times \underline{\ ?\ }$ **15.** $\frac{6}{5} \div (-10) = \underline{\ ?\ } \times \left(-\frac{1}{10}\right)$

16. $-\frac{3}{8} \div 7 = \underline{\ ?\ } \times \frac{1}{7}$ **17.** $\frac{5}{16} \div \frac{1}{8} = \underline{\ ?\ } \times \underline{\ ?\ }$ **18.** $-\frac{3}{4} \div \frac{3}{10} = \underline{\ ?\ } \times \underline{\ ?\ }$

Written Exercises

Divide. Write the answer as a proper fraction in lowest terms or as a mixed number in simple form.

A **1.** $\frac{2}{5} \div \frac{3}{5}$ **2.** $\frac{7}{8} \div \frac{3}{8}$ **3.** $5 \div \frac{1}{5}$ **4.** $10 \div \frac{1}{2}$

5. $\frac{5}{8} \div \frac{9}{5}$ **6.** $\frac{3}{4} \div \frac{7}{8}$ **7.** $\frac{\frac{5}{9}}{\frac{1}{7}}$ **8.** $\frac{\frac{2}{3}}{\frac{3}{8}}$

9. $-\frac{21}{4} \div \left(-\frac{7}{8}\right)$ **10.** $-\frac{4}{5} \div \left(-\frac{36}{25}\right)$ **11.** $3\frac{1}{4} \div \frac{5}{8}$ **12.** $10\frac{1}{2} \div \frac{8}{9}$

13. $-5\frac{5}{8} \div 10$ **14.** $11\frac{1}{9} \div 100$ **15.** $-6\frac{1}{3} \div \left(-\frac{19}{21}\right)$ **16.** $-10\frac{1}{3} \div \left(-\frac{31}{33}\right)$

B **17.** $6\frac{1}{8} \div \left(\frac{8}{3} \times \frac{3}{7}\right)$ **18.** $-7 \div \left(\frac{21}{4} \times \frac{3}{7}\right)$ **19.** $\left(-1\frac{2}{3} \times \frac{18}{5}\right) \div 3$

20. $-\left(\frac{35}{4} \times \frac{2}{7}\right) \div \left(-\frac{4}{3}\right)$ **21.** $-\left(3\frac{1}{5} \times \frac{5}{2}\right) \div \frac{8}{9}$ **22.** $\left(-2\frac{1}{6} \div \frac{1}{9}\right) \times \frac{1}{13}$

23. $-\left(4\frac{1}{6} \div 5\right) \times \left(-\frac{2}{5}\right)$ **24.** $-3\frac{1}{8} \div 4 \div \left(-\frac{5}{4}\right)$ **25.** $5\frac{1}{3} \div 2\frac{2}{3} \div (-4)$

Divide. Simplify the answer.

EXAMPLE **a.** $\frac{5a}{3} \div \frac{2a}{3}$ **b.** $\frac{x}{2} \div \frac{y}{4}$

Solution **a.** $\frac{5a}{3} \div \frac{2a}{3} = \frac{\overset{5}{\cancel{5a}}}{\underset{1}{\cancel{3}}} \times \frac{\overset{1}{\cancel{3}}}{\underset{2}{\cancel{2a}}} = \frac{5 \times 1}{1 \times 2} = \frac{5}{2}$, or $2\frac{1}{2}$

b. $\frac{x}{2} \div \frac{y}{4} = \frac{x}{\underset{1}{\cancel{2}}} \times \frac{\overset{2}{\cancel{4}}}{y} = \frac{x \times 2}{1 \times y} = \frac{2x}{y}$

26. $\frac{6x}{5} \div 2$

27. $-4 \div \frac{1}{2y}$

28. $42r \div \frac{3r}{4}$

29. $\left(-\frac{6a}{7}\right) \div \left(-\frac{3a}{4}\right)$

C 30. $-8b \div \frac{5}{3b}$

31. $\frac{-5}{7c} \div \frac{5c}{14}$

32. $\frac{-8c^2}{9} \div \frac{4c}{5}$

33. $\frac{5de^2}{6} \div \frac{10d^2e}{9}$

Evaluate the expression when $x = \frac{1}{2}$, $y = \frac{2}{3}$, and $z = \frac{5}{6}$.

EXAMPLE $\frac{1 - z}{y}$

Solution $\frac{1 - z}{y} = \frac{1 - \frac{5}{6}}{\frac{2}{3}} = \left(1 - \frac{5}{6}\right) \div \frac{2}{3} = \frac{1}{\cancel{6}_2} \times \frac{\cancel{3}^1}{2} = \frac{1}{4}$

34. $\frac{x}{y}$

35. $\frac{y}{z}$

36. $\frac{2x}{z}$

37. $\frac{z}{3y}$

38. $\frac{x + 1}{z}$

39. $\frac{y}{y + 1}$

Problems

Solve. Write the answer as a whole number, as a proper fraction in lowest terms, or as a mixed number in simple form.

A 1. How many packages will $5\frac{1}{2}$ lb of raisins fill if each package holds 9 oz?

2. Karen Northrup worked $12\frac{1}{2}$ h last week and earned \$50. What was her hourly rate of pay?

3. A television station released 300 balloons at an outdoor celebration. Of these, $\frac{3}{4}$ were orange. How many were orange?

4. Leo Delray earns \$2 an hour for babysitting. If he works $3\frac{1}{4}$ h one evening, how much does he earn?

5. To the nearest million, the number of households in the United States having television sets was 4 million in 1950 and 76 million in 1980. Express the first number as a fraction of the second.

6. A gasoline tank with a capacity of 15 gal is $\frac{3}{4}$ full. How many gallons will it take to fill the tank?

7. A town has raised $\frac{3}{8}$ of the \$12,000 it needs to furnish its new library. How much more is it hoping to raise?

Solve. Simplify the answer.

8. In a recent year there were 32,000 persons in the United States who had celebrated their 100th birthday. Of these, $\frac{3}{4}$ were women. How many were men?

B 9. How much fringe will be needed for all four edges of a rectangular rug measuring $11\frac{3}{4}$ ft by $8\frac{1}{3}$ ft? If the fringe is 3 in. wide, what are the dimensions of the rug after the fringe is added?

10. An advertising sign is to have six lines of printing. The letters are to be $1\frac{1}{2}$ in. high with $\frac{1}{4}$ in. between the lines.
   a. How much vertical space is required for the printing?
   b. If there is a top margin of 3 in. and a lower margin of $3\frac{1}{2}$ in., what will be the total height of the sign?

11. One half of the class voted to have a picnic. One third of the class voted to hold a dinner instead. What fraction of the class wanted neither a picnic nor a dinner?

12. A picture measures $8\frac{3}{4}$ in. by 8 in. When framed it measures $10\frac{3}{4}$ in. by 10 in. How wide is each side of the frame?

C 13. Only $\frac{1}{5}$ of the downtown workers drive to work. Of those who do not drive, $\frac{3}{16}$ ride bicycles to work. What fraction of the workers ride bicycles to work?

14. Kevin's regular rate of pay is \$4 per hour. When he works overtime, he earns $1\frac{1}{2}$ times as much per hour. How much will Kevin earn for $5\frac{1}{2}$ h of overtime work?

Review Exercises

Use the inverse operation to write a related equation. Solve for the variable.

1. $n + 135 = 240$ **2.** $x - 45 = 52$ **3.** $4y = 156$ **4.** $9t = 504$

5. $12x = 432$ **6.** $r \div 17 = 27$ **7.** $38m = 418$ **8.** $a \div 22 = 33$

Challenge

Write a fraction whose value is between the given fractions.

1. $\frac{2}{5} < \underline{\ ?\ } < \frac{3}{5}$ **2.** $-\frac{2}{3} < \underline{\ ?\ } < -\frac{1}{3}$ **3.** $\frac{1}{8} < \underline{\ ?\ } < \frac{1}{4}$

4. $-\frac{2}{7} < \underline{\ ?\ } < -\frac{3}{14}$ **5.** $\frac{1}{6} < \underline{\ ?\ } < \frac{1}{4}$ **6.** $-\frac{5}{6} < \underline{\ ?\ } < -\frac{7}{9}$

4-7 Fractions and Decimals

Any fraction can be represented as a decimal. You may recall that a fraction such as $\frac{3}{4}$ can be easily written as an equivalent fraction whose denominator is a power of 10, and then as a decimal. To represent $\frac{3}{4}$ as a decimal, we first write it as an equivalent fraction with denominator 100.

$$\frac{3}{4} = \frac{3 \times 25}{4 \times 25} = \frac{75}{100} = 0.75$$

For most fractions, however, we use the fact that $\frac{a}{b} = a \div b$ and divide numerator by denominator.

EXAMPLE 1 Write as a decimal: **a.** $-\frac{5}{16}$ **b.** $\frac{24}{55}$

Solution **a.** First find $5 \div 16$.

$$\begin{array}{r} 0.3125 \\ 16\overline{)5.0000} \\ \underline{4\,8} \\ 20 \\ \underline{16} \\ 40 \\ \underline{32} \\ 80 \\ \underline{80} \\ 0 \end{array}$$

Therefore, $-\frac{5}{16} = -0.3125$.

The decimal -0.3125 is called a **terminating decimal** because the final remainder is 0 and the division ends.

b. Find $24 \div 55$.

$$\begin{array}{r} 0.43636 \\ 55\overline{)24.00000} \\ \underline{22\,0} \\ 2\,00 \\ \underline{1\,65} \\ 350 \\ \underline{330} \\ 200 \\ \underline{165} \\ 350 \\ \underline{330} \\ 20 \end{array}$$

Therefore, $\frac{24}{55} = 0.43636\ldots$.

The digits 36 continue to repeat without end. The decimal $0.43636\ldots$ is called a **repeating decimal.** We often write $0.43636\ldots$ as $0.4\overline{36}$, with a bar over the block of digits that repeats.

To say that $\frac{24}{55} = 0.43636\ldots$ means that the successive decimals 0.436, 0.4363, 0.43636, and so on, will come closer and closer to the value $\frac{24}{55}$.

We can predict when a fraction will result in a terminating decimal because the fraction in lowest terms has a denominator with no prime factors other than 2 and 5. Thus, the fraction $\frac{24}{55}$ does not result in a terminating decimal because its denominator has 11 as a prime factor.

When working with a mixed number, such as $-1\frac{5}{16}$ or $1\frac{24}{25}$, we may consider the mixed number as a sum of a whole number and a fraction, or we may rewrite the mixed number as an improper fraction and then divide.

If a and b are integers and $b \neq 0$, the quotient $a \div b$ is either a terminating decimal or a repeating decimal. The reason for this is that, for any divisor, the number of possible remainders at each step of the division is limited to the whole numbers less than the divisor. Sooner or later, either the remainder is 0 and the division ends, as in part (a) of Example 1, or one of the remainders reappears in the division as in part (b) of Example 1. Then the same block of digits will reappear in the quotient.

Property

Every rational number can be represented by either a terminating decimal or a repeating decimal.

You already know how to write a terminating decimal as a fraction. Rewrite the decimal as a fraction whose denominator is a power of 10.

EXAMPLE 2 Write -0.625 as a fraction in lowest terms.

Solution

$$-0.625 = -\frac{625}{1000} = -\frac{625 \div 125}{1000 \div 125} = -\frac{5}{8}$$

The next example shows a method for writing a repeating decimal as a fraction.

EXAMPLE 3 Write $-1.\overline{21}$ as a fraction in lowest terms.

Solution Let $n = 1.\overline{21}$.

Multiply both sides of the equation by a power of 10 determined by the number of digits in the block of repeating digits. Since there are

2 digits that repeat in the number $1.\overline{21}$, we multiply by 10^2, or 100.

$$\begin{array}{lrl} & 100n = & 121.\overline{21} \\ \text{Subtract:} & n = & 1.\overline{21} \\ \hline & 99n = & 120 \\ & n = & \frac{120}{99} = \frac{40}{33} \end{array}$$

Thus, $-1.\overline{21} = -\frac{40}{33}$, or $-1\frac{7}{33}$.

Property

Every terminating or repeating decimal represents a rational number.

Some decimals, such as those below, neither terminate nor repeat.

0.010010001000001 . . .   1.234567891011121314 . . .

The two decimals shown follow patterns, but they are not repeating patterns. The decimal on the right is made up of consecutive whole numbers beginning with 1.

Decimals that neither terminate nor repeat represent **irrational numbers.** Together, the rational numbers and the irrational numbers make up the set of **real numbers.** The number line that you have studied is sometimes called the **real number line.** For every point on the line, there is exactly one real number and for every real number there is exactly one point on the number line.

Class Exercises

Tell whether the decimal for the fraction is terminating or repeating. If the decimal is terminating, state the decimal.

1. $\frac{1}{4}$ **2.** $\frac{5}{6}$ **3.** $2\frac{2}{5}$ **4.** $-\frac{9}{10}$ **5.** $-1\frac{1}{2}$ **6.** $\frac{13}{30}$

State as a fraction in which the numerator is an integer and the denominator is a power of 10.

7. 0.13   **8.** −0.9   **9.** 1.4   **10.** −0.007   **11.** 3.03   **12.** −5.001

State the repeating digit(s) for each decimal.

13. 6.666 . . . **14.** 0.0444 . . . **15.** 6.050505 . . . **16.** 0.1666 . . .

17. $5.1\overline{5}$ **18.** $0.\overline{422}$ **19.** $1.0\overline{6}$ **20.** $0.3\overline{64}$

Written Exercises

Write as a terminating or repeating decimal. Use a bar to show repeating digits.

A **1.** $\frac{1}{4}$ **2.** $\frac{1}{5}$ **3.** $\frac{2}{9}$ **4.** $\frac{3}{16}$ **5.** $\frac{9}{10}$ **6.** $-\frac{1}{18}$

7. $-\frac{2}{3}$ **8.** $\frac{4}{9}$ **9.** $-\frac{3}{8}$ **10.** $\frac{3}{5}$ **11.** $-\frac{3}{25}$ **12.** $\frac{7}{15}$

13. $1\frac{1}{10}$ **14.** $5\frac{2}{5}$ **15.** $\frac{7}{12}$ **16.** $-\frac{3}{11}$ **17.** $\frac{4}{15}$ **18.** $-4\frac{7}{8}$

19. $-1\frac{7}{18}$ **20.** $2\frac{1}{9}$ **21.** $\frac{3}{20}$ **22.** $\frac{17}{36}$ **23.** $3\frac{2}{7}$ **24.** $\frac{5}{13}$

Write as a proper fraction in lowest terms or as a mixed number in simple form.

25. 0.05 **26.** 0.005 **27.** −0.6 **28.** −2.1 **29.** 2.07

30. −0.62 **31.** 5.125 **32.** 4.3 **33.** −1.375 **34.** −10.001

35. 12.625 **36.** 10.3 **37.** 0.225 **38.** 0.8375 **39.** −1.826

B **40.** 0.444 . . . **41.** −0.555 . . . **42.** $0.0\overline{3}$ **43.** $-1.0\overline{1}$ **44.** $5.\overline{9}$

45. 0.1515 . . . **46.** $-1.\overline{20}$ **47.** $0.\overline{35}$ **48.** $0.\overline{72}$ **49.** $-1.\overline{12}$

50. $1.3\overline{62}$ **51.** $2.13\overline{4}$ **52.** $-8.0\overline{16}$ **53.** $0.\overline{123}$ **54.** $-5.\overline{862}$

Tell whether the number is rational or irrational.

55. $\frac{-13}{17}$ **56.** 1.515151 . . . **57.** −3.72 **58.** 2.121121112 . . .

Arrange the numbers in order from least to greatest.

59. 3.0, $3.0\overline{9}$, $3.00\overline{9}$, 3.1 **60.** 0.182, $0.182\overline{5}$, $0.18\overline{2}$, $0.1\overline{8}$

a. Express the first number as a fraction or mixed number.
b. Compare the first number with the second.

C **61.** $0.\overline{9}$; 1 **62.** $0.4\overline{9}$; $\frac{1}{2}$ **63.** $-1.24\overline{9}$; $-\frac{5}{4}$ **64.** $2.3\overline{9}$; $2\frac{2}{5}$

Self-Test B

Multiply or divide. Write the answer as a proper fraction in lowest terms or as a mixed number in simple form.

1. $\frac{3}{4} \times 5$ **2.** $\frac{1}{8} \times \left(-\frac{1}{3}\right)$ **3.** $\frac{28}{35} \times \frac{21}{14}$ [4-5]

4. $8\frac{3}{4} \times \frac{3}{10}$ **5.** $-3\frac{1}{8} \times \left(-4\frac{4}{5}\right)$ **6.** $-2\frac{4}{7} \times 3\frac{1}{6}$

7. $\frac{5}{8} \div \frac{10}{24}$ **8.** $-\frac{11}{16} \div \frac{44}{8}$ **9.** $-\frac{18}{5} \div \left(-\frac{9}{35}\right)$ [4-6]

10. $1\frac{1}{4} \div 25$ **11.** $4\frac{1}{3} \div \left(-\frac{26}{27}\right)$ **12.** $-4\frac{2}{7} \div \left(-2\frac{1}{14}\right)$

Write as a decimal. Use a bar to show repeating digits.

13. $\frac{5}{8}$ **14.** $\frac{2}{11}$ **15.** $-\frac{1}{80}$ **16.** $\frac{7}{6}$ [4-7]

Write as a proper fraction in lowest terms or as a mixed number in simple form.

17. 0.875 **18.** $1.\overline{6}$ **19.** -2.213 **20.** $0.2\overline{3}$

Self-Test answers and Extra Practice are at the back of the book.

Computer Byte

The following program will print a decimal approximation for any positive proper fraction. The first approximation is rounded to the number of digits that the computer usually displays. The computer will then print an approximation to any desired number of digits.

```
10  PRINT "INPUT NUMERATOR, THEN DENOMINATOR"
20  INPUT N,D
30  IF N > D THEN 10
40  PRINT N;"/";D;" = ";N / D
50  PRINT "HOW MANY DIGITS DO YOU WANT ?";
60  INPUT K
70  PRINT "OR .";
80  FOR I = 1 TO K
90  LET P = 10 * N / D
100  PRINT  INT (P);
110  LET N = 10 * N - D *  INT (P)
120  NEXT I
130  END
```

Use the program to discover the repeating pattern for these fractions.

1. $\frac{1}{7}$ **2.** $\frac{2}{7}$ **3.** $\frac{10}{11}$ **4.** $\frac{5}{13}$ **5.** $\frac{76}{99}$ **6.** $\frac{12}{37}$ **7.** $\frac{17}{33}$ **8.** $\frac{134}{333}$

Programming in BASIC

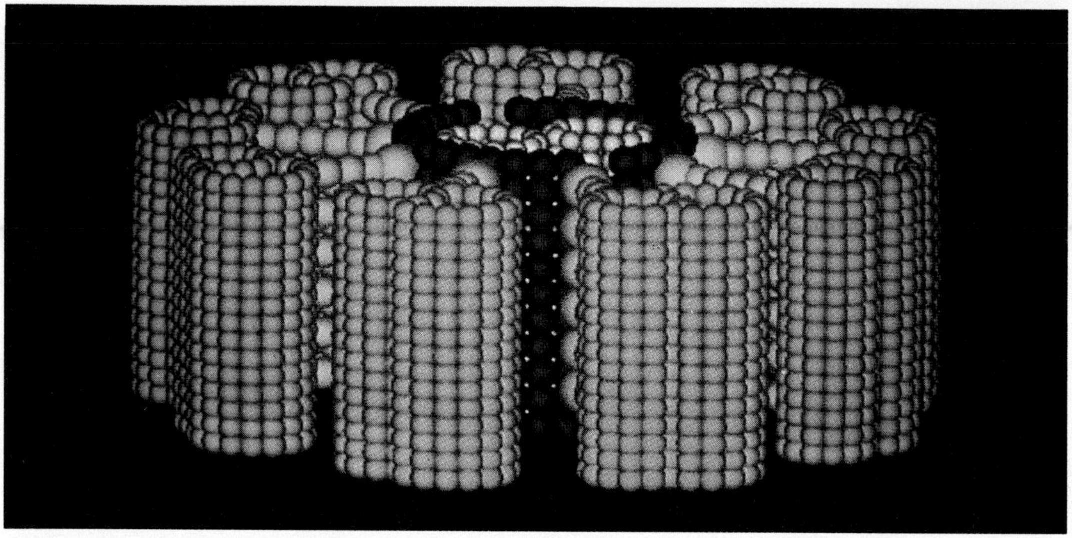

On pages 64–65, you learned about programs that use PRINT, INPUT, and END statements. We can also give a value to a variable by using a **LET** statement, for example, LET A = 215. A LET statement can also be used to evaluate a formula, as shown in this program.

```
10  PRINT "INPUT LENGTH AND WIDTH";
20  PRINT "OF RECTANGLE";
30  INPUT L, W  ◄────────────  For example, type 18, 10
40  LET A = L * W
50  PRINT "AREA = ";A
60  END
```

The programs on pages 58 and 135 use the "greatest integer" function. That is, **INT(X)** represents the greatest integer less than or equal to *X*:

INT(4) = 4 INT(4.9) = 4

The program on page 135 uses two more kinds of statements. Line 30 has an **IF-THEN** statement. It means that if $N > D$, the computer is to go back to line 10. Otherwise (if $N \leq D$), it is to go on to line 40. In the BASIC language, we use the symbols $>$ and $<$ as we do when we write inequalities. To indicate $<$, however, we type in $< =$. To indicate $\geq$, we type in $> =$.

Lines 80–120 in the program on page 135 contain a **FOR-NEXT** *loop*. It tells the computer to perform a computation over and over again for a specific number of times. Here, the variable *I* does not appear in the computation, although in some cases the loop variable may. In this case, the variable *I* is just a counter that allows the computer to repeat the computation *K* times. The variable *N* is given a new value in line 110 each time through.

1. Copy and RUN the program on page 136 for several sets of values of *L* and *W*.
2. Verify on your computer that INT(4) = 4 and INT(4.9) = 4.
3. Use INT to print out quotients and remainders as follows:

```
10  PRINT "TO DIVIDE N BY D, N > D"
20  PRINT "INPUT N, D";
30  INPUT N, D
40  LET Q = N / D
50  LET Q1 = INT(Q)
60  LET R = N - D * Q1
70  PRINT N;"/";D;" = ";Q1;
80  PRINT ", REMAINDER ";R
90  END
```

RUN this for: 60, 14; 100, 9; and 80, 16.

Research Activities

1. Computers can also handle various forms of graphics. Programs can be written to produce drawings that can be made to appear in various or changing forms. The photo on page 136 shows a computer generated picture that is used in biological research to study the make-up of certain fibers. Find out about some other fields in which computer graphics are important.
2. If you were to diagram the programs shown on this page and on page 136, you might use a diagram like the one shown at the right. More elaborate versions of such diagrams are called flow charts. Longer programs would have more sections. When you write longer, more complicated programs, you will want to separate the sections of the programs with REM (remark) statements. Find out about REM statements and how they can help you keep track of what is being done in a program.

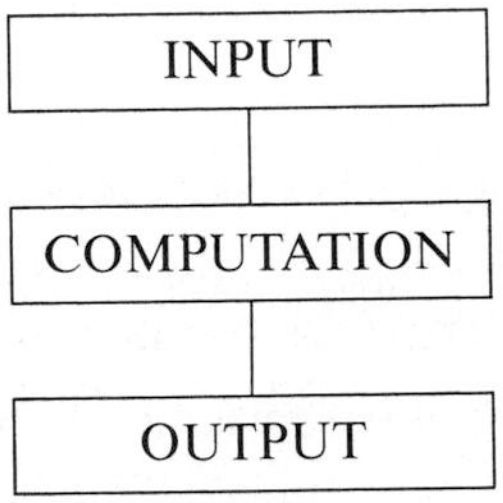

Chapter Review

True or false?

1. $8 \times \frac{1}{9} = \frac{9}{8}$ **2.** $4 \times \left(-\frac{1}{5}\right) = -\frac{4}{5}$ **3.** $\frac{-7}{11} = -\frac{7}{11}$ **[4-1]**

4. $\frac{15}{18}$ in lowest terms is $\frac{3}{5}$. **[4-2]**

5. $-\frac{24}{148}$ in lowest terms is $-\frac{12}{74}$.

6. $\frac{46}{8}$ written as a mixed number in simple form is $5\frac{6}{8}$.

7. $-12\frac{2}{7} = \frac{86}{7}$ **8.** $7\frac{3}{8} = \frac{29}{8}$

9. The LCD of $\frac{2}{3}$ and $\frac{5}{11}$ is 33. **[4-3]**

10. The LCD of $\frac{4}{7}$ and $\frac{5}{42}$ is 6.

11. The LCD of $\frac{7}{30}$ and $-\frac{3}{35}$ is 150.

12. The LCD of $\frac{2}{9}$ and $\frac{4}{5}$ is 36.

Match.

13. $-\frac{5}{12} + \frac{11}{18}$ **14.** $4\frac{2}{5} + 2\frac{3}{10}$ **A.** $-2\frac{11}{18}$ **B.** $-8\frac{17}{18}$ **[4-4]**

15. $1\frac{3}{7} - \frac{5}{8}$ **16.** $-2\frac{1}{6} + \left(-\frac{4}{9}\right)$ **C.** $\frac{7}{36}$ **D.** $\frac{3}{16}$

17. $-\frac{9}{16} - \left(-\frac{3}{4}\right)$ **18.** $\frac{1}{8} - \frac{3}{8}$ **E.** $\frac{27}{28}$ **F.** $-\frac{1}{4}$ **[4-5]**

19. $\frac{1}{4} \times \frac{1}{9}$ **20.** $\frac{4}{5} \times \frac{3}{8}$ **G.** $6\frac{7}{10}$ **H.** $\frac{1}{36}$

21. $-7\frac{2}{3} \times 1\frac{1}{6}$ **22.** $\frac{2}{5} \times 5$ **I.** 2 **J.** $-1\frac{19}{30}$ **[4-6]**

23. $\frac{3}{14} \div \frac{2}{9}$ **24.** $1\frac{2}{5} \div \left(-\frac{6}{7}\right)$ **K.** $\frac{45}{56}$ **L.** $\frac{3}{10}$

Complete. Use a bar to show repeating digits.

25. $\frac{5}{16}$ written as a decimal is __?__. **[4-7]**

26. $\frac{4}{3}$ written as a decimal is __?__.

27. -0.125 written as a fraction in lowest terms is __?__.

28. $2.\overline{42}$ written as a mixed number in simple form is __?__.

Chapter Test

Complete.

1. $5 \times \underline{\ ?\ } = \frac{5}{7}$ **2.** $6 \times \frac{1}{6} = \underline{\ ?\ }$ **[4-1]**

3. $12 \div (-13) = \underline{\ ?\ }$ **4.** $\frac{-1}{4} = \frac{1}{-4} = \underline{\ ?\ }$

Write as a proper fraction in lowest terms or as a mixed number in simple form.

5. $\frac{14}{40}$ **6.** $-\frac{26}{52}$ **7.** $-\frac{136}{160}$ **8.** $\frac{15}{4}$ **9.** $\frac{-83}{9}$ **[4-2]**

Write as an improper fraction.

10. $4\frac{4}{7}$ **11.** $-5\frac{3}{5}$ **12.** $7\frac{8}{9}$ **13.** $-21\frac{3}{10}$

Write each pair of fractions as equivalent fractions with the least common denominator.

14. $\frac{3}{7}, \frac{5}{14}$ **15.** $\frac{1}{9}, \frac{6}{11}$ **16.** $\frac{5}{8}, \frac{13}{36}$ **17.** $\frac{7}{12}, \frac{5}{24}$ **[4-3]**

Add or subtract. Write the answer as a proper fraction in lowest terms or as a mixed number in simple form.

18. $\frac{3}{8} - \frac{1}{7}$ **19.** $\frac{3}{10} - \left(-\frac{1}{4}\right)$ **20.** $-\frac{1}{6} + \frac{3}{14}$ **[4-4]**

21. $1\frac{3}{4} + \left(-2\frac{1}{2}\right)$ **22.** $5\frac{5}{6} - 3\frac{1}{3}$ **23.** $-\frac{7}{9} - \frac{5}{6}$

Multiply. Write the answer as a proper fraction in lowest terms or as a mixed number in simple form.

24. $\frac{4}{7} \times \left(-\frac{4}{11}\right)$ **25.** $3\frac{1}{8} \times 2\frac{3}{5}$ **26.** $-\frac{1}{4} \times \left(-\frac{1}{6}\right)$ **[4-5]**

Divide. Write the answer as a proper fraction in lowest terms or as a mixed number in simple form.

27. $\frac{2}{3} \div \frac{7}{9}$ **28.** $-\frac{6}{19} \div \frac{9}{38}$ **29.** $-1\frac{1}{6} \div \left(-4\frac{2}{3}\right)$ **[4-6]**

Write as a terminating or repeating decimal. Use a bar to show repeating digits.

30. $\frac{6}{25}$ **31.** $\frac{5}{33}$ **32.** $\frac{9}{16}$ **33.** $\frac{4}{9}$ **[4-7]**

Write as a proper fraction in lowest terms or as a mixed number in simple form.

34. 0.04 **35.** −0.375 **36.** 6.125 **37.** $0.\overline{7}$

Cumulative Review (Chapters 1–4)

Exercises

Give the solution of the equation for the given replacement set.

1. $x - 12 = 46$; $\{58, 59, 60\}$
2. $8d = 2$; $\left\{\frac{1}{3}, \frac{1}{4}, \frac{1}{5}\right\}$
3. $3(6 + y) = 39$; $\{7, 14, 21\}$
4. $(5 - a) \div (a + 7) = \frac{1}{5}$; $\{1, 2, 3\}$
5. $16r - 11 = 69$; $\{0, 5, 10\}$
6. $m^2(7 + m) = 176$; $\{3, 4, 5\}$

Evaluate the expression if $a = 3$, $b = 0.2$, and $c = 5$.

7. ab^2
8. $a^2 + b^2$
9. a^2c^2
10. bc^2
11. $2b^2$
12. a^2b^3
13. $(a + b)^2$
14. $c(a^2 + b)$
15. $2ac^2 \div b$
16. $\frac{10b^2}{c^2}$

Use the symbol > to order the numbers from greatest to least.

17. 75.70, 75.40, 75.06
18. 19.05, 19.18, 19.50
19. 0.03, 0.30, 0.33
20. 105.07, 10.507, 1050.7

List the integers that can replace x to make the statement true.

21. $|x| = 7$
22. $|x| = 18$
23. $|x| \geq 5$
24. $|x| < 7.3$
25. $4 < |x| < 6$
26. $6 > |x| > 0$
27. $31 < |x| < 40$
28. $17 \leq |x| \leq 25$

What value of the variable makes the statement true?

29. $-7 + y = 11$
30. $-3n = 51$
31. $-6(-b) = 72$
32. $17 - x = -5$
33. $8(-n) = 32$
34. $-a \div 15 = 3$

Evaluate the expression when $x = 5$, $y = -7$, and $z = -5$.

35. $\frac{y + 3}{x}$
36. $\frac{xy}{z}$
37. $\frac{x + y}{z}$
38. $\frac{yz}{x}$
39. $\frac{x - z}{y}$
40. $\frac{x^2 + y^2}{z^2}$
41. $\frac{x}{7} + \frac{y}{7}$
42. $\frac{2x}{15} + \frac{z}{3}$
43. $\frac{-y + z}{x}$
44. $\frac{-z - x}{-y}$

Solve. Write the answer as a proper fraction in lowest terms or as a mixed number in simple form.

45. $-5 \times \left(\frac{3}{8} \div \frac{1}{3}\right)$
46. $2\frac{1}{2} \div \left(\frac{5}{8} \times 1\frac{3}{4}\right)$
47. $7\frac{3}{8} + \left[-4\frac{1}{2} \div \left(-5\frac{2}{3}\right)\right]$

Problems

Problem Solving Reminders

Here are some reminders that may help you solve some of the problems on this page.

- You may need to supply additional information.
- Some steps in your plan may not involve operations.
- Reread the question to be sure you have answered with the information requested.

Solve.

1. The Maxwell children have hired a caterer to provide food for an anniversary party for their parents. The caterer has quoted a price of $15.75 per person and is asking for an advance payment of $\frac{1}{4}$ of the total bill. If the estimated number of guests is 50, how much is the advance payment?

2. The Clean-as-a-Whistle Company provides a matching service for people looking for home cleaners and people wishing to clean homes. The fees include $6.50 per hour for the cleaner, plus $1.50 per hour for the agency. If you hire a cleaner from the company for 5 h, how much will you pay?

3. As a general rule for brick work, masons estimate 6.5 bricks per square foot. Based on this estimate, will 2500 bricks be enough for a patio that is 396 ft^2?

4. The controller of a hospital found that laundry fees for a four-month period totaled $8755. Based on this total, what would be the estimated fee for an entire year?

5. Store owners at the Wagon Wheel Mall pay a monthly rental fee plus a maintenance fee. The maintenance fee is determined by the number of square feet occupied by the shop. The entire mall is 200,000 ft^2 and the annual fee for the entire mall is $63,000. What is the annual share of the maintenance fee for a store that occupies 2500 ft^2?

6. An investor bought 12 acres of land for $70,000. She later subdivided the land into 22 lots that she sold for $4500 apiece. What was her profit on the sale?

7. Douglas bought 75 shares of Health Care Company (HCC) stock and 150 shares of Bowwow Brands (BWB) stock. Last year HCC paid a dividend of $1.85 per share and BWB paid a dividend of $2.04 per share. What was the total of the dividends that Douglas received?

5

Equations and Inequalities

The trains pictured at the right were introduced in France. They can travel at speeds of up to 160 km/h on conventional tracks and nearly triple that on their own continuously welded tracks. The speed of a train on an actual trip depends, of course, on the number of curves and the type of track. A trip of 425 km from Paris to Lyon that takes about 4 h in a conventional train, for instance, can be completed in about 2.5 h in one of these trains.

The time it takes a train to complete a trip depends on the speed of the train and the distance traveled. Some relationships, such as the relationship between time, rate, and distance, can be expressed as equations. Other relationships can be expressed as inequalities. You will learn more about equations and inequalities and methods to solve both in this chapter. You will also learn how to use equations to help solve problems.

Career Note

Reporters representing newspapers, magazines, and radio and television stations often attend newsworthy events such as the introduction of new trains. Reporters need a wide educational background. They must report facts, not their own opinions. They must be willing to meet deadlines and often to work at irregular hours.

NCF
NCF
SNA

5-1 Properties of Equality

Consider the following examples.

$$8 + 7 = 15 \qquad (8 + 7) + 10 = 15 + 10$$

These examples illustrate that we may add the same number to two equal expressions and the sums that result will be equal.

In general,

Addition Property of Equality

For all numbers a, b, and c:

If $a = b$, then $a + c = b + c$.

If $a + c = b + c$, then $a = b$.

We may also multiply two equal expressions by the same number and the resulting products will be equal.

$$14 - 6 = 8 \qquad (14 - 6)3 = (8)3$$

Multiplication Property of Equality

For all numbers a, b, and c:

If $a = b$, then $ac = bc$.

If $ac = bc$ and $c \neq 0$, then $a = b$.

Notice that if $c = 0$, then $a \times 0 = b \times 0$, but we can still have $a \neq b$. For example, $8 \times 0 = 3 \times 0$ but $8 \neq 3$.

EXAMPLE Use the properties of equality to form a true sentence.

a. If $a + 2 = 12$, then $a = \underline{\ ?\ }$. **b.** If $3r = 15$, then $r = \underline{\ ?\ }$.

Solution

a. $a + 2 = 12$ and $12 = 10 + 2$

$a + 2 = 10 + 2$

So by the addition property of equality, $a = 10$.

b. $3r = 15$ and $15 = 3 \times 5$

$3r = 3 \times 5$

By the multiplication property of equality, $r = 5$.

Class Exercises

Use one of the properties of equality to form a true sentence.

1. If $c + 8 = 15$, then $c = \underline{\ ?\ }$.

2. If $20 = b + 6$, then $\underline{\ ?\ } = b$.

3. If $m + (-11) = -23$, then $m = \underline{\ ?\ }$.

4. If $-30 = b + 10$, then $\underline{\ ?\ } = b$.

5. If $4p = 28$, then $p = \underline{\ ?\ }$.

6. If $15 = -5f$, then $\underline{\ ?\ } = f$.

Written Exercises

Name the property of equality illustrated.

A **1.** If $z + 7 = 11$, then $z = 4$.

2. If $m = 9$, then $4m = 36$.

3. If $8x = 56$, then $x = 7$.

4. If $r + 23 = 51$, then $r = 28$.

5. If $y = 13$, then $y + 8 = 21$.

6. If $72 = 12q$, then $6 = q$.

7. If $90 = 5a$, then $18 = a$.

8. If $46 = 4 + d$, then $42 = d$.

Use one of the properties of equality to form a true sentence.

9. If $x + 4 = 15$, then $x = \underline{\ ?\ }$.

10. If $d + 18 = 14$, then $d = \underline{\ ?\ }$.

11. If $11 = b + 16$, then $\underline{\ ?\ } = b$.

12. If $12 = g + 7$, then $\underline{\ ?\ } = g$.

13. If $13 = -8 + n$, then $\underline{\ ?\ } = n$.

14. If $-14 + j = 6$, then $j = \underline{\ ?\ }$.

15. If $4x = 12$, then $x = \underline{\ ?\ }$.

16. If $5g = 35$, then $g = \underline{\ ?\ }$.

17. If $-6m = 18$, then $m = \underline{\ ?\ }$.

18. If $21 = -3n$, then $\underline{\ ?\ } = n$.

19. If $-56 = -8r$, then $\underline{\ ?\ } = r$.

20. If $7a = 63$, then $a = \underline{\ ?\ }$.

B **21.** If $3x = 3.6$, then $x = \underline{\ ?\ }$.

22. If $4.5 = 4y$, then $\underline{\ ?\ } = y$.

23. If $0.3z = -2.7$, then $z = \underline{\ ?\ }$.

24. If $-2r = 42.6$, then $r = \underline{\ ?\ }$.

25. If $4 = \frac{1}{3}p$, then $\underline{\ ?\ } = p$.

26. If $-4 = \frac{1}{6}m$, then $\underline{\ ?\ } = m$.

C **27.** If $5n = -2$, then $10n + 4 = \underline{\ ?\ }$.

28. If $3s = 5$, then $9s + 6 = \underline{\ ?\ }$.

Review Exercises

Simplify.

1. $46 + 19 \times 3$

2. $57 \div 12 + 5$

3. $33 + 18 \div 9$

4. $2(17 + 5) \div 3$

5. $(54 + 27) \div (6 \times 9)$

6. $[63.7 \div (13.6 - 4.5)]4$

5-2 Equivalent Equations

On page 9, you learned that a *solution* of an equation involving a variable is a value of the variable that makes the equation true. Because the equation

$$x + 5 = 18$$

is true when $x = 13$, 13 is a solution of the equation. An equation may have no solution, one solution, or more than one solution.

The set of numbers that a variable may represent is called the *replacement set*. When the replacement set is small, we may substitute the values for the variable to solve the equation. When the replacement set is larger, for example the rational numbers, substitution may not be practical. In such cases, we use the properties that we have learned to change, or **transform,** the equation into a simpler equation that has the same solution. Two equations that have the same solution are called **equivalent equations.**

One transformation that we may use to obtain an equivalent equation is the following.

> Simplify numerical expressions and variable expressions.

The example that follows shows how to use this transformation to obtain equivalent equations. You will learn how to solve equations in the lessons that follow.

EXAMPLE Simplify the expressions on both sides of the equation to obtain an equivalent equation.

a. $y - 8 + 3 = 24 \div 6$ **b.** $38 = 2n + 6 + 3n$ **c.** $2(a + 3) = 18$

Solution

a. Perform the operations on each side of the equation to simplify the numerical expressions.

$$y - 8 + 3 = 24 \div 6$$
$$y - 5 = 4$$

b. Combine like terms to simplify the variable expressions.

$$38 = 2n + 6 + 3n$$
$$38 = 2n + 3n + 6$$
$$38 = 5n + 6$$

c. Use the distributive property to simplify the left side.

$$2(a + 3) = 18$$
$$2a + 2(3) = 18$$
$$2a + 6 = 18$$

Throughout the rest of the chapter, if no replacement set is given for an equation, assume that the solution can be any number.

Reading Mathematics: ***Study Skills***
When you find a reference in the text to material that you studied earlier, reread the material in the earlier section to help you understand the new lesson. For example, page 146 includes a reference to the definition of *solution* that you learned earlier. Turn back to page 9 to review the definition.

Class Exercises

Simplify the expressions on both sides of the equation to obtain an equivalent equation.

1. $m - 9 + 5 = 32 \div 8$

2. $4 \times 12 = 3 + h - 10$

3. $13 + 8 + k = 11 \times 5$

4. $45 \div 9 = t - 7 - 8$

5. $42 = 3n + 2 + 5n$

6. $8v - 10 + 2v = 30$

7. $7q + 15 - 2q = 25$

8. $35 = y - 7 + 5y$

9. $3(x + 2) = 18$

10. $20 = 5(a - 3)$

Written Exercises

Simplify the expressions on both sides of the equation to obtain an equivalent equation.

A

1. $b + 10 - 3 = 44 \div 2$

2. $5 \times 23 = 8 + k + 7$

3. $24 \times 3 = 8 + 12 + u$

4. $c - 11 + 4 = 54 \div 9$

5. $26 \div 13 = -7 - 5 + v$

6. $8 \times 12 = e + 14 - 2$

7. $4 + 9 + f - 3 = 24 \div 2 \times 3$

8. $6 \times 8 \div 3 = t + 12 - 9 + 6$

9. $33 = 4n - 7 + 6n$

10. $12a + 8 - 3a = 35$

11. $13q - 2q - 2 = 20$

12. $14 = 7d - 2 + d$

13. $15 = 3z + 5 + 2z$

14. $-8v + 2v + 3 = 21$

15. $4x + 8x - 2x + 7 = -13$

16. $18 = 2f - 5f + 9 + 6f$

17. $4(j + 2) = 36$

18. $42 = (g + 3)7$

19. $20 = (e - 5)2$

20. $-8(m - 1) = 24$

Simplify the expressions on both sides of the equation to obtain an equivalent equation.

21. $-6(3 + w) = 48$

22. $27 = (5 - u)3$

23. $14 = 2(13 + b - 5)$

24. $(6 + 4 + p)3 = 21$

25. $(2n + 6 + n)5 = 45$

26. $12 = 4(7 + 8n - 3n)$

B **27.** $0.4 \times 8 = -2.2 + 17.8 + c$

28. $3 \times 10.1 = 17.8 + h - 5.6$

29. $36 \div \frac{3}{2} = \frac{4}{3} + k + \frac{2}{3}$

30. $\frac{1}{2}u + \frac{3}{7} - \frac{4}{7} = 9 \times \frac{1}{3}$

31. $0.6g + 4.3 + 19.4g = 24.3$

32. $19.8 = 17.5y - 3.5y + 8.2$

33. $\frac{-8}{7} = \frac{6}{7} + \frac{5}{4}v - \frac{9}{4}v$

34. $\frac{4}{5}m + \frac{1}{2} + \frac{11}{5}m = \frac{3}{2}$

35. $6.6 = (11 - 10x)0.3$

36. $28 = (10v - 20)0.2$

37. $\frac{1}{2}(4h - 10) = 17$

38. $15 = (6y + 9)\frac{1}{3}$

C **39.** $8m + 5(-3 - 6m) = \frac{27 - 9}{3}$

40. $6q(3.5 + 2.7) - 12q = (3.5 - 2.7)$

41. $\frac{1}{2}(36.8n + 13.2n + 12.6) = 52.6 \div 2$

42. $81 \times \frac{1}{3} = \left(\frac{-9}{4} + 7e - 8e\right)\frac{4}{3}$

43. $\left(8d + \frac{3}{4}\right) \div 6 + \frac{1}{4} + 2d = 99 \div 3$

44. $\frac{2}{5} \times 140 = \left[\left(\frac{5}{8}w - 32\right) \div 4\right] + \frac{3}{8}w - 6$

Review Exercises

What value of the variable makes the statement true?

1. $-x + 9 = 15$

2. $-7 + x = 8$

3. $x - (-8) = -9$

4. $6 - (-x) = 15$

5. $x + (-3) = -11$

6. $6 + x = -13$

7. $-4 - x = -12$

8. $x - 5 = -15$

9. $8 + (-x) = -12$

Challenge

A snail is climbing up the side of a slippery well that is 2.45 m deep. Each hour the snail climbs 45 cm, but falls back 5 cm. How long will it take the snail to climb to the top of the well?

5-3 Solving Equations with Addition and Subtraction

The usual way to solve an equation is to transform it into the form

$$x = c \qquad \text{or} \qquad c = x,$$

where x is the variable alone on one side, and c is a number. Then the solution is simply c.

We know that addition and subtraction are inverse operations. In the example below, the addition of 9 *undoes* the subtraction of 9.

$$17 - 9 = 8 \qquad 8 + 9 = 17$$

We can use this idea and the addition property of equality to transform an equation that involves subtraction into an equivalent equation with the variable alone on one side. If

$$n - 8 = 24$$

then

$$n - 8 + 8 = 24 + 8.$$

When we simplify the numerical expressions on both sides of the equation, we obtain

$$n = 32.$$

Because subtraction of a number is the same as adding the opposite of the number, we may use similar transformations for an equation involving addition, as in the following example.

$$n + 6 = 32$$

$$n + 6 + (-6) = 32 + (-6)$$

$$n + 6 - 6 = 32 - 6$$

$$n = 26$$

In general, we may use the following transformation to solve equations involving addition or subtraction.

> *Transformation by addition or subtraction:* Add the same number to, or subtract the same number from, both sides of an equation.

When you have solved an equation, it is a good idea to check your solution to be sure that you have not made any errors in transforming the equation. To check, simply substitute your answer in the original equation.

EXAMPLE 1 Solve $y - 14.5 = 35$.

Solution Add 14.5 to both sides of the equation to obtain y alone on the left side.

$$y - 14.5 = 35$$
$$y - 14.5 + 14.5 = 35 + 14.5$$
$$y = 49.5$$

The solution is 49.5.

Check:
$$y - 14.5 = 35$$
$$49.5 - 14.5 \stackrel{?}{=} 35$$
$$35 = 35 \ \checkmark$$

We may need to use more than one transformation to solve some equations involving addition or subtraction.

EXAMPLE 2 Solve $18 = -4 + x + 6$.

Solution Simplify the right side of the equation.

$$18 = -4 + x + 6$$
$$18 = x + 2$$

Subtract 2 from both sides of the equation.

$$18 - 2 = x + 2 - 2$$
$$16 = x$$

The solution is 16.

Check:
$$18 = -4 + x + 6$$
$$18 \stackrel{?}{=} -4 + 16 + 6$$
$$18 = 18 \ \checkmark$$

When a solution to an equation involves several steps, be sure that you can identify which transformation you are using in each step.

Class Exercises

Identify the transformation used in each step.

1. $y + 18 = 7$
$y + 18 - 18 = 7 - 18$

2. $m - 9 = 13$
$m - 9 + 9 = 13 + 9$

3. $5 = w - 10$
$5 + 10 = w - 10 + 10$

4. $12 = k + 2$
$12 - 2 = k + 2 - 2$

5. $-3 + d + 8 = 14$
$d + 5 = 14$
$d + 5 - 5 = 14 - 5$

6. $16 = -9 + h + 6$
$16 = h - 3$
$16 + 3 = h - 3 + 3$

Complete in order to solve and identify the transformation used.

7. $21 = r - 19$
   $21 \underline{\ ?\ } 19 = r - 19 \underline{\ ?\ } 19$

8. $u + 15 = 27$
   $u + 15 \underline{\ ?\ } 15 = 27 \underline{\ ?\ } 15$

Written Exercises

Use transformations to solve the equation. Write down all the steps. Check your solution.

A

1. $f + 8 = 23$
2. $p + 4 = 13$
3. $x + 10 = -16$
4. $n - 7 = -12$
5. $w - 5 = 18$
6. $a - 11 = 14$
7. $-15 = v + 9$
8. $-26 = d + 8$
9. $17 = e + 10$
10. $22 = g - 6$
11. $-19 = r - 3$
12. $-28 = q - 11$
13. $9 + y + 6 = 14$
14. $-5 + 8 + l = 26$
15. $13 + u - 7 = -32$
16. $10 - 6 + k = -17$
17. $-5 + m - 12 = 23$
18. $14 - 10 + n = 21$
19. $-18 = 8 + w + 12$
20. $-34 = 9 + h - 4$
21. $24 = a + 17 - 6$
22. $42 = -7 + b + 3$
23. $-25 = j + 5 - 8$
24. $-18 = -10 + w - 9$

B

25. $j + 4\frac{3}{8} = 8$
26. $-5 = t + 6\frac{1}{3}$
27. $-7\frac{1}{4} + m = 2$
28. $7 = k - 4.3$
29. $10 = 3.6 + u$
30. $f - 8.5 = -2$
31. $3 = -8\frac{2}{7} + d + 1\frac{1}{7}$
32. $5\frac{1}{3} + g - 2\frac{1}{6} = -9$
33. $6 = 3\frac{4}{9} + y + 8\frac{5}{9}$
34. $8.4 + h + 1.6 = 11$
35. $2.1 + n - 8.3 = 10$
36. $4 = 6.7 + 3.5 + v$

EXAMPLE $|q| + 8 = 14$

Solution $|q| + 8 - 8 = 14 - 8$, so $|q| = 6$.

By the definition of absolute value, q is 6 or q is -6.

C

37. $|x| + 5 = 7$
38. $5 = |g| - 2$
39. $-3 + |w| = 8$
40. $8 + |d| = 9$

Review Exercises

Evaluate the expression when $a = \frac{1}{2}$ and $b = \frac{2}{3}$.

1. ab
2. $6ab$
3. $\frac{3}{8}ab$
4. $a \div 6$
5. $ab \div 4$
6. $a \div \frac{3}{5}$

5-4 Solving Equations with Multiplication and Division

We can use the multiplication property of equality and the fact that multiplication and division are inverse operations to transform an equation that involves division into an equivalent equation with the variable on one side. For example, if

$$x \div 8 = 12$$

we can multiply both sides by 8 to obtain x alone on the left side.

$$x \div 8 \times 8 = 12 \times 8$$
$$x = 96$$

We can use similar transformations to solve an equation involving multiplication.

$$13y = 195$$
$$13y \times \frac{1}{13} = 195 \times \frac{1}{13}$$

Because the result of multiplying a number by its reciprocal is 1, we obtain the following.

$$y = \frac{195}{13}$$
$$y = 15$$

Because multiplying by $\frac{1}{13}$ is the same as dividing by 13, we could have written the first step above as $\frac{13y}{13} = \frac{195}{13}$.

In general, we can use the following transformation to solve equations involving multiplication or division.

> *Transformation by multiplication or division:* Multiply or divide both sides of an equation by the same nonzero number.

EXAMPLE 1 Solve $-15n = 75$.

Solution Divide both sides of the equation by -15.

$$-15n = 75$$
$$\frac{-15n}{-15} = \frac{75}{-15}$$
$$n = -5$$

The solution is -5.

EXAMPLE 2 Solve $22 = \frac{r}{3.6}$.

Solution Multiply both sides of the equation by 3.6.

$$22 = \frac{r}{3.6}$$

$$22 \times 3.6 = \frac{r}{3.6} \times 3.6$$

$$79.2 = r$$

The solution is 79.2.

When the variable expression in an equation involves a fraction, as in the equation $\frac{1}{5}n = 14$, we can divide both sides of the equation by the fraction. Because dividing by a fraction is the same as multiplying by its reciprocal, we can transform the equation by multiplying both sides of the equation by the reciprocal. To solve $\frac{1}{5}n = 14$, we multiply both sides of the equation by 5, the reciprocal of $\frac{1}{5}$. In general, we can solve equations involving fractions in the following way.

> If an equation has the following form (where a, b, and c are numbers, $a \neq 0$, $b \neq 0$, and x is a variable),
>
> $$\frac{a}{b}x = c,$$
>
> multiply both sides by the reciprocal of $\frac{a}{b}$, namely $\frac{b}{a}$.

EXAMPLE 3 Solve $18 = -\frac{4}{9}m$.

Solution Multiply both sides of the equation by $-\frac{9}{4}$, the reciprocal of $-\frac{4}{9}$.

$$18 = -\frac{4}{9}m$$

$$-\frac{9}{4} \times 18 = -\frac{9}{4} \times \left(-\frac{4}{9}m\right)$$

$$-\frac{9}{\cancel{4}_{2}} \times \cancel{18}^{9} = m$$

$$m = -\frac{81}{2}, \text{ or } -40\frac{1}{2}$$

The solution is $-\frac{81}{2}$, or $-40\frac{1}{2}$.

As shown in Example 3, we may exchange the sides of an equation and still have an equivalent equation.

Class Exercises

a. Identify the transformation you would use to solve the equation.
b. Solve the equation.

1. $5x = 35$ **2.** $\frac{x}{8} = 42$ **3.** $56 = 7x$ **4.** $108 = \frac{x}{12}$

5. $84 = -3x$ **6.** $\frac{x}{9} = -8$ **7.** $\frac{x}{-6} = 30$ **8.** $\frac{x}{1.5} = 10$

9. $2.4x = 12$ **10.** $\frac{1}{5}x = 45$ **11.** $\frac{5}{7}x = 15$ **12.** $-\frac{3}{4}x = 9$

Written Exercises

Use transformations to solve the equation. Write down all the steps. Check your solution.

A **1.** $6x = 36$ **2.** $49 = -7z$ **3.** $-114 = 3y$ **4.** $-9a = -153$

5. $-\frac{5}{7}n = 35$ **6.** $\frac{1}{2}r = 18$ **7.** $-27 = -\frac{3}{11}b$ **8.** $\frac{2}{3}q = -46$

9. $16 = \frac{w}{8}$ **10.** $-7 = \frac{r}{13}$ **11.** $\frac{a}{-24} = 22$ **12.** $\frac{n}{-7} = -12$

13. $-12g = 204$ **14.** $\frac{2}{5}d = 17$ **15.** $-\frac{1}{9}a = 459$ **16.** $837 = -15p$

17. $\frac{m}{18} = 54$ **18.** $62 = \frac{b}{31}$ **19.** $8 = \frac{c}{-612}$ **20.** $\frac{t}{240} = -9$

21. $0.5a = 42$ **22.** $81 = 2.7b$ **23.** $5 = \frac{m}{31.7}$ **24.** $\frac{b}{0.6} = 18$

25. $\frac{t}{0.8} = 19$ **26.** $12 = \frac{a}{2.53}$ **27.** $3604 = -9.01x$ **28.** $-7.3d = -146$

B **29.** $\frac{2}{7}b = \frac{5}{8}$ **30.** $\frac{1}{5}x = -\frac{9}{10}$ **31.** $-\frac{1}{8} = \frac{3}{4}q$ **32.** $\frac{5}{9} = -\frac{2}{3}n$

33. $2.8 = 0.01x$ **34.** $7.9r = -19.75$ **35.** $-3.72y = 5.208$ **36.** $5.01m = 85.671$

C **37.** $-\frac{3}{8}a = 46.5$ **38.** $\frac{x}{3.2} = -\frac{1}{4}$ **39.** $\frac{7}{12} = \frac{d}{5.4}$ **40.** $\frac{5}{9}n = -1.004$

Review Exercises

Find the solutions of the inequality. The replacement set for x is the set of whole numbers.

1. $x < 7$ **2.** $x \geq 19$ **3.** $21 < x$ **4.** $x > 10$

5. $9 \geq x$ **6.** $x \leq 5$ **7.** $4 \leq x \leq 11$ **8.** $6 > x > 1$

5-5 Using Several Transformations

When we simplify the numerical and variable expressions in an equation, we may obtain an equation in one of the following forms, where a, b, and c are numbers and x is a variable.

$$ax + b = c \qquad ax - b = c \qquad b - ax = c$$

For equations such as these, we must use more than one operation to transform the equation into the form $x = c$.

EXAMPLE 1 Solve $9 - 5n = 36 - 12$.

Solution Simplify the numerical expression on the right side of the equation.

$$9 - 5n = 36 - 12$$
$$9 - 5n = 24$$

Subtract 9 from both sides of the equation.

$$9 - 5n - 9 = 24 - 9$$
$$-5n = 15$$

Divide both sides of the equation by -5.

$$\frac{-5n}{-5} = \frac{15}{-5}$$
$$n = -3$$

The solution is -3.

The transformations that we used in Example 1 suggest the following steps for solving equations in which all the variables are on the same side.

> **1.** Simplify each side of the equation.
>
> **2.** If there are still indicated additions or subtractions, use the inverse operations to undo them.
>
> **3.** If there are indicated multiplications or divisions involving the variable, use the inverse operations to undo them.

In steps 2 and 3, always remember to *perform the same operation on both sides of the equation.*

EXAMPLE 2 Solve $35 = \frac{5}{8}(r - 24)$.

Solution Simplify the right side.

$$35 = \frac{5}{8}(r - 24)$$
$$35 = \frac{5}{8}r - \frac{5}{8}(24)$$
$$35 = \frac{5}{8}r - 15$$

Add 15 to both sides.

$$35 + 15 = \frac{5}{8}r - 15 + 15$$
$$50 = \frac{5}{8}r$$

Multiply both sides by $\frac{8}{5}$.

$$\frac{8}{5} \times 50 = \frac{8}{5} \times \frac{5}{8}r$$
$$\frac{8}{\cancel{5}_{1}} \times \overset{10}{\cancel{50}} = r$$
$$80 = r$$

The solution is 80.

Some equations have variables on both sides. To transform equations in this form, we may add a variable expression to both sides or subtract a variable expression from both sides.

EXAMPLE 3 Solve $8x = x + 14$.

Solution Subtract x from both sides.

$$8x = x + 14$$
$$8x - x = x + 14 - x$$
$$7x = 14$$

Divide both sides by 7.

$$\frac{7x}{7} = \frac{14}{7}$$
$$x = 2$$

The solution is 2.

Class Exercises

State which transformations you would use to solve the equation. State them in the order in which you would use them.

1. $8x + 18 = 42$
2. $6t - 2 = 28$
3. $\frac{b}{5} - 3 = 33$
4. $12 + \frac{d}{7} = 18$
5. $9 = \frac{1}{2}r - 10$
6. $\frac{2}{3}n + 6 = 8$
7. $13 + 11 = 5a + 6$
8. $\frac{m}{5} + 8 = 3(2 + 7)$
9. $-4(y + 8) = 16$
10. $5n = 2n - 9$
11. $3b + 6 = \frac{1}{2}b$
12. $11 - 4x = 7x + 8$

Written Exercises

Identify the transformation used in each step.

A

1. $8x - 2x = 54 \times 3$
   $6x = 162$
   $x = \frac{162}{6}$
2. $2x + 3 = 17$
   $2x = 14$
   $x = \frac{14}{2}$
3. $31 = 4 - 3x$
   $27 = -3x$
   $\frac{27}{-3} = x$
4. $5(18 + x) = 45$
   $90 + 5x = 45$
   $5x = -45$
   $x = \frac{-45}{5}$
5. $52 = 4(x - 3)$
   $52 = 4x - 12$
   $64 = 4x$
   $\frac{64}{4} = x$
6. $3x + 13 - 7x = 37$
   $-4x + 13 = 37$
   $-4x = 24$
   $x = \frac{24}{-4}$

Solve.

7. $2w + 1 = 5$
8. $8 + 4q = 16$
9. $11x - 17 = 49$
10. $8d - 31 = 33$
11. $2y - 2 = -3 + 7$
12. $-14 + 5 = 7x - 30$
13. $\frac{a}{2} + 3 = 6$
14. $14 + \frac{t}{11} = 17$
15. $\frac{z}{4} - 5 = 9$
16. $39 = \frac{n}{5} - 21$
17. $\frac{1}{3}x + 4 = -6$
18. $\frac{3}{8}m + 9 = 18$
19. $42 = 6 - \frac{1}{5}q$
20. $\frac{1}{9}e - 8 = 30$
21. $-2(x - 3) = -3(-8)$
22. $\frac{105}{5} = 3(4 - 2b)$
23. $-5a - 9 + a = \frac{45}{3}$
24. $13 + f - 8f = 25 \times 5$
25. $7m = -2m + 10$
26. $3x = -x + 2$
27. $y - 5 = 2y + 10$
28. $3x + 4 = 2x - 6$
29. $5b - 2 = b + 10$
30. $-7r - 8 = -5r + 3$

B

31. $5(y - 1) + 8 = -9$
32. $34 = 3(t + 6) - 8$
33. $9 - 4(x - 3) = 17$

Solve.

34. $15 - 6(x + 2) = 1$

35. $50 = 2(5r + 2) - 1$

36. $26 = -5(4 + 8y) - 6$

37. $3a = 2.5(8 + a)$

38. $0.3(p + 4) = 2.7p$

39. $x(4.8 - 2) = 4.8x - 2$

40. $4q + 19 = \frac{5}{6}q$

41. $\frac{3}{5}c = 2c - 7$

42. $\frac{2}{3}a = -15 - a$

C 43. $\frac{1}{2}b + \frac{3}{5} = 2b - \frac{9}{10}$

44. $\frac{3}{4}f - \frac{1}{2} = 2f + \frac{1}{2}$

45. $-\frac{1}{6}\left(t - \frac{1}{3}t\right) = -t + 36$

46. $-z - 9 = \frac{3}{4}\left(2z + \frac{4}{3}\right)$

47. $\frac{2}{3}\left(m - \frac{1}{2}\right) + 3 = \frac{m}{3} - 7$

48. $\frac{1}{2}(-4x - 5) = 7x - \frac{1}{2}$

Write an equation for the word sentence and solve for y.

49. Nine divided by six is four times the difference of a number y subtracted from four.

50. Five times the sum of a number y and 11 is seventeen minus three.

51. Five eighteenths subtracted from one third of a number y is twice the number y.

52. One half the sum of five and a number y is one quarter y.

Self-Test A

Use one of the properties of equality to form a true sentence.

1. If $35 + p = 47$, then $p = \underline{\ ?\ }$.

2. If $-6a = 48$, then $a = \underline{\ ?\ }$. **[5-1]**

Simplify the expressions on both sides of the equation to obtain an equivalent equation.

3. $17 = 3x - 9 + 5x - 8$

4. $24 \div 3 = 5(m - 9)$ **[5-2]**

Use transformations to solve the equation.

5. $x + 19 = 24$

6. $36 = y - 11$

7. $a + 14 = -9 - 3$ **[5-3]**

8. $-8q - 56$

9. $\frac{m}{18} - 9$

10. $\frac{1}{4}d - 8$ **[5-4]**

11. $27 = 2y - 13$

12. $-2(7 + 2b) = 52$

13. $6n - 9 - 3n = n - 17$ **[5-5]**

Self-Test answers and Extra Practice are at the back of the book.

5-6 Equivalent Inequalities

To solve an inequality, we transform the inequality into an **equivalent inequality.** The transformations that we use are similar to those we use to solve equations.

> Simplify numerical expressions and variable expressions.
>
> Add the same number to, or subtract the same number from, both sides of the inequality.
>
> Multiply or divide both sides of the inequality by the same *positive* number.
>
> Multiply or divide both sides of the inequality by the same *negative number and reverse the direction of the inequality.*

Notice that we do not multiply the sides of an inequality by 0.

The following shows why we must change the inequality when multiplying or dividing by a negative number.

$$\begin{aligned} -6 &< 5 \\ 2(-6) \ &? \ 2(5) \\ -12 &< 10 \end{aligned} \qquad\qquad \begin{aligned} -6 &< 5 \\ -2(-6) \ &? \ -2(5) \\ 12 &> -10 \end{aligned}$$

EXAMPLE 1 Solve each inequality.

a. $x + 7 \leq -18$ **b.** $y - 4.5 > 32$

Solution **a.** Subtract 7 from both sides of the inequality.

$$\begin{aligned} x + 7 &\leq -18 \\ x + 7 - 7 &\leq -18 - 7 \\ x &\leq -25 \end{aligned}$$

The solutions are all the numbers less than or equal to -25.

b. Add 4.5 to both sides of the inequality.

$$\begin{aligned} y - 4.5 &> 32 \\ y - 4.5 + 4.5 &> 32 + 4.5 \\ y &> 36.5 \end{aligned}$$

The solutions are all the numbers greater than 36.5.

EXAMPLE 2 Solve $2\frac{1}{4} - \frac{1}{2} \geq n$.

Solution We may exchange the sides of the inequality and *reverse the inequality sign* before we simplify the numerical expression.

$$2\frac{1}{4} - \frac{1}{2} \geq n$$

$$n \leq 2\frac{1}{4} - \frac{1}{2}$$

$$n \leq \frac{7}{4}, \text{ or } 1\frac{3}{4}$$

The solutions are all the numbers less than or equal to $\frac{7}{4}$.

EXAMPLE 3 Solve each inequality.

a. $7a < 91$ **b.** $-3x \geq 18$ **c.** $26 \leq \frac{y}{4}$ **d.** $\frac{d}{-9} > -108$

Solution **a.** Divide both sides by 7.

$$7a < 91$$

$$\frac{7a}{7} < \frac{91}{7}$$

$$a < 13$$

The solutions are all the numbers less than 13.

b. Divide both sides by -3 and *reverse the inequality sign.*

$$-3x \geq 18$$

$$\frac{-3x}{-3} \leq \frac{18}{-3}$$

$$x \leq -6$$

The solutions are all the numbers less than or equal to -6.

c. Multiply both sides by 4.

$$26 \leq \frac{y}{4}$$

$$4 \times 26 \leq 4 \times \frac{y}{4}$$

$$104 \leq y$$

The solutions are all the numbers greater than or equal to 104.

d. Multiply both sides by -9 and *reverse the inequality sign.*

$$\frac{d}{-9} > -108$$

$$-9 \times \frac{d}{-9} < -9 \times (-108)$$

$$d < 972$$

The solutions are all the numbers less than 972.

Class Exercises

Identify the transformation used to transform the first inequality into the second.

1. $e + 5 > 8$
   $e + 5 - 5 > 8 - 5$

2. $q - 3 < 7$
   $q - 3 + 3 < 7 + 3$

3. $\frac{1}{2}k < 4$
   $2 \times \frac{1}{2}k < 2 \times 4$

4. $6a > 12$
   $\frac{6a}{6} > \frac{12}{6}$

5. $-\frac{1}{4}u > 3$
   $-4 \times -\frac{1}{4}u < -4 \times 3$

6. $-9m < 27$
   $\frac{-9m}{-9} > \frac{27}{-9}$

Identify each transformation and complete the equivalent inequality.

7. $n - 6 > 9$
   $n - 6 + 6 \underline{\ ?\ } 9 + 6$

8. $d + 4 < -3$
   $d + 4 - 4 \underline{\ ?\ } -3 - 4$

9. $3r < 15$
   $\frac{3r}{3} \underline{\ ?\ } \frac{15}{3}$

10. $\frac{1}{5}v > 6$
    $5 \times \frac{1}{5}v \underline{\ ?\ } 5 \times 6$

11. $-4z > 32.8$
    $\frac{-4z}{-4} \underline{\ ?\ } \frac{32.8}{-4}$

12. $-\frac{1}{3}s < 2\frac{1}{3}$
    $-3 \times -\frac{1}{3}s \underline{\ ?\ } -3 \times \frac{7}{3}$

Written Exercises

Use transformations to solve the inequality. Write down all the steps.

A

1. $-4 + 16 > k$
2. $g < -18 - 9$
3. $(17 + 4)2 < j$
4. $f \geq 7(23 - 9)$
5. $a + 7 < 10$
6. $c + 8 > 13$
7. $e - 11 \geq 9$
8. $m - 5 \leq 15$
9. $-16 > n + 2$
10. $-13 < q - 6$
11. $8w < 56$
12. $7y > 42$
13. $-5t > 35$
14. $-6a < 18$
15. $-48 \leq -4b$
16. $-49 \geq -7m$
17. $\frac{u}{3} \leq 5$
18. $\frac{w}{4} \geq 9$

Use transformations to solve the inequality. Write down all the steps.

19. $\frac{f}{-2} > 13$

20. $\frac{n}{-5} < 12$

21. $-10 \leq \frac{y}{-6}$

22. $-9 \geq \frac{d}{4}$

23. $\frac{4h - 2h}{2} \leq -6 - 5$

24. $\frac{16}{4} > \frac{7n - 2n}{5}$

B 25. $-8(13.4 + 7.6) > a$

26. $12 \leq p - 4.27$

27. $3r > 63.9$

28. $10\left(3\frac{1}{2} + 4\frac{2}{5}\right) \geq g$

29. $j + 3\frac{4}{7} < 9$

30. $d + 5\frac{1}{4} > -8$

31. $-10 \geq n - 6.13$

32. $c < (18.7 - 7.6)4$

33. $e \leq \left(5\frac{1}{3} + 2\frac{1}{2}\right)6$

34. $42.4 < 4t$

35. $\frac{d}{0.6} \leq -18$

36. $\frac{1}{5}w \geq \frac{2}{5}$

37. $\frac{3}{4} \leq \frac{1}{4}n$

38. $\frac{m}{3.1} \geq 12$

39. $-7 > -\frac{1}{3}d$

40. $-\frac{1}{2}f \leq -13$

41. $-6y < 24.6$

42. $42.5 > -5b$

43. $\frac{a}{-13.2} \geq 7$

44. $\frac{x}{-0.3} < -9$

45. $h - 10\frac{2}{3} > 12\frac{1}{5}$

46. $-8.27 \leq k + 17.41$

47. $22.5 \geq -2.5m$

48. $3.2u \geq 25.6$

C 49. $\frac{3}{4}n + \frac{1}{2}n > \frac{2}{3} \times \frac{3}{8}$

50. $\frac{-5}{8}p - \frac{1}{8}p > \frac{1}{4} \div 7$

51. $3.4(21.2 - 18.9) < 4.6(-3b + 2b)$

52. $\frac{5(-1.6t)}{2.5} < -14.3 - 9.6$

Review Exercises

Write the numbers in order from least to greatest.

1. $-1.4,\ 1.2,\ -2.6,\ 3.2$

2. $3.7,\ 4.02,\ -3.07,\ -4.1,\ 3$

3. $12,\ -12.2,\ -12.09,\ 112,\ -11.2$

4. $9.8,\ -8.09,\ 0.89,\ -0.98,\ -9$

5. $-5.03,\ 3.05,\ -30.05,\ 0.35,\ -5.3$

6. $-0.2,\ -0.02,\ -2,\ -20,\ 200$

7. $2.89,\ 2.089,\ -2.8,\ 28.9,\ -2.89$

8. $-7.6,\ -0.76,\ -7.06,\ -0.076,\ -76.0$

5-7 Solving Inequalities by Several Transformations

We may need to use more than one transformation to solve some inequalities. It is helpful to follow the same steps that we use for solving equations.

1. Simplify each side of the inequality.
2. Use the inverse operations to undo any indicated additions or subtractions.
3. Use the inverse operations to undo any indicated multiplications or divisions.

EXAMPLE 1 Solve $-4r + 6 + 2r - 18 < -8$.

Solution Simplify the left side.

$$-4r + 6 + 2r - 18 < -8$$
$$-2r - 12 < -8$$

Add 12 to both sides.

$$-2r - 12 + 12 < -8 + 12$$
$$-2r < 4$$

Divide both sides by -2 and reverse the inequality sign.

$$\frac{-2r}{-2} > \frac{4}{-2}$$
$$r > -2$$

The solutions are all the numbers greater than -2.

The solutions to the inequality in Example 1 include all numbers greater than -2. We show the graph of the solutions on the number line in the following way.

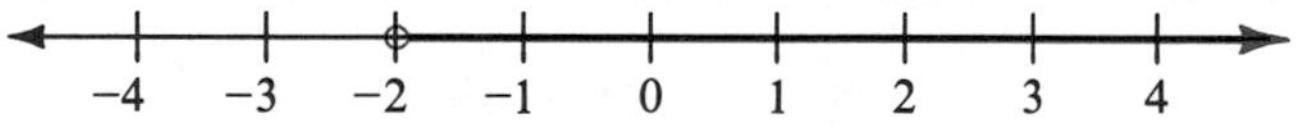

The open dot at -2 indicates that -2 is not on the graph of the solutions of the inequality.

We use a solid dot to show that a number is on the graph of the solutions. We graph the solutions of $r \geq -2$ in the following way.

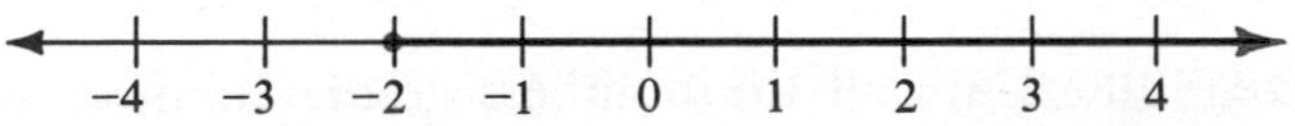

EXAMPLE 2 Solve $3(5 + x) \leq -3$ and graph the solutions.

Solution Simplify the left side.

$$\begin{aligned} 3(5 + x) &\leq -3 \\ 3(5) + 3x &\leq -3 \\ 15 + 3x &\leq -3 \end{aligned}$$

Subtract 15 from both sides.

$$\begin{aligned} 15 + 3x - 15 &\leq -3 - 15 \\ 3x &\leq -18 \end{aligned}$$

Divide both sides by 3.

$$\begin{aligned} \frac{3x}{3} &\leq \frac{-18}{3} \\ x &\leq -6 \end{aligned}$$

The solutions are all the numbers less than or equal to -6.

Because -6 is on the graph, we used a solid dot to graph the solutions of the inequality.

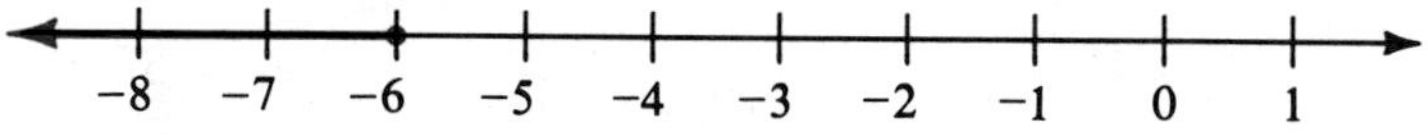

Like equations, inequalities may have variables on both sides. We may add a variable expression to both sides or subtract a variable expression from both sides to obtain an equivalent inequality.

EXAMPLE 3 Solve $-z + 7 \leq 3z - 18$.

Solution Add z to both sides.

$$\begin{aligned} -z + 7 &\leq 3z - 18 \\ z + (-z) + 7 &\leq z + 3z - 18 \\ 7 &\leq 4z - 18 \end{aligned}$$

Add 18 to both sides.

$$\begin{aligned} 7 + 18 &\leq 4z - 18 + 18 \\ 25 &\leq 4z \end{aligned}$$

Divide both sides by 4.

$$\begin{aligned} \frac{25}{4} &\leq \frac{4z}{4} \\ 6.25 &\leq z \end{aligned}$$

The solutions are all the numbers greater than or equal to 6.25.

Class Exercises

State which transformations you would use to solve the inequality. State them in the order in which you would use them.

1. $8x + 7 - 5x + 2 \leq 30$
2. $-29 > 5 - 2y - 10 - 4y$
3. $7 \geq \frac{-4}{5}m + 6 + \frac{3}{5}m - 4$
4. $\frac{6}{7}k - 8 - \frac{5}{7}k + 3 < -3$
5. $4(h - 3) > 16$
6. $-4 \geq \frac{1}{2}(w + 12)$
7. $2 < (k + 45)\frac{-1}{5}$
8. $(3 - s)7 \leq 42$
9. $-u + 8 \geq 4u - 10$
10. $a - 6 < -5a - 18$

Written Exercises

Solve and graph the solutions.

A 1. $3q + 5 < -13$

2. $-7 + 5m > 28$
3. $30 \geq -4b - 6$
4. $-57 \leq -8z - 9$
5. $-\frac{w}{2} + 8 > 23$
6. $-\frac{c}{3} + 7 < -18$
7. $-12 \leq -5 + \frac{r}{6}$
8. $13 \geq 6 + \frac{e}{4}$

Solve.

9. $3v + 11 - 8v - 5 < -21$
10. $9 - 12u + 4 + 6u > -5$
11. $12 \geq \frac{3}{5}f + 6 - \frac{4}{5}f + 4$
12. $19 \leq 7 + \frac{1}{3}k + 2 - \frac{2}{3}k$
13. $h > -5h + 18 - 6$
14. $t < 17 - 4t - 2$
15. $38 - 8 - 7n \leq 3n$
16. $-9q + 18 - 3 \geq 6q$
17. $\frac{1}{4}(20 - x) < 6$
18. $\frac{1}{6}(42 - p) > 12$
19. $21 \geq 7(m - 2)$
20. $-25 \leq 5(w + 3)$
21. $j + 8 > 4j - 16$
22. $-6f + 7 < 2f - 9$
23. $10 + \frac{3}{4}a \leq \frac{-7}{8}a + 5$
24. $\frac{5}{6}g - 4 \geq \frac{2}{3}g + 6$

B 25. $-12.8c + 8 + 7.8c - 6 \geq 17$

26. $4 + 7.5y - 9 + 2.5y > 25$

Solve.

27. $1\frac{4}{5} < 8m + 4\frac{1}{5} - 3m - 7\frac{2}{5}$

28. $-2\frac{2}{3} \le 5\frac{2}{3} - 9u + 4\frac{2}{3} + 3u$

29. $0.2(40k + 62.5) \le -3.5$

30. $-0.5(12v - 18.6) < 21.3$

31. $-2\frac{7}{8} > \left(\frac{5}{8} - t\right)\frac{1}{5}$

32. $5\frac{3}{4} \le \frac{1}{3}\left(x - \frac{3}{4}\right)$

33. $2.7e + 8.2 < -9.3e + 32.2$

34. $5.4 - 10.9w \ge 9.1w - 14.6$

35. $\frac{5}{6}f - 2\frac{4}{5} > 1\frac{1}{5} + \frac{2}{3}f$

36. $-2\frac{1}{9}d + \frac{3}{5} \le -3\frac{2}{9}d - 4\frac{2}{5}$

C 37. $0.11(360 + 25n) < (1.86n \div 6) - 3.06n$

38. $\frac{1}{5}\left(w - 5\frac{5}{9}\right) + \frac{2}{9} + \frac{3}{4}w \ge \frac{1}{8}w - 1 + \frac{5}{8}w$

39. $[(250.25x - 10.5) \div -5] - 14.6 \le -0.05x + 502.5$

40. $9\frac{4}{5} + \frac{2}{7}k - 7\frac{3}{5} > -\frac{11}{12} + \left[\left(\frac{4}{7}k + 2\frac{1}{3}\right) \div \frac{4}{5}\right]$

Review Exercises

Use *n* to write a variable expression for the word phrase.

1. A number increased by nine
2. Twice a number
3. Sixteen less than a number
4. Half of a number
5. The sum of a number and three
6. Six more than a number
7. A number divided by five
8. Eight times a number

Calculator Key-In

Do the following on your calculator.

1. Press any 3 digits.	852
2. Repeat the digits.	852,852
3. Divide by 7.	?
4. Divide by 11.	?
5. Divide by 13.	?

What is your answer? Now multiply your answer by 1001. Try again using three different digits. Explain your results.

5-8 Equations into Word Problems

An equation such as

$$12x = 132$$

can be used to represent many real-life problems. For example:

> To pay back \$132 that his father lent him, Carlton will make 12 equal payments. How much will each be?
>
> 12 payments $\times$ x dollars $=$ \$132
>
> One hundred thirty-two people have signed up for a tour of the planetarium. If 12 people are in each group, how many tour groups will there be?
>
> 12 people $\times$ x groups $=$ 132 people

In each of the problems, the variable x was used to represent an unknown number. In each case, the product of 12 and the unknown number equals 132. Notice that the equation $12x = 132$ does not answer the question in each problem. We must solve the equation for x to find the answer to the question.

EXAMPLE 1 State two word problems that can be represented by the equation $42 - x = 19$.

Solution The following are two possibilities.

a. This morning Phyllis must deliver 42 copies of the *Herald News*. After delivering the papers on River Road, she has 19 papers left to deliver. How many copies did she deliver on River Road?

b. Forty-two students had planned to audition for the school play this week. On Wednesday 19 students were still waiting to audition. How many students had auditioned so far?

EXAMPLE 2 Which of the following equations represents the problem below?

a. $15 + x = 60$ **b.** $15 - x = 60$ **c.** $15x = 60$ **d.** $\frac{x}{15} = 60$

Jeff must be at his music teacher's studio in 60 min. If it takes 15 min for him to reach the studio, how much extra time does Jeff have?

Solution The unknown number in the problem is the number of minutes of extra time Jeff has. The variable x represents this number. The problem states that the travel time, 15 min, and the extra time, x min, together must equal 60 min. Answer (a), $15 + x = 60$, represents the problem.

Class Exercises

State a problem that the equation could represent. Use the words in parentheses as the subject of the problem.

1. $x + 18 = 362$ (attendance at a game)

2. $x - 10 = 24$ (a garden)

3. $15x = 75$ (bicycling)

4. $\frac{x}{4} = 28$ (carpentry)

Written Exercises

Write a problem that the equation could represent.

A

1. $80 + x = 84$ **2.** $95 + x = 159$ **3.** $x - 8 = 24$ **4.** $x - 45 = 47$

5. $50 - x = 37$ **6.** $243 - x = 96$ **7.** $52x = 728$ **8.** $8x = 96$

9. $\frac{x}{36} = 27$ **10.** $\frac{x}{24} = 378$ **11.** $\frac{1}{4}x = 7$ **12.** $\frac{1}{8}x = 5$

B

13. $3x + 5 = 60$ **14.** $2x - 8 = 26$ **15.** $x + 2x = 15$ **16.** $x + \frac{1}{2}x = 48$

Match.

17. Photo Mart received 32 cartons of photo albums. If each carton contains 10 albums, how many albums were received?

18. If Jocelyn earns \$10 a week for mowing the lawn, in how many weeks will she have \$32?

19. A single row of 32 square tiles of the same size covers a length of 10 ft. How wide is each tile?

20. Bay Village is 32 km from Londonderry. If a car traveling between the two cities is 10 km from Londonderry, how far is the car from Bay Village?

21. After grading 10 tests, a teacher has 32 tests left to grade. How many tests were there in all?

A. $10 + x = 32$

B. $x - 10 = 32$

C. $10x = 32$

D. $32x = 10$

E. $\frac{x}{10} = 32$

Review Exercises

Solve.

1. $-\frac{2}{3}x = -3$ **2.** $3.2 = t + 4.2$ **3.** $c - 9 = 35$ **4.** $28 = -4 + \frac{a}{3}$

5. $-3 = \frac{1}{6}a$ **6.** $-2(n + 8) = 45$ **7.** $6 + 3b = 4b$ **8.** $\frac{a}{-7} = 31 - 22.8$

5-9 Word Problems into Equations

Usually a word problem states some numerical relationships and asks a question. We may write an equation to represent the given information and then solve the equation to answer the question. The following five-step plan is helpful in solving word problems using equations.

Solving a Word Problem Using an Equation

Step 1 Read the problem carefully. Make sure that you understand what it says. You may need to read it more than once.

Step 2 Decide what numbers are asked for. Choose a variable and use it with the given conditions of the problem to represent the number(s) asked for.

Step 3 Write an equation based on the given conditions.

Step 4 Solve the equation and find the required numbers.

Step 5 Check your results with the words of the problem. Give the answer.

EXAMPLE 1 Karyn has earned \$56.25 at her afternoon job. If she earns \$2.50 per hour, how many more hours must she work to earn a total of \$225 to buy a cassette player?

Solution

- The problem says Karyn has earned \$56.25, she earns \$2.50 per hour, and she would like to earn \$225.
- The problem asks how many more hours Karyn must work to have \$225. Let x = the number of hours. Since Karyn earns \$2.50 per hour, the money after x more hours $= 56.25 + 2.50x$.
  We have two expressions for the total amount of money:
  $$225 \qquad \text{and} \qquad 56.25 + 2.50x.$$
- Use the expressions to write an equation: $225 = 56.25 + 2.50x$.
- Solve.
  $$\begin{aligned} 225 &= 56.25 + 2.50x \\ 225 - 56.25 &= 56.25 + 2.50x - 56.25 \\ 168.75 &= 2.50x \\ 67.5 &= x \end{aligned}$$
- Check: If Karyn earns \$2.50 per hour, in 67.5 h she will earn $67.5 \times \$2.50$, or \$168.75. She now has \$56.25, and $56.25 + 168.75 = 225$. ✓

Karyn must work 67.5 h, or $67\frac{1}{2}$ h, more.

EXAMPLE 2 Mark estimates that it will take 7 h to sand and paint the porch floor. He estimates that it will take twice as long to sand the floor as to paint the floor. How long does he expect to spend on each part of the job?

Solution

- The problem says that sanding and painting take 7 h, and sanding takes twice as long as painting.
- The problem asks for the length of time to do each part.
  Let x = the time it takes to paint.
  Use a chart to help organize the information.

paint	sand	total time
x	$2x$	7

The time for sanding and the time for painting make up the total time. We are given 7 as the numerical expression for the total time. From the chart we see that $x + 2x$ is a variable expression for the total time.

- Using the two expressions for the total time, write an equation:
  $x + 2x = 7.$
- Solve.

$$x + 2x = 7$$
$$3x = 7$$
$$x = \frac{7}{3}, \text{ or } 2\frac{1}{3}$$

Therefore, $2x = 2 \times 2\frac{1}{3} = 4\frac{2}{3}$.

- Check: Is the total time 7 h? $2\frac{1}{3} + 4\frac{2}{3} = 7$

  Is $4\frac{2}{3}$ twice as much as $2\frac{1}{3}$? $4\frac{2}{3} \div 2 = 2\frac{1}{3}$ ✓

Mark expects to spend $4\frac{2}{3}$ h sanding and $2\frac{1}{3}$ h painting.

We may need to round the answers to some problems. When rounding an answer that is the result of division, we must consider whether it is reasonable to round the answer up or down.

EXAMPLE 3 The eighth-grade classes are taking a bus trip to the art museum. There is room for 60 people on each bus. If 175 students and 23 adults go on the trip, how many buses are needed?

Solution

- The problem says that 175 and 23 people will take the bus trip, and 60 people can fit on each bus.

- The problem asks how many buses are needed. If we let $x =$ the number of buses, then the number of people on the buses is $60x$. We know that there are $175 + 23$ people.
- Using the two expressions for the number of people, write an equation: $60x = 175 + 23$.
- Solve.

$$60x = 175 + 23$$
$$60x = 198$$
$$x = 3.3$$

  To have enough buses for all of the people on the trip, round the answer *up* to the nearest whole number, 4.
- Check: Four buses with 60 people each will carry 4×60, or 240, people; and $240 \geq 175 + 23$. ✓

  Four buses are needed.

Class Exercises

Write an equation for each problem. Do not solve.

1. Electricity usage is measured in kilowatt hours (kW·h). A water heater uses an estimated 4219 kW·h of electricity each year. About how many kilowatt hours is this per day?

2. Television advertising costs $200,000 per minute. How many minutes can be purchased for $350,000?

3. A delivery truck is carrying an 8713 lb load of pet food. At a weighing station the loaded truck weighs 17,200 lb. What is the weight of the empty truck?

4. On a recent trip to Paris, Janet spent $75 on gifts. If a franc was then worth $.1236, how many francs did she spend?

5. Harry spent his birthday money on a flying lesson. Mel spent $75 more than Harry. Together they spent $143. How much did Harry get for his birthday?

6. Condominiums in a new building cost $95 per square foot. Sam is looking at a unit that costs $83,125. How large is the unit?

7. Gerry bought some plants at $2.49 each. Her total bill before deducting a $10 coupon was $24.90. How many plants did she buy?

8. The Spanish Club raised $131.25 by having a garage sale and car wash. The amount raised at the car wash was half the amount raised at the garage sale. How much was raised at each event?

Problems

A periodic table displays the elements in order of increasing atomic number. Also shown, below the symbol for the element, is its atomic weight. Use the selected entries below, from the periodic table, for Problems 1–6.

10	36	53	76	79
Neon	Krypton	Iodine	Osmium	Gold
Ne	Kr	I	Os	Au
20.183	83.80	126.9044	190.2	196.967

Follow the five-step plan for using an equation to solve.

A **1.** Three times the atomic weight of an element is 60.549. What is the element?

2. The atomic weight of an element divided by 8 is 15.86305. What is the element?

3. The total atomic weight of three elements is 407.35. If two of the elements are neon and gold, what is the third?

4. The atomic weight of an element is the sum of the protons and neutrons in the element. The atomic number indicates the number of protons. How many neutrons are in an atom of iodine?

5. The quotient of one element's atomic number divided by another's is $2.\overline{1}$. If the second element is krypton, what is the first?

6. The total atomic weight of two elements is 274. The atomic weight of the first is 106.4 less than that of the second. What are the two elements?

7. The Plantery delivered a shipment of 300 plants to the Pine Grove Mall. If the shipment is to be divided equally among 27 planters, how many plants will be in each planter?

8. The eighth-grade teachers allow three quality points for each book report. How many reports must be written to earn 25 quality points?

B 9. Dan has saved 235 trading stamps. He needs a total of 685 stamps to get a pair of skis. If he gets 10 stamps for every dollar he spends at the supermarket, how much must he spend to earn enough stamps for the skis?

10. Darla made 512 g of energy snack. She used twice as many grams of sunflower seeds as of peanuts and 12 more grams of pumpkin seeds than of peanuts. How much of each ingredient did she use?

11. Byrne, Chang, and Weinstein pooled their funds to purchase a car wash franchise. They spent a total of \$677,000. Byrne spent five times as much as Chang but \$17,000 less than Weinstein. How much did each spend?

12. Steven tutors 3 students for a total of 8 hours each week. He charges the second student \$4 more per week than the first. He charges the third student $1\frac{1}{2}$ times the amount he charges the second student per week. He earns a total of \$52 each week. How much does each student pay?

C 13. Lianne has some dimes and nickels with a total value of \$4.60. The number of dimes she has is 4 more than 3 times the number of nickels. How many nickels does she have?

Self-Test B

Use transformations to solve the inequality.

1. $y - 19 > 27$ **2.** $\frac{b}{7} \geq -14$ **3.** $107 < 36 + t$ **4.** $-9a \leq -45$ **[5-6]**

5. $\frac{2}{3}p + 6 \leq -11$ **6.** $\frac{n}{-2} - 10 > 24$ **[5-7]**

7. $16 < 4(3 - x)$ **8.** $-3d + 18 \geq 2d - 12$

Write a problem that the equation could represent.

9. $x - 15 = 85$ **10.** $3x = 54$ **[5-8]**

Use an equation to solve.

11. Fran spent 3 times as long on her homework for English class as on her science homework. If she spent 60 min on her homework for both classes, how long did she spend on her science homework? **[5-9]**

Self-Test answers and Extra Practice are at the back of the book.

Credit Balances

Before stores or banks issue credit cards, they do a complete credit check of the prospective charge customer. Why? Because issuing credit is actually lending money. When customers use credit cards they are getting instant loans. For credit loans, interest, in the form of a *finance charge,* is paid for the favor of the loan.

To keep track of charge account activity, monthly statements are prepared. The sample statement below is a typical summary of activity.

Customer's Statement			Billing Cycle Closing Date 9/22	
Account Number 35-0119-4G			Payment Due Date 10/17	
Date	**Dept. No.**	**Description**	**Purchases & Charges**	**Payments & Credits**
9/3	753	TOYS	30.00	
9/14	212	HOUSEWARES	12.50	
9/17		PAYMENT		20.00

Previous Balance	Payments & Credits	Unpaid Balance	Finance Charge	Purchases & Charges	New Balance	Minimum Payment
40.99	20.00	20.99	.61	42.50	64.10	20.00

Statements usually show any finance charges and a complete list of transactions completed during the billing cycle. Finance charges are determined in a variety of ways. One common method is to compute the amount of the unpaid balance and make a charge based on that amount. Then new purchases are added to compute the new balance on which a minimum payment is due.

To manage the masses of data generated by a credit system, many merchants use computerized cash registers. The cash registers work in the following way. When a customer asks to have a purchase charged, the salesperson enters the amount of the purchase and the customer's credit card number into the computer. The computer then retrieves the account balance from memory, adds in the new purchase, and compares the total to the limit allowed for the account. If the account limit has not been reached, the transaction is completed and the amount of the new purchase is stored in memory. At the end of the billing cycle, the computer totals the costs of the new purchases, deducts payments or credits, adds any applicable finance charges, and prints out a detailed statement.

Copy and complete. Use the chart below to find the minimum payment.

	Previous Balance	Payments and Credits	Unpaid Balance	Finance Charge	Purchases and Charges	New Balance	Minimum Payment
1.	175.86	50.00	?	1.89	35.00	?	?
2.	20.00	20.00	?	0	30.00	?	?
3.	289.75	40.00	?	5.25	68.80	?	?
4.	580.00	52.00	?	8.00	189.65	?	?
5.	775.61	110.00	?	10.48	0	?	?

Solve.

6. Debra Dinardo is comparing her sales receipts to her charge account statement for the month. The billing cycle closing date for the statement is 4/18. Debra has sales receipts for the following dates and amounts.
3/30 $17.60 4/8 $21.54
4/16 $33.12 4/26 $9.75
On April 14, Debra paid the balance on her last statement with a check for $139.80. Her statement shows the information below. Is the statement correct? Explain.

New Balance	Minimum Payment
Up to $20.00	New Balance
$ 20.01 to $200.00	$20.00
$200.01 to $250.00	$25.00
$250.01 to $300.00	$30.00
$300.01 to $350.00	$35.00
$350.01 to $400.00	$40.00
$400.01 to $450.00	$45.00
$450.01 to $500.00	$50.00
Over $500.00	$50.00 plus $10.00 for each $50.00 (or fraction thereof) of New Balance over $500

Previous Balance	Payments & Credits	Unpaid Balance	Finance Charge	Purchases & Charges	New Balance	Minimum Payment
139.80	139.80	0	0	72.26	72.26	20.00

Research Activity Find out why stores and banks are willing to extend credit. How are the expenses of running the credit department paid for? Why do some stores offer discounts to customers who pay cash?

Chapter Review

True or false?

1. If $m = -3$, then $6 + m = 9$. **2.** If $t + 9 = 24$, then $t = 15$. [5-1]

3. If $3q = -15$, then $q = -5$. **4.** If $a = 12$, then $6a = 2$.

5. These equations are equivalent: [5-2]

$2(4n + 8) = 32 \qquad 8n + 16 = 64$

6. These equations are equivalent:

$-4b + 8 - 3 - 2b = 50 \qquad 5 - 6b = 50$

7. If $x - 24 = 13$, $x = -11$. **8.** If $46 = m + 18$, $28 = m$. [5-3]

9. If $13d = 533$, $d = 41$. **10.** If $\frac{x}{-8} = 16$, $x = -2$. [5-4]

11. If $\frac{f}{9} + 11 = 2$, $f = -1$. **12.** If $4 + 6y = 40$, $y = 6$. [5-5]

13. If $3a - 12 = 9a + 18$; $-5 = a$. **14.** If $4(6 + x) = 76$, $x = 13$.

Match the equivalent inequalities.

15. $x + 15 < 25$ **16.** $x - 20 \leq 5$ **A.** $x > 10$ **B.** $x \leq 25$ [5-6]

17. $-5x < -50$ **18.** $3x \geq 50 + x$ **C.** $x < 40$ **D.** $x < 10$ [5-7]

19. $\frac{1}{2}x + 6 < 26$ **20.** $\frac{x}{-5} + 5 \geq 10$ **E.** $x \geq 25$ **F.** $x \leq -25$

Choose the best answer.

21. Which of the equations represents the problem? [5-8]
In a survey for orange juice, one fifth of the people questioned were under 20 years old. If 45 people were under 20, how many people were questioned?

a. $\frac{1}{5}x = 20$ **b.** $5x = 45$ **c.** $\frac{1}{5}x = 45$ **d.** $20x = 45$

22. Jess travels twice as far to school as Lee does. If together they travel 6.9 km to school, how far does Jess travel to school? [5-9]

a. 2.3 km **b.** 3.45 km **c.** 4.6 km **d.** 1.725 km

23. TriCity Taxi Company charges \$1 for the first mile and \$.60 for every mile thereafter. If your trip is measured in tenths of a mile, how far can you ride in a TriCity Taxi for \$12?

a. 6.6 mi **b.** 18.3 mi **c.** 19.3 mi **d.** 19.4 mi

Chapter Test

Use one of the properties of equality to form a true sentence.

1. If $-8 + x = 9$, then $x = \underline{\ ?\ }$. **2.** If $8 + y = 14$, then $y = \underline{\ ?\ }$. [5-1]

3. If $5m = 35$, then $m = \underline{\ ?\ }$. **4.** If $-28 = 4d$, then $\underline{\ ?\ } = d$.

Simplify the expressions on both sides of the equation to obtain an equivalent equation.

5. $-2a - 3 + 4 + 6a = 27$ **6.** $3(x + 7) = -41 - 8$ [5-2]

Use transformations to solve the equation.

7. $m - 21 = -16$ **8.** $32 = a + 9$ **9.** $-11 + r = 25$ [5-3]

10. $7p = 49$ **11.** $\frac{1}{2}y = 14$ **12.** $\frac{n}{-3} = 12$ [5-4]

13. $-3b + 4 = -19$ **14.** $\frac{x}{6} - 17 = 5$ [5-5]

15. $-8 - 2y = 6y + 4$ **16.** $3(5t - 6) = 72$

Use transformations to solve the inequality.

17. $a + 12 < 19$ **18.** $\frac{m}{4} > -8$ **19.** $-3y \leq 42$ [5-6]

20. $\frac{w}{-6} \geq 9$ **21.** $75 < 5p$ **22.** $27 \geq n - 16$

Solve and graph the solutions.

23. $\frac{1}{4}d - 2 > 18$ **24.** $-35 \leq -5(r + 8)$ [5-7]

25. $\frac{a}{9} + 17 \geq 20$ **26.** $8x - 4 < 5x + 23$

Write a problem that the equation could represent.

27. $7m = 21$ **28.** $32 + r = 76$ [5-8]

Use an equation to solve.

29. Judith McSweeny plans to interview 18 applicants for a job. If she spends 3 h interviewing each day and she spends $\frac{3}{4}$ h interviewing each applicant, how many days will she need for the interviews? [5-9]

30. Ross bought 2 books yesterday. The price of one was 3 times as much as the price of the other. If the sum of the prices was \$8.60, what was the price of each book?

Cumulative Review (Chapters 1–5)

Exercises

Replace the variable with the given value and tell whether the resulting statement is true or false.

1. $x + 4 \geq 10;\ 7$ **2.** $3y - 5 = 12;\ 2\frac{1}{3}$ **3.** $6a + 1 < 5;\ 1$

4. $b + 5 < b - 3;\ 7$ **5.** $2a + 6 = 3a - 1;\ 5$ **6.** $3x \geq x + 5;\ 10$

Graph the numbers on a number line.

7. 0, −3.5, 4.0, 1.0, −1.0 **8.** 6, 3, −2, −1.5, 5, 0

9. 4, 8, 3, −2, 0, 1, 5 **10.** −10, −12, −5, −11, −8

Write the fractions as equivalent fractions with the least common denominator (LCD).

11. $\frac{1}{8}, \frac{2}{5}$ **12.** $\frac{4}{9}, \frac{6}{7}$ **13.** $\frac{2}{3}, \frac{1}{6}$ **14.** $\frac{5}{11}, \frac{2}{9}$

15. $\frac{-6}{11}, \frac{-3}{8}$ **16.** $\frac{3}{4}, \frac{-2}{7}$ **17.** $\frac{5}{6}, \frac{-7}{8}$ **18.** $\frac{-3}{4}, \frac{-1}{2}$

Perform the indicated operation.

19. $-35.7 + (-42.81)$ **20.** $1\frac{1}{3} \times \left(-2\frac{2}{5}\right)$ **21.** $-14.4 \div 0.12$

22. $-2\frac{1}{5} - 1\frac{7}{8}$ **23.** $-16.781 - (0.086)$ **24.** $-\frac{7}{8} \div 4\frac{1}{5}$

Express as a fraction or mixed number in lowest terms.

25. 0.75 **26.** 1.35 **27.** 46.55 **28.** 0.375 **29.** 6.88

30. 17.86 **31.** 4.08 **32.** 100.100 **33.** 99.44 **34.** 0.885

Round to the place specified.

35. hundredths: 6.0871 **36.** tens: 116.033 **37.** thousandths: 5.6568

38. tenths: 38.555 **39.** hundreds: 4010.6 **40.** tenths: 89.659

Solve.

41. $x + 5 = 17$ **42.** $3x - 5 < 8$ **43.** $4 + 2x > 7$

44. $15x \div 3 = 21$ **45.** $12 - 8x \geq 10$ **46.** $42x + 10 = 94$

47. $2x + (x - 3) = 18$ **48.** $5x = 9x - 14$ **49.** $-2x + 16 = 4x - 12$

Problems

Problem Solving Reminders
Here are some problem solving reminders that may help you solve some of the problems on this page.
- Determine which facts are necessary to solve the problem.
- Check your answer by using rounding to find an estimated answer.
- Supply additional information if necessary.

Solve.

1. Calculator batteries are being sold at 2 for 99¢. How much will 6 batteries cost?
2. "My new camera cost a fortune," boasted Frank. "Mine cost twice as much as yours," returned Eddie. If together the two cameras cost $545.25, how much did Frank's camera cost?
3. A newspaper with a circulation of 1.1 million readers estimates $\frac{1}{5}$ of its readers have subscriptions. About how many readers have subscriptions?
4. Amos Ellingsworth earns $455 per week. About $\frac{1}{4}$ of his pay is deducted for taxes, insurance, and Social Security. To the nearest dollar, how much does Amos take home each week?
5. Sally Gray takes home $378.50 per week. She will get a $50 per week raise in her next weekly check. If Sally takes home $\frac{4}{5}$ of her raise, what will be her new take-home pay?
6. The Denver Ducks won $\frac{2}{3}$ of their games. The Minneapolis Moles won half of their games. The two teams played the same number of games and together won a total of 49 games. How many games did each team win?
7. The Carpenters make annual mortgage payments of $6430.56 and property tax payments of $1446.00. What are the combined monthly payments for mortgage and taxes?
8. At a recent sales banquet, diners had a choice of beef, chicken, or fish. Four times as many people chose chicken as fish. Five times as many people chose beef as chicken. If 325 people had dinner, how many dinners of each type were served?
9. At a recent job fair, there were $\frac{2}{3}$ as many inquiries about jobs in health care as in electronics. A reported 250 inquiries were made about both fields. How many inquiries were made about health care?

6

Geometry

The photograph at the right shows a part of the interior of the East Building of the National Gallery of Art in Washington, D.C. The building was designed by I. M. Pei and completed in 1978. Although the architecture of the East Building is in sharp contrast to the architecture of the older West Building, the same Tennessee marble was used in the outside construction of both.

The planning and construction of a museum presents some unique problems. Conditions such as temperature, humidity, and adequate space must be carefully considered for the proper care of valuable works of art. The building itself must also reflect a high degree of artistic taste. Notice, for example, how the portion of the National Gallery shown contains triangles, rectangles, and other geometric shapes in repeating patterns.

Career Note

Being an architect involves many years of continuous study in the fields of art, mathematics, and engineering. In designing a building, an architect faces a variety of challenges arising from the purpose and location of the structure. Factors such as the space available and the appearance of adjacent buildings must be taken into account. Architects must also have a current knowledge of the many different types of building materials available.

6-1 Points, Lines, and Planes

In geometry, we start with three undefined terms: **point, line,** and **plane.** We indicate an exact location by a point. In a drawing, we represent a point by a dot. You probably know the following important fact about lines.

> Through any two distinct points there is exactly one line. That is, two points *determine* a line.

We think of the line AB, below, as passing through points A and B and extending without end in both directions.

Line AB: $\overleftrightarrow{AB}$, or $\overleftrightarrow{BA}$

Points, such as X, Y, and Z below, through which one line can be drawn are said to be **collinear.**

The drawing below shows a **line segment,** or simply a **segment,** which we denote as $\overline{AB}$ (or $\overline{BA}$). The segment is made up of the points A and B and the part of the line $\overleftrightarrow{AB}$ lying between A and B. The points A and B are called the **endpoints** of the segment.

Segment AB: $\overline{AB}$, or $\overline{BA}$

The length of $\overline{AB}$ is denoted by AB (no bar over the letters). Two segments that have the same length are said to be **congruent.** When $AB = CD$, we write $\overline{AB} \cong \overline{CD}$ to mean $\overline{AB}$ *is congruent to* $\overline{CD}$.

On any segment, such as $\overline{AB}$ below, there is exactly one point M such that $AM = MB$. The point M is called the **midpoint** of $\overline{AB}$.

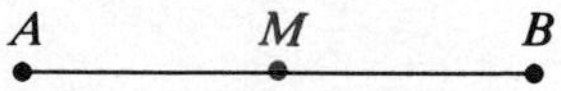

If we imagine $\overline{AB}$ extended without end in only one direction from endpoint A through point B, we have a **ray,** denoted by $\overrightarrow{AB}$.

Ray AB: $\overrightarrow{AB}$

A **plane** can be thought of as a flat surface extending infinitely in all directions. We often draw a portion of a plane to suggest the whole plane, as in the diagram. Points that all lie on one plane are said to be **coplanar.**

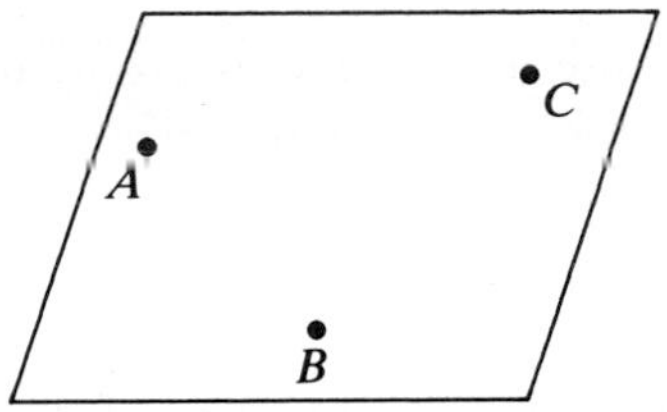

Plane ABC

> Through any three noncollinear points there is exactly one plane. That is, three noncollinear points determine a plane.

EXAMPLE 1 Write a symbol that denotes each figure.

a. The points of $\overrightarrow{RP}$ between and including P and R

b. The line containing T and Q

c. The point Q and all the points to the left of Q on the line that contains P and Q

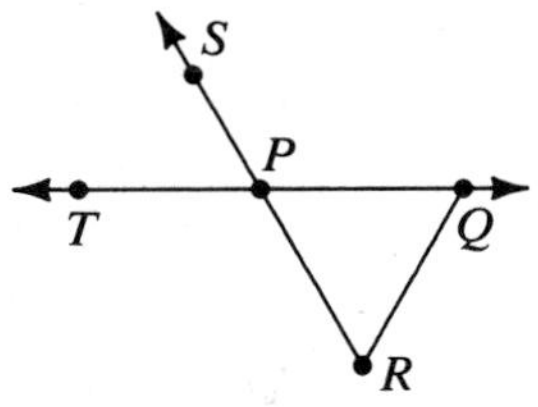

Solution

a. $\overline{PR}$ (or $\overline{RP}$)

b. $\overleftrightarrow{TQ}$ (or any of these: $\overleftrightarrow{QT}$, $\overleftrightarrow{PQ}$, $\overleftrightarrow{QP}$, $\overleftrightarrow{PT}$, $\overleftrightarrow{TP}$)

c. $\overrightarrow{QT}$ (or $\overrightarrow{QP}$)

Reading Mathematics: *Symbols*
Some mathematical symbols, such as those for segments, rays, and lines, look very much alike. When you read such symbols, be sure to give them their complete meanings.

$\overline{AB}$ is read as *segment AB*.
$\overrightarrow{AB}$ is read as *ray AB*.
$\overleftrightarrow{AB}$ is read as *line AB*.

A **geometric construction** is a special kind of drawing for which we use only a compass and a straightedge. For a construction, we may use a ruler as a straightedge to help draw segments but we may not use the ruler to measure length.

EXAMPLE 2 Construct a segment that is congruent to $\overline{AB}$.

Solution

1. Use your straightedge to draw a ray with endpoint O.

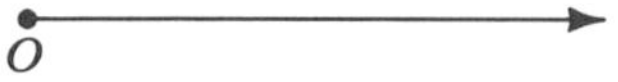

2. Open your compass until the point is on A and the pencil tip is on B. Then, without changing the setting of the compass, place the point of the compass at O and move the pencil end so that the pencil makes a mark crossing the ray. Call the point of intersection P. Then $\overline{OP} \cong \overline{AB}$.

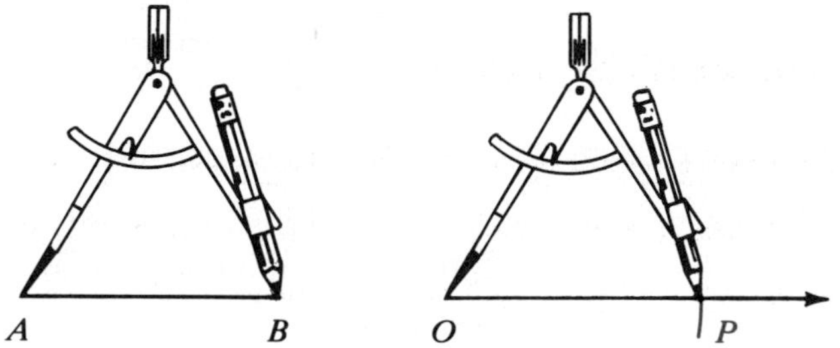

Class Exercises

Write a symbol that denotes each drawing.

1.

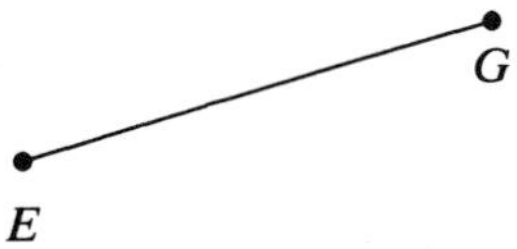

2.

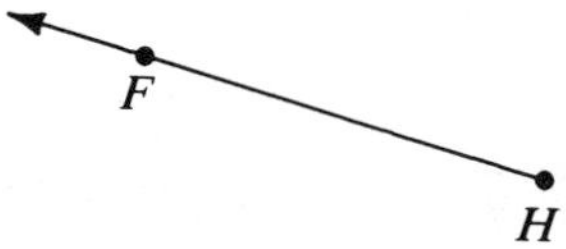

3.

Write two symbols that could be used to denote each drawing.

4.

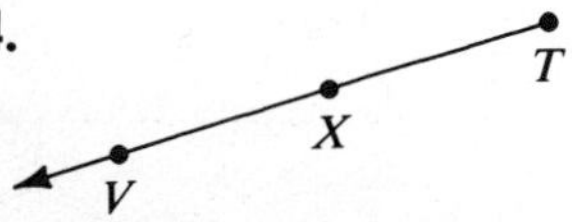

5.

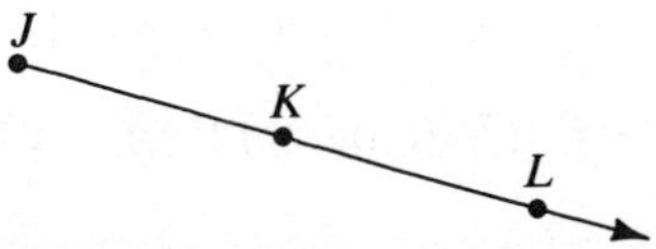

6.

Exercises 7–10 refer to the diagram at the right.

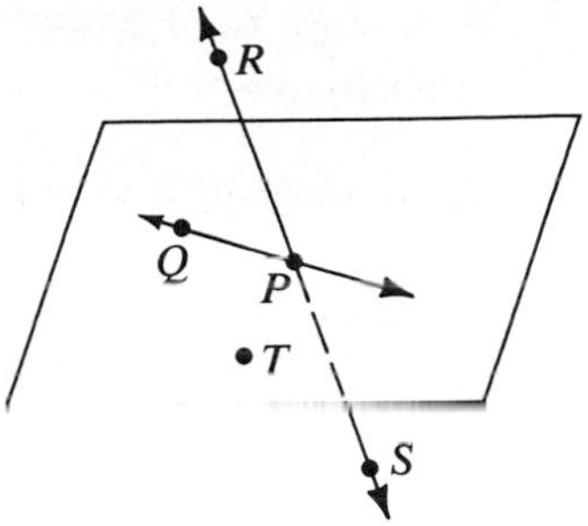

7. Name three collinear points.
8. Name three coplanar points that are not collinear.
9. How many lines can be drawn through both Q and T?
10. True or false? Points P, Q, and R are coplanar.

Written Exercises

Exercises 1–4 refer to the diagram at the right. Use the symbol for a line, a ray, or a segment to denote each set of points.

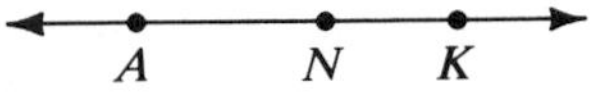

A 1. The point A and all points to the right of A
2. N and A and all points between N and A
3. The point N and all points to the left and right of N
4. The point K and all points to the left of K

Draw a labeled diagram to illustrate each description.

5. $\overleftrightarrow{MX}$ and point P on $\overleftrightarrow{MX}$ but not on $\overrightarrow{MX}$
6. $\overrightarrow{QR}$ and point S on $\overrightarrow{QR}$ but not on $\overline{QR}$
7. $\overleftrightarrow{SP}$ and point R not on $\overleftrightarrow{SP}$
8. $\overleftrightarrow{AB}$ and $\overleftrightarrow{BC}$ intersecting at B
9. Noncollinear points P, Q, and R, $\overline{PQ}$, $\overline{QR}$, $\overline{PR}$, and point X on $\overline{PR}$
10. Noncollinear points D, E, and F, $\overline{DE}$, and $\overrightarrow{EF}$
11. Noncollinear points C, A, T, and O, $\overrightarrow{CT}$, and $\overleftrightarrow{OT}$
12. Noncollinear points D, E, F, and G, $\overline{DE}$, and $\overrightarrow{EF}$

Exercises 13–16 refer to the diagram at the right.

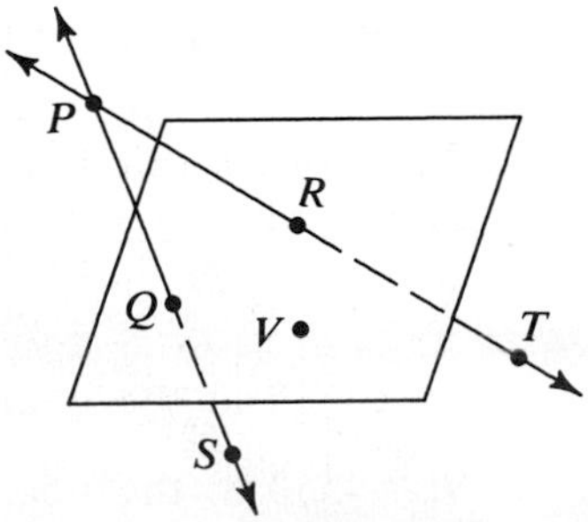

13. Name three collinear points.
14. Name three coplanar points that are not collinear.
15. Do the points P, Q, and R determine a plane?
16. Name four coplanar points.

Referring to $\overline{AB}$ below, use a straightedge and a compass to construct each figure.

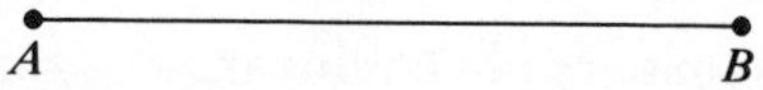

17. $\overline{CD}$ congruent to $\overline{AB}$

18. $\overline{EF}$ such that $EF = 2(AB)$

Exercises 19–22 refer to the diagram at the right. Name each figure, using the symbol for a line, a ray, or a segment.

B 19. All the points that are on both $\overrightarrow{FD}$ and $\overrightarrow{EG}$

20. All the points that are on either $\overline{EF}$ or $\overline{FG}$

21. All the points that are on either $\overline{DE}$ or $\overrightarrow{EG}$

22. All the points that are on both $\overrightarrow{EG}$ and $\overrightarrow{FG}$

Use a straightedge and a compass to construct each figure.

23. Points A, B, and C and $\overline{AB}$, $\overline{BC}$, and $\overline{AC}$ such that B is the midpoint of $\overline{AC}$

24. Points P, Q, and R and $\overline{PQ}$, $\overline{QR}$, and $\overline{PR}$ such that $PQ = QR = PR$

In Exercises 25–32, M is the midpoint of $\overline{CD}$. Find the missing length.

25. $CM = 12$, $CD =$ _?_

26. $CD = 37$, $MD =$ _?_

27. $CD = 3x$, $CM = 15$, $x =$ _?_

28. $CD = 48$, $MD = 8x + 4$, $x =$ _?_

C 29. $CM = x$, $MD = 3x - 8$, $x =$ _?_

30. $CM = 2x$, $MD = x + 6$, $x =$ _?_

31. $MD = x + 4$, $CD = 5x - 13$, $x =$ _?_

32. $CM = 3x$, $CD = 8x - 14$, $x =$ _?_

Review Exercises

Round each number to the place indicated.

1. 56.0425 to the nearest tenth

2. 2.072 to the nearest hundredth

3. 1.2012 to the nearest thousandth

4. 7435.807 to the nearest tenth

5. 2842.349 to the nearest hundredth

6. 269.196 to the nearest tenth

7. 0.8625 to the nearest thousandth

8. 83.025 to the nearest tenth

9. 7.4553 to the nearest thousandth

10. 14.297 to the nearest hundredth

6-2 Circles

A **circle** is the set of all points in a plane that are a given distance from a given point in that plane. The given point is called the **center** of the circle, and the given distance is called **the radius** of the circle. A segment joining the center of a circle and a point on the circle is called **a radius** (plural: *radii*) of the circle. In the circle at the right, P is the center and $\overline{PQ}$ is a radius.

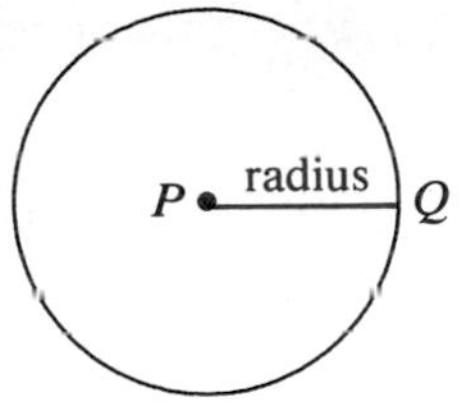

A segment joining two points on a circle is called a **chord.** A chord that passes through the center of the circle is called **a diameter.** We refer to the length of such a chord as **the diameter** of the circle. Thus, the diameter of any circle is twice the radius of the circle. Two points on a circle and the part of the circle between them form an **arc.** If the points are at the ends of a diameter, the arc is a **semicircle.**

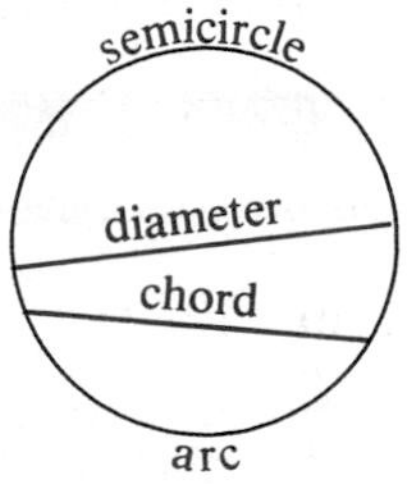

EXAMPLE 1 Construct a circle and a chord that has the same length as the radius of the circle.

Solution

1. With your compass, draw a circle with center O.

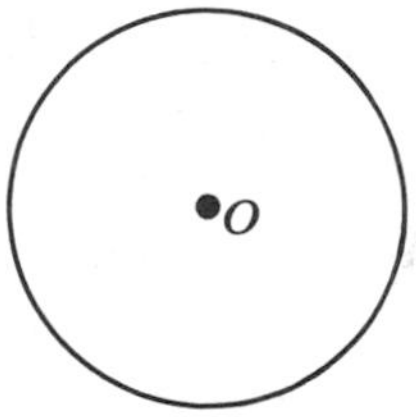

2. Without changing the setting of the compass, place the point of the compass at a point X on the circle. Draw an arc that intersects the circle, say at point P.

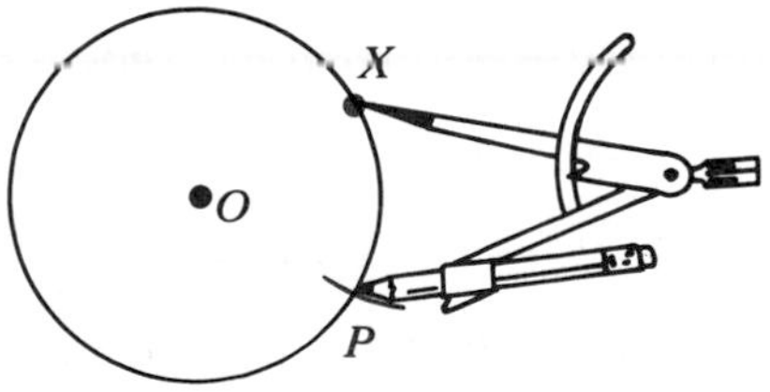

3. With a straightedge, draw $\overline{PX}$. Then $PX = OP$.

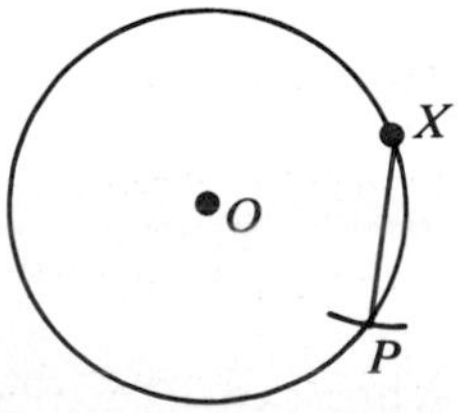

The distance around a circle is called the **circumference** of the circle. For any circle the circumference, C, divided by the diameter, d, is a fixed number called π (a Greek letter, pronounced "pie"). That is, for any circle

$$\frac{C}{d} = \pi.$$

This relationship can be expressed in several forms.

Formulas for Circles

$$C = \pi \times d = \pi d \qquad \text{or} \qquad C = \pi \times 2r = 2\pi r$$

The number π cannot be expressed exactly as a fraction because π is irrational. Two common approximations of π are 3.14 and $\frac{22}{7}$. Because the approximation of 3.14 is good to only three digits, answers should be given to only three digits when 3.14 is used for π.

EXAMPLE 2 Find the circumference of a circle with radius 4 cm. Use $\pi \approx 3.14$.

Solution Use the formula $C = 2\pi r$.

$$C \approx 2 \times 3.14 \times 4$$
$$C \approx 25.12$$

The circumference is approximately 25.1 cm.

EXAMPLE 3 Find the diameter of a circle with a circumference of 66 cm. Use $\pi \approx \frac{22}{7}$.

Solution Use the formula $C = \pi d$.

$$66 \approx \frac{22}{7} \times d$$

Multiply both sides by $\frac{7}{22}$.

$$\frac{7}{22} \times 66 \approx \frac{7}{22} \times \frac{22}{7} \times d$$
$$21 \approx d$$

The diameter of the circle is approximately 21 cm.

Note that when we use an approximation for π, we use the symbol $\approx$.

Class Exercises

Tell whether each segment is a chord, a radius, a diameter, or none of these, in relation to the circle with center O shown in the diagram.

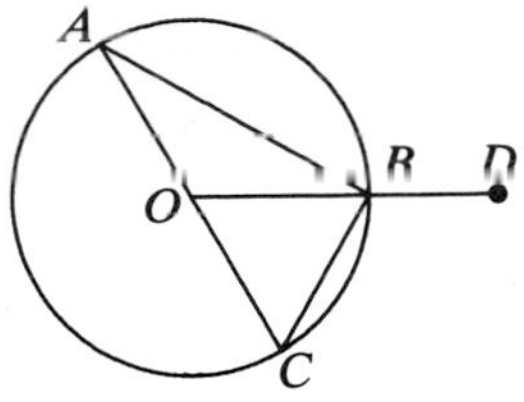

1. $\overline{BC}$ **2.** $\overline{OB}$ **3.** $\overline{OD}$ **4.** $\overline{AC}$ **5.** $\overline{AB}$ **6.** $\overline{OA}$

7. Name two segments of the same length in the diagram.

8. What is the relationship between AC and OC in the diagram?

Written Exercises

Draw a labeled diagram to illustrate each description.

A **1.** A circle with center O and a radius $\overline{OP}$

2. A circle with center T and two diameters, $\overline{XY}$ and $\overline{UV}$

3. A circle with center D and chords $\overline{AB}$ and $\overline{BC}$

4. A circle with center P, radii $\overline{PM}$ and $\overline{PQ}$, and chord $\overline{MQ}$ not a diameter

Referring to $\overline{AB}$ below, use a straightedge and a compass to construct each figure.

5. Two circles, each with radius AB, that intersect at two points

6. A semicircle with radius AB

Find the circumference of a circle with the given radius r or the given diameter d.
For Exercises 7–10, use $\pi \approx 3.14$.

7. $d = 750$ m **8.** $d = 500$ km **9.** $r = 25$ cm **10.** $r = 6.5$ m

For Exercises 11–14, use $\pi \approx \frac{22}{7}$.

11. $d = \frac{14}{11}$ **12.** $d = \frac{7}{33}$ **13.** $r = 21$ **14.** $r = 17.5$

Find the radius of a circle with the given circumference. Use $\pi \approx \frac{22}{7}$.

B **15.** $C = 110$ **16.** $C = 242$ **17.** $C = 0.44$ **18.** $C = 4840$

The equator of Mars is approximately a circle with diameter 6787 km. The equator of Earth is approximately a circle with radius 6378 km. Use $\pi \approx 3.14$ to answer the following.

19. What is the approximate difference, in kilometers, between the circumference of Earth and the circumference of Mars?

20. If the circumference of Jupiter's equator is approximately 448,800 km, about how much greater (in kilometers) is the diameter of Jupiter than the diameter of Earth?

Use a straightedge and a compass to construct each figure.

21. A circle and two congruent chords

22. Two circles of equal radius intersecting in two points, and four radii of these circles forming a four-sided closed figure

C 23. A circle and 6 chords of the circle such that each chord has the same length as a radius and each chord shares an endpoint with another chord

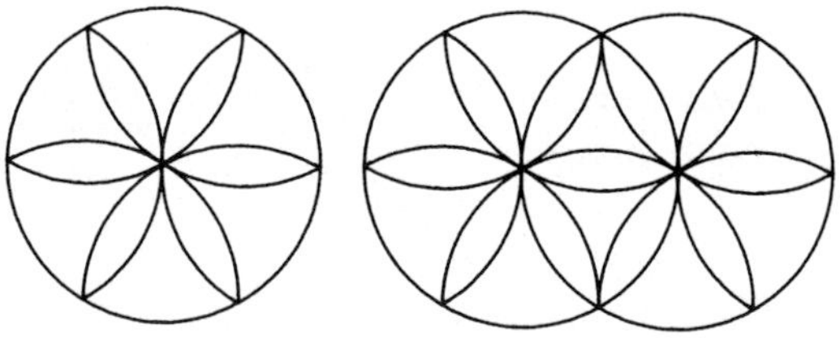

24. See if you can figure out how to construct the figures shown using only a compass. (*Hint:* See Exercise 23.)

Review Exercises

Replace each _?_ with >, <, or = to make a true sentence.

1. 46 _?_ 90	**2.** 118 _?_ 180	**3.** 107 _?_ 170	**4.** 875 _?_ 857
5. 40 + 30 _?_ 80	**6.** 75 _?_ 66 + 33	**7.** 95 − 27 _?_ 56	**8.** 114 − 24 _?_ 90

Calculator Key-In

Over two thousand years ago, Archimedes found that the number π is between the fractions $3\frac{10}{71}$ and $3\frac{1}{7}$. Use your calculator to find decimal approximations of these numbers to complete the following statement:

$$\underline{\ ?\ } < \pi < \underline{\ ?\ }$$

6-3 Angles

An **angle** is formed by two rays with a common endpoint, called the **vertex** of the angle. The rays are called the **sides** of the angle. We use the angle symbol ($\angle$) with letters or with numbers, as shown below, to denote angles. By general agreement, when an angle is named with three letters, the middle letter always indicates the vertex of the angle.

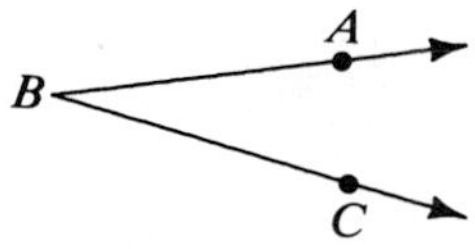

$\angle ABC$, $\angle CBA$, or $\angle B$

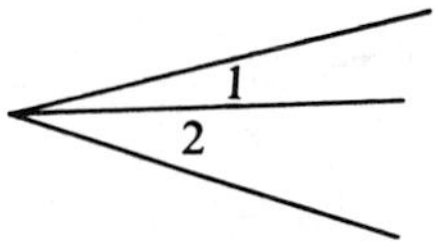

$\angle 1$ and $\angle 2$

Although angles are formed by rays, we sometimes show only segments of these rays as the sides of an angle, as in the diagram at the right above.

We measure angles with a **protractor,** as shown below. The measure of angle QOP is 40 degrees. We write this fact as $m\angle QOP = 40°$.

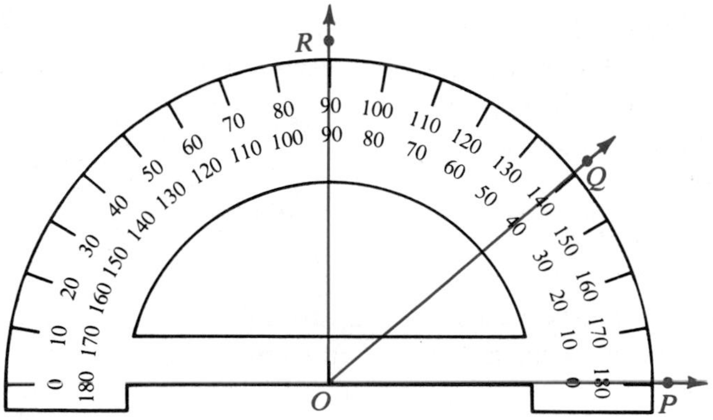

$m\angle QOP = 40°$ $m\angle ROP = 90°$

We classify angles according to their measures as shown in the table below. Angles that have the same measure are called **congruent angles.**

Name	Measure
Acute	Between 0° and 90°
Right	90°
Obtuse	Between 90° and 180°

EXAMPLE 1 Construct an angle that is congruent to $\angle A$.

Solution

1. Draw a ray with endpoint O.

2. Draw two arcs of the same radius, with centers A and O. Label the points of intersection of the arc and $\angle A$ as X and Y. Label the intersection of the arc and $\vec{O}$ as C.

3. Put the compass point at Y and open the compass so that you can draw an arc through X. Using this radius, draw an arc with center C. Label the point where the two arcs intersect as B.

4. Draw $\overrightarrow{OB}$. Now $\angle BOC$ is congruent to $\angle A$.

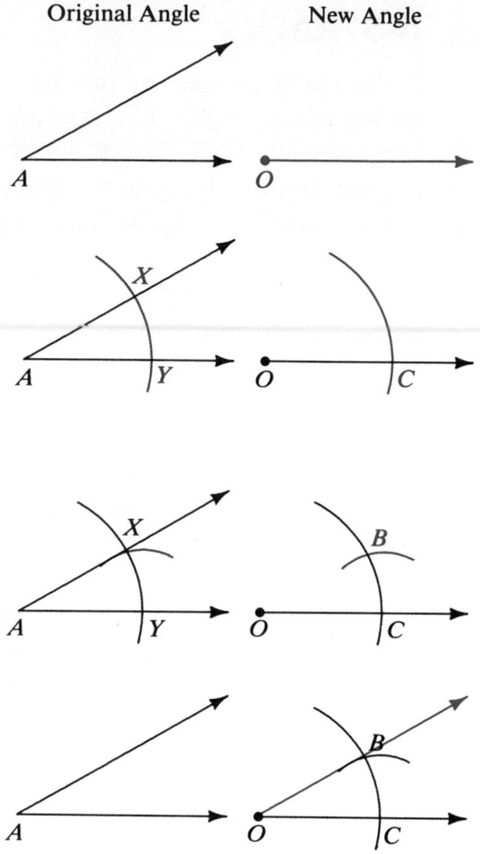

We may write $\angle BOC$ *is congruent to* $\angle A$ as $\angle BOC \cong \angle A$.

Two angles, like $\angle 1$ and $\angle 2$ in the diagram at the right, that have a common side and a common vertex but do not "overlap" are called **adjacent angles.** If you know the measures of $\angle 1$ and $\angle 2$ in the diagram, you can find the measure of $\angle AOC$. For example,

if $m\angle 1 = 60°$ and $m\angle 2 = 20°$,
then $m\angle AOC = 60° + 20° = 80°$.

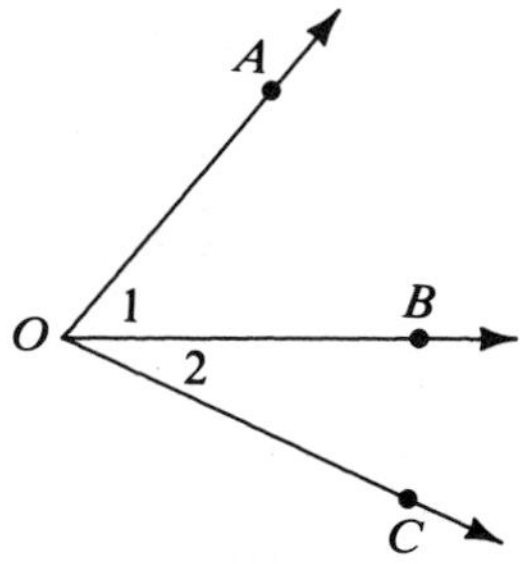

A ray that divides an angle into two congruent angles is said to **bisect** the angle. The ray is called the **angle bisector.** In the diagram at the right, $\overrightarrow{OP}$ is the angle bisector of $\angle ROQ$. Angles 1 and 2 are marked in the same way to show that they are congruent.

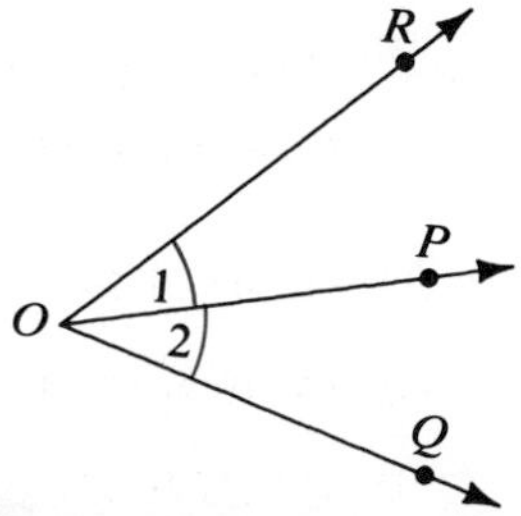

EXAMPLE 2 Construct the bisector of $\angle O$.

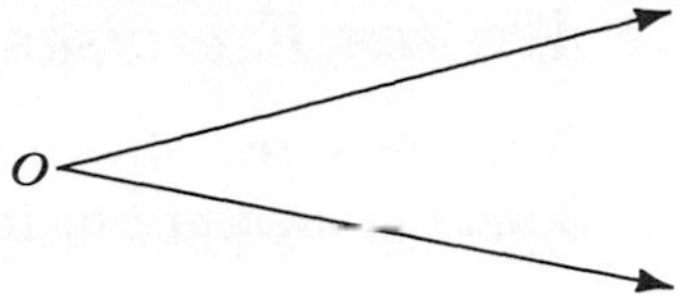

Solution

1. With a compass, draw an arc with center O, intersecting the sides of the angle. Label the points of intersection X and Y.

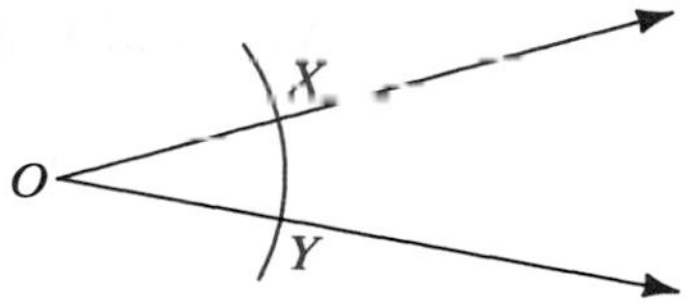

2. Draw an arc inside the angle with center X. With center Y and the *same* radius, draw another arc intersecting the arc inside the angle. Label the point of intersection C.

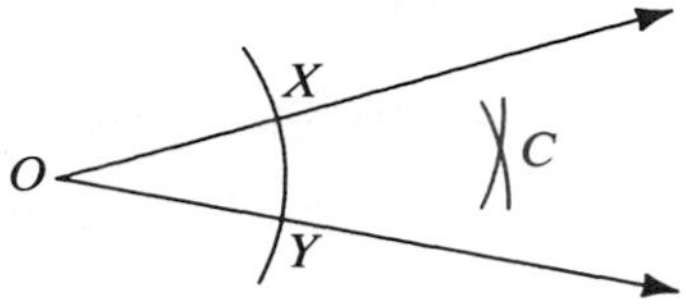

3. Draw $\overrightarrow{OC}$.
Now $\angle XOC \cong \angle YOC$, and $\overrightarrow{OC}$ bisects $\angle XOY$.

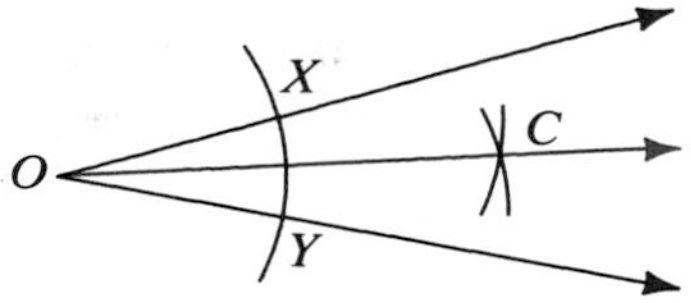

Class Exercises

Exercises 1–7 refer to the diagram at the right.

1. Name two acute angles.
2. Name two obtuse angles.
3. Name two angles that appear to be right angles.
4. Name a pair of adjacent angles.
5. Name a pair of nonadjacent angles.
6. Name two angles that appear to be congruent but are not right angles.
7. Do $\angle AXC$ and $\angle AXB$ have a common side and a common vertex? Are they adjacent?

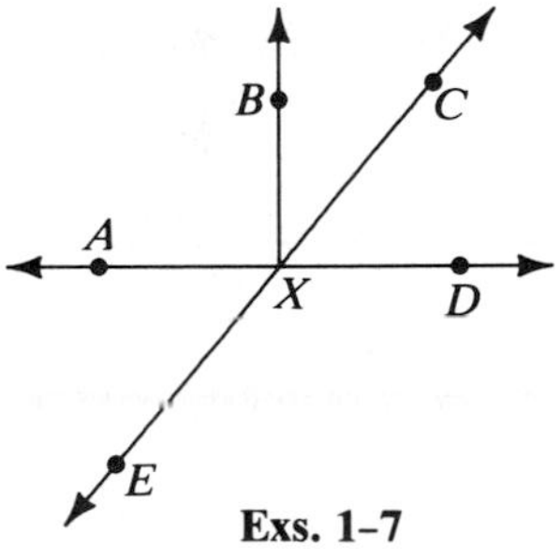

Exs. 1–7

Exercises 8 and 9 refer to the diagram at the right.

8. $m\angle MOP + m\angle COP = m\angle$ __?__
9. If $\angle MOP \cong \angle COP$, then __?__ bisects $\angle$ __?__.

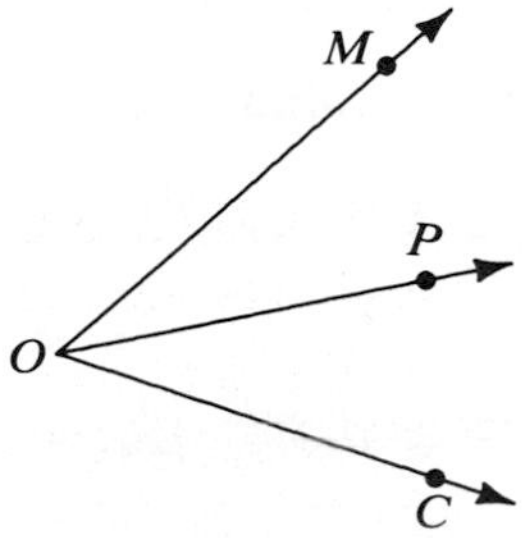

Exs. 8, 9

Written Exercises

The measures of two angles in the diagram are given. Find the measure of the third angle.

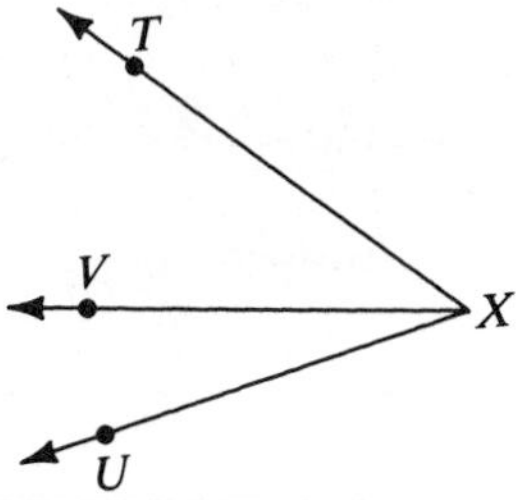

A 1. m∠TXV = 33°; m∠VXU = 17°; m∠TXU = __?__°

2. m∠TXU = 57°; m∠VXU = 21°; m∠TXV = __?__°

3. m∠TXU = 62°; m∠TXV = 28°; m∠VXU = __?__°

4. m∠VXU = 19°; m∠TXV = 35°; m∠UXT = __?__°

5. Draw an acute angle, ∠P. Construct an angle congruent to ∠P.

6. Draw an obtuse angle, ∠Q. Construct an angle congruent to ∠Q.

7. Draw an obtuse angle and construct its bisector.

8. Draw an acute angle and construct its bisector.

In the diagram at the right, ∠*COB* is a right angle and m∠*EOD* = 82°. Find the measure of each angle.

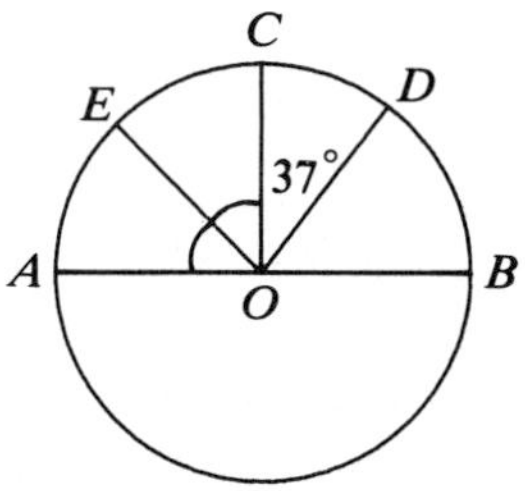

B 9. ∠EOC 10. ∠DOB

11. ∠AOC 12. ∠EOB

13. Draw two acute angles, ∠A and ∠B. Construct ∠C such that m∠C = m∠A + m∠B.

14. Draw any obtuse ∠A and any acute ∠B. Then construct ∠D such that m∠D = m∠A − m∠B.

C 15. Draw a line. Mark points A, X, and B (in that order) on the line. Choose any point C not on the line. Draw $\overrightarrow{XC}$. Bisect ∠AXC and ∠BXC. What appears to be true of the two bisectors?

Review Exercises

Evaluate the expression for the given value of the variable.

1. $n + 60;\ n = 54$
2. $r - 40;\ r = 90$
3. $8s;\ s = 14$
4. $\frac{1}{4}y;\ y = 56$
5. $2m + 36;\ m = 24$
6. $5x - 25;\ x = 36$
7. $\frac{1}{2}t + 45;\ t = 30$
8. $3(z + 20);\ z = 12$
9. $6(x - 30);\ x = 42$
10. $(d + 15)7;\ d = 8$
11. $18 + 12w;\ w = 10$
12. $29 - 5c;\ c = 3$

6-4 Special Angles

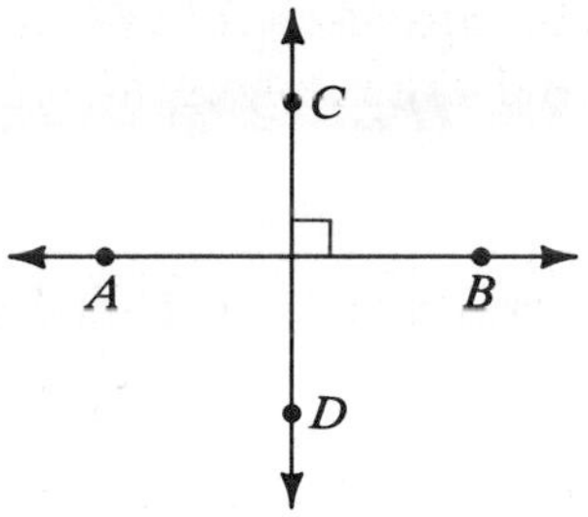

If two lines intersect to form four congruent angles, the lines are **perpendicular.** (Rays or segments are said to be perpendicular if the lines containing them are perpendicular.) Each of the congruent angles is a right angle. In the diagram at the right, $\overleftrightarrow{AB}$ is perpendicular to $\overleftrightarrow{CD}$. We can write $\overleftrightarrow{AB} \perp \overleftrightarrow{CD}$ (or $\overleftrightarrow{CD} \perp \overleftrightarrow{AB}$). The mark (⏋) in the diagram indicates that the lines are perpendicular.

Two angles whose measures have a sum of 90° are called **complementary** angles. Complementary angles may or may not be adjacent.

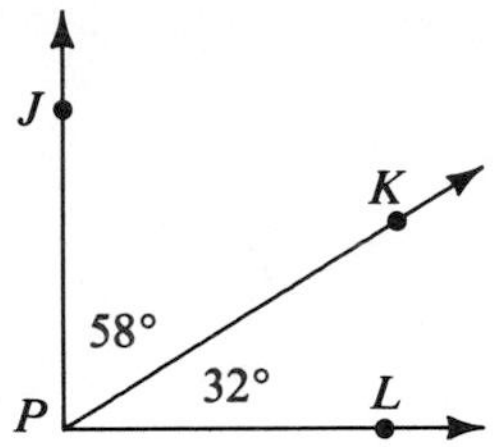

$\angle JPK$ and $\angle KPL$ are complementary.

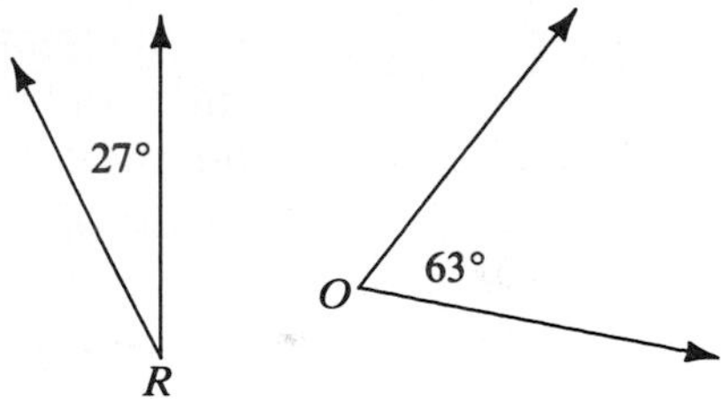

$\angle R$ and $\angle O$ are complementary.

EXAMPLE 1 One of two complementary angles has measure 6° greater than the other. What are the measures of the two angles?

Solution Let n be the measure of the smaller angle.
Then $n + 6°$ is the measure of the larger.
Because the two angles are complementary, we have

$$\begin{aligned} n + (n + 6°) &= 90° \\ 2n + 6° &= 90° \\ 2n + 6° - 6° &= 90° - 6° \\ 2n &= 84° \\ n &= \frac{84°}{2} = 42° \end{aligned}$$

The smaller angle has measure 42°.
The larger angle has measure 42° + 6°, or 48°.

Problem Solving Reminder
When checking your answer to a problem, reread the problem to be sure to *answer the question asked.* Notice that in Example 1, the solution of the first equation was the measure of one angle. The question asks for two angle measures, however, so a second value was needed to complete the solution.

You can construct perpendicular lines with a straightedge and compass by thinking of the construction as bisecting a "180° angle."

EXAMPLE 2 Construct a line perpendicular to $\overleftrightarrow{AB}$ at point P.

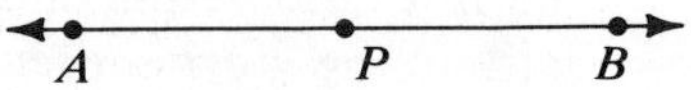

Solution

1. Draw any arc with center P, intersecting $\overleftrightarrow{AB}$ at C and D.

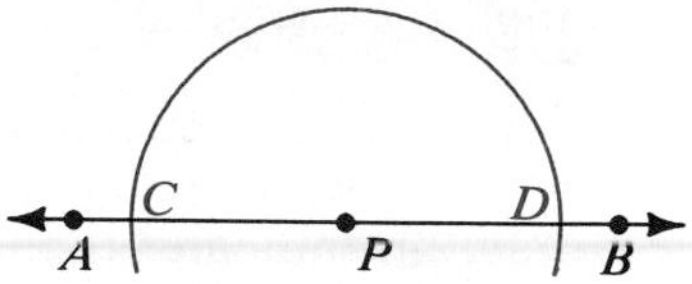

2. Open the compass more. Then draw two intersecting arcs of the same radius with centers C and D. Label the point of intersection of the arcs Q.

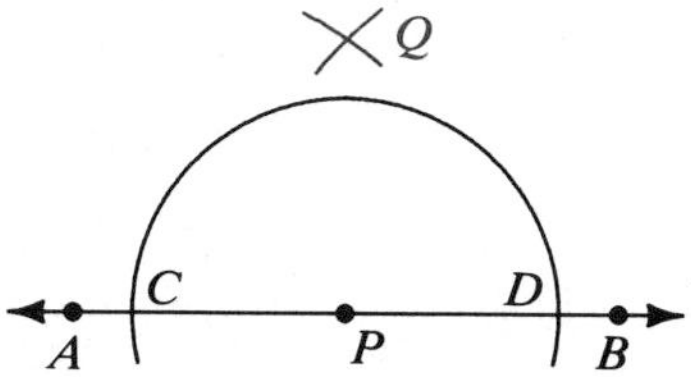

3. Draw $\overleftrightarrow{PQ}$.
Then $\overleftrightarrow{PQ} \perp \overleftrightarrow{AB}$.

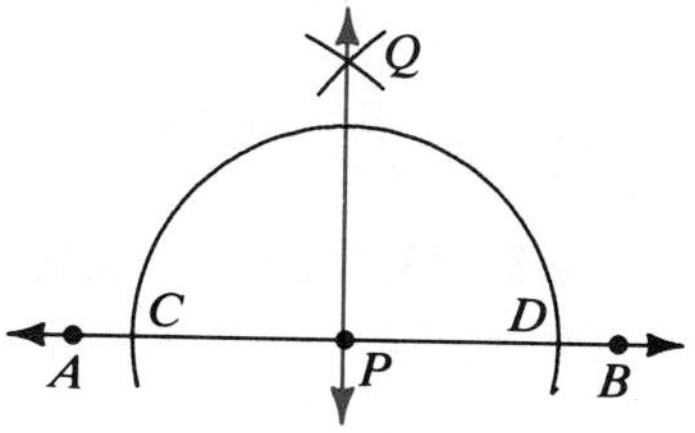

If the sum of the measures of two angles is 180°, the angles are called **supplementary** angles. Like complementary angles, supplementary angles need not be adjacent.

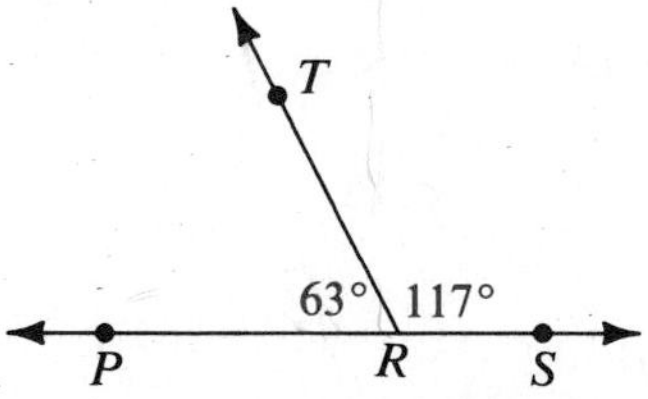

$\angle PRT$ and $\angle SRT$ are supplementary.

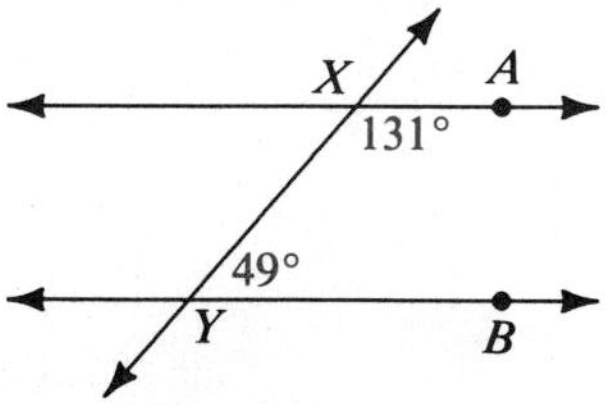

$\angle AXY$ and $\angle BYX$ are supplementary.

Notice that if two supplementary angles are adjacent, as $\angle PRT$ and $\angle SRT$ at the left above, their noncommon sides ($\overrightarrow{RP}$ and $\overrightarrow{RS}$) lie on one line.

Whenever two lines intersect to form four angles, the nonadjacent angles are called **vertical** angles. In the diagram, ∠1 and ∠2 are vertical angles. ∠3 and ∠4 are also vertical angles.

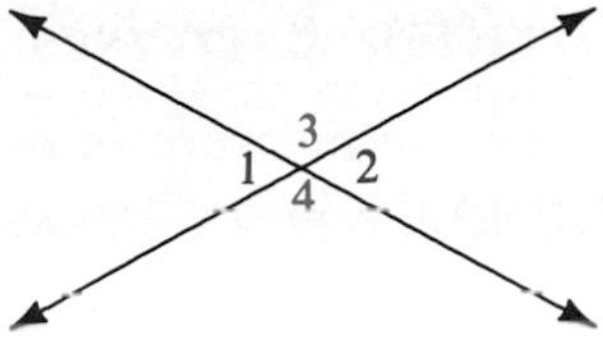

When two lines intersect, the vertical angles formed are congruent.

To see why vertical angles are congruent, note that in the diagram,

$m\angle 1 + m\angle 3 = 180°$ and $m\angle 2 + m\angle 3 = 180°$.

If we subtract $m\angle 3$ from both sides of each equation,

$m\angle 1 = 180° - m\angle 3$ and $m\angle 2 = 180° - m\angle 3$.

Therefore, $m\angle 1 = m\angle 2$.

Class Exercises

Tell which of the following describe the given pair of angles (more than one may be correct).

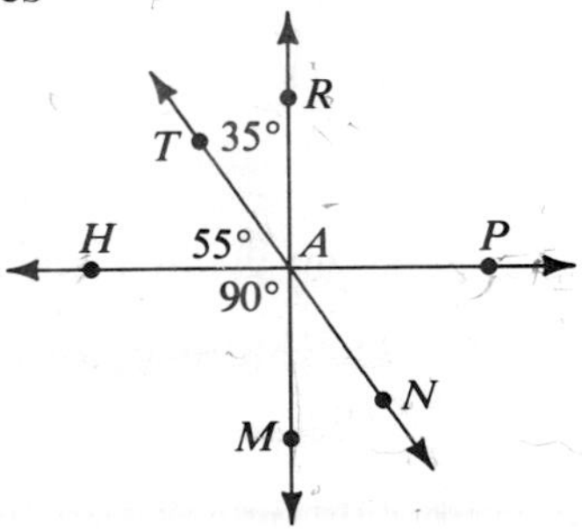

a. **complementary** **b.** **supplementary**

c. **adjacent** **d.** **vertical**

1. ∠*TAR* and ∠*RAP* **2.** ∠*TAR* and ∠*HAT*

3. ∠*RAH* and ∠*HAM* **4.** ∠*TAR* and ∠*MAN*

5. ∠*HAT* and ∠*MAN* **6.** ∠*HAT* and ∠*TAP*

True or false?

7. Complementary angles are always adjacent.

8. Vertical angles are always complementary.

9. Two right angles are complementary.

10. Two right angles are supplementary.

11. Two supplementary angles with equal measure are right angles.

12. Vertical angles may be adjacent.

Written Exercises

Find the measure of each angle labeled ∠1.

A **1.**

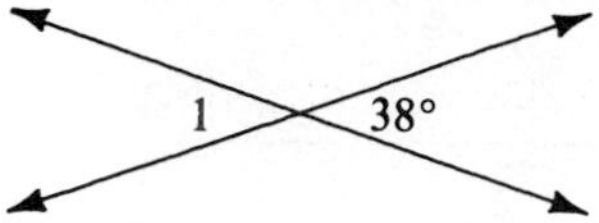

2.

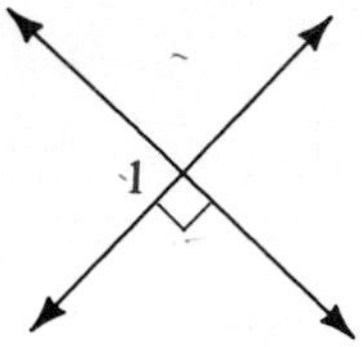

3.

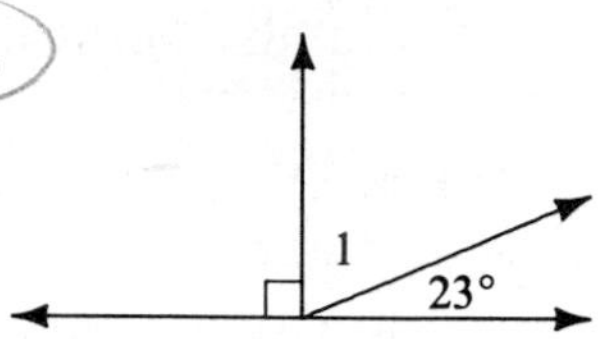

4.

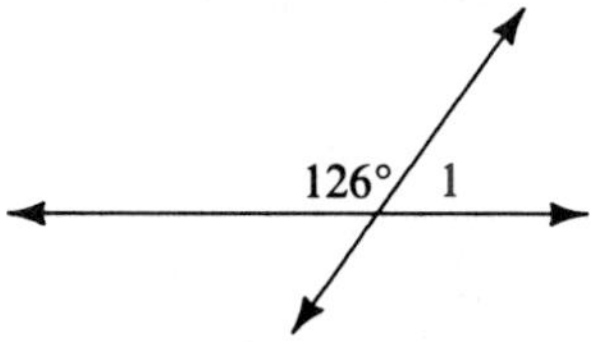

5.

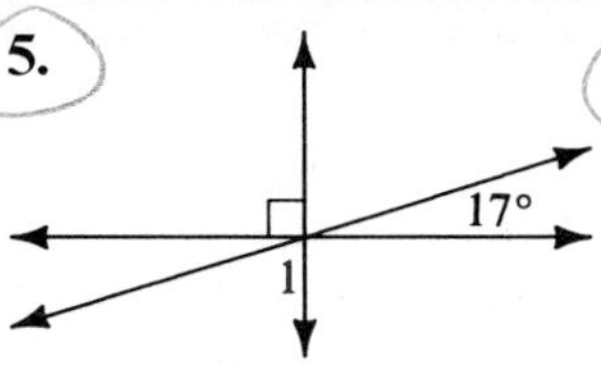

6.

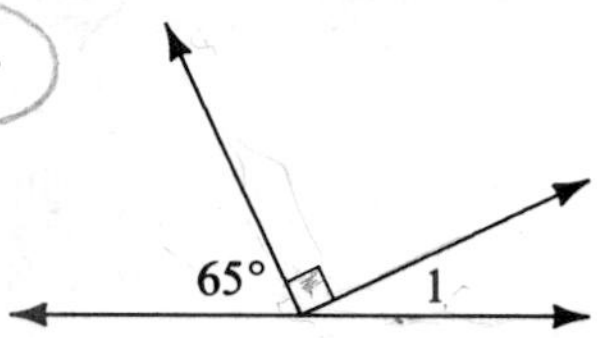

Find the measure of each angle in the diagram at the right.

7. ∠ *RWS* **8.** ∠ *TWU*

9. ∠ *TWS* **10.** ∠ *PWQ*

11. ∠ *QWS* **12.** ∠ *PWT*

13. ∠ *QWU* **14.** ∠ *PWR*

15. ∠ *SWU* **16.** ∠ *RWT*

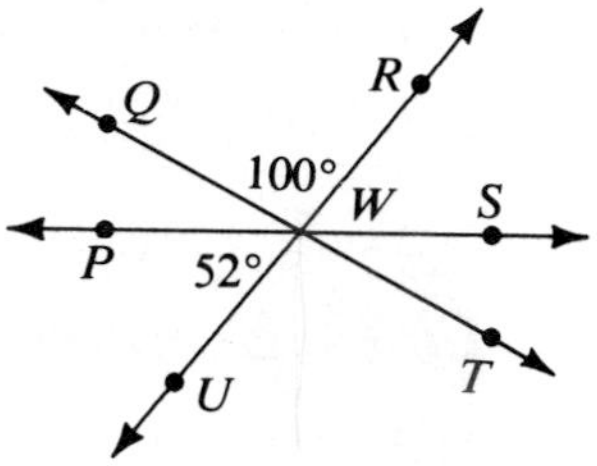

Exs. 7–16

In Exercises 17–20, find the measures of two *complementary* angles satisfying the given conditions.

17. The measure of one angle is 24° greater than the measure of the other.

18. The measure of one angle is 8° less than the measure of the other.

19. The measure of one angle is 30° greater than the measure of the other.

20. The measure of one angle is 70° less than the measure of the other.

In Exercises 21–23, find the measures of two *supplementary* angles satisfying the given conditions.

B **21.** The measure of one angle is 5 times the measure of the other.

22. The measure of one angle is 8 times the measure of the other.

23. The measure of one angle is $\frac{2}{3}$ the measure of the other.

24. If two vertical angles are complementary, what is the measure of each angle?

25. If two vertical angles are supplementary, what is the measure of each angle?

26. a. Draw any $\overleftrightarrow{LM}$ and a point P on $\overleftrightarrow{LM}$. Construct a line perpendicular to $\overleftrightarrow{LM}$ at P.

b. Use the right angle constructed in part (a) to construct a 45° angle.

27. Construct a 135° angle.

28. As illustrated in the diagram at the right, the common chord of two circles of the same radius is perpendicular to the segment joining the centers of the circles and divides this segment exactly in half. That is, in the diagram, $\overline{AB} \perp \overline{PQ}$ and $\overline{PX} \cong \overline{QX}$. $\overline{AB}$ is called the **perpendicular bisector** of $\overline{PQ}$.
Draw any $\overline{RS}$. Use the fact stated above to construct the perpendicular bisector of $\overline{RS}$.

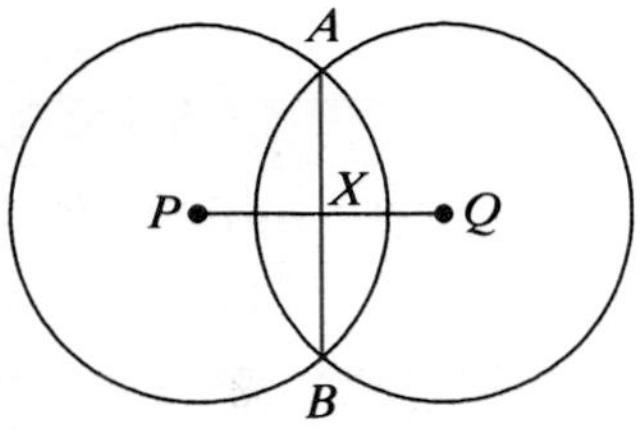

Ex. 28

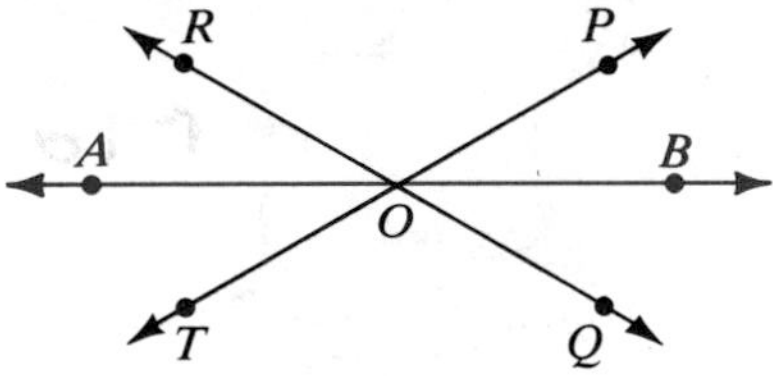

Ex. 29

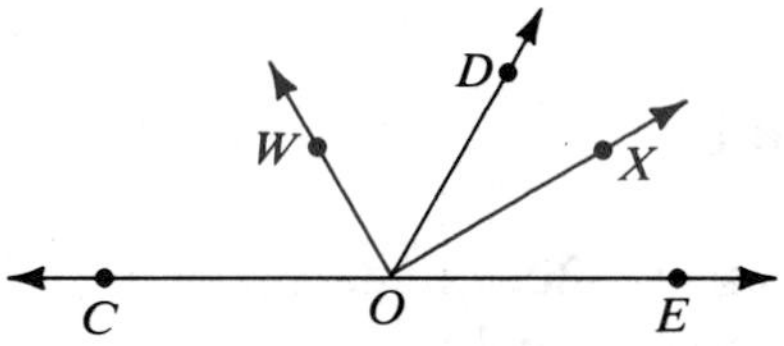

Ex. 30

C 29. In the diagram, $\overrightarrow{OB}$ bisects $\angle POQ$. Explain how you know that $\overrightarrow{OA}$ bisects $\angle ROT$.

30. In the diagram, $\overrightarrow{OW}$ bisects $\angle COD$ and $\overrightarrow{OX}$ bisects $\angle DOE$. Explain how you know that $m\angle WOX = 90°$.

Review Exercises

Solve.

1. $\frac{y}{7} = 49$

2. $2t + 24 = 73$

3. $5x - 2x = 18$

4. $130 - 45 = 2n - 20$

5. $180 - 4x = 95$

6. $z(4 - 2) = 40$

7. $5(3 + s) = 65$

8. $t = 2t - 80$

9. $5r - 25 = r + 17$

6-5 Parallel Lines

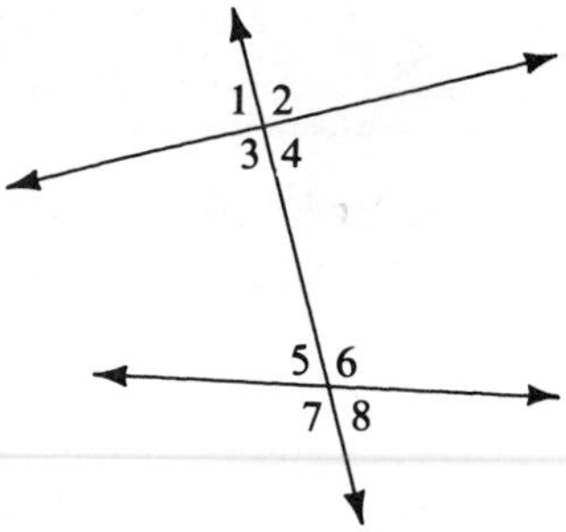

Sometimes a line is denoted by a single lower-case letter, as line *n* at the right. A line, such as line *n*, that intersects two other coplanar lines is called a **transversal.** The following pairs of angles formed by two lines and a transversal are called **alternate interior angles:**

$\angle 3$ and $\angle 6$ $\qquad$ $\angle 4$ and $\angle 5$

The following pairs of angles are called **corresponding angles:**

$\angle 1$ and $\angle 5$ $\qquad$ $\angle 2$ and $\angle 6$
$\angle 3$ and $\angle 7$ $\qquad$ $\angle 4$ and $\angle 8$

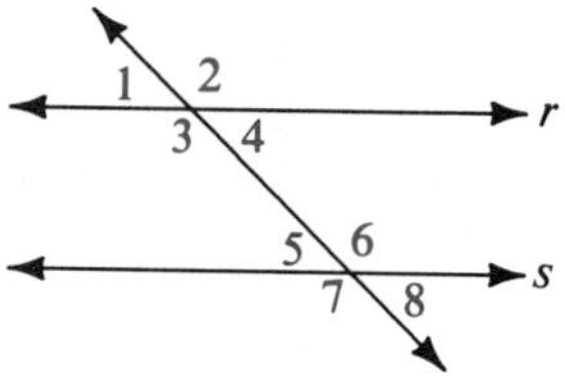

If two lines lie in one plane and do not meet, they are called **parallel lines.** We abbreviate the statement *r is parallel to s* by writing $r \parallel s$. If a transversal intersects two parallel lines, then each pair of angles listed above is a pair of congruent angles. In the diagram at the right,

$\angle 3 \cong \angle 6$ $\qquad$ $\angle 1 \cong \angle 5$ $\qquad$ $\angle 2 \cong \angle 6$
$\angle 4 \cong \angle 5$ $\qquad$ $\angle 3 \cong \angle 7$ $\qquad$ $\angle 4 \cong \angle 8$

EXAMPLE 1 Lines *l* and *m* are parallel and $m\angle 1 = 117°$. Find the measures of the other angles.

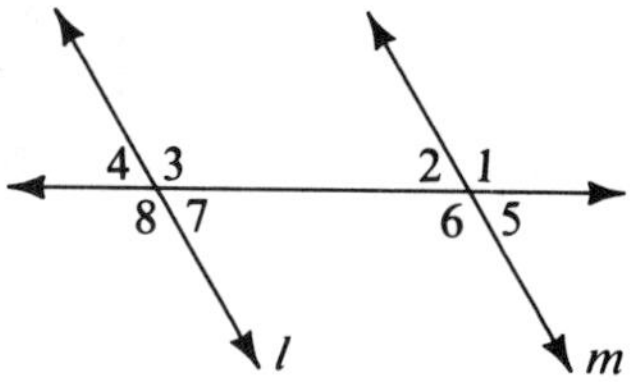

Solution Since $m\angle 1 = 117°$,

$m\angle 3 = m\angle 1 = 117°$ (corresponding angles)

$m\angle 6 = m\angle 3 = 117°$ (alternate interior angles)

$m\angle 8 = m\angle 6 = 117°$ (corresponding angles)

Since $m\angle 2 + m\angle 1 = 180°$,

$m\angle 2 = 63°$ $(63 + 117 = 180)$

$m\angle 5 = m\angle 2 = 63°$ (vertical angles)

$m\angle 7 = m\angle 5 = 63°$ (corresponding angles)

$m\angle 4 = m\angle 7 = 63°$ (vertical angles)

If two lines are cut by a transversal and any two alternate interior angles (or any two corresponding angles) are congruent, then the other pairs are also congruent and the two given lines are parallel. This fact enables us to construct parallel lines by copying one angle.

EXAMPLE 2 Construct a line through point P and parallel to line m.

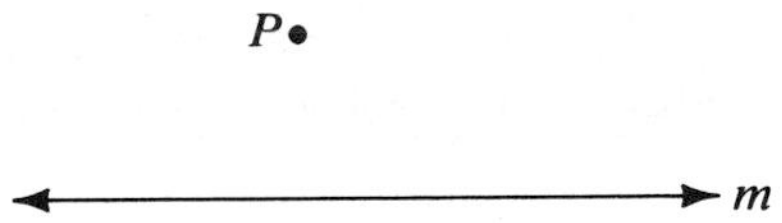

Solution

1. Draw any line through P intersecting m at Q.

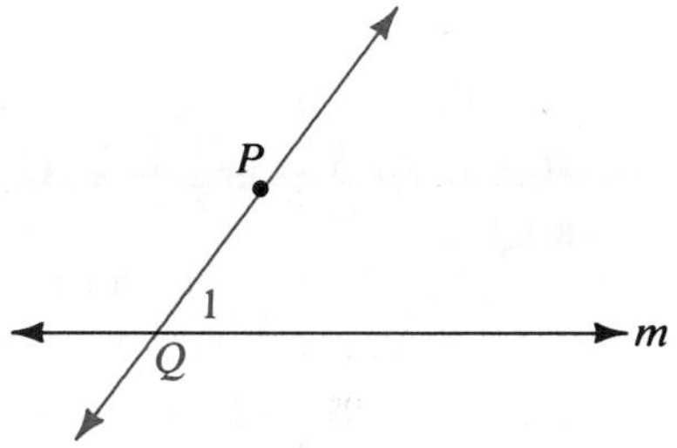

2. At P, construct an angle congruent to $\angle 1$ (by the method already learned). Label the line you have just drawn as n. Then, since lines m and n form congruent corresponding angles with transversal $\overleftrightarrow{PQ}$, $n \parallel m$.

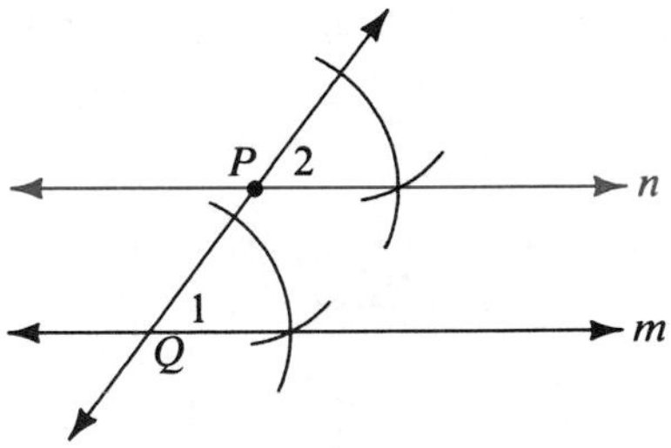

Class Exercises

Exercises 1–8 refer to the diagram at the right.

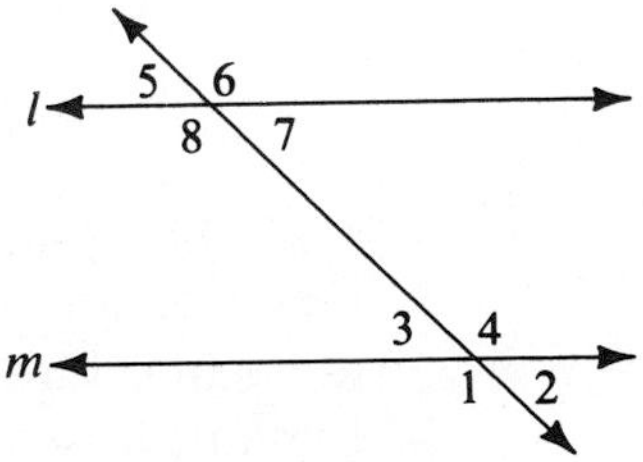

Exs. 1–8

1. Name two pairs of alternate interior angles.

2. Name four pairs of corresponding angles.

Assume that $l \parallel m$ in Exercises 3–8. If $m\angle 3 = 42°$, find the measure of each angle.

3. $\angle 6$ **4.** $\angle 7$ **5.** $\angle 4$

6. $\angle 5$ **7.** $\angle 2$ **8.** $\angle 8$

Written Exercises

Exercises 1–16 refer to the diagram at the right. Name a pair of alternate interior angles, one of which is the given angle.

A **1.** $\angle 5$ **2.** $\angle 3$ **3.** $\angle DBC$ **4.** $\angle 6$

Name a pair of corresponding angles, one of which is the given angle.

5. $\angle 2$ **6.** $\angle 5$ **7.** $\angle DBC$ **8.** $\angle FBE$

In the diagram, suppose that $\overleftrightarrow{DE} \parallel \overleftrightarrow{AC}$ and $\overleftrightarrow{BC} \perp \overleftrightarrow{DE}$. If $m\angle 1 = 32°$, find the measure of each angle.

9. $\angle 2$ **10.** $\angle 3$ **11.** $\angle 4$ **12.** $\angle 5$

13. $\angle 6$ **14.** $\angle 7$ **15.** $\angle 8$ **16.** $\angle ABE$

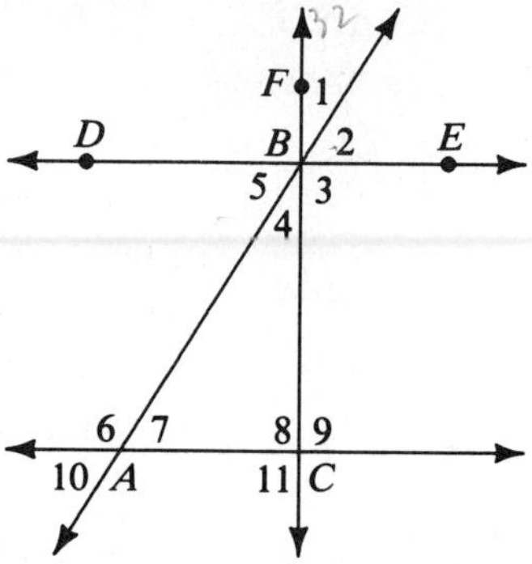

Exs. 1–16

17. Draw a line l and a point B not on l. Construct a line parallel to l through B.

18. Draw any $\angle TAP$. Construct a line through point P parallel to $\overleftrightarrow{AT}$.

B **19.** In the diagram, $l \parallel m$. What relationship is there between $\angle 6$ and $\angle 4$? (*Hint:* Consider $\angle 5$.)

20. If $l \parallel m$ in the diagram, what is the relationship between $\angle 8$ and $\angle 1$? Explain.

21. Suppose $\angle 3 \cong \angle 8$. Make a sketch of how the diagram would look. Explain how you know that $\angle 2 \cong \angle 8$ also.

22. Suppose $\angle 1 \cong \angle 7$. Make a sketch of how the diagram would look. Explain how you know that $\angle 4 \cong \angle 7$ also.

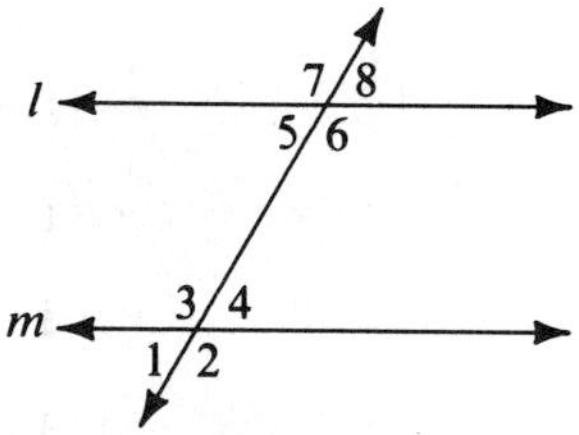

Exs. 19–22

23. Use the idea suggested by the diagram.

a. Describe an alternative method of constructing a line through point P parallel to line m.

b. Explain how you know that the method you described produces parallel lines.

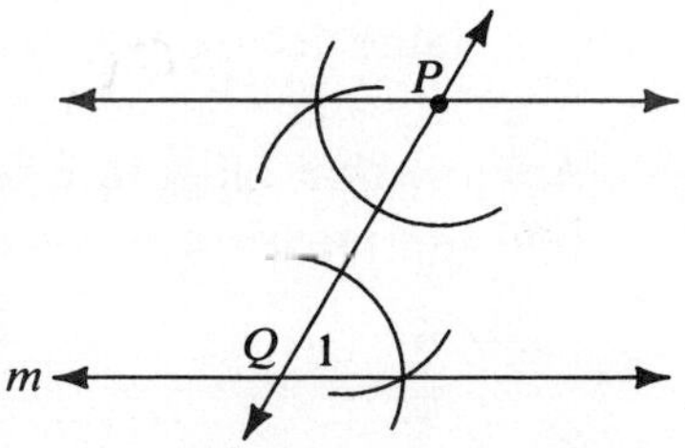

Ex. 23

24. In the diagram, $ABCD$ is a figure in which *both* pairs of opposite sides are parallel. Explain why $\angle 1 \cong \angle 2$.

25. In the diagram, suppose $\angle 1 \cong \angle 2$ and $\overline{AD} \parallel \overline{BC}$. Explain how you know also that $\overline{AB} \parallel \overline{DC}$.

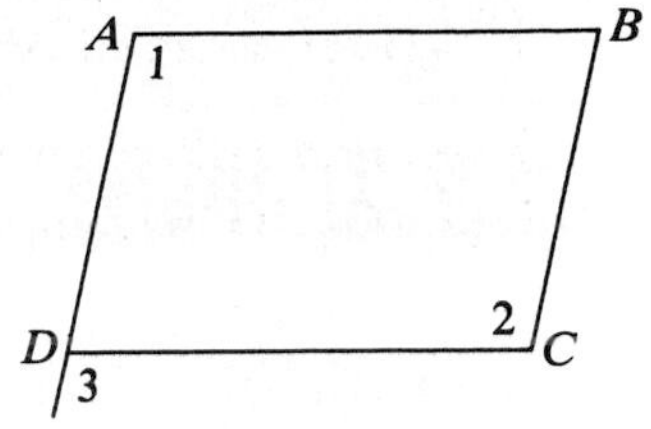

Exs. 24, 25

26. Construct two parallel lines and a transversal and construct the bisectors of two interior angles on the *same side* of the transversal (like $\angle 1$ and $\angle 2$ in the diagram). What appears to be true of these bisectors? Explain why.

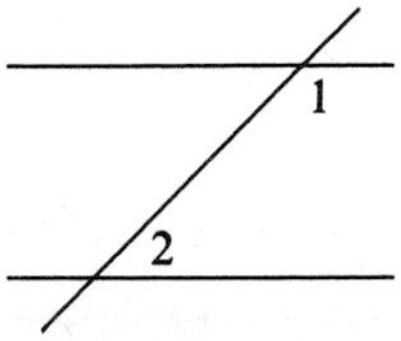

Ex. 26

C 27. If all sides of a four-sided figure are congruent, then the opposite sides of the figure are parallel. Use this fact to construct two parallel lines.

Self-Test A

Draw a labeled diagram to illustrate each description in Exercises 1–5.

1. $\overline{RS}$ 2. $\overrightarrow{AB}$ 3. Plane X 4. $\overleftrightarrow{ST}$ **[6–1]**

5. A circle with center P, a radius $\overline{QP}$, a diameter $\overline{TW}$, and a chord $\overline{XY}$ **[6–2]**

6. Find the circumference of a circle with diameter 49. Use $\pi \approx \frac{22}{7}$.

7. Draw an acute angle and construct its bisector. **[6–3]**

8. In the diagram, if $m\angle BAD = 137°$ and $m\angle CAD = 55°$, what is $m\angle BAC$?

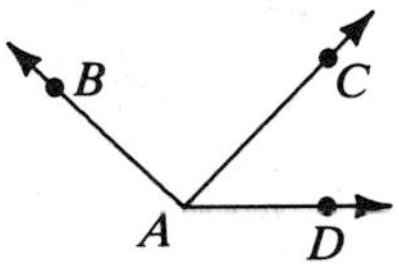

9. $\angle ARQ$ and $\angle QRT$ are complementary. If $m\angle ARQ$ is 18° greater than $m\angle QRT$, what is the measure of each angle? **[6–4]**

10. $\angle XYZ$ and $\angle ABC$ are supplementary. If $m\angle ABC$ is 54° less than $m\angle XYZ$, what is the measure of each angle?

In the diagram, $\overleftrightarrow{WX} \parallel \overleftrightarrow{TS}$.

11. $\angle WYQ$ and $\angle$ _?_ are alternate interior angles. **[6–5]**

12. $\angle YXQ$ and $\angle$ _?_ are corresponding angles.

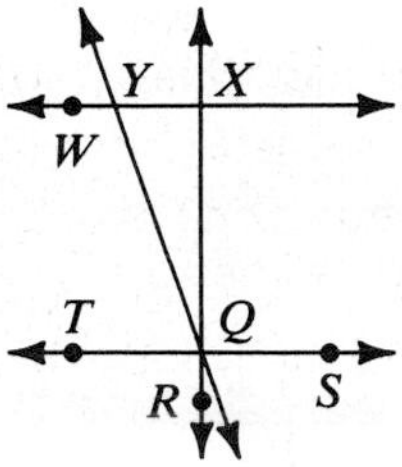

Self-Test answers and Extra Practice are at the back of the book.

6-6 Triangles

If we join three points that are noncollinear, we obtain a **triangle.** Each of the three points is a **vertex** (plural: *vertices*) of the triangle. The triangle with vertices A, B, and C can be denoted as $\triangle ABC$.

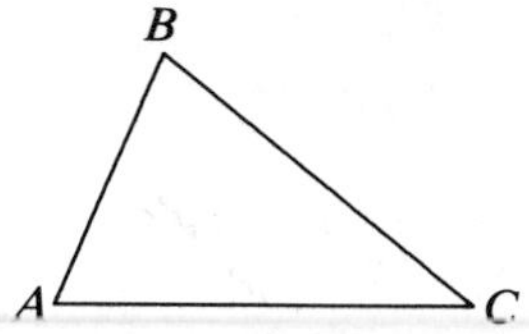

Sides of $\triangle ABC$: $\overline{AB}$, $\overline{BC}$, $\overline{AC}$
Angles of $\triangle ABC$: $\angle A$, $\angle B$, $\angle C$

To find the sum of the angle measures of a $\triangle ABC$, draw a line l through one vertex, parallel to the opposite side. Since l is a line, we know that $m\angle 4 + m\angle 2 + m\angle 5 = 180°$. But since $\angle 1$ and $\angle 4$ are alternate interior angles, as are $\angle 3$ and $\angle 5$,

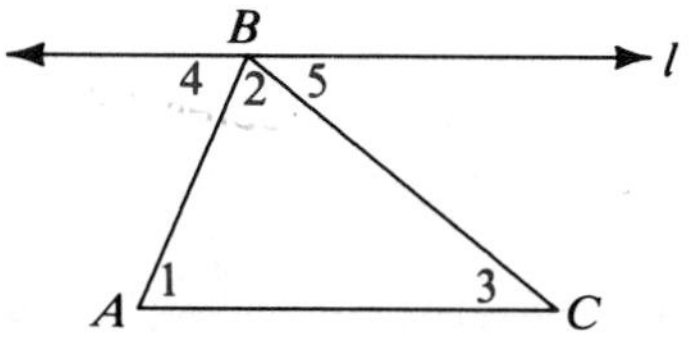

$$m\angle 1 = m\angle 4 \qquad \text{and} \qquad m\angle 3 = m\angle 5.$$

Therefore, $m\angle 1 + m\angle 2 + m\angle 3 = m\angle 4 + m\angle 2 + m\angle 5 = 180°$.

> The sum of the angle measures of any triangle is 180°.

EXAMPLE 1 Two angles of a triangle are congruent, and the third angle has measure 38°. Find the measure of one of the congruent angles.

Solution Let x represent the measure of one of the congruent angles. Then the sum of the three angle measures is $x + x + 38°$.

$$\begin{aligned} x + x + 38° &= 180° \\ 2x + 38° &= 180° \\ 2x &= 142° \\ x &= 71° \end{aligned}$$

Each of the congruent angles has measure 71°.

We can classify triangles by their angles as follows:

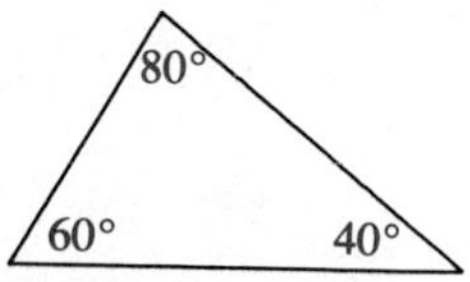

Acute Triangle
Three acute angles

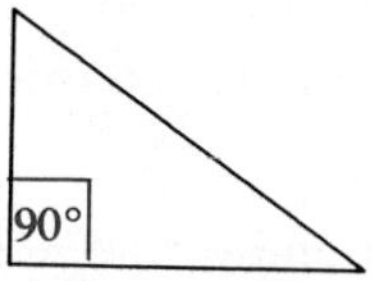

Right Triangle
One right angle

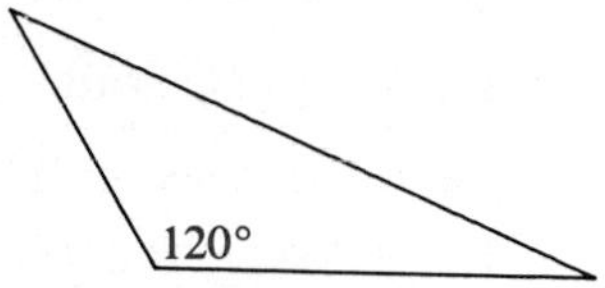

Obtuse Triangle
One obtuse angle

We can also classify triangles by their sides (marks indicate congruent sides):

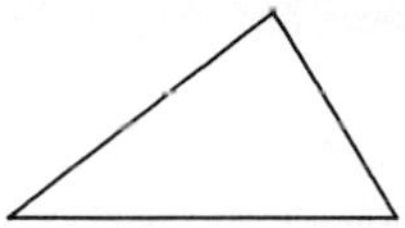

Scalene Triangle
No two sides congruent

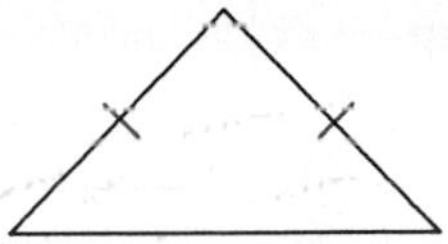

Isosceles Triangle
At least two sides congruent

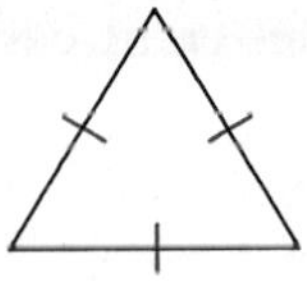

Equilateral Triangle
All sides congruent

In an isosceles triangle, the angles opposite congruent sides are congruent.

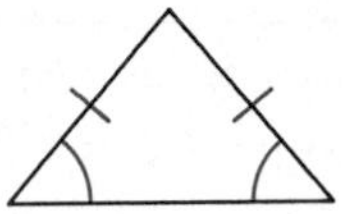

EXAMPLE 2 Find the measure of one angle of an equilateral triangle.

Solution Sketch a triangle to help you plan your solution. In your sketch, mark congruent sides alike.

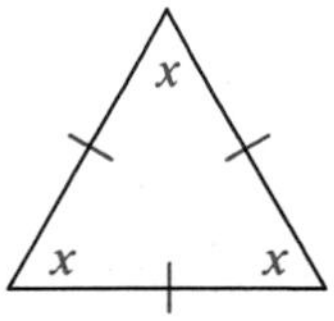

Since all sides of the triangle are congruent, all angles of the triangle are congruent, according to the fact above. Let x represent the measure of one of the three congruent angles. Then each angle has measure x, so

$$\begin{aligned} x + x + x &= 180° \\ 3x &= 180° \\ x &= 60° \end{aligned}$$

Each angle of an equilateral triangle has measure 60°.

Problem Solving Reminder
You may want to *make a sketch* to help plan your solutions for some problems. In Example 2 above, sketching the equilateral triangle helped to identify the relationships among the sides and the angles, making it easier to write an equation.

Class Exercises

Refer to the triangles shown. State the letter of each triangle that appears to be

1. acute
2. obtuse
3. right
4. isosceles
5. scalene
6. equilateral
7. isosceles right
8. scalene obtuse

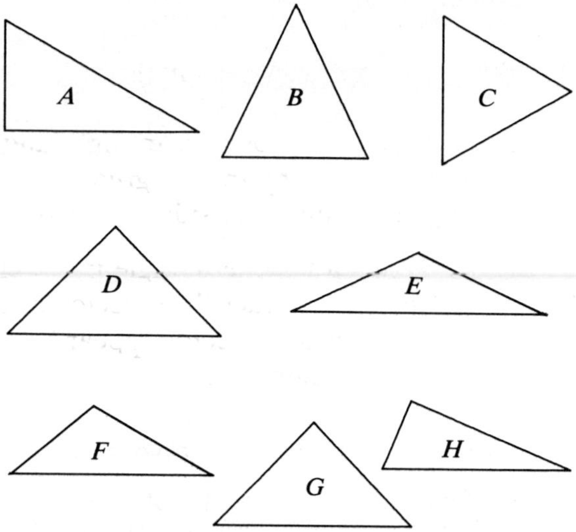

Without using a protractor, find the measure of the unknown angle.

9. 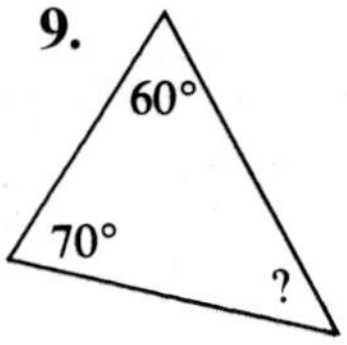

10. 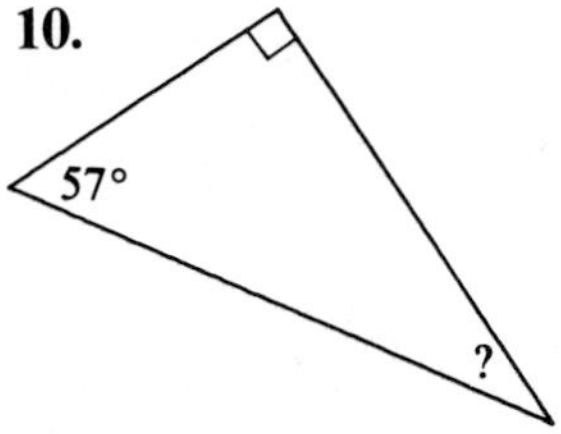

11. 

12. 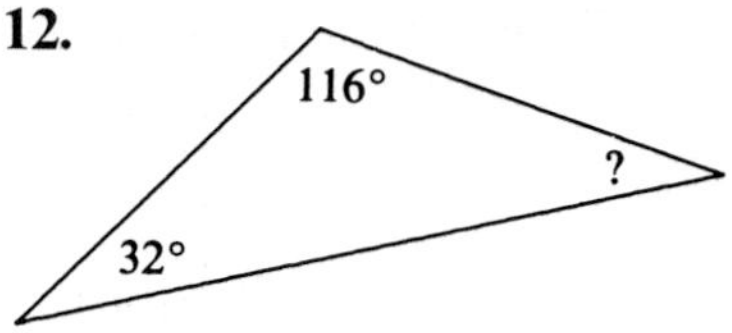

Written Exercises

Without using a protractor, find the measure of each unknown angle.

A 1. 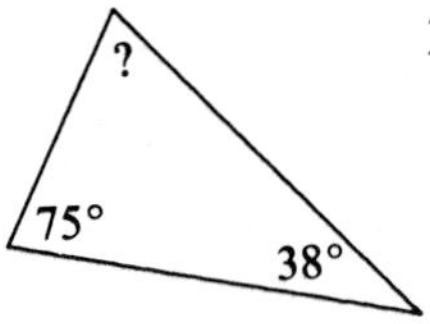

2. 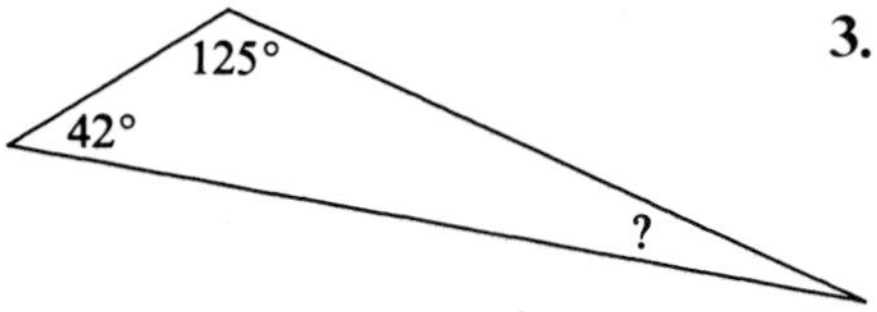

3. 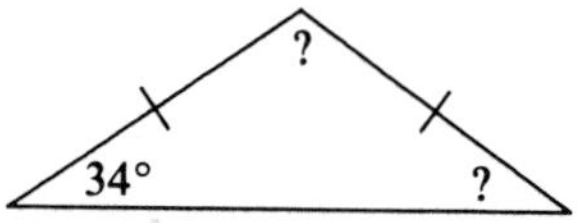

4. 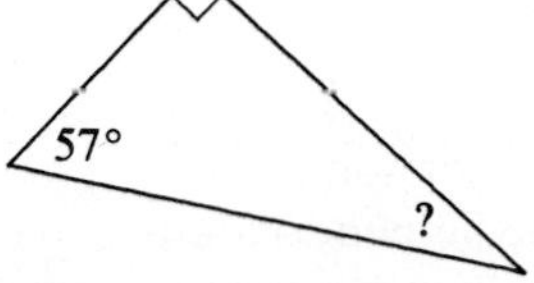

5. 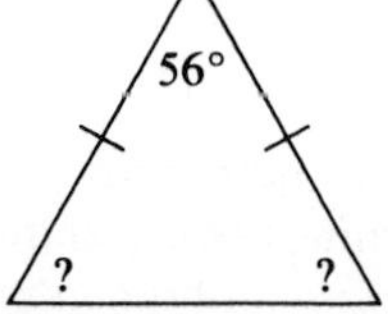

6. 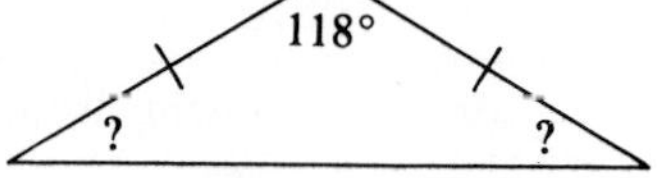

Construct each figure.

7. an isosceles right triangle
8. an isosceles obtuse triangle
9. an isosceles acute triangle
10. an equilateral triangle

11. Construct an isosceles triangle and construct the bisector of the angle formed by the congruent sides. Does the bisector appear to divide the opposite side into two congruent segments?

12. Construct a scalene triangle in which one side is much longer than another. Construct the bisector of the angle formed by these two sides. Does the bisector appear to divide the opposite side into two congruent segments?

13. Find the measure of each angle of an isosceles right triangle.

14. One of the acute angles of a right triangle has measure twice as great as the other. What are the measures of the three angles of the triangle?

Find the values of x and y in each diagram.

B 15.

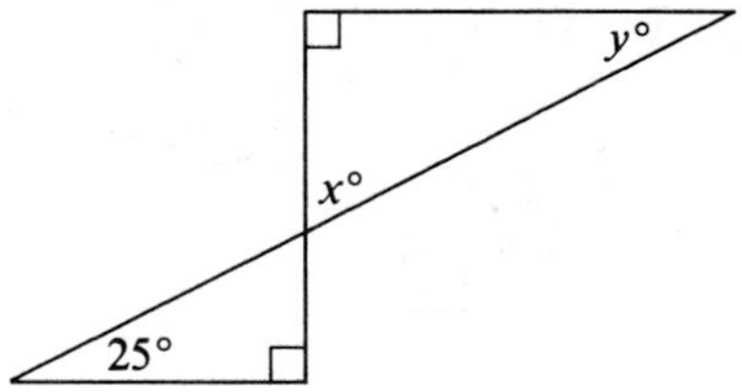

16.

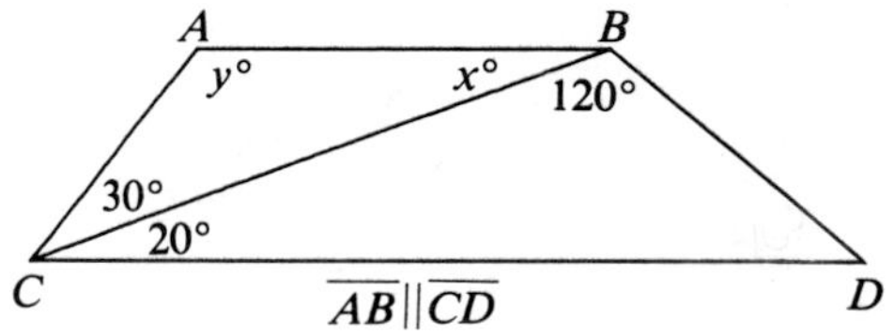

17.

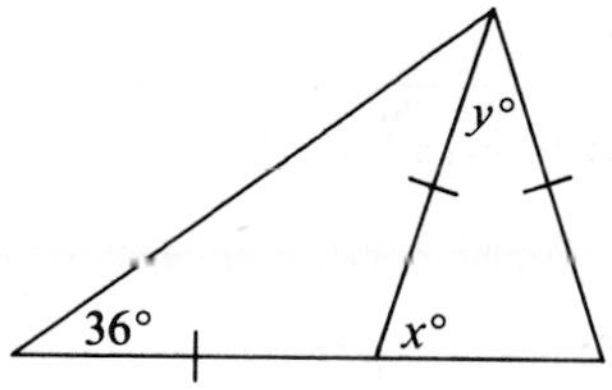

18.

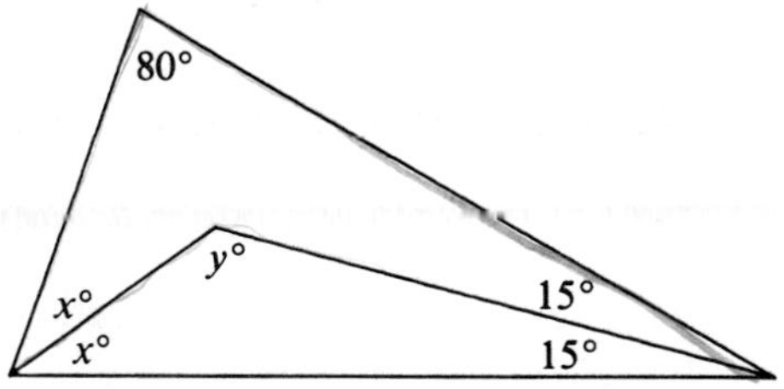

19.

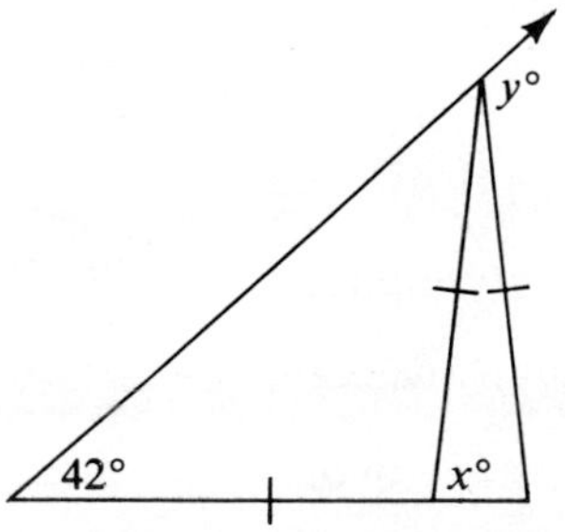

20.

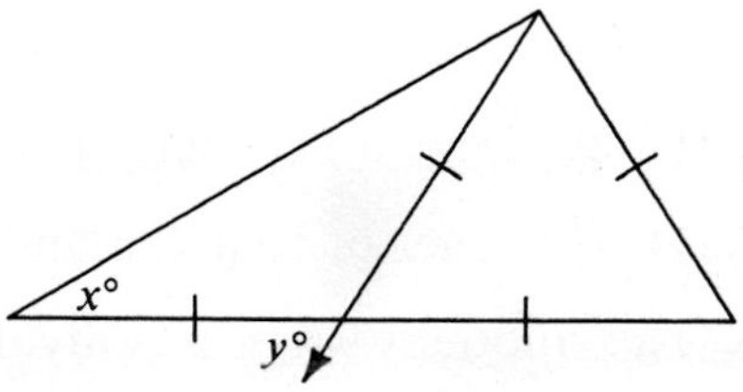

21. a. Draw an acute triangle DEF.

b. Construct a new triangle PRO such that $\angle P \cong \angle D$ and $\angle R \cong \angle E$ but with $\overline{PR}$ twice as long as $\overline{DE}$.

c. Repeat part (b) but make $\overline{PR}$ three times as long as $\overline{DE}$.

d. What appears to be true of the other sides of the new triangle relative to $\triangle DEF$?

22. a. Draw a large acute triangle. Bisect each angle.

b. Repeat part (a) with a large obtuse triangle.

c. What do you notice about the angle bisectors?

23. Construct a circle and a diameter $\overline{AB}$. Choose any point C on the circle and draw triangle ABC. What special kind of triangle does it appear to be?

24. Construct a circle and a diameter $\overline{DE}$. Construct a chord $\overline{FG}$ that is perpendicular to $\overline{DE}$ but is *not* a diameter. Draw triangles DFG and EFG. What special kind of triangle do these appear to be?

C **25.** In $\triangle ABC$, $m\angle C = 70°$. The bisectors of $\angle A$ and $\angle B$ meet at point X. Find $m\angle AXB$.

26. In $\triangle DEF$, there is a point M of $\overline{EF}$ such that $ME = MF = MD$. Find $m\angle EDF$.

27. In equilateral triangle JKL, there is a point Y of $\overline{JK}$ such that $\overline{LY} \perp \overline{JK}$. Find $m\angle KLY$.

28. In isosceles triangle RST, $\overline{RT} \perp \overline{ST}$. The bisector of $\angle T$ meets side $\overline{RS}$ at point Z. Find $m\angle RZT$.

Review Exercises

Write an equation or an inequality for the sentence.

1. The difference when nine is subtracted from d is five.

2. A number n is the product of three and eleven.

3. Negative four is the sum of a number x and twenty.

4. Three times a number y is the sum of sixty-four and nineteen.

5. The product of fourteen and z is greater than ninety-eight.

6. The quotient when a is divided by eight is less then twelve.

7. The difference when ten is subtracted from twice m is two.

8. The product of six and the sum of t and three is thirty-six.

6-7 Special Quadrilaterals

Any four-sided closed figure is called a **quadrilateral.** A special kind of quadrilateral in which both pairs of opposite sides are parallel is called a **parallelogram.**

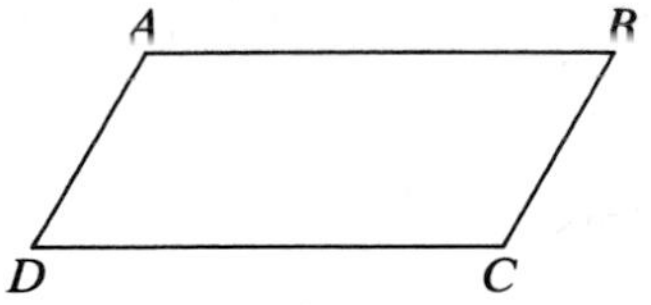

Parallelogram $ABCD$

$\overline{AB} \parallel \overline{CD}$

$\overline{AD} \parallel \overline{BC}$

In any parallelogram, opposite sides are congruent. In the diagram,

$$\overline{AB} \cong \overline{CD} \quad \text{and} \quad \overline{AD} \cong \overline{BC}.$$

Also, opposite angles of a parallelogram are congruent. In the diagram,

$$\angle A \cong \angle C \quad \text{and} \quad \angle B \cong \angle D.$$

EXAMPLE 1 Find each angle measure.

a. m$\angle BCD$

b. m$\angle 1$

c. m$\angle D$

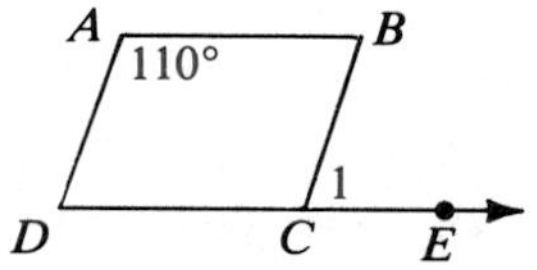

Solution

a. $\angle BCD \cong \angle A$, so m$\angle BCD = 110°$

b. $m\angle BCD + m\angle 1 = 180°$
$110° + m\angle 1 = 180°$
$m\angle 1 = 70°$

c. $\overline{AB} \parallel \overline{DE}$
$m\angle B = m\angle 1 = 70°$ (alternate interior angles)
$\angle D \cong \angle B$, so $m\angle D = 70°$

You may be familiar with the names of the following special parallelograms.

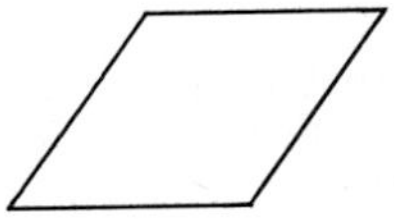

Rhombus
Opposite sides parallel
All sides congruent
Opposite angles congruent

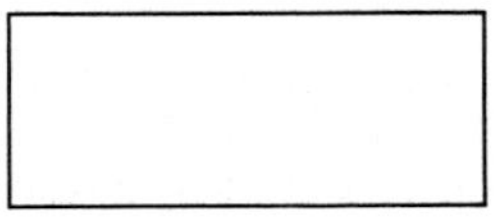

Rectangle
Opposite sides parallel
Opposite sides congruent
Four right angles

Square
Opposite sides parallel
All sides congruent
Four right angles

EXAMPLE 2 Construct a parallelogram.

Solution

1. Draw a line and a point not on the line. Construct a pair of parallel lines and a transversal (by the method already learned). Label the points where the lines intersect as P and Q.

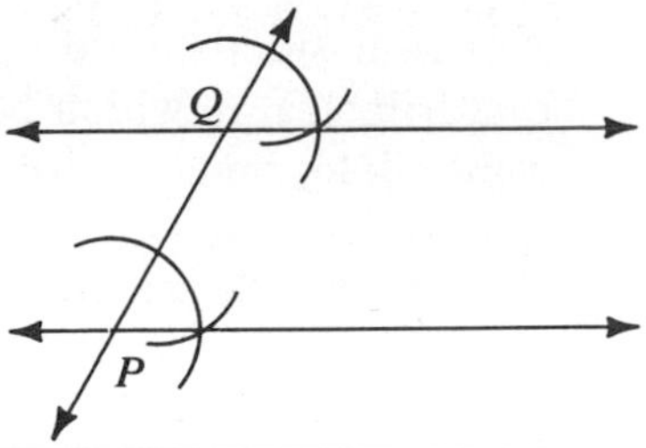

2. Choose any point S on one of the parallel lines. Construct a line parallel to $\overleftrightarrow{PQ}$ through S, using the same method. Label the point where this line intersects the line through Q as R.

   Then $PQRS$ is a parallelogram.

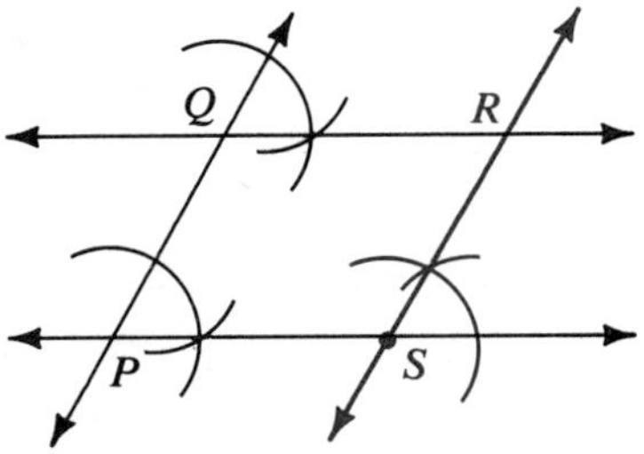

A rhombus, a rectangle, and a square are parallelograms because they each have *two* pairs of parallel sides. A quadrilateral that has exactly *one* pair of parallel sides is called a **trapezoid.** If the nonparallel sides of a trapezoid are congruent, then the trapezoid is called an **isosceles trapezoid.** An isosceles trapezoid also has two pairs of congruent angles.

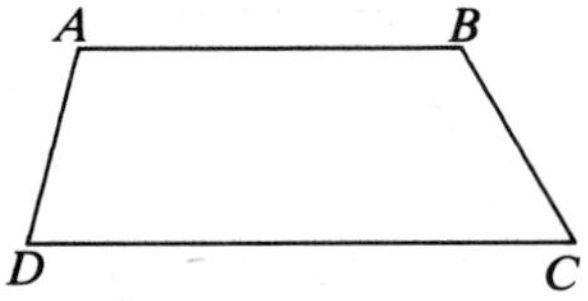

Trapezoid $ABCD$
$\overline{AB} \parallel \overline{CD}$

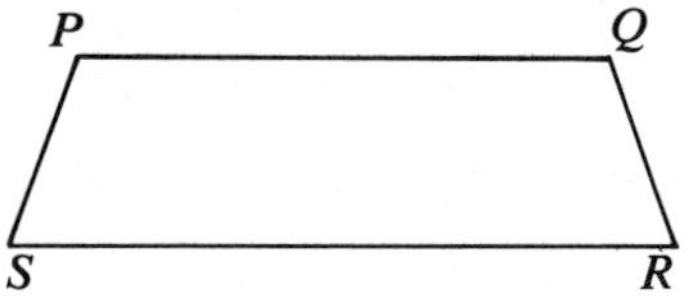

Isosceles trapezoid $PQRS$
$\overline{PQ} \parallel \overline{RS}$
$\overline{PS} \cong \overline{QR}$
$\angle P \cong \angle Q$
$\angle S \cong \angle R$

A segment that joins opposite vertices of a quadrilateral is called a **diagonal.** In the diagram, $\overline{TR}$ and $\overline{QS}$ are the diagonals of quadrilateral $QRST$.

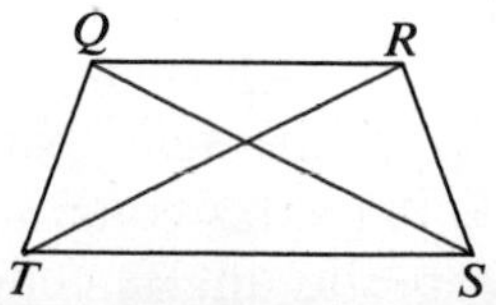

Class Exercises

Choose each name that describes the figure.

quadrilateral	**rectangle**	**parallelogram**	**rhombus**
square	**trapezoid**	**isosceles trapezoid**	

1. 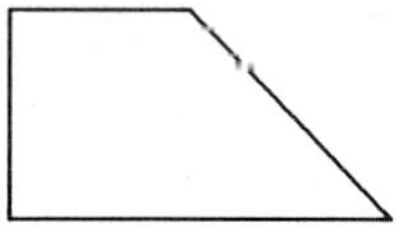

2. 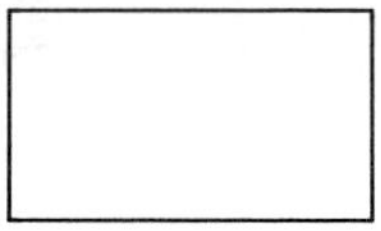

3. 

4. 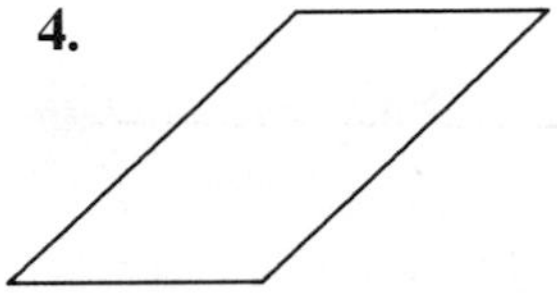

5. 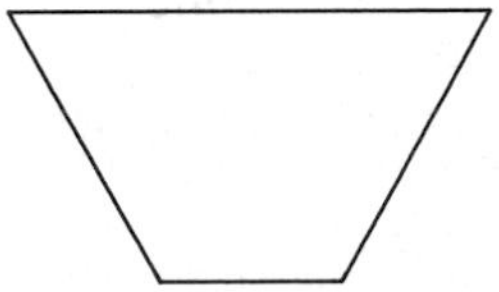

6. 

7. 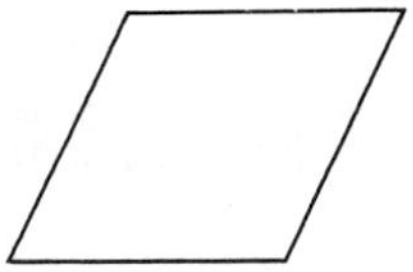

Written Exercises

In the diagram, *PQRS* is a parallelogram. Find each angle measure or each length.

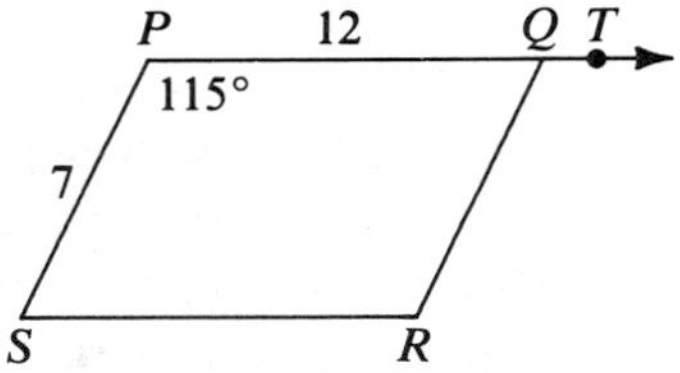

Exs. 1–6

A **1.** m∠*RQT* **2.** m∠*PQR* **3.** m∠*R*

4. m∠*S* **5.** *RS* **6.** *QR*

In the diagram, *ABCD* is an isosceles trapezoid and *ABCE* is a parallelogram.

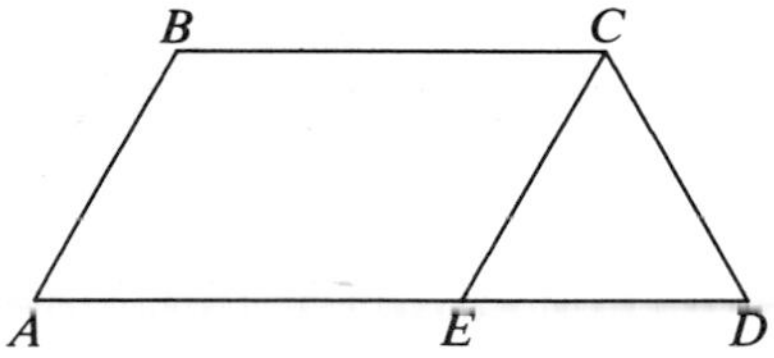

Exs. 7–10

7. Name three congruent segments.

8. Give a reason why ∠*CED* ≅ ∠*A*.

9. Name two other angles congruent to ∠*A*.

10. Name an angle congruent to ∠*B*.

True or false?

11. All squares are rhombuses. **12.** All rectangles are squares.

13. A rhombus with at least one right angle must be a square.

14. A trapezoid can have two right angles.

15. A parallelogram with at least one right angle must be a rectangle.

16. If two sides of a quadrilateral are parallel and the other two sides are congruent, the quadrilateral must be a parallelogram.

17. Draw a line l and a point P not on l. Construct a parallelogram with one side on l and with P as one vertex.

18. If two sides of a quadrilateral are congruent *and* parallel, then the quadrilateral is a parallelogram. Use this fact to construct a parallelogram.

B 19. If the opposite sides of a quadrilateral are congruent, then the quadrilateral is a parallelogram. Use this fact to construct a parallelogram (without copying any angles).

20. Construct a rhombus. Draw the diagonals of the rhombus. What appears to be true of the diagonals?

21. Construct an isosceles trapezoid.

22. Construct a rectangle. Draw the diagonals of the rectangle and let O be their intersection point. Draw a circle with center O that passes through one vertex of the rectangle. Does it also pass through the other vertices?

Find the value of x in each diagram.

23.

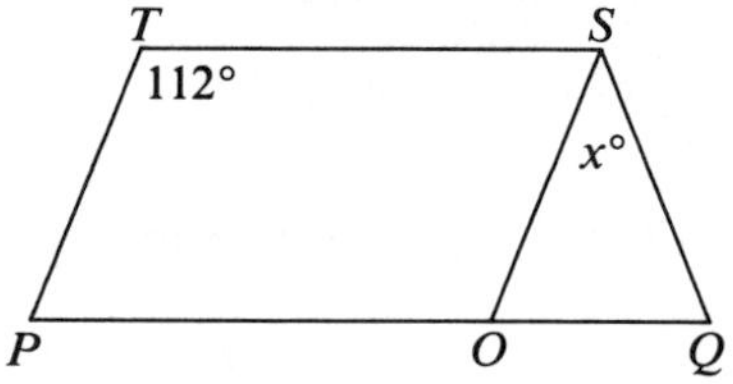

$POST$ is a parallelogram.
$SO = SQ$

24.

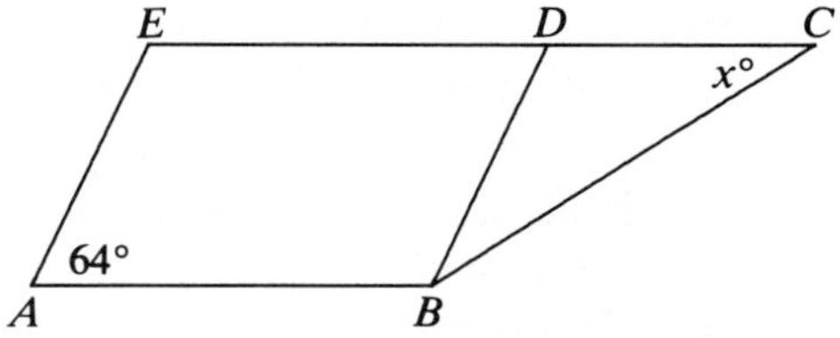

$ABDE$ is a parallelogram.
$DB = DC$

C 25. A line segment that joins the midpoints of the nonparallel sides of a trapezoid is called the **median** of the trapezoid.
a. Construct a trapezoid and the median of the trapezoid.
b. What relationship between the median and the parallel sides of the trapezoid appears to be true?

Review Exercises

Simplify.

1. $2.5(-3.67)$
2. $5.32 \div (-1.4)$
3. $-12.4(-7.9)$
4. $-5.616 \div 3.9$
5. $-8.5(4.16)$
6. $-62.5(-2.8)$
7. $-14.4 \div (-1.6)$
8. $17.5(-6.4)$
9. $46.8 \div (-7.5)$

6-8 Polygons and Their Perimeters

A **polygon** is a closed figure consisting of segments joined at their endpoints. The points are the **vertices** and the segments are the **sides** of the polygon. You know that a triangle is a three-sided polygon and a quadrilateral is a four-sided polygon. Some other special polygons also have names depending on the number of their sides.

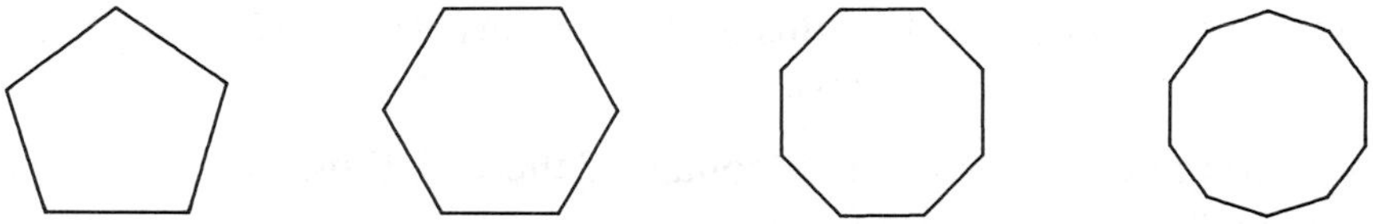

Pentagon	**Hexagon**	**Octagon**	**Decagon**
5 sides	6 sides	8 sides	10 sides

The **perimeter** of a polygon is the sum of the lengths of the sides.

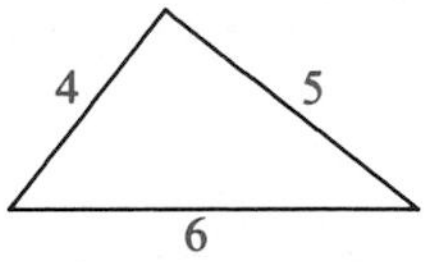

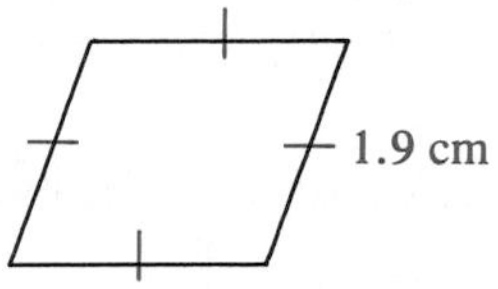

Perimeter $= 4 + 5 + 6 = 15$

Perimeter $= 4 \times 1.9 = 7.6$ (cm)

If all the sides and all the angles of a polygon are congruent, the polygon is called **regular.**

EXAMPLE The perimeter of a regular hexagon is 256.2 cm. Find the length of one side of the hexagon.

Solution Recall that a regular hexagon has 6 sides of the same length. Let s be the length of one side. Then the perimeter is $6 \times s$.

$$256.2 = 6 \times s$$
$$6s = 256.2$$
$$s = \frac{256.2}{6} = 42.7$$

The length of one side is 42.7 cm.

Problem Solving Reminder
To solve some problems, you may have to *supply additional information* such as a mathematics fact that you have learned. In the Example, it was necessary to recall that a regular hexagon has 6 congruent sides in order to find the length of one side.

Class Exercises

Find the perimeter of each polygon.

1.
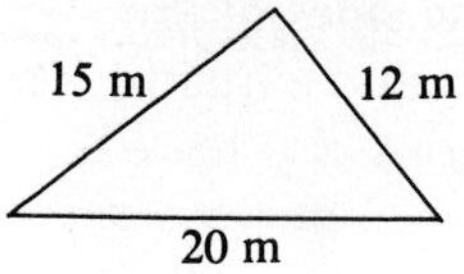

2.
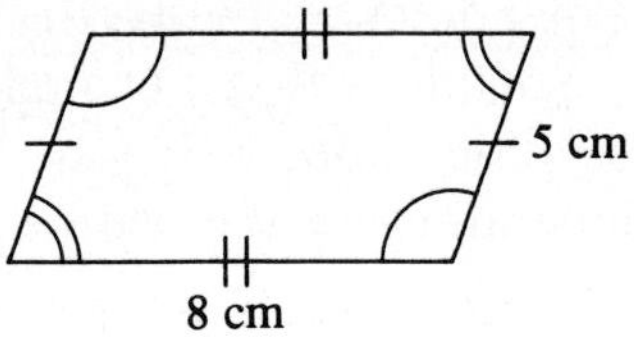

3.
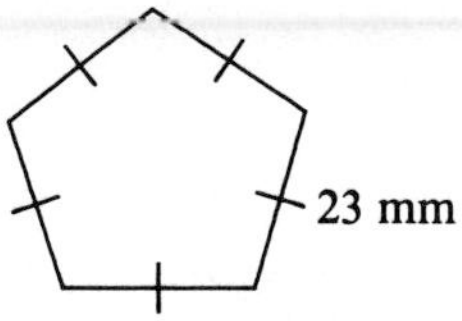

4.
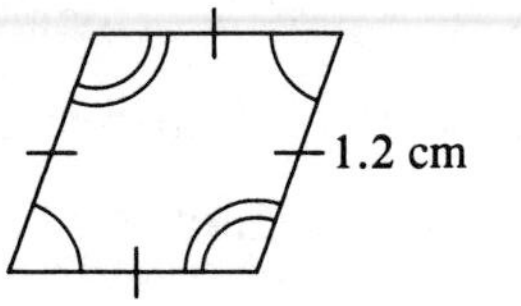

In Exercises 5–8, all the angles in the figures are right angles. Find the perimeter of each figure.

5.
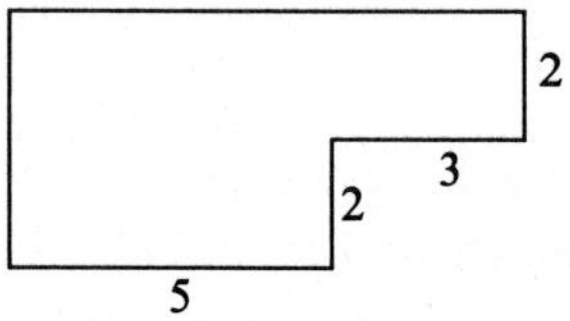

6.
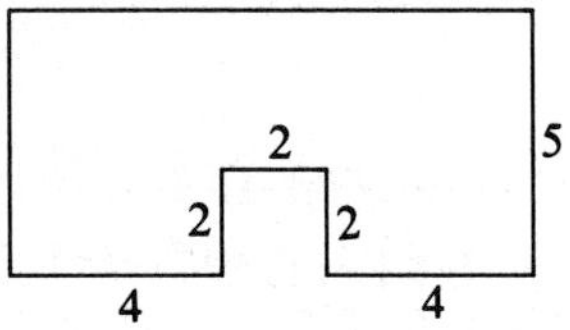

7.
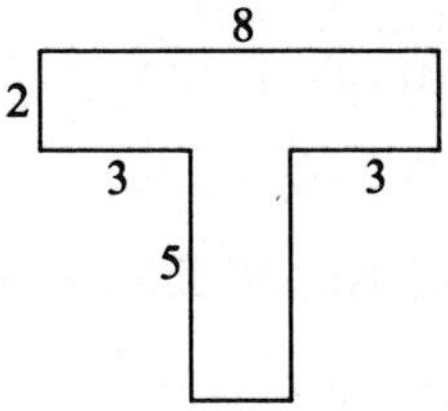

8.
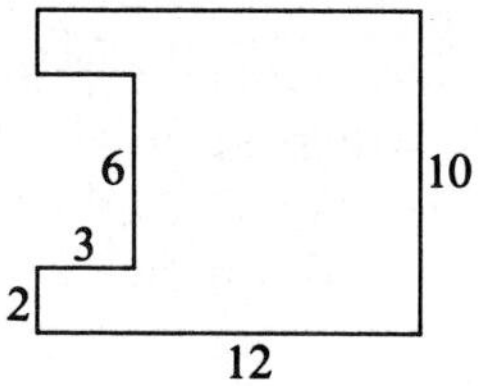

Give another name for each.

9. a regular triangle

10. a regular quadrilateral

Written Exercises

Find the perimeter of each.

A **1.** A regular pentagon with sides of length 3.2 cm

2. A regular octagon with sides of length 12.5 m

3. An isosceles triangle with two sides of length 18.5 m and the third side of length 13 m

Find the perimeter of each.

4. A parallelogram with sides of length 23.6 cm and 52.9 cm

5. A regular decagon with sides of length 4.25 mm

6. A pentagon with three sides of length 26 cm and two sides of length 14.5 cm

Find the length of each side of the figure described.

7. A regular hexagon with perimeter 427.2 mm

8. A regular octagon with perimeter 392.8 cm

9. A square with perimeter 25 in.

10. An equilateral triangle with perimeter 572.4 m

11. A rectangle with perimeter 148.6 m and width 29.2 m

12. An isosceles trapezoid with parallel sides of lengths $26\frac{1}{4}$ ft and $38\frac{1}{4}$ ft and perimeter 86 ft

A polygon is *inscribed* in a circle if all of its vertices lie on the circle. Draw a circle for each exercise and construct each figure so that it is inscribed in the circle.

B 13. A regular hexagon (*Hint:* The length of each side of a regular hexagon equals the radius of the circle on which the vertices lie.)

14. A square (*Hint:* The diagonals of a square are perpendicular.)

15. An equilateral triangle (*Hint:* Construct a regular hexagon first.)

16. A regular octagon (*Hint:* Construct two perpendicular diameters and bisect two of the right angles formed.)

If the vertex of an angle is the center of a circle, the angle is called a *central angle*. Use each figure to calculate the measure of one angle formed by two adjacent sides of the given polygon.

17.

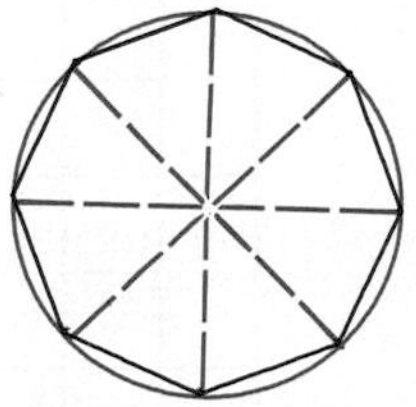

A regular octagon
Each central angle is 45°.

18.

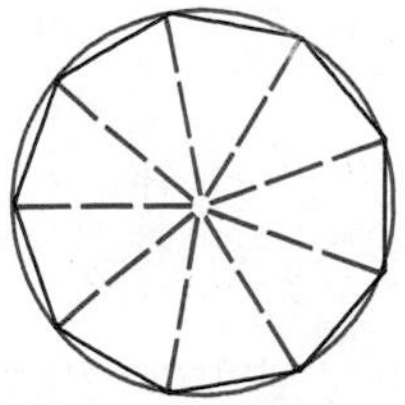

A regular 9-sided polygon
Each central angle is 40°.

Use a method such as the one used for Exercises 17 and 18 to find the measure of one angle formed by two adjacent sides of the given polygon.

19. a regular decagon

20. a regular 12-sided polygon

C **21. a.** Draw any quadrilateral $ABCD$ and draw the diagonal $\overline{AC}$. What is the sum of the measures of the angles of $ABCD$?

b. Draw a pentagon $PQRST$ and diagonals $\overline{RP}$ and $\overline{RT}$. What is the sum of the measures of the angles of $PQRST$?

c. In a polygon with n sides, how many triangles can be made by drawing diagonals from one vertex of the polygon?

d. Use your answer to part (c) to write a formula for finding the sum of the angles of a polygon with n sides.

22. In the diagram below, $ABCDE$ is a regular pentagon. Find the value of y. (*Hint:* See Exercise 21.)

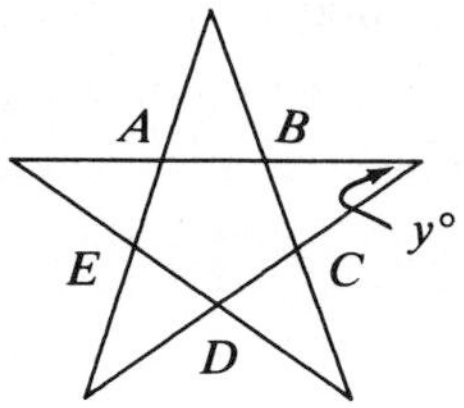

Review Exercises

Simplify.

1. $1.45 + 2.36$

2. $-7.82 + 52.4$

3. $-3.75 + (-4.2)$

4. $-95 + 14.9$

5. $3.82 - (-46)$

6. $-18 - 33$

7. $-64.5 - (-27.3)$

8. $0.75 - 26.15$

Challenge

1. Can you remove 8 squares from the figure at the right without changing the perimeter?

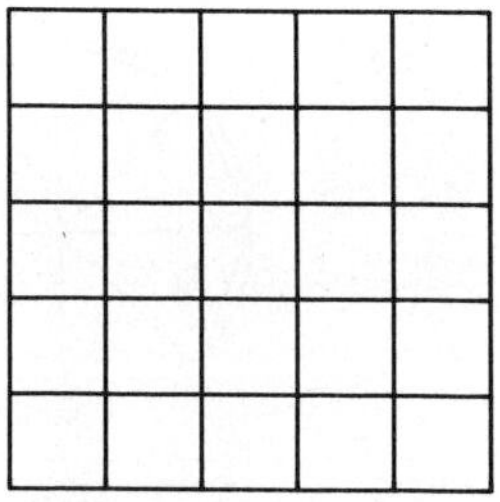

2. Can you remove 8 squares to increase the perimeter by 16?

3. Can you rearrange the squares to obtain a perimeter of 36?

4. Rearrange the squares to obtain the greatest possible perimeter.

5. Can you rearrange the squares to obtain a perimeter less than the perimeter shown?

6-9 Congruent Polygons

Two polygons are **congruent** if there is a way to match the vertices of one with the vertices of the other so that the *corresponding sides are congruent and the corresponding angles are congruent.* In the diagram at the right,

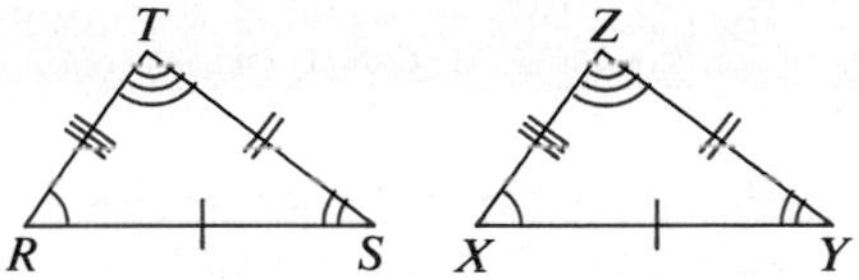

$$\angle R \cong \angle X \qquad \angle S \cong \angle Y \qquad \angle T \cong \angle Z$$

and

$$\overline{RS} \cong \overline{XY} \qquad \overline{ST} \cong \overline{YZ} \qquad \overline{RT} \cong \overline{XZ}$$

Notice that since vertices R and S are matched with vertices X and Y, side $\overline{RS}$ must be matched with side $\overline{XY}$. Notice also that the order in which the vertices are named in the statement tells how the vertices are matched:

$$\triangle RST \cong \triangle XYZ.$$

If two figures are congruent, we can match their vertices by using one or more of the basic **rigid motions.**

Translation **Rotation** **Reflection**

We can use translation to match triangles RST and XYZ above.

EXAMPLE 1 In the diagram, $ABCD \cong HGFE$.

a. $\angle B \cong \angle$ _?_

b. $\overline{AD} \cong$ _?_

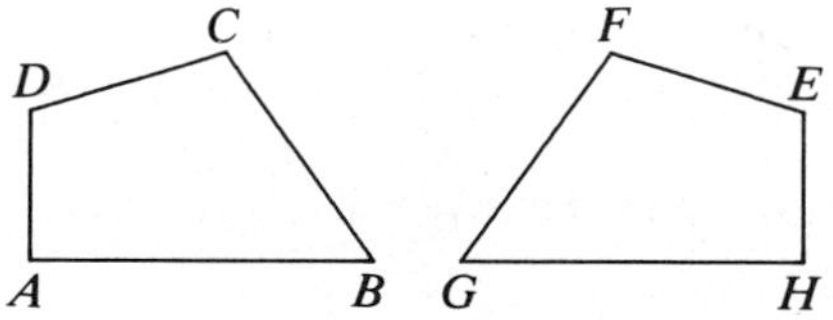

Solution The statement $ABCD \cong HGFE$ indicates that B corresponds to G and $\overline{AD}$ corresponds to $\overline{HE}$. (Note that the polygons can be matched by using reflection.) Therefore,

a. $\angle B \cong \angle G$

b. $\overline{AD} \cong \overline{HE}$

When working with triangles, we do not need to check all sides and all angles to establish congruence. Suppose that in the two triangles below, the sides and the angles marked alike are congruent.

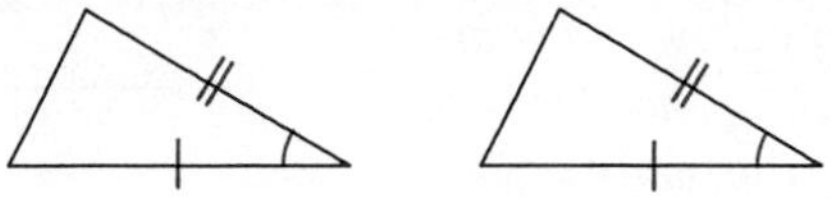

If we were to match the congruent parts by using translation, we would find that all other corresponding sides and angles are congruent also. Thus we can use the following method to establish congruence in two triangles.

The side-angle-side (SAS) test for congruence
If two sides of one triangle and the angle they form (the *included angle*) are congruent to two sides and the included angle of another triangle, then the two triangles are congruent.

Two other methods that we can use to establish congruence in triangles are:

The angle-side-angle (ASA) test for congruence
If two angles and the side between them (the *included side*) are congruent to two angles and the included side of another triangle, then the two triangles are congruent.

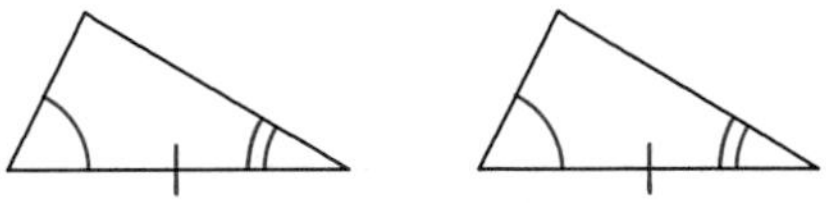

The side-side-side (SSS) test for congruence
If three sides of one triangle are congruent to the three sides of another triangle, then the two triangles are congruent.

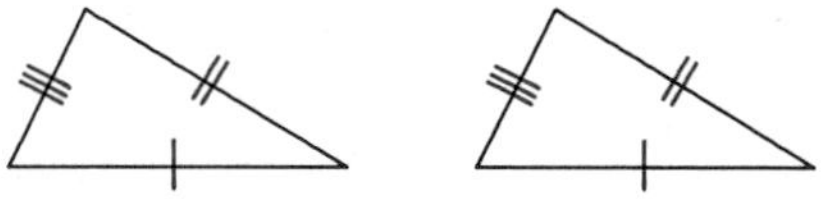

EXAMPLE 2 In the diagram, triangle ABC is isosceles, with $\overline{AB} \cong \overline{CD}$. $\overline{BD}$ bisects $\angle ABC$. Explain why $\triangle ABD \cong \triangle CBD$.

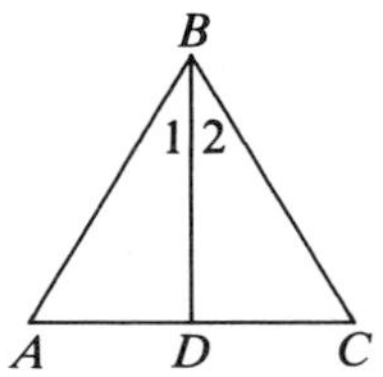

Solution We know that $\overline{AB} \cong \overline{CB}$.
Since $\overline{BD}$ bisects $\angle ABC$, $\angle 1 \cong \angle 2$.
Also, $\overline{BD}$ is a side of both triangles.
Therefore, by the SAS test,
$\triangle ABD \cong \triangle CBD$.

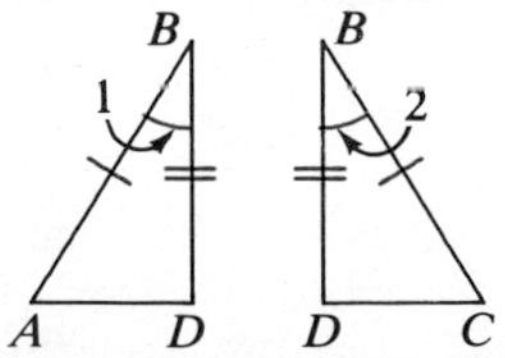

Class Exercises

In the diagram, $\triangle HJK \cong \triangle DOT$.

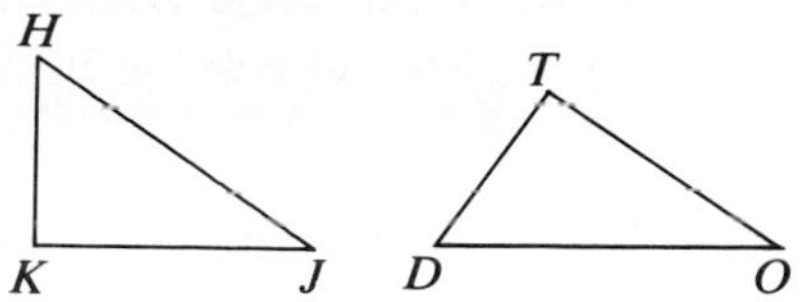

1. $\angle J \cong \angle$ __?__
2. $\angle T \cong \angle$ __?__
3. $\overline{KJ} \cong$ __?__
4. $\overline{DO} \cong$ __?__

In the diagram, $QRST \cong BAKE$.

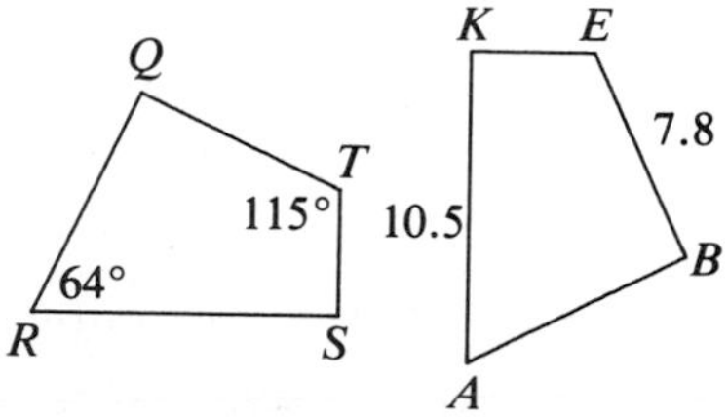

5. $\angle A \cong \angle$ __?__
6. In $BAKE$, m$\angle$ __?__ $= 115°$
7. $QT =$ __?__
8. $\overline{TS} \cong$ __?__

State which of the rigid motions is needed to match the vertices of the triangles in each pair and give a reason why the triangles are congruent.

9. 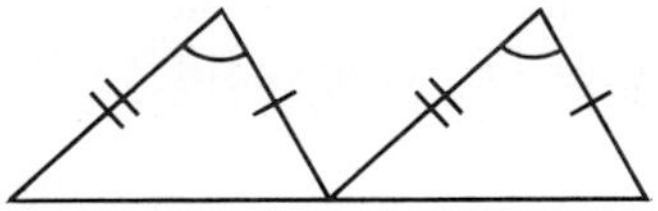

10. 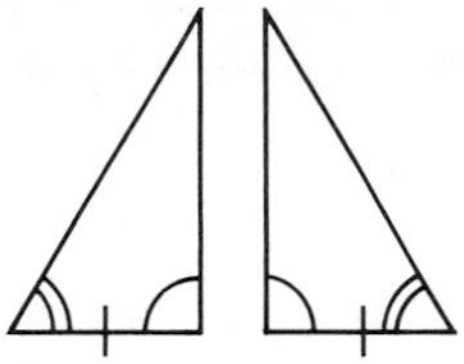

11. 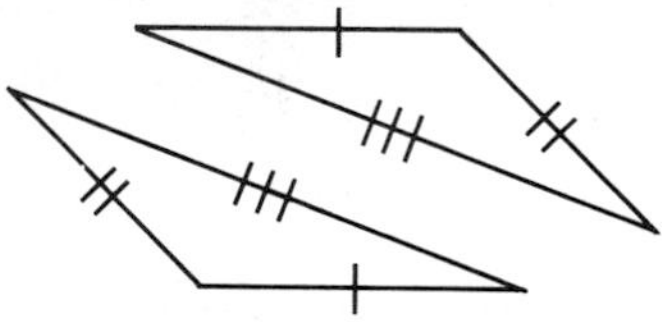

Written Exercises

Explain why the triangles in each pair are congruent.

A 1. 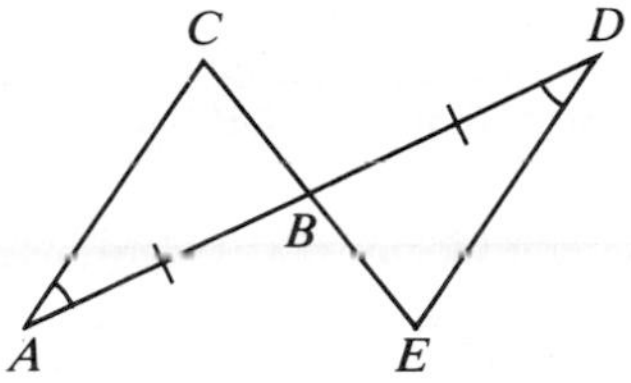

$\triangle ABC \cong \triangle DBE$

2. 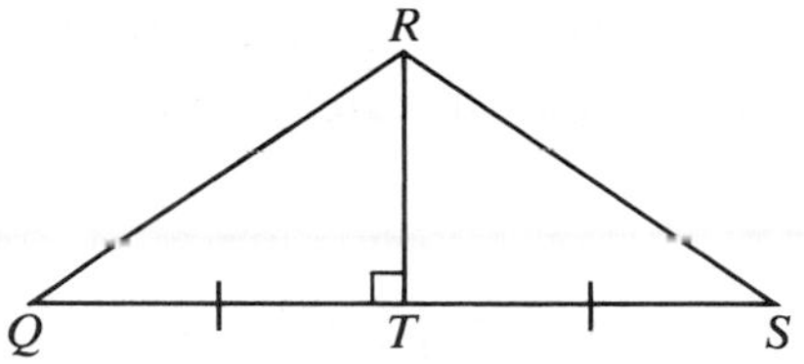

$\triangle QRT \cong \triangle SRT$

3. 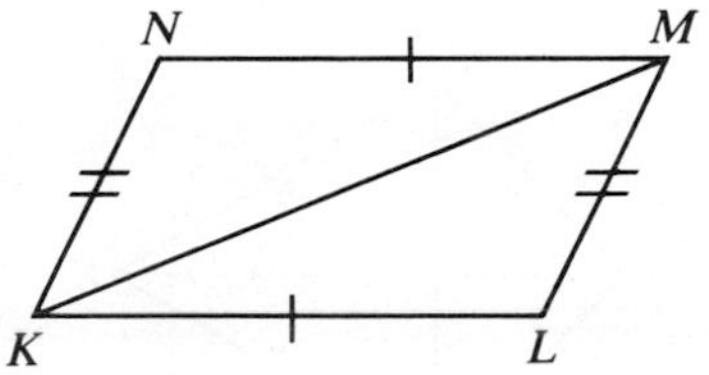

$\triangle KLM \cong \triangle MNK$

4. 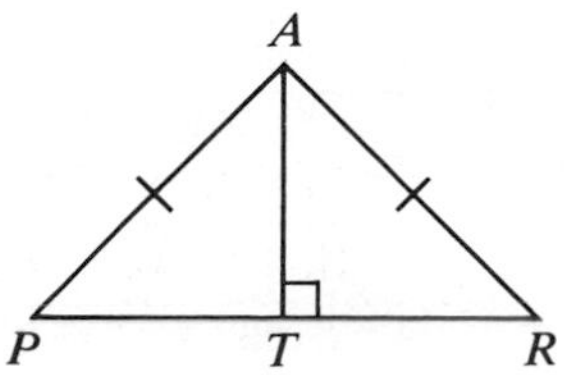

$\triangle PAT \cong \triangle RAT$

5. Draw an acute triangle *ABC*. Use the SAS test to construct a triangle *DEF* such that $\triangle ABC \cong \triangle DEF$. With a compass, check the third sides of the triangles for congruence.

6. Draw an acute triangle *RST*. Use the ASA test to construct a triangle *XYZ* such that $\triangle RST \cong \triangle XYZ$. Use your compass to check the two remaining sides of the triangles to see if the corresponding sides are congruent.

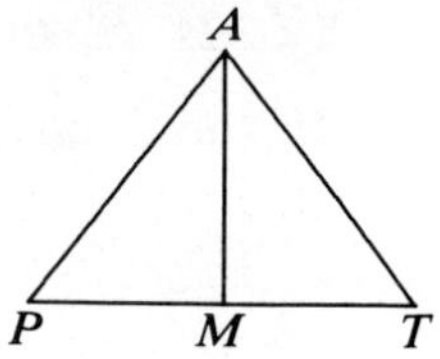

Ex. 7

7. $\overline{AM} \perp \overline{PT}$; $PM = MT$. Explain why $\triangle PAM \cong \triangle TAM$.

8. *LMNO* is a rhombus. Explain why $\triangle LMN \cong \triangle NOL$.

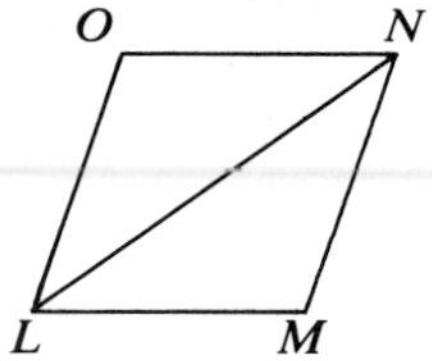

Ex. 8

For Exercises 9–12, name the congruent triangles, state which of the rigid motions (you may use more than one) are needed to match the vertices of the triangles, and explain why the triangles are congruent.

B **9.**

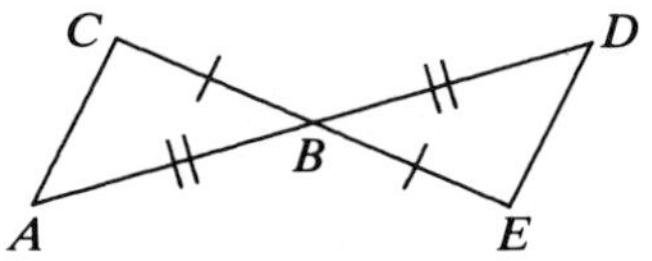

10.

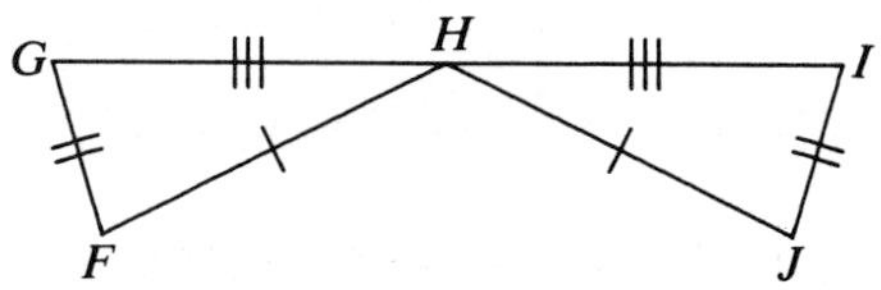

11.

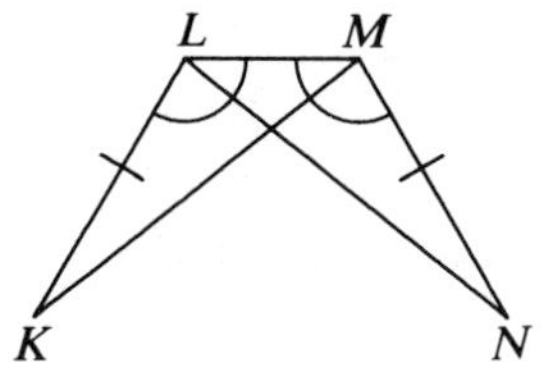

12.

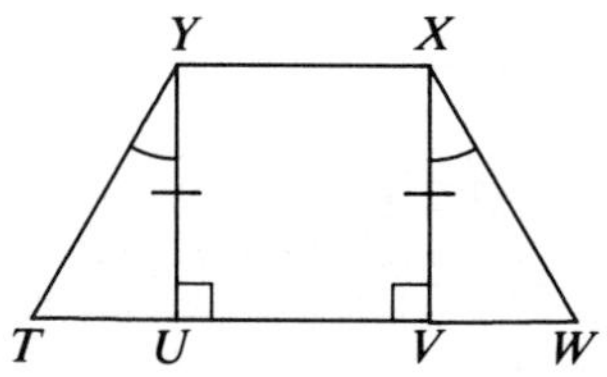

Name a pair of congruent triangles and explain why they are congruent.

13.

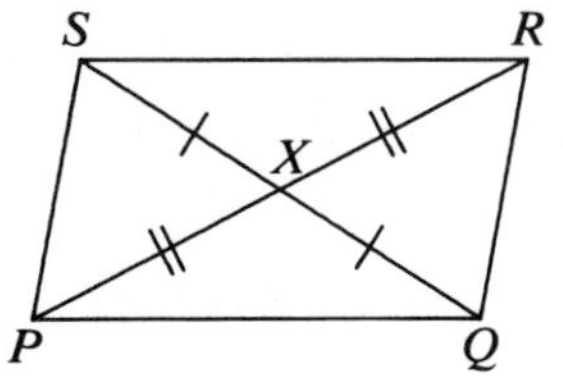

14.

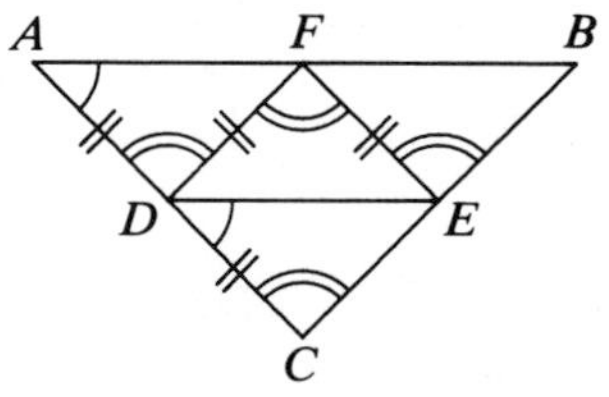

15.

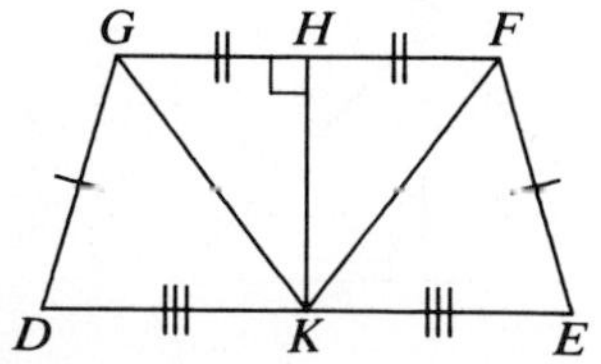

16.

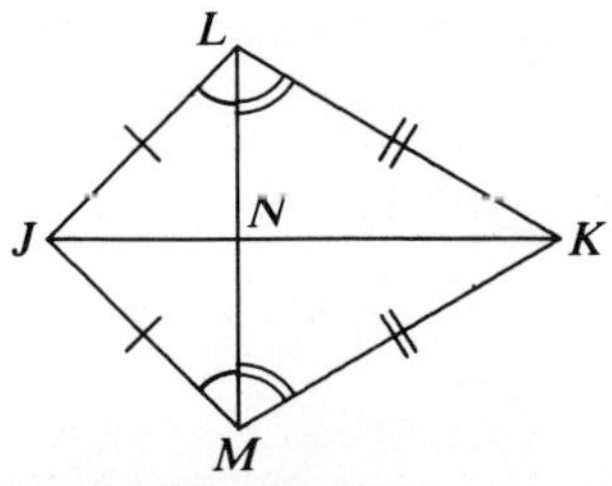

17. $FDCA$ is a parallelogram and $AB = ED$. Explain why $\triangle ABC \cong \triangle DEF$.

18. $FDCA$ is a parallelogram and $\angle ACB \cong \angle EFD$. Explain why $\triangle ABC \cong \triangle DEF$.

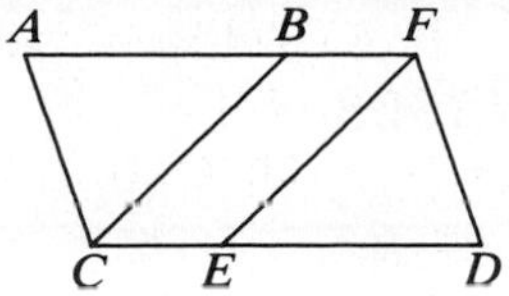

19. $\overline{RS} \parallel \overline{XY}$ and $XO = SO$. Explain why $\triangle XOY \cong \triangle SOR$.

20. $\overline{RS} \parallel \overline{XY}$ and $RS = XY$. Explain why $\triangle XOY \cong \triangle SOR$.

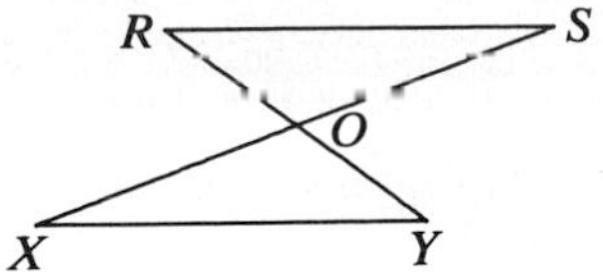

Self-Test B

Find the measure of each unknown angle in the triangle and tell whether the triangle is acute, right, or obtuse.

1. A scalene triangle with angles of measure 38° and 52° **[6-6]**
2. An equilateral triangle
3. An isosceles triangle with angles of measure 110° and 35°

***QTWX* is an isosceles trapezoid. *RSWX* is a rectangle.**

4. Find $m\angle XRS$. **[6-7]**
5. Find $m\angle XQR$.
6. Name a segment congruent to $\overline{XQ}$.
7. Name a segment congruent to $\overline{WS}$.

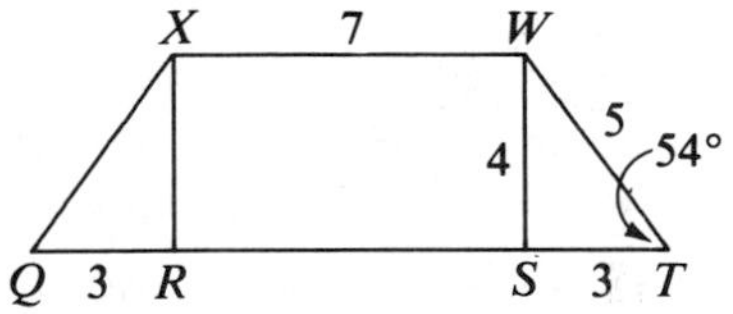

8. Find the perimeter of $QTWX$. **[6-8]**
9. Find the perimeter of $RSWX$.

10. If a regular pentagon has perimeter 321 cm, what is the length of each side?

True or false?

11. $\overline{RS} \cong \overline{BA}$ **[6-9]**

12. $\angle T \cong \angle C$

13. This statement indicates the corresponding parts correctly:

$\triangle RTS \cong \triangle CBA$.

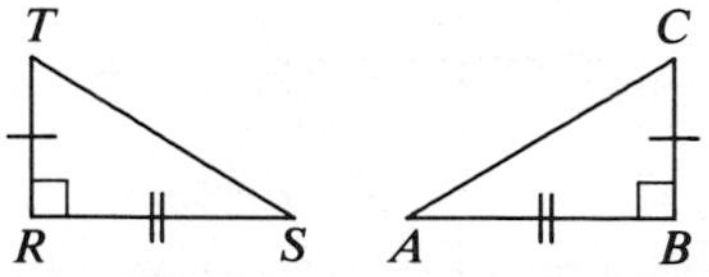

Self-Test answers and Extra Practice are at the back of the book.

Ellipses

An **ellipse** is a curve that is important in astronomy. The orbit of every planet in our solar system, including Earth, is an ellipse.

You can draw an ellipse with the aid of a piece of string, a pencil, and two nails driven into a piece of wood. Make a loop of string that fits loosely around the nails and put the pencil point inside the loop. Keeping the loop taut with the pencil, draw the largest closed curve you can. The resulting curve is an ellipse. Notice that for every point on the curve that you have drawn, the sum of its distances from the two nails ($p + q$ in the drawing below) is always the same. This is true because the loop has a fixed length. Every ellipse has two points corresponding to the nails above. Each of these points is called a **focus** (plural: *foci*) of the ellipse.

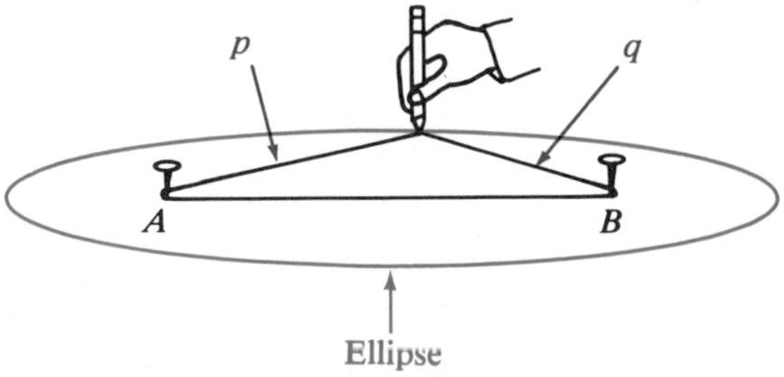

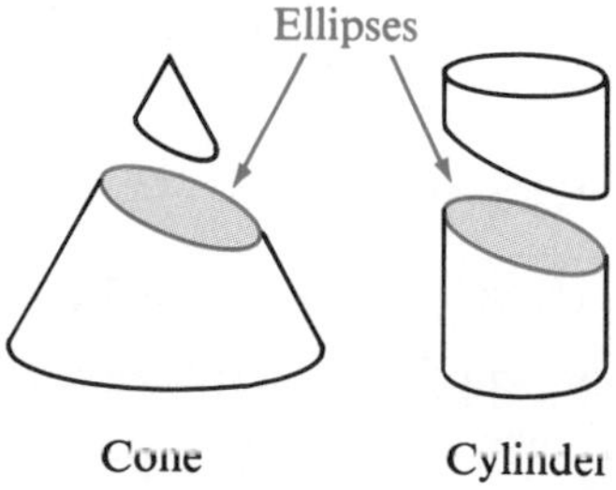

Ellipses occur as cross sections of common geometric solids as shown at the right above.

To illustrate an ellipse, shine a flashlight at a piece of paper. If you hold the paper at a slant through the "cone" of light, you will see an ellipse.

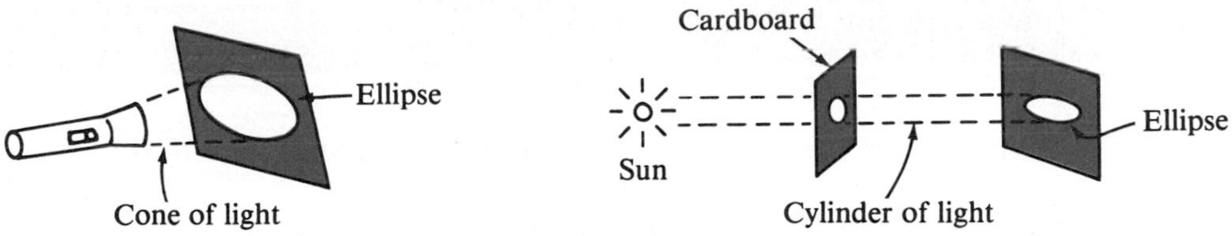

If you let the sun's rays shine through a circular hole in a piece of cardboard and hold a piece of paper at a slant through the "cylinder" of light, you will also see an ellipse.

1. Using an old piece of wood, draw an ellipse using the string method described. Start with a fairly large loop of string. Then shorten the loop by tying a small knot in it and draw another ellipse using the same nails as foci.

2. Make an ellipse by either the flashlight method or the sunlight method described above. Vary the dimensions of the ellipse by changing the slant of the sheet of paper.

3. You can also make an ellipse by folding paper. First cut out a circle of paper. Mark the center of the circle and any other point P inside the circle. Then fold the circle so that the edge just touches the point P and make a crease. Unfold the circle and then repeat the folding process several times, folding from a different direction each time. Do you see an ellipse after making several folds? What appear to be its foci?

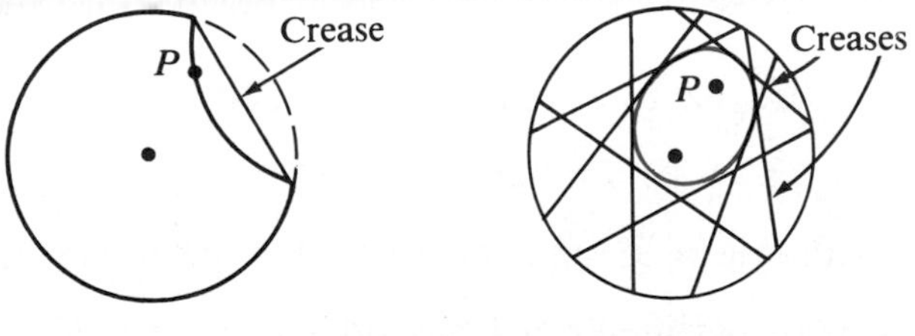

Career Activity

Astronomical instruments have changed greatly since the first telescope was invented in the 1600's. If you were an astronomer today, what are some of the instruments that you might be using?

Chapter Review

Complete. Use the appropriate symbols for segments, lines, and rays.

1. __?__ is a ray through point E that begins at point O. **[6-1]**
2. __?__ is a segment with endpoints A and E.
3. __?__ is a line through points A and C.
4. If the radius of a circle is 17, the circumference is __?__. Use $\pi \approx 3.14$. **[6-2]**
5. If the circumference of a circle is 37, the diameter is __?__. Use $\pi \approx 3.14$.
6. The measure of an obtuse angle is between __?__° and __?__°. **[6-3]**
7. The measure of an acute angle is between __?__° and __?__°.
8. Two angles that have a common side and a common vertex but do not overlap are called __?__ angles.

True or false?

9. Complementary angles have a sum of 90°. **[6-4]**
10. Supplementary angles are always congruent.
11. Vertical angles always have a sum of 90°.
12. Parallel lines meet in a single point. **[6-5]**
13. Alternate interior angles are always congruent.
14. $\triangle NOQ$ is an isosceles obtuse triangle. **[6-6]**
15. $\triangle QOP$ is a scalene acute triangle.
16. $m\angle QPO$ is 55°.

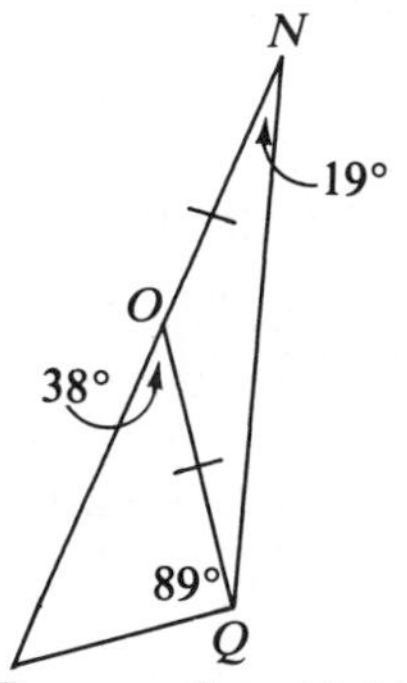

Exs. 14–16

17. Opposite angles of a trapezoid are always congruent. **[6-7]**
18. All sides and all angles of a rhombus are congruent.
19. A parallelogram with width 53 and length 84 has perimeter 272. **[6-8]**
20. A regular octagon with perimeter 564 has sides of length 70.5.
21. Two triangles are always congruent if three sides of one triangle are congruent to three sides of the other. **[6-9]**
22. Two triangles are always congruent if three angles of one triangle are congruent to three angles of the other.

Chapter Test

1. Draw a labeled diagram to illustrate points A, B, and C, $\overrightarrow{AB}$, $\overleftrightarrow{BC}$, and $\overline{AC}$. [6–1]
2. Draw any $\overline{LM}$ and construct $\overline{XY}$ congruent to $\overline{LM}$.
3. Draw a circle with radius $\overline{OM}$, a diameter $\overline{KL}$, and a chord $\overline{NP}$. Label an arc and a semicircle. [6–2]
4. Find the circumference of a circle with radius 42 cm. Use $\pi \approx \frac{22}{7}$.
5. Draw an obtuse angle and construct a congruent angle. [6–3]
6. $\angle GFH$ and $\angle EFG$ are adjacent angles. $m\angle GFH = 52°$. $m\angle EFG = 76°$. What is $m\angle EFH$?
7. $\angle XYZ$ and $\angle RST$ are supplementary angles. If $m\angle XYZ$ is 9° less than $m\angle RST$, what is the measure of each angle? [6–4]
8. $\angle ABC$ and $\angle DBE$ are vertical angles. $m\angle DBE = 62°$. Find $m\angle ABC$.

In the diagram, lines *l* and *m* are parallel.

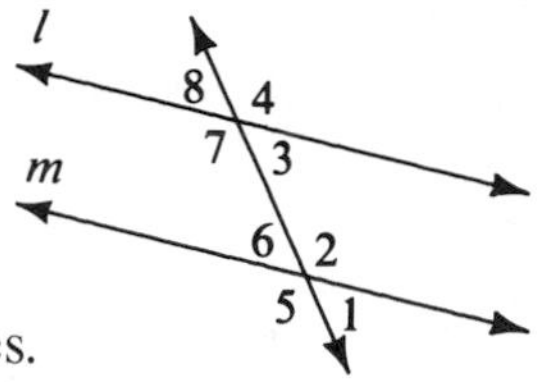

9. $\angle 3$ and $\angle$ _?_ are alternate interior angles. [6–5]
10. $\angle 6$ and $\angle$ _?_ are corresponding angles.
11. $m\angle 4 = 138°$. Find the other angle measures.
12. $\triangle OPQ$ is an isosceles obtuse triangle. If $m\angle QOP$ is 28°, what are the measures of the other angles? [6–6]
13. $\triangle RST$ is a scalene acute triangle. If $m\angle SRT$ is 64° and $m\angle STR$ is 77°, what is $m\angle RST$?
14. Name two quadrilaterals in which all sides are congruent. [6–7]
15. Name two quadrilaterals that have two pairs of congruent angles.
16. A regular decagon has perimeter 377.5. Find the length of a side. [6–8]
17. A rectangle has length 18 and width 12. Find the perimeter.

Are the triangles in each pair congruent? If so, name the triangles that are congruent and explain why they are congruent.

18.

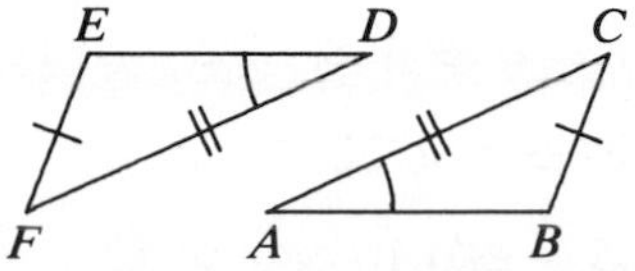

19. [6–9]

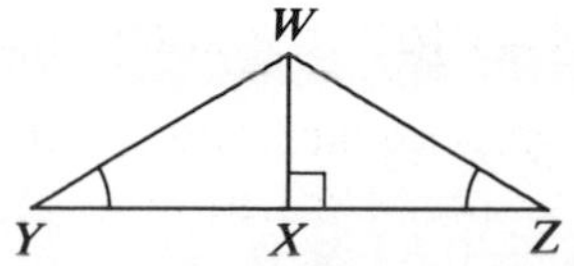

Cumulative Review (Chapters 1–6)

Exercises

Round to the nearest cent.

1. \$12.453 **2.** \$39.995 **3.** \$160.870 **4.** \$.955

5. \$821.099 **6.** \$.006 **7.** \$375.902 **8.** \$7.9048

Simplify.

9. $(36 + 18)y$ **10.** $x + 0.4x$ **11.** $\frac{500r}{5}$ **12.** $1200 \times b \times 0.3$

13. $4(a + 5a)$ **14.** $100n \div 2.5$ **15.** $1.6(n - 4.2)$ **16.** $\frac{14t}{40} \times 200$

17. $-9.7 + (-6.1)$ **18.** $6.14 + (-12.5)$ **19.** $-4.032 + 9.25$

20. $42.9 - (-3.7)$ **21.** $-3.4 - (-12.5)$ **22.** $-76 - 27.82$

23. -4.23×3.5 **24.** $-12.3 \times (-5.4)$ **25.** 13.5×24

26. $-64 \div 8$ **27.** $-30 \div (-12)$ **28.** $-28 \div 0.2$

Write the fraction in lowest terms.

29. $-\frac{84}{116}$ **30.** $\frac{20}{74}$ **31.** $-\frac{116}{164}$ **32.** $-\frac{36}{64}$ **33.** $\frac{24}{148}$

Express as a fraction or mixed number in lowest terms.

34. 0.45 **35.** 0.036 **36.** 2.01 **37.** 11.84 **38.** 4.832

Express as a decimal. Use a bar to indicate a repeating decimal.

39. $\frac{2}{3}$ **40.** $\frac{5}{11}$ **41.** $3\frac{5}{6}$ **42.** $2\frac{4}{9}$ **43.** $8\frac{1}{12}$

Express the repeating decimal as a fraction or mixed number in lowest terms.

44. $0.\overline{4}$ **45.** $0.8\overline{3}$ **46.** $1.\overline{3}$ **47.** $2.\overline{42}$ **48.** $5.2\overline{13}$

Solve the equation.

49. $b + 17 = 39$ **50.** $1.7 + x = 2.3$

51. $d - 65 = 104$ **52.** $526 - a = 438.5$

53. $n = 0.5 \times 38$ **54.** $1056 = r \times 22$

55. $44.688 = 0.84 \times q$ **56.** $2745.6 = 0.16 \times t \times 52$

Problems

Problem Solving Reminders
Here are some reminders that may help you solve some of the problems on this page.
- Consider whether drawing a sketch will help.
- Check by using rounding to find an estimated answer.
- Reread the question to be sure that you have answered with the information requested.

Solve.

1. The perimeter of an equilateral triangle is 45 cm. What is the length of each side?
2. A photographer works 35 h a week and earns $295. What is the hourly rate to the nearest cent?
3. Elena commutes to work. She travels 2.6 km by subway and 1.8 km by bus. How far is that in all?
4. The temperature at 11:30 P.M. was 7° below zero. By the next morning, the temperature had fallen 6°. What was the temperature then?
5. During one week, the stock of DataTech Corporation had the following daily changes in price: Monday, up $1\frac{1}{2}$ points; Tuesday, down 2 points; Wednesday, down $\frac{3}{4}$ of a point; Thursday, up $3\frac{1}{8}$ points; Friday, up $2\frac{3}{4}$ points. What was the change in the price of the stock for the week?
6. A rope 25 m long is cut into 2 pieces so that one piece is 9 m shorter than the other. Find the length of each piece.
7. Michael spent $16.00 on tickets to the game. Adult tickets cost twice as much as student tickets. If he bought 2 adult tickets and 4 student tickets, how much does each kind of ticket cost?
8. The difference between the measures of two supplementary angles is 8°. What is the measure of each angle?
9. The length of a rectangle is 5 cm greater than the width. The perimeter is 70 cm. Find the length and the width.
10. The two equal sides of an isosceles triangle are each 11 cm longer than the third side. The perimeter of the triangle is 58 cm. What is the length of each side?
11. The perimeter of a regular octagon is 121.6 m. What is the length of each side?

7

Ratio, Proportion, and Percent

Before the invention of the microscope, objects appeared to consist only of those materials seen with the unaided eye. Today the ability to magnify objects, such as the salt crystals shown at the right, has enabled scientists to understand the structures of various compounds in detail. The most advanced microscopes in use at the present time are electron microscopes. Electron microscopes can magnify objects hundreds of thousands of times by using beams of focused electrons.

The visibility of fine detail in a magnification depends on several factors, including the light and the magnifying power of the microscope. For a simple microscope, the magnifying power can be expressed as this ratio:

$$\frac{\text{size of the image on the viewer's eye}}{\text{size of the object seen without a microscope}}.$$

In this chapter, you will learn how scales and ratios are used.

Career Note

When you think of photography, you probably think of it as a means of portraying people and places. When used in conjunction with a microscope (photomicrography), or with infrared or ultraviolet light, photography can become an important research tool. Scientific photographers must have a knowledge of film, filters, lenses, illuminators, and all other types of camera equipment. They must also have a thorough understanding of scale and proportion in order to find the best composition for a particular photograph.

7-1 Ratio and Proportion

A **ratio** is an indicated quotient of two numbers. For example,

$$\frac{4}{6} \qquad 4:6 \qquad 4 \text{ to } 6$$

are three ways of writing *the ratio of 4 to 6.* Note that the first number is always divided by the second. We usually write ratios in lowest terms. Because $\frac{4}{6} = \frac{2}{3}$, the ratio of 4 to 6 is the same as the ratio of 2 to 3, that is, $4:6 = 2:3$. The terms of a ratio are usually whole numbers. Because $\frac{\frac{1}{2}}{5} = \frac{1}{10}$, the ratio of $\frac{1}{2}$ to 5 is the same as the ratio of 1 to 10.

Ratios can be used to compare two quantities. Example 1 illustrates that we must use the same unit of measure to express the ratio of two quantities of the same kind.

EXAMPLE 1 An airport runway is 120 m wide and 5 km long. Use a ratio to compare its length to its width.

Solution 5 km = 5000 m

$$\begin{array}{l} \text{length} \longrightarrow \\ \text{width} \longrightarrow \end{array} \frac{5000}{120} = \frac{125}{3}$$

The ratio of length to width is $\frac{125}{3}$, or 125:3.

Example 2 illustrates that we may use a ratio to compare quantities of different kinds.

EXAMPLE 2 Roger's car traveled 120 mi on 9 gal of gas. Express the ratio of miles to gallons in lowest terms.

Solution The ratio of miles to gallons is $\frac{120}{9}$, or $\frac{40}{3}$.

A **proportion** is a statement of equality of two ratios, for example,

$\frac{2}{5} = \frac{6}{15}$ or $2:5 = 6:15$. (Read *2 is to 5 as 6 is to 15.*)

The numbers 2, 5, 6, and 15 are called the **terms** of the proportion. The numbers 2 and 15 are called the **extremes** and the numbers 5 and 6 are called the **means.** Notice that

$$2 \times 15 = 5 \times 6.$$

The product of the extremes equals the product of the means.
In general,

Property

If $\frac{a}{b} = \frac{c}{d}$, or $a:b = c:d$, where $b \neq 0$ and $d \neq 0$, then $ad = bc$.

Since $ad = bc$ is an equation equivalent to the proportion $\frac{a}{b} = \frac{c}{d}$, we can use this property to *solve* a proportion. That is, we can find one term of a proportion when we know the other three terms.

EXAMPLE 3 The directions on a bag of concrete mix call for the addition of 3 qt of water to 40 lb of mix. How much water should be added if only 30 lb of mix is used?

Solution In planning the solution, ask yourself the following questions.

- What quantity is to be found?
  The amount of water needed for 30 lb of mix.
  Let w represent this quantity.
- Do the given facts involve any ratios?
  Yes, 3 qt of water to 40 lb of mix and w qt of water to 30 lb of mix.

Since ratios are involved, equate them in a proportion and solve.

$$\begin{array}{l} \text{water} \longrightarrow \\ \text{mix} \longrightarrow \end{array} \frac{3}{40} = \frac{w}{30}$$

$$3 \times 30 = 40w$$

$$\frac{90}{40} = w$$

$$2\frac{1}{4} = w$$

For 30 lb of mix, $2\frac{1}{4}$ qt of water are needed.

Problem Solving Reminder
After you read a problem, it is a good idea to *ask yourself questions* to help plan your solution. Notice how the two questions in Example 3 help to identify the problem as one that can be solved by using a proportion.

Class Exercises

State each ratio in lowest terms. The terms should be whole numbers.

1. $\frac{7}{14}$ **2.** 8:6 **3.** 2 to 1 **4.** $\frac{\frac{1}{4}}{6}$ **5.** A dozen to a pair

6. The number of days in a week to the number of days in June

7. The number of walls in your classroom to the number of doors

For each proportion (a) state an equivalent equation that does not involve fractions and (b) solve the equation.

8. $\frac{n}{8} = \frac{5}{2}$ **9.** $\frac{3}{n} = \frac{6}{10}$ **10.** $\frac{8}{5} = \frac{w}{15}$ **11.** $\frac{21}{15} = \frac{7}{r}$

a. State the quantity to be represented by a variable in the problem.
b. Set up a proportion whose solution would answer the question.

12. A recipe for 20 rolls calls for 5 tablespoons of butter. How many tablespoons are needed for 30 rolls?

13. A car goes 140 mi on 5 gal of gas. How many miles could it go on 7 gal?

Written Exercises

Write each ratio as a fraction in lowest terms.

A **1.** 35 to 28 **2.** 15 to 21 **3.** $\frac{24}{56}$ **4.** 132:36

5. $\frac{98}{49}$ **6.** 9 to 54 **7.** $\frac{5}{8}:\frac{1}{5}$ **8.** 1 to $\frac{1}{3}$

Compare the product of the means and the product of the extremes. Is the proportion true?

9. $\frac{4}{6} \stackrel{?}{=} \frac{9}{12}$ **10.** $\frac{6}{5} \stackrel{?}{=} \frac{12}{10}$ **11.** $\frac{9}{15} \stackrel{?}{=} \frac{12}{20}$ **12.** $\frac{1}{8} \stackrel{?}{=} \frac{7}{56}$

Solve each proportion.

13. $\frac{m}{15} = \frac{16}{20}$ **14.** $\frac{24}{n} = \frac{8}{7}$ **15.** $\frac{42}{14} = \frac{18}{c}$ **16.** $\frac{2}{9} = \frac{x}{36}$

17. $\frac{s}{14} = \frac{3}{4}$ **18.** $\frac{8}{3} = \frac{36}{d}$ **19.** $\frac{5}{4} = \frac{a}{2.4}$ **20.** $\frac{4}{n} = \frac{15}{10}$

B **21.** $\frac{2n}{8} = \frac{7}{10}$ **22.** $\frac{15}{4} = \frac{9}{2r}$ **23.** $\frac{9}{10} = \frac{3b}{5}$ **24.** $\frac{9}{4n} = \frac{1.5}{7}$

25. $\frac{11}{10} = \frac{x+2}{5}$ **26.** $\frac{n-3}{16} = \frac{5}{8}$ **27.** $\frac{24}{t+8} = \frac{5}{3}$ **28.** $\frac{7}{8} = \frac{35}{w-1}$

Problems

A **1.** Five cans of paint will cover 130 m^2 of wall space. How many cans will be needed to cover 208 m^2?

2. To obtain the correct strength of a medicine, 5 cm^3 of distilled water is added to 12 cm^3 of an antibiotic. How much water should be added to 30 cm^3 of the antibiotic?

3. A recipe that serves 8 calls for 15 oz of cooked tomatoes. How many ounces of tomatoes will be needed if the recipe is reduced to serve 6? How many servings can be made with 20 oz of cooked tomatoes?

4. A geologist found that silt was deposited on a river bed at the rate of 4 cm every 170 years. How long would it take for 5 cm of silt to be deposited? How much silt would be deposited in 255 years?

B **5.** Five vests can be made from $2\frac{1}{2}$ yd of fabric. How many vests can be made from 6 yd of fabric?

6. A fruit punch recipe calls for 3 parts of apple juice to 4 parts of cranberry juice. How many liters of cranberry juice should be added to 4.5 L of apple juice?

7. A bag of 3 lb of Fairlawn's Number 25 grass seed covers a 4000 ft^2 area. How great an area will 16 oz of the same seed cover?

8. A wall hanging requires 54 cm of braided trim. How many wall hangings can be completed if 3 m of braided trim is available?

C **9.** In a recent election, the ratio of votes *for* a particular proposal to votes *against* the proposal was 5 to 2. There were 4173 more votes for the proposal than against the proposal. How many votes were for and how many votes were against the proposal?

10. A certain soil mixture calls for 8 parts of potting soil to 3 parts of sand. To make the correct mixture, Vern used 0.672 kg of sand and 2 bags of potting soil. How much potting soil was in each bag?

Review Exercises

Write as a proper fraction in lowest terms or as a mixed number in simple form.

1. $\frac{60}{180}$ **2.** $\frac{48}{28}$ **3.** $\frac{54}{63}$ **4.** $\frac{105}{70}$ **5.** $\frac{66}{84}$ **6.** $\frac{107}{12}$ **7.** $\frac{79}{7}$ **8.** $\frac{62}{155}$

7-2 Rates and Problem Solving

Ratios that compare quantities of different kinds are also called **rates.** A rate is usually simplified to a *per-unit* form, that is, a form involving the ratio of some number to 1. The rate is then expressed simply as a whole number, a mixed number, or a decimal.

EXAMPLE 1 If a car travels 195 km in 3 h, what is its average rate of travel?

Solution

$$\text{rate} = \frac{195}{3}$$

$$= \frac{65}{1} = 65 \text{ (kilometers per hour)}$$

The car traveled at an average rate of 65 kilometers per hour (km/h).

When we know the rate of travel and the time someone has traveled, we can find the distance traveled by the following formula.

Formula

The distance d, traveled in time t, at a constant rate r, is given by

$$\text{distance} = \text{rate} \times \text{time}$$
$$d = rt$$

A rate of the form *distance per unit time* is often called **speed.** In Example 1, the average speed is 65 km/h.

EXAMPLE 2 A car made a trip of 225 mi at an average speed of 50 mi/h. How long did the trip take?

Solution Substitute 225 for d and 50 for r in the distance formula:

$$d = rt$$
$$225 = 50t$$
$$t = \frac{225}{50}$$
$$t = 4\frac{1}{2}$$

The trip took $4\frac{1}{2}$ h.

If a rate is the price of one item, it is called the **unit price.** For example, if 2 peaches sell for 78¢, the unit price is $\frac{78}{2}$, or 39, cents per peach.

EXAMPLE 3 If 5 oranges sell for 95¢, what is the cost of 12 oranges?

Solution *Method 1*

You can plan to find the price of one orange and then multiply by 12 to answer the question in the problem.

$$\text{unit price} = \frac{95}{5} = 19 \text{ (cents per orange)}$$

$$\text{cost of 12 oranges} = 12 \times 19 = 228 \text{ (cents)}$$

Method 2

Since the facts of the problem involve a rate and a rate is a ratio, you can plan to write a proportion for the statement:

If 5 oranges cost 95¢, then 12 oranges cost __?__ ¢.

Let c = cost in cents of 12 oranges.

$$\begin{array}{r} \text{oranges} \longrightarrow \\ \text{cents} \longrightarrow \end{array} \frac{5}{95} = \frac{12}{c}$$

$$5c = 95 \times 12$$

$$c = \frac{95 \times 12}{5} = 228 \text{ (cents)}$$

By either method, the cost of 12 oranges is 228¢, or \$2.28.

There is often more than one correct way to solve a problem. In Example 3, one plan used a per-unit rate and the other plan used a proportion. In Example 2 a formula was used, but the problem could also have been solved using the proportion $\frac{50}{1} = \frac{225}{t}$.

Class Exercises

a. Express each rate as a fraction.
b. Write the rate in a per-unit form.

1. Three melons for \$1.59

2. Two cans of tennis balls for \$5.88

3. 6 cans of water per 2 cans of juice

4. 28 bicycles sold in 7 days

5. 192.5 km in 3.5 h

6. A dozen eggs for \$1.08

7. Ten oranges for \$1.65

8. 225 m in 25 s

Solve each problem by (a) using a unit rate and (b) using a proportion.

9. A hardware store sells 8 stove bolts for $1.20. How much will 11 stove bolts cost?

10. If 720 pencils are packaged in 5 boxes, how many pencils are packaged in 7 boxes?

11. Light bulbs are selling at the rate of 3 for $2.07. How many bulbs can you buy for $4.83?

Problems

Give the unit price of each item.

A

1. 7 oz of crackers for $1.19

2. 14 oz of cottage cheese for $1.19

3. 5 yd of upholstery fabric for $80

4. 16 boxes of raisins for $5.60

Solve.

5. A certain kind of lumber costs $3.00 for 8 ft. At this rate, how much does a piece that is 14 ft long cost?

6. A package of 3 lb of ground beef costs $5.10. How much ground beef could you buy for $3.40 at this rate?

7. A car travels for 3 h at an average speed of 65 km/h. How far does the car travel?

8. A boat covers 48 km in 2 h. What is the boat's average speed?

9. A homing pigeon flies 180 km in 3 h. At this average speed, how far could the pigeon travel in 4 h?

10. A bicyclist travels for 2 h at an average speed of 12 km/h. How far does the bicyclist travel? At this speed, how long will it take the bicyclist to travel 54 km?

Determine the better buy based on unit price alone.

B

11. A can of 35 oz of Best Brand Pear Tomatoes is on sale for 69¢. A can of 4 lb of Sun Ripe Pear Tomatoes costs $1.88. Which brand is the better buy?

12. A can of Favorite Beef Dog Food holds $14\frac{1}{2}$ oz. Four cans cost $1.00. Three cans of Delight Beef Dog Food, each containing 12 oz, cost $.58. Which is the better buy?

13. Three bottles of Bright Shine Window Cleaner, each containing 15 oz, cost \$2.75. Two bottles of Sparkle Window Cleaner, each containing 18.75 oz, can be purchased for \$1.98. Which is the better buy?

14. A bottle of Harvest Time Apple Juice contains 64 oz and costs 99¢. Farm Fresh Juice is available in bottles that contain 1 gal for \$1.88 each. Which is the better buy?

Solve.

15. A car uses 3 gal of gasoline every 117 mi. During the first part of a trip, the car traveled 130 mi in 4 h. If the car continues to travel at the same average speed and the trip takes a total of 6 h, how many gallons of gasoline will be consumed?

16. Emily Depietro purchased 3 trays of strawberry plants for \$16.47. Emily also purchased 10 trays of ivy plants. If the ratio of the price per tray of strawberry plants to the price per tray of ivy plants is 3 to 2, what is the total cost of the plants?

C **17.** In the time that it takes one car to travel 93 km, a second car travels 111 km. If the average speed of the second car is 12 km/h faster than the speed of the first car, what is the speed of each car?

Review Exercises

Find the perimeter of a regular polygon whose sides have the given length.

1. pentagon, 4 cm
2. square, 6.2 m
3. octagon, 10.5 cm
4. triangle, 8.9 m
5. rhombus, 35.6 m
6. hexagon, 21.75 cm
7. quadrilateral, 14.35 m
8. decagon, 64.87 cm

7-3 Scale Drawings

A **scale drawing** is a drawing of a real object in which all lengths are proportional to the corresponding actual lengths. The scale of such a drawing indicates the ratio of length in the drawing to the actual length. For example, the scale

1 cm: 1 km

on a map means that a length of 1 cm on the map represents an actual distance of 1 km. Because 1 km = 100,000 cm, the scale ratio of distances on the map to the actual distances is $\frac{1}{100,000}$.

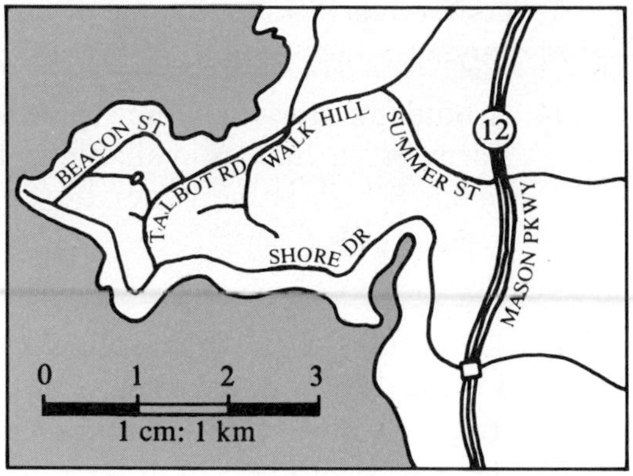

EXAMPLE A scale drawing of a car chassis uses the scale 1 cm:0.125 m. The length of the chassis is 42 cm in the drawing. What is the actual length of the chassis?

Solution Let n = the actual length. Write a proportion.

$$\begin{array}{r} \text{length in scale drawing} \longrightarrow \\ \text{actual length} \longrightarrow \end{array} \frac{1}{0.125} = \frac{42}{n}$$

$$n = 0.125 \times 42 = 5.25$$

The length of the car chassis is 5.25 m, or 525 cm.

Class Exercises

In the scale drawing at the right, the scale is 1 cm:2 m. Use the measurements on the drawing to find the actual length of each.

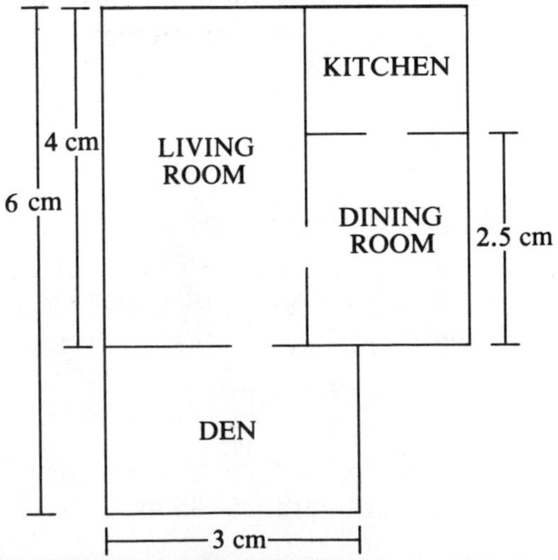

1. living room **2.** den

3. dining room **4.** entire house

A scale drawing uses the scale 1 cm:4 m. Find the measurement on the drawing.

5. The actual width is 6 m.

6. The actual length is 12 m.

Written Exercises

A scale drawing of a desk uses the scale 1 in. : 2.5 in. Find the actual measurement for the given measurement in the drawing.

A **1.** The width is 16 in.

2. The height is 15 in.

3. The depth is 9 in.

4. The depth of the lid is 6.4 in.

5. A leg is 0.8 in. thick.

6. A drawer is 7 in. wide.

A scale drawing of a solar heating system uses a scale of 4 cm : 1 m. Find the measurement in the drawing that corresponds to the given actual measurement.

7. The width of one solar panel is 1 m.

8. The height of one panel is 3 m.

9. The length of a vertical section of hot water pipe is 7.5 m.

10. The height of a hot water storage tank is 2 m.

Solve.

11. In a drawing, the length of an amoeba is 6.3 cm. The scale of the drawing is 1 cm : 0.1 mm. What was the actual length?

12. A drawing of a hummingbird has the scale 5 cm : 1 cm. The actual distance from the tip of the hummingbird's beak to the end of its tail feathers is 6.4 cm. What is this length in the drawing?

B **13.** A bicycle frame is to have the shape of a triangle ABC with the following measurements:

$m\angle A = 73^\circ$

$AB = 60$ cm

$AC = 58$ cm

a. Make a scale drawing of this triangle using the scale 1 cm : 4 cm.

b. What are the lengths in the drawing of $\overline{AB}$ and $\overline{AC}$?

c. By measuring $\overline{BC}$ in the drawing, determine the actual length of $\overline{BC}$ to the nearest centimeter.

14. A trestle bridge is to be constructed in the shape of an isosceles trapezoid $PQRS$ with these actual measurements:

$PQ = 40$ m $\qquad PS = 12$ m $\qquad QR = 12$ m

$m\angle P = 70°$ $\qquad m\angle Q = 70°$

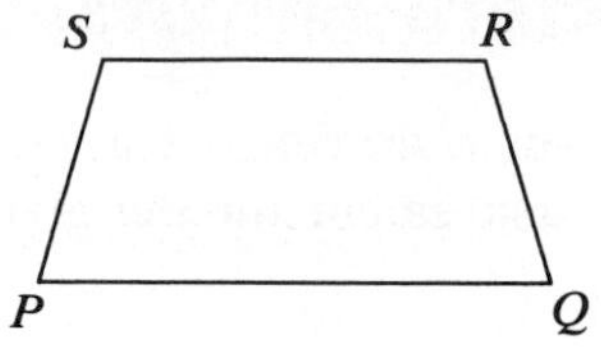

a. Make a scale drawing of the bridge using the scale 1 cm:2 m.

b. Use the scale drawing to determine the actual length RS to the nearest meter.

Review Exercises

Round to the nearest thousandth.

1. 0.3651 **2.** 0.6977 **3.** 46.7746 **4.** 321.0055

5. 60.0059 **6.** 4.01086 **7.** 99.9009 **8.** 6.00808

Computer Byte

The following program will solve a proportion. Note that -1 is used to indicate which term you want to find.

```
10  PRINT "INPUT TERMS IN THE ORDER SHOWN."
20  PRINT "USE -1 FOR THE MISSING TERM."
30  PRINT
40  PRINT  TAB( 5);"(1)"; TAB( 13);"(3)"
50  PRINT  TAB( 4);"----- = -----"
60  PRINT  TAB( 5);"(2)"; TAB( 13);"(4)"
70  PRINT
80  PRINT "INPUT TERMS";
90  INPUT A,B,C,D
100  IF A * D < 0 THEN 140
110  IF B * C > 0 THEN 20
120  LET N = (A * D) / ( - 1 * B * C)
130  GOTO 150
140  LET N = (B * C) / ( - 1 * A * D)
150  PRINT "THE MISSING TERM IS ";N
160  END
```

Use the program to solve. If your answer to Exercise 1 is not correct, check for a typing mistake.

1. $\frac{1}{2} = \frac{n}{4}$ **2.** $\frac{n}{12} = \frac{6}{8}$ **3.** $\frac{9}{n} = \frac{2}{3}$ **4.** $\frac{6.4}{8.4} = \frac{8}{n}$

7-4 Percents, Fractions, and Decimals

A **percent** is an amount *per hundred,* or a number of hundredths. The symbol for percent is %.

$$30\% = \frac{30}{100} = 0.30 \qquad 0.4\% = \frac{0.4}{100} = \frac{4}{1000} = 0.004$$

Note that

$$100\% = \frac{100}{100} = 1.$$

Percents greater than 100% name numbers greater than 1.

$$350\% = \frac{350}{100} = 3.5$$

EXAMPLE 1 Express 63.5% as (a) a fraction in lowest terms and (b) a decimal.

Solution **a.** $63.5\% = \frac{63.5}{100} = \frac{635}{1000} = \frac{127}{200}$

b. $63.5\% = \frac{63.5}{100} = \frac{635}{1000} = 0.635$

Short cut: Move the decimal point two places to the left and remove the % symbol.

EXAMPLE 2 Express each as a fraction in lowest terms.

a. $\frac{7}{8}\%$ **b.** $66\frac{2}{3}\%$

Solution **a.** $\frac{7}{8}\% = \frac{\frac{7}{8}}{100}$

$= \frac{7}{8} \times \frac{1}{100}$

$= \frac{7}{800}$

b. $66\frac{2}{3}\% = \frac{66\frac{2}{3}}{100}$

$= \frac{200}{3} \times \frac{1}{100}$

$= \frac{200}{300}$

$= \frac{2}{3}$

EXAMPLE 3 Express each as a percent.

a. 0.036 **b.** $\frac{3}{5}$ **c.** $\frac{1}{6}$

Solution **a.** $0.036 = \frac{36}{1000} = \frac{3.6}{100} = 3.6\%$

Short cut: Move the decimal point two places to the right and add the % symbol.

b. *Method 1*

$$\frac{3}{5} = \frac{n}{100}$$

$$5n = 300$$

$$n = \frac{300}{5} = 60$$

Thus, $\frac{3}{5} = \frac{60}{100} = 60\%$.

Method 2

Divide to express as a decimal first.

$$\frac{3}{5} = 0.6$$

Now move the decimal point two places to the right and add the % symbol.

$$\frac{3}{5} = 60\%$$

c. $\frac{1}{6} = \frac{n}{100}$

$$6n = 100$$

$$n = \frac{100}{6} = 16\frac{2}{3}$$

Therefore, $\frac{1}{6} = 16\frac{2}{3}\%$.

In part (c) of Example 3, dividing the numerator of the fraction by the denominator does not result in a terminating decimal. If we divide to express such a fraction as a percent, we must round the answer before writing the decimal as a percent.

EXAMPLE 4 Express $\frac{5}{7}$ as a percent to the nearest tenth of a percent.

Solution Divide to the ten-thousandths' place to express the fraction as a decimal.

$$\frac{5}{7} \approx 0.7142$$

Round the decimal to the nearest thousandth and then write the rounded decimal as a percent.

$$0.7142 \approx 0.714 = 71.4\%$$

Class Exercises

Express each fraction as a percent.

1. $\frac{1}{2}$ **2.** $\frac{1}{3}$ **3.** $\frac{1}{4}$ **4.** $\frac{1}{5}$ **5.** $\frac{3}{4}$ **6.** $\frac{2}{3}$

Express each percent as a proper fraction in lowest terms or as a mixed number in simple form.

7. 45% **8.** 8% **9.** 0.5% **10.** $\frac{3}{4}$% **11.** 175% **12.** 2.5%

Written Exercises

Express each fraction or decimal as a percent.

A **1.** 0.83 **2.** 3.62 **3.** 0.0052 **4.** 0.094

5. 4.72 **6.** 13.08 **7.** 0.003 **8.** 6.003

9. $\frac{4}{5}$ **10.** $\frac{7}{20}$ **11.** $\frac{3}{8}$ **12.** $\frac{5}{8}$

13. $\frac{11}{40}$ **14.** $\frac{9}{16}$ **15.** $\frac{5}{6}$ **16.** $\frac{7}{9}$

Express each fraction as a percent to the nearest tenth of a percent.

17. $\frac{5}{11}$ **18.** $\frac{9}{22}$ **19.** $\frac{3}{14}$ **20.** $\frac{7}{12}$

21. $\frac{15}{19}$ **22.** $\frac{1}{21}$ **23.** $\frac{6}{13}$ **24.** $\frac{4}{9}$

Express each percent as (a) a proper fraction in lowest terms or a mixed number in simple form and (b) a decimal.

25. 36% **26.** 75% **27.** 248% **28.** 1.25% **29.** 0.45%

30. 150% **31.** 2.8% **32.** 0.6% **33.** 5.75% **34.** 12.5%

Express each percent as a proper fraction in lowest terms.

35. $\frac{3}{8}$% **36.** $\frac{2}{5}$% **37.** $\frac{5}{6}$% **38.** $\frac{7}{9}$% **39.** $3\frac{1}{5}$%

40. $14\frac{7}{8}$% **41.** $16\frac{2}{3}$% **42.** $33\frac{1}{3}$% **43.** $11\frac{1}{9}$% **44.** $24\frac{1}{6}$%

Replace _?_ with <, >, or = to make a true statement.

B **45.** $\frac{7}{8}$ _?_ 78% **46.** 0.5 _?_ 50% **47.** 0.02 _?_ 20%

Replace $\underline{?}$ with $<$, $>$, or $=$ to make a true statement.

48. $\frac{2}{3}$ $\underline{?}$ $66\frac{2}{3}\%$

49. 0.25 $\underline{?}$ 2.5%

50. $\frac{5}{8}$ $\underline{?}$ 62.5%

51. 9.5 $\underline{?}$ 950%

52. 4.6 $\underline{?}$ 46%

53. $\frac{4}{9}$ $\underline{?}$ $44\frac{4}{9}\%$

Problems

Write a fraction and a percent for each. Round to the nearest tenth of a percent when necessary.

A **1.** At the Sailboat Restaurant 7 out of 10 people ordered the seafood special.

2. Julia completed 8 out of 12 projects without extra help.

3. In the hockey playoffs, the Silver Skates won 3 out of 5 games.

4. In a consumer opinion survey, 400 out of 1000 people preferred liquid soap to bar soap.

5. The average person spends 8 out of every 24 hours sleeping.

6. In a class of 178 students, 49 tried out for the class play.

Review Exercises

Solve.

1. $n - 12 = 3$

2. $r + 16 = 49$

3. $56.45 - p = 16.94$

4. $y - 12.75 = 8.90$

5. $-4 + 9 = 15 + m$

6. $18 + b = 43 - 9$

7. $4x + 21.50 = 5x$

8. $t - 2t = -35.98$

Challenge

You have taken a part-time job at a nearby shopping mall. Your assignment is to hand out 500 advertising leaflets. You have decided to work in a pattern. You will hand out 1 leaflet on the first day, 2 on the second day, 4 on the third day, 8 on the fourth day, and so on. How many days will it take to complete your assignment?

7-5 Working with Percents

When we say *38% of 50 is 19,* we mean

$$\frac{38}{100} \times 50 = 19 \qquad \text{or} \qquad 0.38 \times 50 = 19.$$

The percent, 38%, is called the **rate,** r.
The word "of" indicates multiplication.
The number, 50, following the word "of" is called the **base,** b.
The number, 19, that is the product of the rate and the base is called the **percentage,** p.

Formula

percentage = rate × base

$$p = rb$$

EXAMPLE 1 What is 18% of 35?

Solution p is to be found, r is 18%, and b is 35.

$$p = 0.18 \times 35 = 6.3$$

18% of 35 is 6.3.

EXAMPLE 2 What percent of 40 is 27?

Solution r is to be found, p is 27, and b is 40.

$$27 = r \times 40$$

$$\frac{27}{40} = r$$

$$r = 0.675 = 67.5\%$$

27 is 67.5% of 40.

EXAMPLE 3 48 is 16% of what number?

Solution b is to be found, p is 48, and r is 16%.

$$48 = 0.16 \times b$$

$$b = \frac{48}{0.16} = 300$$

48 is 16% of 300.

Sometimes when we use the formula $p = rb$, it is easier to rewrite the rate as a fraction.

EXAMPLE 4 56 is $66\frac{2}{3}\%$ of what number?

Solution b is to be found, p is 56, and r is $66\frac{2}{3}\%$, or $\frac{2}{3}$.

$$56 = \frac{2}{3}b$$

$$b = \frac{56}{\frac{2}{3}} = 56 \times \frac{3}{2} = 84$$

56 is $66\frac{2}{3}\%$ of 84.

Class Exercises

Identify the given numbers as percentage, rate, or base and tell which number is to be found.

1. 12 is 4% of what number?

2. What is 35% of 60?

3. What percent of 80 is 56?

4. 81 of 360 students at Jefferson Junior High are taking French. What percent of students are taking French?

5. 68% of the 300 people interviewed in an opinion poll were against a tax increase. How many people were against the increase?

6. One day the quality control department at the Sure-Fire Sparkplug Company reported that 35 plugs were defective. This is 0.25% of the daily output. What is the daily output?

Written Exercises

Solve.

A

1. What is 24% of 550?

2. 4 is 16% of what number?

3. What percent of 500 is 35?

4. What is 31% of 425?

5. 1.6 is 8% of what number?

6. What percent of 220 is 187?

7. 15 is 37.5% of what number?

8. What is 32.5% of 840?

9. What percent of 75 is 25?

10. What is 0.04% of 9936?

B 11. 27 is $16\frac{2}{3}\%$ of what number?

12. What is $33\frac{1}{3}\%$ of 162?

13. What is $\frac{1}{9}\%$ of 17?

14. 45 is $\frac{5}{6}\%$ of what number?

15. 52 is what percent of 78?

16. What percent of 126 is 42?

17. What percent of 84 is 147?

18. 33 is what percent of 4400?

Problems

Solve.

A 1. In one game a quarterback completed 13 of 25 passes. What percent of the passes were completed?

2. On a 75-question test Maureen got 84% correct. How many questions did she answer correctly?

3. 15% of the contents of a 454 g can of dog food is protein. How many grams of protein are in the can?

4. A town with a population of 27,530 has voted to allot 37.5% of the entire budget to education. If the education budget is $285,000, what is the total budget?

5. 12% of the total worth of a certain pension fund is invested in oil stocks. If $45 million is invested in oil stocks, what is the total worth of the fund?

6. A stereo system is marked with a price of $479. The sales tax on the system is $28.74. What is the sales tax rate?

B 7. On Saturday 78% of the breakfast customers at Mark's Restaurant ordered orange juice. If 33 customers did *not* order orange juice, how many breakfast customers were there altogether?

8. In a state with a 5% sales tax, a tennis racket cost $60.85, including tax. What was the selling price of the racket?

9. The Masons allocated 35% of their budget for housing and insurance, 15% for food, and 15% for education. If their total budget is $52,000, how much do they spend on other items?

10. A pair of jeans costs $8.00 to manufacture. If the designer, distributor, and wholesaler each add a 50% markup of the price paid, what is the final price of the jeans?

C **11.** In a student opinion poll at Polk Junior High, 27.5% of the students who responded chose football as their favorite sport. Basketball was chosen by 17.5% of the students who responded. Other sports were chosen by 44 people in the poll.
a. What is the total number of people who responded to the poll?
b. How many people preferred basketball?

12. The Sound Off Siren Company tests every fifth siren for sound quality and every eighth siren for mechanical quality. The daily output is 350 sirens.
a. What percent is tested for sound quality?
b. What percent is tested for mechanical quality?
c. What percent is tested for both types of quality?

Self-Test A

Write each ratio as a fraction in lowest terms.

1. $\frac{9}{15}$ **2.** 12:4 **3.** 16 cm to 2 m [7-1]

Solve each proportion.

4. $\frac{4}{a} = \frac{24}{18}$ **5.** $\frac{40}{100} = \frac{x}{6}$ **6.** $\frac{21}{n} = \frac{7}{18}$

Solve.

7. If 6 apples cost $1.50, how much will 10 apples cost? [7-2]

8. Ken drives for 2 h at an average speed of 55 km/h. How far does he travel?

A map uses the scale 1 cm : 190 km. Find the actual distance for each distance on the map.

9. 3 cm **10.** 6.5 cm **11.** 14 cm [7-3]

Express each fraction or decimal as a percent.

12. 0.66 **13.** 0.327 **14.** $2\frac{1}{2}$ **15.** $\frac{1}{6}$ [7-4]

Solve.

16. What is 12% of 37? **17.** 12 is 24% of what number? [7-5]

18. What percent of 81 is 27? **19.** What is $\frac{1}{5}$% of 885?

Self-Test answers and Extra Practice are at the back of the book.

7-6 Percent of Increase and Decrease

Many everyday problems involve the **percent of change** in a given quantity. Whether the change is an increase or a decrease, the amount of change is always a percentage of the *original* amount, not of the new amount. The formula $p = r \times b$ is easily applied:

amount of change (p) = percent of change (r) $\times$ original amount (b)

EXAMPLE 1 The selling price of a baseball glove was \$32.50. After sales tax was added, the total cost was \$33.80. What percent of the selling price was the tax?

Solution *Method 1*

First subtract to find the amount of tax.

$$33.80 - 32.50 = 1.30$$

Then express the amount of tax as a percent of the selling price.

$$1.30 = r \times 32.50$$

$$r = \frac{1.30}{32.50}$$

$$r = 0.04 = 4\%$$

Method 2

First express the total cost as a percent of the selling price.

$$33.80 = r \times 32.50$$

$$r = \frac{33.80}{32.50}$$

$$r = 1.04 = 104\%$$

Because the total cost is 104% of the selling price, the tax is

$$104\% - 100\% = 4\%.$$

By either method, the tax is 4% of the selling price.

Problem Solving Reminder

When planning your solution, remember that there are often *alternate methods of solution.* In Example 1, one plan subtracted first to find the amount of change and then used the formula to find the percent. The other plan applied the formula first and then subtracted to find the percent.

EXAMPLE 2 A share of stock in the Bonanza Gold Mine sold for \$15 at the beginning of one day and dropped 32% by the end of the day. What was the price at the end of the day?

Solution *Method 1*

First use the formula $p = rb$ to find the amount of the decrease.

$$p = 0.32 \times 15 = 4.80$$

Then subtract the decrease from the original price.

$$15 - 4.80 = 10.20$$

Method 2

Because the change is a decrease of 32%, the new price is 100% − 32%, or 68%, of the original price.

$$p = 0.68 \times 15 = 10.20$$

By either method, the price at the end of the day was \$10.20.

EXAMPLE 3 The number of people who attended the Wildcats' basketball game on Wednesday was 20% lower than the number of people who attended on Friday. On Wednesday 612 people attended the game. How many people attended on Friday?

Solution Because the change is a decrease of 20%, the number of people on Wednesday is 100% − 20%, or 80%, of the number of people on Friday. Therefore,

$$612 = 0.80b$$

$$b = \frac{612}{0.80} = 765$$

On Friday, 765 people attended the game.

Problems

A 1. The selling price of a bicycle that had sold for \$220 last year was increased by 15%. What is the new price?

2. The weight of a granola bar was decreased by 20%. What is the new weight if the original weight was 4.5 oz?

3. The membership in the Fair Oaks Chess Club increased from 256 to 288. What is the percent of increase?

4. Orders for milling machines from Precision Machine Company dropped from 150 one year to 123 the next. What is the percent of decrease?

5. The fuel economy in the new Desert Rat 2000 compact wagon is advertised to be a 24% increase over the old model. If the new model gets 31 miles per gallon, what was the fuel economy of the old model?

6. After a 16% increase, the price of a pair of running shoes was \$40.60. What was the old price of the shoes?

7. The Calorie count of a container of Seaside Cottage Cheese was reduced by 8% to 414 Calories. What was the old Calorie count?

8. The number of seats on the new Icarus 525 airliner is a 36% increase over the old model. The new plane seats 374 passengers. How many passengers did the old model seat?

B 9. Last year the population of Spoon Forks grew from 1250 to 1300. If the population of the town grows by the same percent this year, what will the population be?

10. This year, Village Realty sold 289 homes. Last year the realty sold 340 homes. If sales decrease by the same percent next year, many homes can Village Realty expect to sell?

C 11. Contributions to the annual Grayson School fund raising campaign were 10% greater in 1984 than they were in 1983. In 1983, contributions were 15% greater than they were in 1982. If contributions for 1984 total \$8855, what was the total in 1982?

12. In July the price of a gallon of gasoline at Quick Sale Service Station rose 12%. In August it fell 15% of its final July price, ending the month at \$1.19. What was its price at the beginning of July?

Review Exercises

Solve.

1. $p = 0.36 \times 27$ **2.** $1.89 = r \times 7$ **3.** $144.5 = 8.5n$

4. $21.65 \times 0.7 = m$ **5.** $156 = 0.3q$ **6.** $a \times 0.15 = 4.125$

7. $\frac{x}{21} = 10.5$ **8.** $91.53 \times 0.4 = t$ **9.** $\frac{324}{y} = 8100$

7-7 Commissions, Discounts, Royalties

Percents are important in business and consumer situations. The following terms are frequently associated with percents.

Commission An amount paid to a salesperson, often in addition to a regular salary, for selling an item or service. The **rate of commission** is generally a percent of the value of the sales that the person makes.

Royalty An amount paid to the creator or owner of a musical or literary work, an invention, or a service. The **royalty rate** is a percent of the money earned by the sale of the creation or service.

Discount A reduction in the original price of an item or service. The **discount rate** is a percent of the original price. The new, lower price is called the **sale price,** or the **net price.**

EXAMPLE 1 Last year Jonathan Stubbs received a commission of \$18,000 on sales of appliances totaling \$225,000. What was his rate of commission?

Solution Use the formula $p = rb$.
r is to be found, p is \$18,000, and b is \$225,000.

$$18{,}000 = r \times 225{,}000$$

$$r = \frac{18{,}000}{225{,}000} = 0.08 = 8\%$$

Jonathan's rate of commission is 8%.

EXAMPLE 2 Nina Boldoni receives a royalty of 15% of the selling price of each of her record albums. The recording company receives the remaining portion of the selling price. What is the selling price of each album if the company receives \$9.52 for each album sold?

Solution Because Nina receives 15% of the selling price, the record company receives 100% − 15%, or 85%, of the selling price.
Therefore,

$$9.52 = 0.85b$$

$$b = \frac{9.52}{0.85} = 11.2, \text{ or } 11.20$$

The selling price is \$11.20.

EXAMPLE 3 The sale price of a clothes dryer is \$252. The original price was \$288. What is the discount rate?

Solution Subtract to find the amount of the discount.

$$288 - 252 = 36$$

Then express the amount of the discount as a percent of the original price.

$$36 = r \times 288$$

$$r = \frac{36}{288} = 0.125 = 12.5\%$$

The discount rate is 12.5%.

Problems

A

1. A pair of slacks that sold for \$17.75 is on sale for \$14.91. What is the discount rate?

2. A video game system that sold for \$135 is discounted 24%. What is the net price?

3. A carpet salesperson receives a 6% commission on her sales. If her commission was \$216 last week, what was the total value of her sales?

4. A guitarist earns a royalty of 22% of the selling price of a record album. If he earns \$2.64 on each record album sold, what is the selling price of the album?

5. The author of a book on running receives a royalty of 75¢ per copy sold. If the royalty rate is 12% of the single copy price, how much money per copy does *not* go to the author?

6. The publisher of *Lost in the Jungle* receives \$12.60 from each copy sold. The remaining portion of the \$15 selling price goes to the author. What royalty rate does the author earn?

7. The discount rate on a coat at Adelphi Clothing is 30% of the original price. The sale price is $50.40. What was the original price?

8. The creator of a new game receives a royalty of 8% of the selling price of each game sold. The company that produces the game receives the remaining amount. If the company receives $10.10 per game, what is the selling price of the game?

B 9. A sales representative for Data Electronics earns a salary of $1314 per month plus a commission based on the total value of her sales. If she earns $1484.40 for the month and her sales totaled $5680, what is her rate of commission?

10. A radio that originally sold for $59.85 was discounted 15% in April. In May, the sale price was discounted 25%. What is the new sale price in May?

A real estate agent earns a commission of 6% of the selling price of a house. If the selling price is a multiple of $100 and the owner wants to keep *at least* the following amount, what is the minimum selling price?

11. $75,000 12. $69,000 13. $84,000 14. $91,000

C 15. An insurance salesperson earns a commission of 3% of the first $5000 of insurance that he sells each week and 4% of the value in excess of $5000. One week he earned a commission of $320. What was the total value of the insurance that he sold during the week?

16. At a clearance sale, a gas-powered lawnmower was discounted 32%. The lawnmower sold for $117.81, including a sales tax of 5% of the sale price. What was the original price of the mower?

Review Exercises

Explain the meaning of each term.

1. ratio 2. proportion 3. percent 4. rate

5. base 6. percentage 7. increase 8. decrease

Calculator Key-In

How can you use your calculator to solve the exercise without using the percent key and using only one of the keys +, −, ×, or ÷?

1. $25.00 + (5% of $25.00) 2. $43.99 − (15% of $43.99)

7-8 Percents and Proportions

You have learned to solve problems involving percents by using the formula $p = rb$. You can also use proportions to solve problems involving percents. The following discussion shows how we may write a proportion that relates percentage, rate, and base.

Consider the statement *9 is 15% of 60.* Because a percent is an amount *per hundred,* we can think of 15% as 15 per hundred, or the ratio of 15 to 100:

$$15\% = \frac{15}{100}.$$

Using the formula $p = rb$, we have

$$9 = \frac{15}{100} \times 60.$$

Dividing both sides of the equation by 60, we obtain the proportion

$$\frac{9}{60} = \frac{15}{100},$$

or 9 is to 60 as 15 is to 100.

Note that $\frac{9}{60}$ is the ratio of the percentage (p) to the base (b).

> Percentage, base, and rate are related as shown in the following proportion:
>
> $$\frac{p}{b} = \frac{n}{100},$$
>
> where $\frac{n}{100}$ is the rate expressed as an amount per hundred.

EXAMPLE 1 143 is 65% of what number?

Solution The rate, 65%, expressed in the form $\frac{n}{100}$ is $\frac{65}{100}$.

The percentage, p, is 143. Write a proportion to find the base, b.

$$\frac{p}{b} = \frac{n}{100}$$

$$\frac{143}{b} = \frac{65}{100}$$

$$65b = 100 \times 143$$

$$b = \frac{14{,}300}{65} = 220$$

EXAMPLE 2 In a recent survey, 38 of 120 people preferred the Bright Light disposable flashlight to other flashlights. What percent of the people surveyed preferred Bright Light?

Solution The question asks what percent, or how many people per hundred, prefer Bright Light.

Let n equal the number per hundred.
You know that p is 38 and b is 120.
Set up a proportion and then solve for n.

$$\frac{p}{b} = \frac{n}{100}$$

$$\frac{38}{120} = \frac{n}{100}$$

$$38 \times 100 = 120n$$

$$\frac{3800}{120} = n$$

$$n = 31\frac{2}{3}$$

In the survey, $31\frac{2}{3}\%$ of the people preferred Bright Light.

EXAMPLE 3 The price of a pocket cassette player has been discounted 25%. The original price was \$59. What is the sale price?

Solution The question asks you to find the sale price.

First find the amount of the discount.
p is to be found, b is 59, and n is 25.
Set up a proportion and then solve for p.

$$\frac{p}{b} = \frac{n}{100}$$

$$\frac{p}{59} = \frac{25}{100}$$

$$100p = 59 \times 25$$

$$p = \frac{1475}{100} = 14.75$$

The amount of the discount is \$14.75.

Next find the sale price.

$$59 - 14.75 = 44.25$$

The sale price is \$44.25.

Class Exercises

For each exercise, set up a proportion to find the number or percent. Do not solve the proportion.

1. What percent of 32 is 20?

2. 14 is 25% of what number?

3. What is 58% of 24?

4. A digital clock is selling at a discount of 15%. The original price was $8.98. How much money will you save by buying the clock at the sale price?

5. Catherine answered 95% of the test questions correctly. If she answered 38 questions correctly, how many questions were on the test?

6. This year, 360 people ran in the town marathon. Only 315 people finished the race. What percent of the people finished the race?

Written Exercises

Use a proportion to solve.

A **1.** What is 16% of 32?

2. 306 is 51% of what number?

3. What percent of 20 is 16?

4. What is 104% of 85?

5. 15 is 37.5% of what number?

6. What percent of 72 is 18?

Problems

Use a proportion to solve.

A **1.** The Plantery received a shipment of 40 plants on Wednesday. By Friday, 33 of the plants had been sold. What percent of the plants were sold?

2. The Eagles have won 6 of the 8 games they have played this season. What percent of this season's games have the Eagles won?

3. The library ordered 56 new books. 87.5% of the books are nonfiction. How many books are nonfiction?

4. This year 18.75% more students have joined the Long Hill High School Drama Club. The records show that 6 new students have joined. How many students were members last year?

5. A water purifier is discounted 20% of the original price for a saving of \$6.96. What is the original price of the water purifier? What is the sale price?

6. The original price of a Sportsmaster 300 fishing pole was \$37.80. The price has now been discounted 15%. What is the amount of the discount? What is the sale price?

B 7. Steve recently received a raise of 6% of his salary at his part-time job. He now earns \$38.69 per week. How much did he earn per week before his raise?

8. Since the beginning of the year, the number of subscriptions to *New Tech Magazine* has increased by 180%. The number of subscriptions is now 140,000. What was the number of subscriptions at the beginning of the year?

EXAMPLE This **pie chart,** or **circle graph,** shows the distribution of the Valley Springs annual budget. Use a proportion to find the measure of the angle for the wedge for education.

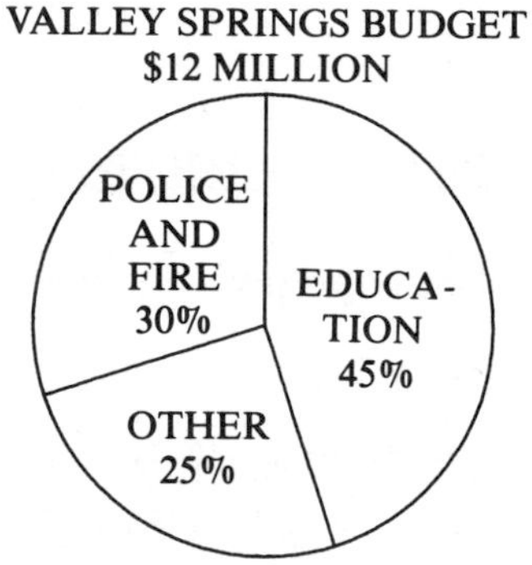

Solution The number of degrees in a circle is 360°. The circle represents the total budget. 45% of the total budget is for education. Therefore,

$$\frac{45}{100} = \frac{n}{360}$$

$$100n = 45 \times 360$$

$$n = \frac{16{,}200}{100}$$

$$n = 162$$

There are 162° in the wedge for education.

Use proportions to answer these questions about the pie chart above.

9. **a.** What is the measure of the angle for the wedge for police and fire expenses?
   b. How much money is budgeted for police and fire expenses?

10. **a.** What is the measure of the angle for the wedge for other expenses?
    b. How much money is budgeted for other expenses?

For Exercises 11–13, (a) use a compass and protractor to draw a pie chart to represent the budget, and (b) use proportions to find the dollar value of each expense.

C **11.** The monthly budget of the Miller family allows for spending 25% on food, 15% on clothing, 30% on housing expenses, 10% on medical expenses, and 20% on other expenses. The budget totals $1800.

12. The weekly expenses of Daisy's Diner total $8400. Of this total, 20% is spent for employees' salaries, 60% is spent on food, 5% is spent on advertising, 10% is spent on rent, and 5% is used for other expenses.

13. The Chimney Hill school budget allows 72% for salaries, 8% for maintenance and repair, and 5% for books and supplies. The remainder is divided equally among recreation, after-school programs, and teacher training. The budget totals $680,000.

Review Exercises

Write as a decimal. Use a bar to indicate a repeating decimal.

1. $\frac{1}{2}$ **2.** $\frac{1}{3}$ **3.** $\frac{1}{6}$ **4.** $\frac{1}{4}$ **5.** $2\frac{1}{4}$ **6.** $\frac{2}{3}$ **7.** $\frac{3}{4}$ **8.** $1\frac{5}{12}$

Computer Byte

The following program converts fractions with numerators and denominators from 1 through 15 to percents.

```
10  PRINT "FRACTION","PERCENT"
20  FOR A = 1 TO 15
30  FOR B = 1 TO 15
40  IF A < B THEN 60
50  PRINT B;"/";A; TAB( 17);100 * B / A;"%"
60  NEXT B
70  NEXT A
80  END
```

1. RUN the program to generate a list of fractions and their equivalent percents.

2. Change line 40 to IF B < A THEN 60 to generate a list of the reciprocals of the fractions in Exercise 1 and their percents.

3. Change the program to generate a list of fractions with any denominators and numerators and their percents.

7-9 Interest

Interest is money that is paid for the use of money that is borrowed or invested. If you borrow money from a bank, for example, the bank will charge you interest for the use of the money. On the other hand, if you deposit money in a bank or invest money in stocks or bonds, you are lending money and you will receive interest.

The amount of interest, I, depends on the three things listed below.

P, the **principal,** the amount borrowed or invested

r, the **annual rate** of interest, a percent

t, the **time,** in years, over which the money is used

In the simplest case, we use this formula:

Formula

Interest = Principal × rate × time

$$I = Prt$$

EXAMPLE 1 Martina Lopez deposits $11,500 in a six-month savings certificate at County Bank. She can make no additional deposits to the certificate during the six months that it is invested. At the end of six months, Martina will receive $603.75 in interest on her original deposit. What is the annual interest rate?

Solution Use the formula, $I = Prt$.
Because the rate of interest in the formula is the annual, or yearly, interest, express the time, 6 months, as 0.5 year.

$$603.75 = 11{,}500 \times r \times 0.5$$

$$603.75 = 5750r$$

$$r = \frac{603.75}{5750} = 0.105 = 10.5\%$$

The annual rate of interest is 10.5%.

Interest paid only on the original principal, as in Example 1, is called **simple interest.** Banks and savings-and-loan companies usually pay **compound interest.** That is, when interest is calculated, it is added to the original principal (or **compounded**). Thus the principal grows. The new principal is used in the next calculation of interest.

EXAMPLE 2 Roy Henderson has deposited \$2500 in a special Vacation Club savings plan through his company's credit union. The plan pays 8% interest, compounded quarterly. If Roy makes no additional deposits, what is the value of his investment after 9 months?

Solution For each interest computation, the rate is 0.08 and the time is 0.25 (one quarter of a year). Note that the principal changes after each three months.

For the first three months: $P = 2500 \quad r = 0.08 \quad t = 0.25$
$I = 2500 \times 0.08 \times 0.25 = 50$

For the second 3 months: $P = 2500 + 50 = 2550$
$I = 2550 \times 0.08 \times 0.25 = 51$

For the third 3 months: $P = 2550 + 51 = 2601$
$I = 2601 \times 0.08 \times 0.25 = 52.02$

$2601 + 52.02 = 2653.02$

The value of the investment after 9 months is \$2653.02.

Reading Mathematics: *Vocabulary*
Interest problems often use expressions describing time. Use the meanings of common word parts, such as the prefix *semi-* ("half"), the root *-annu-* ("year"), and the suffix *-ly* ("happening each," or "once per") to remember the meanings of these terms: *annually* ("once per year"), *semiannually* ("once per half year," or "twice a year"), *quarterly* ("once per quarter," or "4 times a year"), and *monthly* ("once per month").

Problems

Complete the following table.

	Amount Borrowed	Annual Rate	Time	Simple Interest
A **1.**	\$4000	7.5%	2 years	?
2.	\$ 150	8%	3 years	?
3.	\$6000	?	18 months	\$1125
4.	\$1250	?	30 months	\$500
5.	\$4800	9%	?	\$2160
6.	?	12%	3 years	\$342

7. A loan of $6400 at 12.5% simple interest is to be repaid in $4\frac{1}{2}$ years. What is the total amount to be repaid?

8. A $6500 automobile loan is to be repaid in 3 years. The total amount to be repaid is $9230. If the interest were simple interest, what would be the annual rate?

9. Mac Deweese invested $3500 in a money market fund that pays 8.5% compounded quarterly. If he makes no deposits or withdrawals, how much money will be in the fund at the end of 6 months?

10. Al Grey borrowed $8000 at 9% compounded semiannually. When the entire interest and principal are repaid at the end of two years, how much will Al owe?

11. A savings account was opened with $4000. The bank pays $5\frac{1}{2}$% interest, compounded monthly. How much money is in the account after 4 months?

12. You borrow $2500 at 16% interest, compounded semiannually. No interest is due until you repay the loan. If you repay the loan at the end of 18 months, how much will you pay?

13. Steve Burgess and Sarah Keller each invested in 3-month savings certificates that pay simple interest. They made no other deposits or withdrawals. Steve invested $8000 at an annual rate of 8%. Sarah invested $7600 at an annual rate of 8.2%. Who had the greater amount of money after 3 months?

14. Julian Dolby invested $5000 in a special savings account that pays 8% interest, compounded quarterly. How long must Julian keep his money in the account to earn at least $250 in interest?

B 15. Anita Ramirez owns two bonds, one paying 8.5% interest and the other paying 9% interest. Every six months Anita receives a total of $485 in interest from both bonds. If the 8.5% bond is worth $4000, how much is the 9% bond worth?

16. Mike Robarts owns two bonds, one worth $3000, the other worth $5000. The $3000 bond pays 12% interest. Every 6 months, Mike receives a total of $530 interest from both bonds. What is the annual rate of the $5000 bond?

17. Ellen Holyoke borrowed $500 for three months. Interest was charged at a rate of 18%, compounded monthly. Ellen made a payment of $200 after the interest for the second month was compounded. How much did she owe at the end of the third month?

18. David Cho deposited $10,000 in a six-month savings certificate that paid simple interest at an annual rate of 12%. After 6 months, David deposited the total value of his investment in another six-month savings certificate. David made no other deposits or withdrawals. After 6 months, David's investment was worth $11,130. What was the annual simple interest rate of the second certificate?

C **19.** A savings account pays 5% interest, compounded annually. Show that if $1000 is deposited in the account, the account will contain

1000×1.05 dollars after 1 year,
$1000 \times (1.05)^2$ dollars after 2 years,
$1000 \times (1.05)^3$ dollars after 3 years, and so on.

Self-Test B

Solve.

1. Stuart increased his typing speed from 40 to 48 words per minute. What is the percent of increase? **[7-6]**

2. The number of books borrowed from the library in March was 25% greater than the number borrowed in February. If 744 books were borrowed in February, how many were borrowed in March?

3. Lin Hong receives an 8% commission on the selling price of each stereo system that she sells. What is her commission on a stereo system that has a selling price of $1498? **[7-7]**

4. A television that usually sells for $139 is discounted 15%. How much money do you save by buying the television at the sale price?

5. A pair of shoes with an original price of $37 has been discounted 25%. What is the amount of the discount? Use a proportion to solve. **[7-8]**

6. Jake received $35 for his birthday. He has $14.70 left. What percent of the money is left? Use a proportion to solve.

7. Erica borrowed $1800 for one year at 17% simple interest. What was the total amount to be repaid? **[7-9]**

8. You deposit money in a savings account and make no other deposits or withdrawals. How much is in the account at the end of three months if you deposit $350 at 6% interest, compounded monthly?

Self-Test answers and Extra Practice are at the back of the book.

Fibonacci Numbers

In the thirteenth century, an Italian mathematician named Leonardo of Pisa, nicknamed Fibonacci, discovered a sequence of numbers that has many interesting mathematical properties, as well as applications to biology, art, and architecture. Fibonacci defined the sequence as the number of pairs of rabbits you would have, starting with one pair, if each pair produced a new pair after two months and another new pair every month thereafter.

The diagram below illustrates the process that Fibonacci described for the first six months:

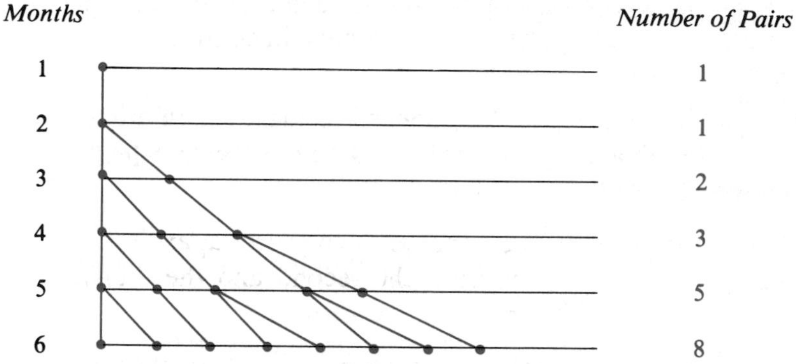

The sequence formed by the numbers of pairs is called the **Fibonacci sequence.** Note that any number in the sequence is the sum of the two numbers that precede it (for example, $2 + 3 = 5$, $3 + 5 = 8$). Thus the sequence would continue

1, 1, 2, 3, 5, 8, 13, 21, 34, 55, 89, 144, 233, 377, 610, . . .

To see one of the many mathematical properties of this sequence, study the sums of the squares of some pairs of consecutive Fibonacci numbers:

$$2^2 + 3^2 = 4 + 9 = 13$$
$$5^2 + 8^2 = 25 + 64 = 89$$
$$13^2 + 21^2 = 169 + 441 = 610$$

Note that in each case the sum is another number in the sequence.

The Fibonacci sequence also relates to a historically important number called the **Golden Ratio,** or the **Golden Mean.** The Golden Ratio is the ratio of the length to the width of a "perfect" rectangle. A rectangle was considered to be "perfect" if the ratio of its length to its width was the same as the ratio of their sum to its length, as written in the proportion at the right. If we let the width of the rectangle be 1, the length is the nonterminating, nonrepeating decimal 1.61828 . . . . Thus, the Golden Ratio is the ratio 1.61828 . . . to 1.

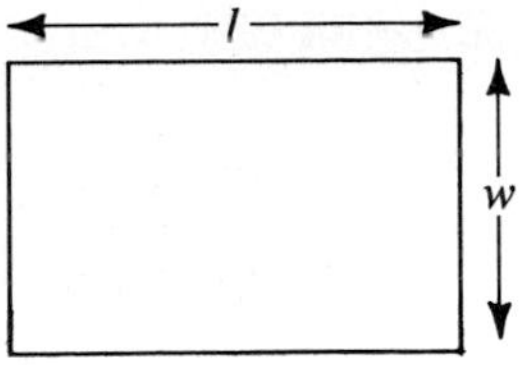

$$\frac{l}{w} = \frac{l + w}{l}$$

It is remarkable that the ratios of successive terms of the Fibonacci sequence get closer and closer to this number. For example,

$\frac{8}{5} = 1.6$ $\qquad$ $\frac{13}{8} = 1.625$ $\qquad$ $\frac{21}{13} = 1.615384\ldots$

$\frac{34}{21} = 1.61904\ldots$ $\qquad$ $\frac{55}{34} = 1.61764\ldots$ $\qquad$ $\frac{89}{55} = 1.61818\ldots$

1. Examine the fourth, eighth, twelfth, and sixteenth terms of the Fibonacci sequence. What do these numbers have in common? Try the fifth, tenth, and fifteenth terms.

Find some other numerical patterns by performing these calculations with the numbers in the Fibonacci sequence listed on the previous page. Tell what you notice about each new pattern.

2. Find the difference of two numbers that are two places apart in the sequence (the first and the third terms, the second and the fourth terms, the third and the fifth terms, and so on).

3. Subtract the squares of two numbers that are two places apart (as in Exercise 2).

4. Multiply two consecutive numbers (the first and second terms), multiply the next two consecutive numbers (the second and third terms), and then add the products.

5. Multiply two numbers that are two places apart (begin with the second and fourth terms), multiply two other numbers that "straddle" one of these (the first and third terms), and then add the products.

Career Activity Botanists have discovered that Fibonacci numbers occur naturally in many plant forms. For example, a pine cone is made up of 8 spirals swirling upward in one direction and 13 spirals swirling upward in the opposite direction. Find some other instances of Fibonacci numbers that botanists have found in nature.

Chapter Review

Complete.

1. If $\frac{14}{7} = \frac{8}{x}$, then $14x =$ __?__. [7-1]

2. If 3 cans of tuna cost \$3.27, the unit price is __?__. [7-2]

3. If Melissa drove 130 km at an average speed of 60 km/h, she traveled for __?__.

4. A map has the scale 1 cm:0.5 km. A map distance of __?__ corresponds to an actual distance of 12 km. [7-3]

5. 0.625 = __?__ % [7-4]

6. $\frac{3}{5}$ = __?__ %

7. 154% of 50 is __?__. [7-5]

8. 3 is 4% of __?__.

9. 17 is __?__ % of 20.

10. 8.5% of 400 is __?__.

11. A stock sold for \$18 per share two months ago. Today its price is \$15 per share. The percent of decrease is __?__. [7-6]

12. The Cortells' heating bill is 24% higher this month than last month. The bill this month is \$75.52. Last month the bill was __?__.

13. The price of a jacket was \$25. It has been discounted \$7.50. The discount rate is __?__. [7-7]

14. Claire Nolan receives a commission of 6% of her total sales. Last week her commission was \$34.32. The total value of her sales for the week was __?__.

Match the proportion to the problem.

15. The Ski Club has 50 members. If 36 members attend the ski trip, what percent attends the ski trip? [7-8]

A. $\frac{36}{100} = \frac{n}{50}$

16. There are 50 families on Jamie's paper route. If 36% receive the Sunday paper, how many families receive the Sunday paper?

B. $\frac{n}{100} = \frac{36}{50}$

True or false?

17. A savings account was opened with \$200. No other deposits or withdrawals were made. If the bank pays $5\frac{1}{4}$% interest compounded quarterly, \$226.25 will be in the account after 3 months. [7-9]

18. If George's aunt gives him a loan of \$650 for one year at 12% simple interest, George will owe \$728 at the end of the year.

Chapter Test

State each ratio as a fraction in lowest terms.

1. $\frac{46}{60}$ **2.** 16 mm to 3 cm **3.** 18:15 **[7-1]**

Solve each proportion.

4. $\frac{n}{63} = \frac{42}{27}$ **5.** $\frac{4.8}{r} = \frac{1.2}{3}$ **6.** $\frac{7}{21} = \frac{t}{9}$

7. A train travels 442 km in $5\frac{1}{2}$ h. Find the average speed. **[7-2]**

8. Country Market is selling 2 containers of yogurt for $1.18. How many containers can you buy for $2.95?

9. The actual distance between two cities is 340 km. A map that shows the cities has a scale of 1 cm:10 km. What is the distance on the map? **[7-3]**

Express each fraction or decimal as a percent.

10. 0.93 **11.** 0.0724 **12.** $\frac{25}{1000}$ **13.** $\frac{5}{8}$ **[7-4]**

14. What is 53% of 244? **15.** 1.6 is 8% of what number? **[7-5]**

16. 35 is what percent of 140? **17.** What is $15\frac{2}{3}\%$ of 60?

18. The total cost of a camera, including sales tax of 6% of the selling price, is $169.55. What is the selling price? **[7-6]**

19. Margaret Sherman's annual business expenses have increased from $2500 to $3175. What is the percent of increase?

20. A salesperson earns a salary plus a commission of 9% of total sales. How much is the commission on sales totaling $1654? **[7-7]**

21. A refrigerator was discounted 30% of the original price. The discounted price is $447.30. What was the original price?

Use proportions to solve Exercises 22 and 23.

22. The Pro Shop sold 6 of 20 tennis rackets in May. What percent of the tennis rackets were sold? **[7-8]**

23. This term, 36% of the students in one class are on the honor roll. If 9 students are on the honor roll, how many students are in the class?

24. You invest $500 at 6% interest, compounded monthly. If you make no other deposits or withdrawals, what is the value of your investment after 3 months? **[7-9]**

Cumulative Review (Chapters 1–7)

Exercises

Evaluate the expression if $x = 3$ and $y = 5$.

1. $x + y$ **2.** $2x + y$ **3.** $2y - x$ **4.** $x + 6y$

5. $y + x + 4$ **6.** $-x - y$ **7.** $-3x - 2y$ **8.** $5x + (-y) - 7$

9. x^2 **10.** xy^2 **11.** $(-x)^2y$ **12.** $-(xy)^2$

Write the numbers in order from least to greatest.

13. 3, −2.5, 0, −7, 6.4, −2.2 **14.** 4, −6.2, −7.3, 0, 3.5, 2.5

15. −1.6, −8.4, −3, −1.0, 0.5 **16.** −4.7, −11.9, 1, 3.8, 0.7, −0.6

Tell whether the statement is true or false for the given value of the variable.

17. $t - 3 \leq -6;\ -4$ **18.** $-m - 3 > 0;\ -3$ **19.** $2b < 3;\ 1$

20. $3 - x = 2;\ 5$ **21.** $n + 1 \geq -7;\ -6$ **22.** $r < -2r - 4;\ -2$

Write the fractions as equivalent fractions having the least common denominator (LCD).

23. $\frac{2}{3}, \frac{5}{9}$ **24.** $-\frac{3}{5}, \frac{7}{20}$ **25.** $-\frac{8}{3}, \frac{9}{11}$ **26.** $-\frac{5}{7}, -\frac{12}{17}$

27. $\frac{7}{3}, \frac{3}{4}$ **28.** $\frac{8}{45}, \frac{11}{75}$ **29.** $\frac{17}{32}, -\frac{3}{128}$ **30.** $\frac{3}{34}, \frac{5}{39}$

Solve the inequality and draw its graph.

31. $x + 1 \geq 2$ **32.** $\frac{1}{3}a < -3$ **33.** $6m < -18$

34. $\frac{3}{5}n \geq -6$ **35.** $4t + 1 > 13$ **36.** $4(w - 2) \leq 10$

State which of the rigid motions are needed to match the vertices of the triangles and explain why the triangles are congruent.

37.

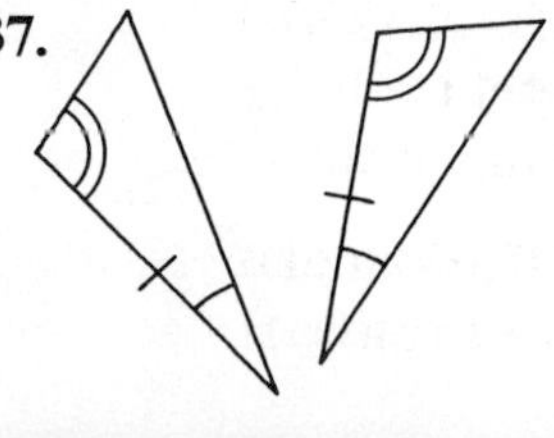

38.

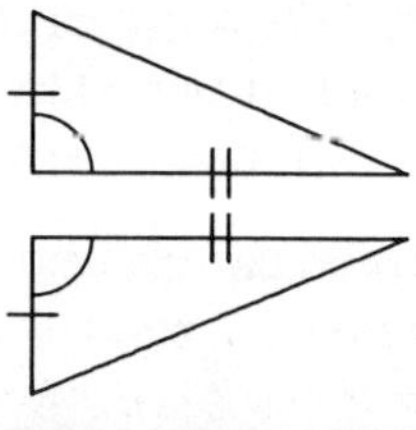

39.

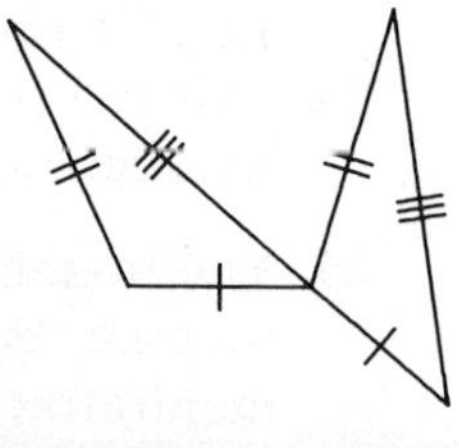

Problems

Problem Solving Reminders
Here are some reminders that may help you solve some of the problems on this page.

- Consider whether a chart will help to organize information.
- Supply additional information if needed.
- Reread the problem to be sure that your answer is complete.

Solve.

1. Donald bought a pair of hiking boots for \$35.83, a sweater for \$24.65, and a backpack for \$18. The tax on his purchase was \$.90. How much did Donald spend?
2. This week, Marisa worked $1\frac{1}{2}$ h on Monday, $2\frac{1}{4}$ h on Tuesday, $1\frac{1}{3}$ h on Wednesday, and $7\frac{1}{2}$ h on Saturday. How many hours did she work this week?
3. An airplane flying at an altitude of 25,000 ft dropped 4000 ft in the first 25 s and rose 2500 ft in the next 15 s. What was the altitude of the airplane after 40 s?
4. Carolyn Cramer spent 3 h and 15 min mowing and raking her lawn. She spent twice as long raking as she did mowing. How long did she spend on each task?
5. At a milk processing plant 100 lb of farm milk are needed to make 8.13 lb of nonfat dry milk. To the nearest pound, how many pounds of farm milk are needed to produce 100 lb of nonfat dry milk?
6. A highway noise barrier that is 120 m long is constructed in two pieces. One piece is 45 m longer than the other. Find the length of each piece.
7. The perimeter of a rectangle is 40 m. The length of the rectangle is 10 m greater than the width. Find the length and the width.
8. Oak Hill School, Longview School, and Peabody School participated in a clean-up campaign to collect scrap aluminum. Oak Hill School collected 40% more scrap aluminum than Longview School. Longview School collected 25% more than Peabody School. If the total collected by the 3 schools was 560 kg, how much did Oak Hill School collect?
9. Eladio invested \$200 at 6% annual interest and \$350 at 5.75% annual interest, both compounded annually. If he makes no deposits or withdrawals, how much will he have after two years?

8

The Coordinate Plane

One of the most fascinating aspects of computer science is the field of computer-aided design (C.A.D.). Computers are used to design a wide variety of goods ranging from televisions and cars to skyscrapers, airplanes, and spacecraft. Computers are also used to generate designs for decorative purposes, such as the rug pattern shown at the right. A particular advantage of using the computer is the ease with which the design can be prepared and modified. The designer may use a light pen to create the design on the computer screen and may type in commands to tell the computer to enlarge, reduce, or rotate the design. Although the actual programs for computer graphics are often complicated, the underlying idea is based on establishing a grid with labeled reference points. The grid is actually an application of the coordinate plane that is presented in this chapter.

Career Note

If you enjoy working with fabrics and drawing your own patterns, you might consider a career as a textile designer. Textile designers create the graphic designs printed or woven on all kinds of fabrics. In addition to having a good understanding of graphics, textile designers must possess a knowledge of textile production. Another important part of textile design is the ability to appeal to current tastes.

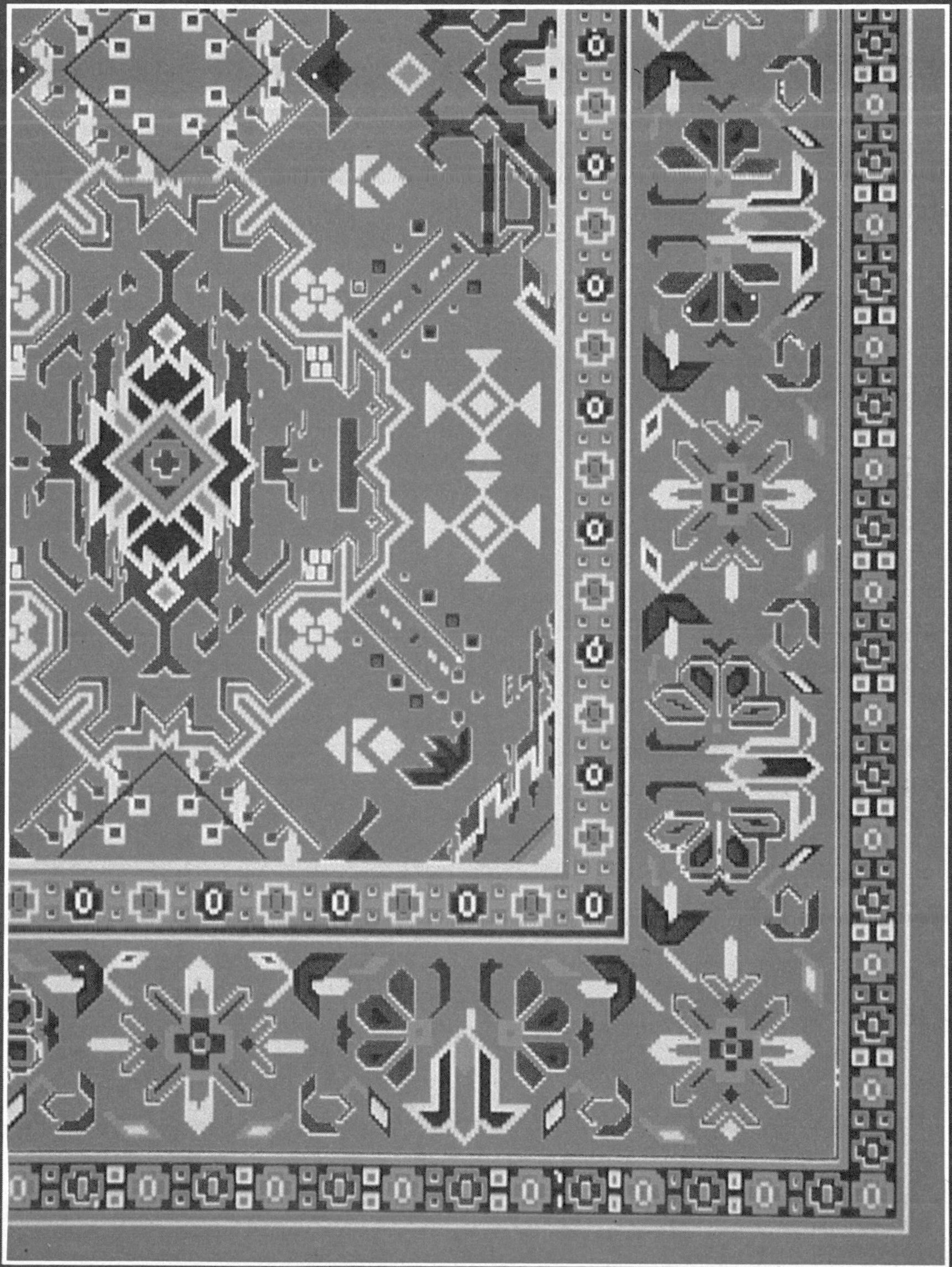

8-1 The Coordinate Plane

We describe the position of a point on a number line by stating its coordinate. Similarly, we can describe the position of a point in a plane by stating a pair of coordinates that locate it in a **rectangular coordinate system.** This system consists of two number lines perpendicular to each other at point O, called the **origin.** The horizontal line is called the **x-axis,** and the vertical line is called the **y-axis.** The positive direction is to the right of the origin on the x-axis and upward on the y-axis. The negative direction is to the left of the origin and downward.

Reading Mathematics: *Diagrams*
As you read text that is next to a diagram, stop after each sentence and relate what you have read to what you see in the diagram. For example, as you read the first paragraph next to the diagram below, locate point M on the graph, and find the vertical line from M to the x-axis.

To assign a pair of coordinates to point M located in the **coordinate plane,** first draw a vertical line from M to the x-axis. The point of intersection on the x-axis is called the **x-coordinate,** or **abscissa.** The abscissa of M is 5.

Next draw a horizontal line from M to the y-axis. The point of intersection on the y-axis is called the **y-coordinate,** or **ordinate.** The ordinate of M is 4.

Together, the abscissa and ordinate form an **ordered pair of numbers** that are the coordinates of a point. The coordinates of M are (5, 4).

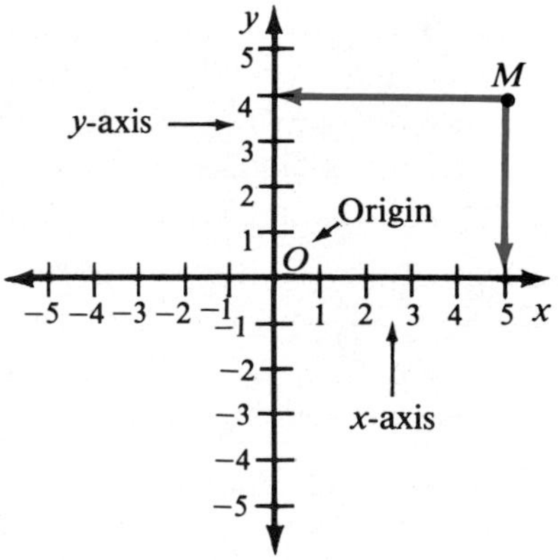

EXAMPLE 1 Give the coordinates of each point.
a. F **b.** S **c.** P **d.** T

Solution **a.** Point F has x-coordinate 4 and y-coordinate -3.
F has coordinates $(4, -3)$.

Similarly,

b. S has coordinates (0, 2).

c. P has coordinates $(-3, 4)$.

d. T has coordinates $(-5, -5)$.

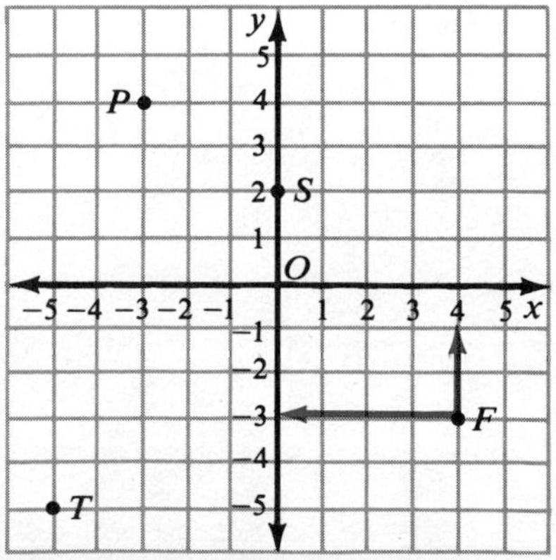

Notice that (4, −3) and (−3, 4) are coordinates of different points. In an ordered pair of numbers the x-coordinate is listed first, followed by the y-coordinate, in the form **(x, y).**

Just as each point in the plane is associated with exactly one ordered pair, each ordered pair of numbers determines exactly one point in the plane.

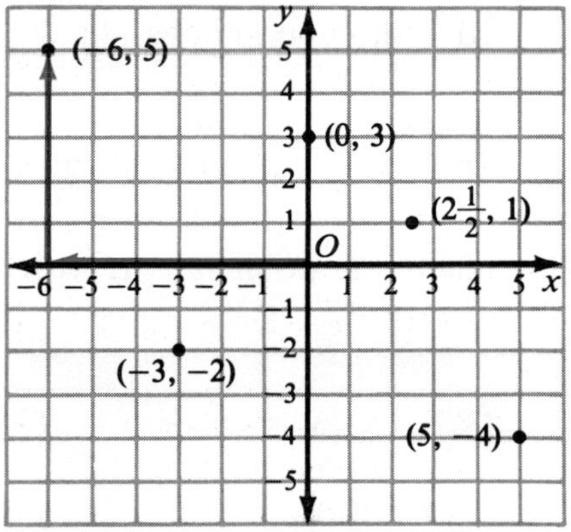

EXAMPLE 2 Graph these ordered pairs: (−6, 5), (5, −4), (0, 3), (−3, −2), and $\left(2\frac{1}{2}, 1\right)$.

Solution First locate the x-coordinate on the x-axis. Then move up or down to locate the y-coordinate.

The x- and y-axes divide the coordinate plane into **Quadrants I, II, III,** and **IV.** The ranges of values for the x-coordinate and y-coordinate of any point in each quadrant are shown at the right.

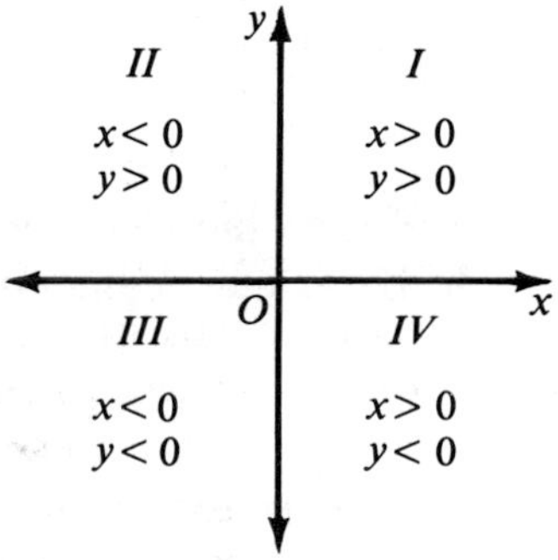

Class Exercises

Give the coordinates of the point.

1. A
2. K
3. E
4. J
5. L
6. F

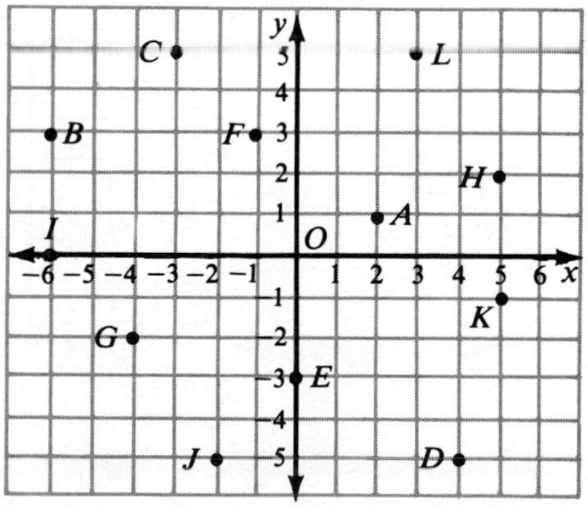

Name the point for the ordered pair.

7. (5, 2)
8. (−6, 0)
9. (4, −5)
10. (−4, −2)
11. (−3, 5)
12. (−6, 3)

Name the quadrant containing the point.

13. F
14. D
15. H
16. J
17. K

Written Exercises

For Exercises 1-18, use the graph at the right.

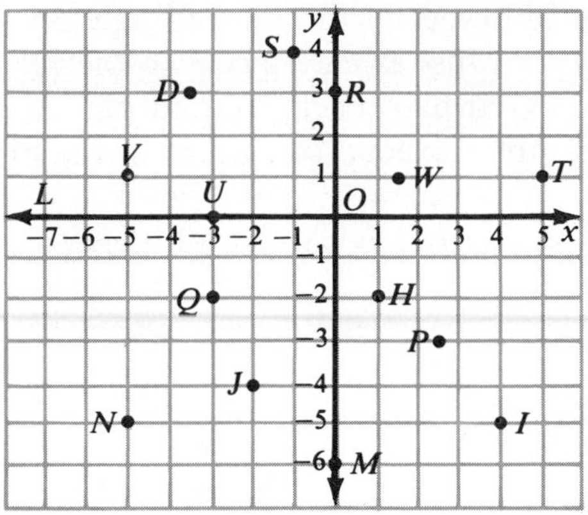

Give the coordinates of the point.

A **1.** N **2.** P **3.** T **4.** R

5. Q **6.** M **7.** S **8.** V

Name the point for the ordered pair.

9. $(4, -5)$ **10.** $(-3, -2)$

11. $(-5, 1)$ **12.** $\left(\frac{5}{2}, -3\right)$

13. $\left(-\frac{7}{2}, 3\right)$ **14.** $(1, -2)$ **15.** $\left(\frac{3}{2}, 1\right)$

16. $(-1, 4)$ **17.** $(0, -6)$ **18.** $(0, 3)$

a. Graph the given ordered pairs on a coordinate plane.
b. Draw line segments to connect the points in the order listed and to connect the first and last points.
c. Name the closed figure as specifically as you can.

EXAMPLE $(-3, -2)$, $(-1, 2)$, $(4, 2)$, $(2, -2)$

Solution **a.**

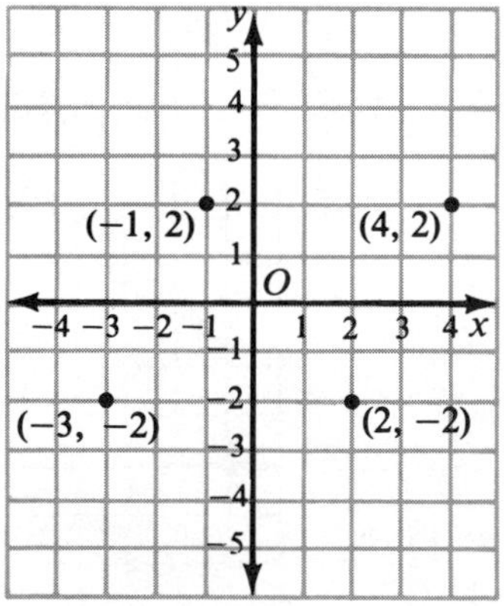

b.

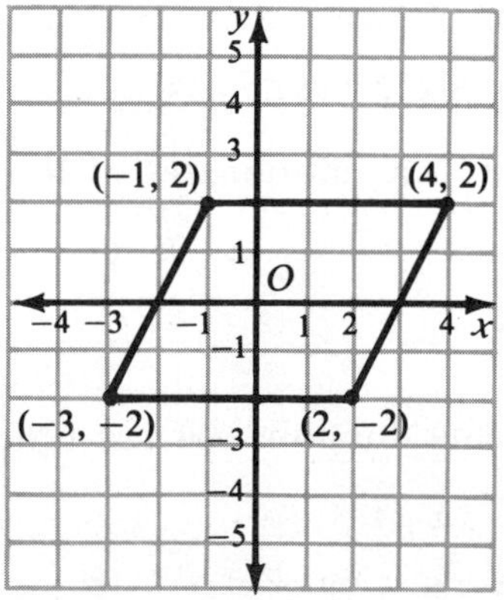

c. parallelogram

B **19.** $(1, -2)$, $(3, -2)$, $(3, 4)$, $(1, 4)$

20. $(0, 1)$, $(3, -2)$, $(6, 1)$, $(3, 4)$

21. $(0, -5)$, $(0, 2)$, $(-3, 6)$, $(-3, -1)$

22. $(-5, 0)$, $(-1, 2)$, $(1, 6)$, $(-3, 4)$

We can translate a figure on a coordinate plane by changing the ordered pairs. We can reflect a figure on a coordinate plane by changing the signs of the ordered pairs.

a. Graph the given ordered pairs on a coordinate plane, connect the points in the order listed, and connect the first and last points.
b. Change the values of the coordinates as directed.
c. Graph and connect all the new points to form a second figure.
d. Identify the change as translation or reflection.

C **23.** $(-5, 4), (-2, 1), (2, 1), (2, 4)$
Decrease all y-coordinates by 3.
(*Hint:* $(-5, 4)$ becomes $(-5, 1)$)

24. $(1, 5), (1, 1), (5, 3)$
Decrease all x-coordinates by 2.

25. $(-2, -2), (2, -2), (4, -4), (4, -6), (1, -4), (-1, -4), (-4, -6), (-4, -4)$
Increase all y-coordinates by 5.

26. $(-8, 4), (-4, 4), (-4, 5), (-1, 3), (-4, 1), (-4, 2), (-8, 2)$
Increase all x-coordinates by 9.

27. $(6, 5), (2, 1), (9, 3)$
Multiply all x-coordinates by -1.

28. $(1, 7), (4, 2), (7, 3), (4, 8)$
Multiply all y-coordinates by -1.

Review Exercises

Complete.

1. If $x + 5 = 13$, then $x =$ __?__.

2. If $8 + x = -1$, then $x =$ __?__.

3. If $9x = 243$, then $x =$ __?__.

4. If $-4x = 52$, then $x =$ __?__.

5. If $2x + 11 = 1$, then $x =$ __?__.

6. If $99 - 9x = 18$, then $x =$ __?__.

7. If $-\frac{4}{3}x = 12$, then $x =$ __?__.

8. If $9 + \frac{2}{3}x = 15$, then $x =$ __?__.

Challenge

Set up a pair of coordinate axes on graph paper. Connect the following points in the order given:

$$(-9, 3), (-4, 3), (-1.5, 1), (2, -1),$$
$$(2, -4), (8.5, -5), (9.5, -1), (2, -1)$$

Do you recognize the figure? (*Hint:* It is a well-known group of stars that is part of the constellation *Ursa Major.*)

8-2 Equations in Two Variables

The equation

$$x + y = 5$$

has two variables, x and y. A solution to this equation consists of two numbers, one for each variable. The solution can be expressed as an ordered pair of numbers, (x, y). There are many ordered pairs that satisfy this equation. Some solutions are

$$(-3, 8), (5, 0), (4, 1), (0, 5), (11, -6).$$

In fact, there are *infinitely* many ordered pairs that satisfy this equation.

EXAMPLE 1 Tell whether each ordered pair is a solution of the equation $2x + y = 7$.

a. $(4, -1)$ **b.** $(-4, 1)$

Solution Substitute the given values of x and y in the equation.

a.
$$\begin{aligned} 2x + y &= 7 \\ 2(4) + (-1) &\stackrel{?}{=} 7 \\ 8 - 1 &\stackrel{?}{=} 7 \\ 7 &= 7 \end{aligned}$$

$(4, -1)$ is a solution.

b.
$$\begin{aligned} 2x + y &= 7 \\ 2(-4) + 1 &\stackrel{?}{=} 7 \\ -8 + 1 &\stackrel{?}{=} 7 \\ -7 &\neq 7 \end{aligned}$$

$(-4, 1)$ is not a solution.

An equation in the two variables x and y establishes a correspondence between values of x and values of y. To find a solution of a given equation in x and y, we can choose any value for x, substitute it in the equation, and solve for the corresponding value for y.

EXAMPLE 2 Give one solution of the equation $x - 3y = 2$.

Solution Choose any value for x. For example, if $x = 14$:

$$\begin{aligned} x - 3y &= 2 \\ 14 - 3y &= 2 \\ -3y &= 2 - 14 \\ y &= \frac{-12}{-3} = 4 \end{aligned}$$

The values $x = 14$ and $y = 4$ correspond.

$(14, 4)$ is one solution of the equation.

To find the value of y corresponding to any given value of x, we could substitute the value of x into a given equation and solve for y, as in Example 2. An easier method is to solve for y in terms of x first, and then substitute, as in Example 3.

EXAMPLE 3 Find the solutions for $2x + 3y = 6$ for the following values of x: -9, -3, 0, 3, 6.

Solution First solve for y in terms of x by writing an equation with y on one side and x on the other.

$$2x + 3y = 6$$
$$3y = 6 - 2x$$
$$y = 2 - \frac{2}{3}x$$

Then substitute the values of x in the new equation and solve for the corresponding values of y.

x	$y = 2 - \frac{2}{3}x$	(x, y)
-9	$2 - \frac{2}{3}(-9) = 8$	$(-9, 8)$
-3	$2 - \frac{2}{3}(-3) = 4$	$(-3, 4)$
0	$2 - \frac{2}{3}(0) = 2$	$(0, 2)$
3	$2 - \frac{2}{3}(3) = 0$	$(3, 0)$
6	$2 - \frac{2}{3}(6) = -2$	$(6, -2)$

Thus $(-9, 8)$, $(-3, 4)$, $(0, 2)$, $(3, 0)$, and $(6, -2)$ are solutions of the equation for the given values of x.

Notice in the table above that each given value of x corresponds to exactly one value of y. In general, any set of ordered pairs such that no two different ordered pairs have the same x-coordinate is called a **function.** An equation, as the one above, that produces such a set of ordered pairs defines a function.

Class Exercises

Tell whether the ordered pair is a solution of the given equation.

$2x + y = 7$

1. (2, 3) **2.** (1, 5) **3.** (7, 0) **4.** (0,7)

$x - 3y = 1$

5. (2, 1) **6.** (4, 1) **7.** (7, 2) **8.** (−2, 1)

Solve the equation for y in terms of x.

9. $x - y = 5$ **10.** $x - y = 9$ **11.** $-3x + y = 7$

If $y = x - 12$, give the value of y such that the ordered pair is a solution of the equation.

12. (9, ?) **13.** (−4, ?) **14.** (0, ?) **15.** (−6, ?)

Written Exercises

Tell whether the ordered pair is a solution of the given equation.

A $-x + 3y = 15$

1. (0, 5) **2.** (6, −7) **3.** (6, 7) **4.** (−3, 6)

$x - 4y = 12$

5. (4, 2) **6.** (−6, −12) **7.** (0, 3) **8.** $\left(13, \frac{1}{4}\right)$

$3x - 2y = 8$

9. (1, 6) **10.** (0, 4) **11.** (4, 0) **12.** $\left(3, \frac{1}{2}\right)$

$-5x - 2y = 18$

13. (−2, −4) **14.** (−4, 1) **15.** $\left(1, -\frac{23}{2}\right)$ **16.** (0, 0)

Solve the equation for y in terms of x.

17. $2x + y = 7$ **18.** $-8x + 5y = 10$ **19.** $-12x + 3y = 48$

20. $4x - 9y = 36$ **21.** $x - \frac{3}{2}y = 3$ **22.** $5x - 4y = 20$

a. Solve the equation for y in terms of x.
b. Find the solutions of the equation for the given values of x.

23. $y - x = 7$
values of x: 2, −5, 7

24. $x + y = -1$
values of x: 3, 1, −2

25. $-x + 2y = 10$
values of x: 4, 0, 6

26. $x - 3y = 12$
values of x: -3, 6, 12

27. $x + 4y = 20$
values of x: 4, -8, 0

28. $-x - 2y = 8$
values of x: -6, -2, 10

B 29. $3x - 2y = 6$
values of x: 4, -2, -8

30. $-2x + 3y = 12$
values of x: 3, -3, -12

31. $2y - x = 5$
values of x: 3, 5, -1

32. $-3y + x = 7$
values of x: 1, 7, -5

33. $2y - 5x = 6$
values of x: 2, 1, -3

34. $4y - 3x = 1$
values of x: 9, -1, -5

Give any three ordered pairs that are solutions of the equation.

35. $y + x = -1$

36. $x - y = 6$

37. $x + y = 0$

38. $4y - x = 7$

39. $5x - y = -5$

40. $-3x - 2y = 0$

41. $2x - 3y = 12$

42. $-\frac{1}{4}y - x = 0$

43. $-x + \frac{1}{2}y = 3$

Write an equation that expresses a relationship between the coordinates of each ordered pair.

EXAMPLE (1, 4), (2, 3), (5, 0), (-1, 6)

Solution Notice that all the coordinates share a common property: the sum of the coordinates in each pair is 5. You can express this relationship by the equation $x + y = 5$.

C 44. (7, 6), (11, 10), (4, 3)

45. (3, -3), (6, -6), (-4, 4)

46. (-2, -4), (-3, -5), (4, 2)

47. (3, -6), (-3, 0), (6, -9)

Review Exercises

Solve.

1. $8a = 24$

2. $6 - 5m = 11$

3. $6t - 31 = 137$

4. $-7x + 4 = -10$

5. $9c = 18 + 3c$

6. $\frac{4}{5}y = 16$

7. $2 + \frac{7}{8}d = -47$

8. $-10 - \frac{2}{3}f = 12$

9. $5(8 + 2h) = 0$

8-3 Graphing Equations in the Coordinate Plane

The equation in two variables

$$x + 2y = 6$$

has infinitely many solutions. The **table of values** below lists some of the solutions. When we graph the solutions on a coordinate plane, we find that they all lie on a straight line.

$x + 2y = 6$

x	y
-2	4
0	3
6	0
10	-2

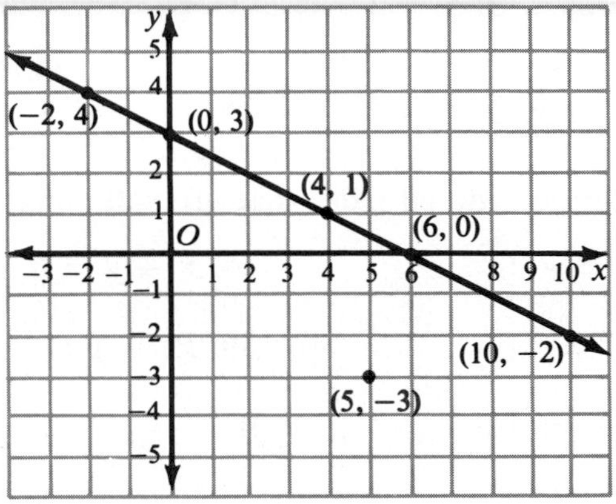

If we choose any other point on this line, we will find that the coordinates also satisfy the equation. For example, the ordered pair (4, 1) is a solution:

$$x + 2y = 6$$
$$4 + 2(1) = 6$$

If we choose a point *not* on this line, such as the graph of (5, −3), we find that its coordinates *do not* satisfy the equation:

$$x + 2y = 6$$
$$5 + 2(-3) \neq 6$$

The graph of an ordered pair is on the line if and only if it is a solution of the equation. The set of all points that are the graphs of solutions of a given equation is called the **graph of the equation.**

Note that the graph of $x + 2y = 6$ crosses the y-axis at (0, 3). The y-coordinate of a point where a graph crosses the y-axis is called the ***y*-intercept** of the graph. In this case, the y-intercept is 3. Since the graph also crosses the x-axis at (6, 0), the ***x*-intercept** of the graph is 6.

In general, any equation that can be written in the form

$$ax + by = c$$

where x and y are variables and a, b, and c are numbers (with a and b

not both zero), is called a **linear equation in two variables** because its graph is always a straight line in the plane.

In order to graph a linear equation, we need to graph only two points whose coordinates satisfy the equation and then join them by means of a line. It is wise, however, to graph a third point as a check.

EXAMPLE Graph the equation $x + 3y = 6$.

Solution First find three points whose coordinates satisfy the equation. It is usually easier to start with the y-intercept and the x-intercept, that is, $(0, y)$ and $(x, 0)$.

If $x = 0$: $0 + 3y = 6$, $3y = 6$, $y = 2$

If $y = 0$: $x + 3(0) = 6$, $x = 6$

As a check, if $x = 3$: $3 + 3y = 6$, $3y = 3$, $y = 1$

$x + 3y = 6$

x	y
0	2
6	0
3	1

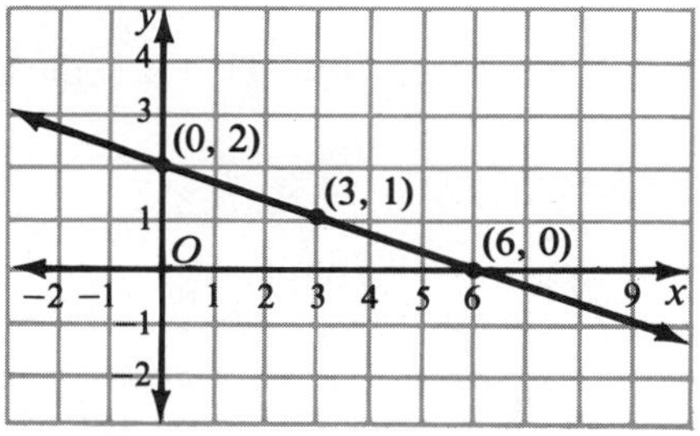

Class Exercises

Find three solutions of the linear equation. Include those that are in the form $(0, y)$ and $(x, 0)$.

1. $x - y = 7$

2. $y + x = -4$

3. $-x - 2y = 8$

4. $3y - x = 9$

5. $2x + y = 10$

6. $3x - 2y = 3$

7. $y = x$

8. $y = 3x$

9. $y = \frac{1}{2}x$

Written Exercises

A **1–9.** Graph each equation in Class Exercises 1–9. Use a separate set of coordinate axes for each equation.

Graph the equation on a coordinate plane. Use a separate set of axes for each equation.

10. $x + y = 5$ **11.** $x - 6 = y$ **12.** $y - x = 4$

13. $y + x = -3$ **14.** $2x - y = 10$ **15.** $8x + 2y = 8$

16. $3y + x = 0$ **17.** $3x - y = -6$ **18.** $-2x + 3y = 12$

19. $2y - \frac{1}{2}x = 4$ **20.** $\frac{1}{3}y + 2x = 3$ **21.** $4y - 3x = 12$

22. $4x - 3y = 6$ **23.** $-2x + 5y = 5$ **24.** $\frac{1}{2}y + 2x = 3$

B **25.** $\frac{x + y}{3} = 2$ **26.** $\frac{x - y}{4} = -1$ **27.** $\frac{3x - y}{2} = 3$

28. $\frac{2x + y}{3} = 1$ **29.** $\frac{x - 2y}{3} = -4$ **30.** $\frac{x + 3}{4} = y$

31. $\frac{3x - 1}{2} = y$ **32.** $\frac{-3y + 2x}{4} = -2$ **33.** $\frac{-4x + 3y}{6} = -4$

Graph the equation. Use a separate set of axes for each equation.

EXAMPLE $y = 6$

Solution Rewrite the equation in the form

$$y = 0x + 6.$$

Find three solutions.

If $x = -1$: $y = 0(-1) + 6 = 6$

If $x = 2$: $y = 0(2) + 6 = 6$

If $x = 3$: $y = 0(3) + 6 = 6$

Three solutions are $(-1, 6)$, $(2, 6)$, and $(3, 6)$. Graph these points and draw the line.

The graph of $y = 6$ is a horizontal line.

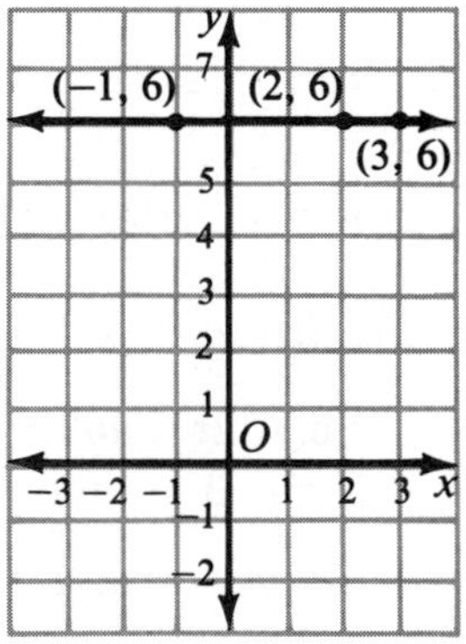

34. $y = 2$ **35.** $x = -4$ **36.** $y = 0$

37. $y = -3$ **38.** $x = 6$ **39.** $y = \frac{3}{2}$

C **40.** Graph the equation $y = x^2$ by graphing the points with x-coordinates -3, -2, -1, 0, 1, 2, and 3. Join the points by means of a curved line. (This curve is called a **parabola.**)

41. Graph the equation $xy = 12$ by graphing the points with x-coordinates 1, 3, 6, and 12. Join the points by means of a curved line. On the same set of axes, graph the points with x-coordinates -1, -3, -6, and -12. Join the points by means of a curved line. (This two-branched curve is called a **hyperbola.**)

Graph the equation using the following values of x: -5, -2, 0, 2, 5. Join the points by means of a straight line.

42. $y = |x|$ **43.** $y = -|x|$ **44.** $y = |x - 3|$ **45.** $y - 4 = |x|$

For what value of k is the graph of the given ordered pair in the graph of the given equation?

46. $(3, -2)$; $2y + kx = 14$ **47.** $(-5, 4)$; $3x - ky = -12$

Self-Test A

Exercises 1-6 refer to the diagram. Give the coordinates of each point.

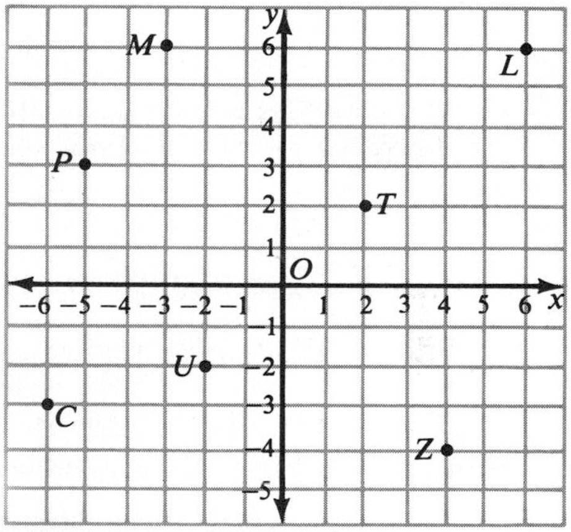

1. M **2.** Z **3.** L **[8-1]**

Name the point for the given ordered pair.

4. $(-6, -3)$ **5.** $(2, 2)$ **6.** $(-5, 3)$

Graph the given ordered pairs on one set of axes.

7. $(-3, 5)$ **8.** $(9, 7)$ **9.** $(-4, -8)$

10. $(11, -10)$ **11.** $(0, -2)$ **12.** $(-4, 2)$

Find the solutions of the equation for the given values of x.

13. $4y - x = 2$
values of x: 0, -4, 9

14. $y + 2x = 6$ **[8-2]**
values of x: -3, $\frac{1}{2}$, 11

Graph each equation on a coordinate plane. Use a separate set of axes for each equation.

15. $y = x - 1$ **16.** $y = 2x$ **17.** $4x - y = 9$ **18.** $x = 7$ **[8-3]**

Self-Test answers and Extra Practice are at the back of the book.

8-4 Graphing a System of Equations

Two equations in the same variables are called a **system of equations.** If the graphs of two linear equations in a system have a point in common, the coordinates of that point must be a solution of both equations. We can find a solution of a system of equations such as

$$x - y = 2$$
$$x + 2y = 5$$

by finding the *point of intersection* of the graphs of the two equations.

The graphs of the two equations above are shown on the same set of axes. The point with coordinates (3, 1) appears to be the point of intersection of the graphs. To check whether (3, 1) satisfies the given system, we substitute its coordinates in both equations:

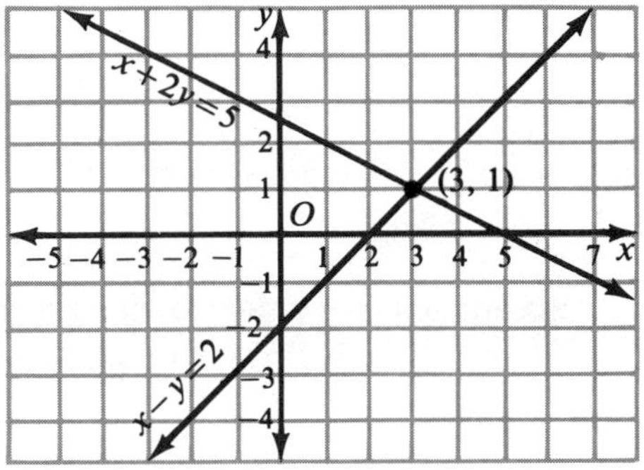

$x - y = 2$	$x + 2y = 5$
$3 - 1 = 2$	$3 + 2(1) = 5$

Since the coordinates satisfy both equations, (3, 1) is the solution of the given system of equations.

EXAMPLE 1 Use a graph to solve the system of equations:

$$y - x = 4$$
$$3y + x = 8$$

Solution First make a table of values for each equation, then graph both equations on one set of axes.

$y - x = 4$

x	y
0	4
−4	0
−2	2

$3y + x = 8$

x	y
−1	3
5	1
2	2

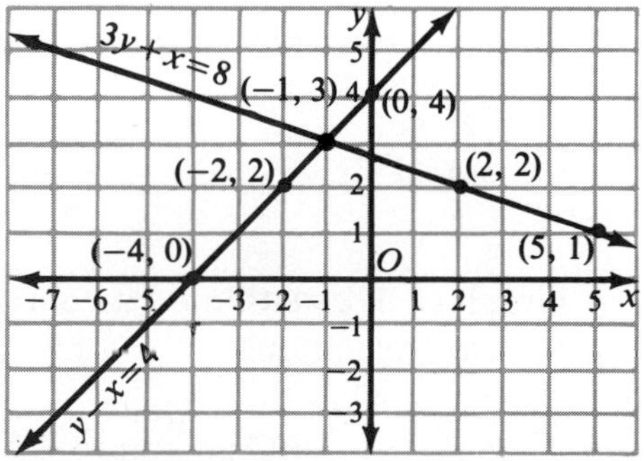

The point of intersection appears to be (−1, 3).

To check, substitute the coordinates $(-1, 3)$ in both equations:

$$y - x = 4 \qquad\qquad 3y + x = 8$$
$$3 - (-1) \stackrel{?}{=} 4 \qquad\qquad 3(3) + (-1) \stackrel{?}{=} 8$$
$$3 + 1 = 4 \checkmark \qquad\qquad 9 - 1 = 8 \checkmark$$

The solution for the given system is $(-1, 3)$.

EXAMPLE 2 Use a graph to solve the system of equations: $2y - x = 2$
$2y - x = -4$

Solution Make a table of values for each equation and graph both equations on one set of axes.

$2y - x = 2$

x	y
0	1
−2	0
2	2

$2y - x = -4$

x	y
0	−2
4	0
2	−1

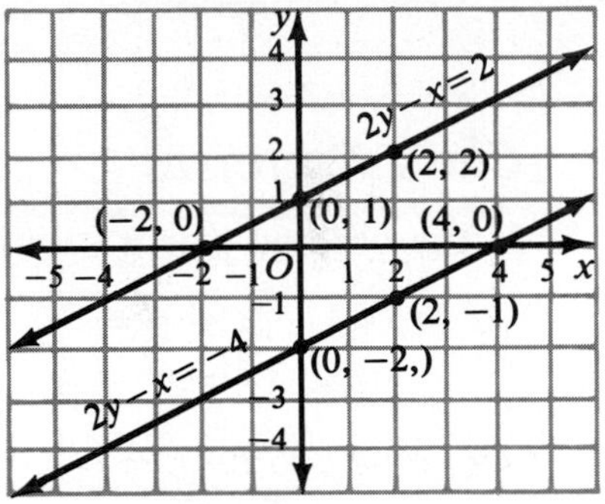

The graphs do not intersect; they are **parallel lines.** Thus, the system has *no solution.*

A system may have infinitely many solutions, as the following example illustrates.

EXAMPLE 3 Use a graph to solve the system of equations: $6x + 3y = 18$
$2x + y = 6$

Solution Make a table of values for each equation and graph both equations on one set of axes.

$6x + 3y = 18$

x	y
0	6
3	0
1	4

$2x + y = 6$

x	y
0	6
3	0
1	4

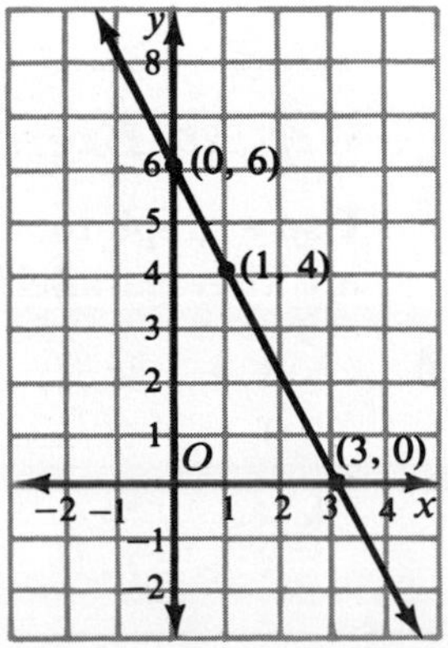

The graphs *coincide.* The coordinates of all points on the line satisfy both equations. This system has *infinitely many solutions.*

To solve a system of equations, first graph the equations on one set of axes. Then consider:

If the graphs intersect, the system has one solution. The coordinates of the point of intersection form the solution.

If the graphs are parallel, the system has no solution.

If the graphs coincide, the system has infinitely many solutions.

Class Exercises

Is the ordered pair a solution of the system of equations?

1. $(4, -1)$ $x + y = 3$, $x - y = 5$

2. $(5, -1)$ $x + y = -6$, $x - y = 4$

3. $(3, 1)$ $x + 2y = 5$, $x - y = 2$

4. $(-4, -4)$ $2x + y = -12$, $x - y = 0$

5. A system of two linear equations has no solution. What does the graph of this system look like?

6. The coordinates $(-3, -1)$, $(0, 0)$, and $(3, 1)$ are solutions of a system of two linear equations. What does the graph of this system look like?

7. The graphs of two equations appear to intersect at $(-4, 5)$. How can you check to see whether $(-4, 5)$ satisfies the system?

Written Exercises

Use a graph to solve the system. Do the lines intersect or coincide, or are they parallel?

A

1. $x + y = 6$, $x - y = 0$

2. $x + y = 5$, $3y + 3x = 15$

3. $x - y = -3$, $x - y = 2$

4. $x - y = 4$, $x + y = 0$

5. $-2y - 2x = -6$, $x + y = 3$

6. $2x - y = 4$, $y + 2x = 2$

7. $x - 2y = 8$
$2y - x = 4$

8. $6y + 4x = 24$
$2x + 3y = 12$

9. $3x - y = -6$
$y - x = 6$

10. $x - 2y = -8$
$2y - 3x = 12$

11. $7x - 14y = 70$
$x - 2y = 10$

12. $3x + 2y = 6$
$3x + 2y = 12$

B 13. $2x + \frac{3}{2}y = 2$
$x + 2y = 6$

14. $x + 3y = 2$
$2x + 5y = 3$

15. $\frac{2}{3}x - y = 2$
$6y - 4x = 18$

16. $3x - 5y = 9$
$\frac{1}{2}x - 2y = 5$

17. $\frac{3}{2}x + 2y = 4$
$2x + 5y = 3$

18. $-7x - 2y = 7$
$-\frac{7}{2}x - y = 1$

C 19. Find the value of k in the equations

$$6x - 4y = 12$$
$$3x - ky = 6$$

such that the system has infinitely many solutions.

20. Find the value of k in the equations

$$5x - 3y = 15$$
$$kx - 9y = 30$$

such that the system has no solution.

Review Exercises

Write in lowest terms.

1. $\frac{18}{16}$
2. $\frac{12}{27}$
3. $\frac{49}{56}$
4. $\frac{18}{81}$
5. $\frac{24}{30}$
6. $\frac{48}{144}$
7. $\frac{13}{169}$
8. $\frac{17}{101}$

Calculator Key-In

On Roger's first birthday he received a dime from his parents. For each birthday after that, they doubled the money. How much will Roger receive for his eighteenth birthday?

8-5 Using Graphs to Solve Problems

In the drawing at the left below, the slope of the hill changes. It becomes steeper partway up, and then flattens out near the top.

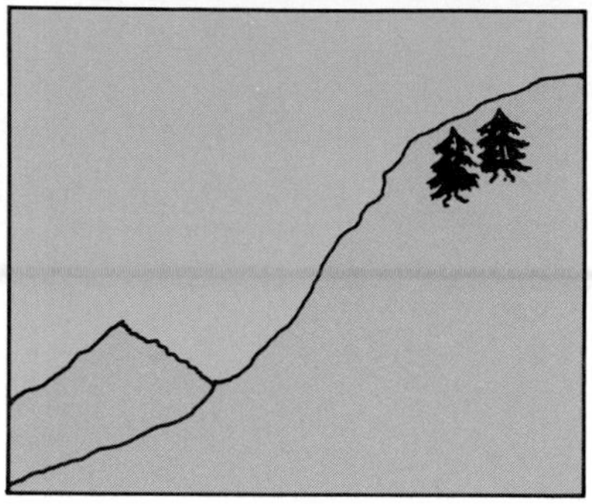

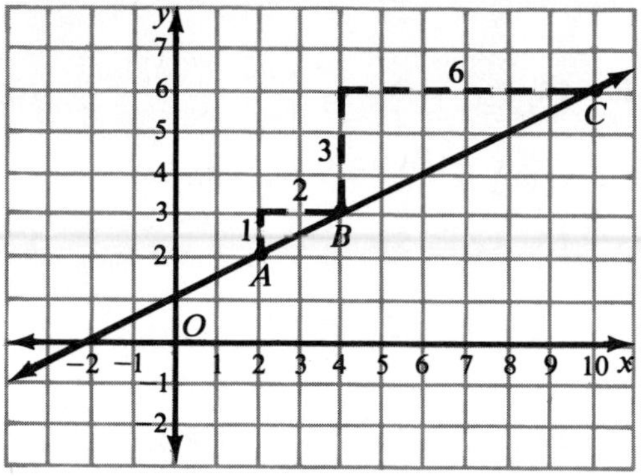

On the other hand, the slope of the straight line shown in the graph above does not change. It remains constant. The **slope of a line** is the ratio of the change in the y-coordinate to the change in the x-coordinate when moving from one point on the line to another.

Moving from A to B: $\text{slope} = \dfrac{\text{change in } y}{\text{change in } x} = \dfrac{1}{2}$

Moving from B to C: $\text{slope} = \dfrac{\text{change in } y}{\text{change in } x} = \dfrac{3}{6} = \dfrac{1}{2}$

A basic property of a straight line is that its slope is constant.

A straight-line graph sometimes expresses the relationship between two physical quantities. For example, such a graph can represent the conditions of temperature falling at a constant rate or of a hiker walking at a steady pace. If we can locate two points of a graph that is known to be a straight line, then we can extend the graph and get more information about the relationship.

EXAMPLE 1 The temperature at 8 A.M. was 3°C. At 10 A.M. it was 7°C. If the temperature climbed at a constant rate from 6 A.M. to 12 noon, what was it at 6 A.M.? What was it at 12 noon?

Solution Set up a pair of axes.

Let the coordinates on the horizontal axis represent the hours after 6 A.M.

Let the vertical axis represent the temperature.

Use the information given to plot the points.

At 8 A.M., or 2 h after 6 A.M., the temperature was 3°C. This gives us the point (2, 3).

At 10 A.M., or 4 h after 6 A.M., the temperature was 7°C. This gives us the point (4, 7).

Since we know that the temperature climbed at a constant rate, we can first graph the two points and then draw a straight line through them.

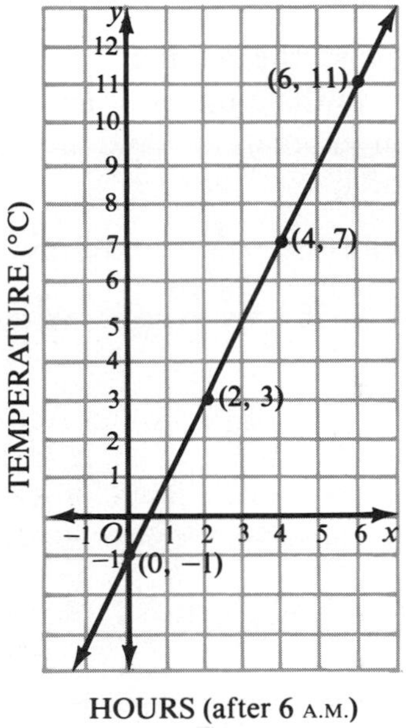

We can see that the line crosses the vertical axis at -1. Therefore, at 6 A.M., or 0 h after 6 A.M., the temperature was -1°C. At 12 noon, or 6 h after 6 A.M., the temperature was 11°C.

Sometimes we are given information about the relationship between two quantities. We can use the information to write and graph an equation. We can then read additional information from the graph.

EXAMPLE 2 Maryanne uses 15 Cal of energy in stretching before she runs and 10 Cal for every minute of running time. Write an equation that relates the total number of Calories (y) that she uses when she stretches and goes for a run to the number of minutes (x) that she spends running. Graph this equation. From your graph, determine how long Maryanne must run after stretching to use a total of 55 Cal.

(The solution is on the next page.)

Solution Consider the facts given:

15 Cal used in stretching
10 Cal/min used in running

Use the variables suggested.

If x = running time in minutes, then $10x$ = Cal used in running for x min.
If y = Cal used in stretching *and* running for x min, then $y = 15 + 10x$.

Make a table of values to locate two points. Because the number of Calories is large compared with the number of minutes, mark the vertical axis in intervals of 5 and the horizontal axis in intervals of 1.

$y = 15 + 10x$

x	y
0	15
2	35

Plot the points and draw the graph.

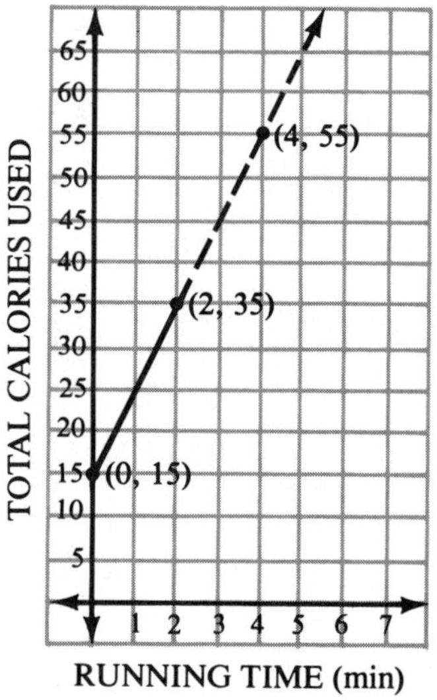

From the graph, you can see that Maryanne must run 4 min after stretching to use a total of 55 Cal.

Problem Solving Reminder
To help identify the conditions of a problem, it may be useful strategy to *rewrite the facts in simpler form.* In Example 2, we list the given facts before writing an equation based on the conditions of the problem.

Class Exercises

Complete for each graph.

1. change in y = ?
   change in x = ?
   slope = ?

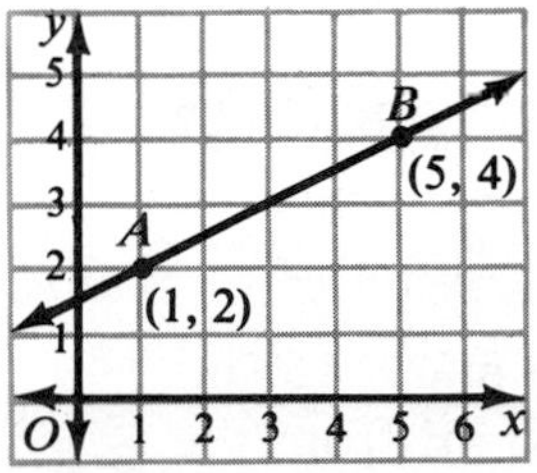

2. change in y = ?
   change in x = ?
   slope = ?

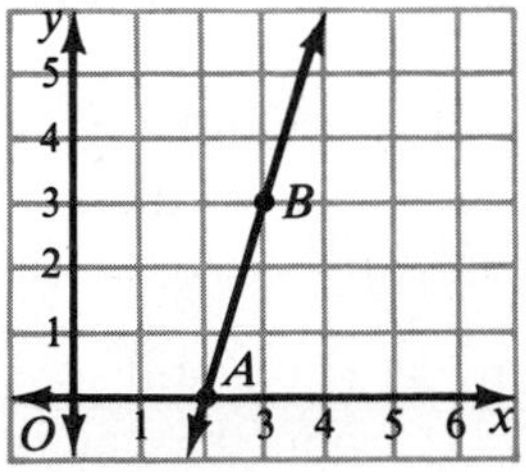

3. change in y = ?
   change in x = ?
   slope = ?

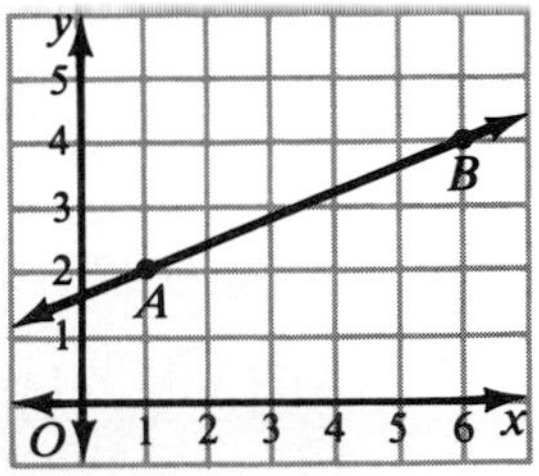

Use a straight-line graph to complete the ordered pairs, then find the slope.

4. $A(1, 3)$, $B(5, 5)$, $C(9, ?)$, $D(?, -1)$
5. $A(0, -3)$, $B(2, 2)$, $C(4, ?)$, $D(?, -8)$
6. $A(8, 4)$, $B(-1, -8)$, $C(5, ?)$, $D(?, -4)$
7. $A(0, 1)$, $B(2, 3)$, $C(-2, ?)$, $D(?, 0)$
8. $A(-1, 6)$, $B(0, 4)$, $C(2, ?)$, $D(?, -4)$

Problems

Solve. Use the same intervals for both axes.

A 1. A pack of greeting cards costs \$1.50. Five packs will cost \$7.50. Draw a straight-line graph to show the relationship between the number of packs and the cost. Let the x-axis represent the number of packs and the y-axis represent the cost in dollars. What is the slope of the line?

2. An object of 2 g suspended from a spring stretches the spring to a length of 6 cm. An object of 5 g stretches the spring to a length of 11 cm. Draw a straight-line graph to show the relationship between the number of grams of the object and the length of the stretched spring. Let the x-axis represent grams, and the y-axis represent centimeters. What is the slope of the line?

Use a graph to solve the problem.

B 3. At 1 A.M. the temperature was $-6°C$. At 5 A.M. it was $-1°C$. If the temperature continues to rise steadily, what will the temperature be at 9 A.M.?

4. Hernando is saving money for a camping trip. Each week he deposits \$5 in the bank. He had \$25 to start the account. In 3 weeks he had \$40 in the account.
   a. How much money will Hernando have by the seventh week?
   b. If the trip costs \$85, how long will it take him to save enough money?

5. At 9 A.M. a test car driving at a constant speed passes a marker 50 mi from its starting point. At noon the car is about 130 mi from the marker. If the test drive ends at 1:30 P.M., how far will the car be from its starting point?

6. Between 1970 and 1980, the Rockfort Corporation used a 10-year expansion plan to increase its annual earnings steadily. The corporation had earnings of \$3.6 million in 1975 and \$6 million in 1977.
   a. About how much were the corporation's annual earnings in 1972?
   b. About how much did it earn by the end of the 10-year plan?

a. Write an equation relating the quantity labeled y to the quantity labeled x.
b. Graph the equation.
c. Use the graph to answer the question.

C 7. A butcher charges \$4.50 a pound for the best cut of beef. For an additional \$2.00, any order will be delivered. Relate the total cost (y) to the amount of beef (x) ordered and delivered. How many pounds of beef can be ordered and delivered for \$33.50?

8. It takes a work crew 15 min to set up its equipment, and 3 min to paint each square meter of a wall. Relate the number of minutes (y) it takes to complete a job to the number of square meters (x) to be painted. If it took the crew 33 hours to complete the job, about how many square meters was the wall?

9. A word processor can store documents in its memory. It takes about 10 s to get the information, and about 35 s to print each page of it. Therefore, in about 360 s, or 6 min, the processor can complete a 10-page document. Relate the time (y) in minutes it takes to complete a document to the number of pages (x) to be typed. How many minutes will it take to complete an 18-page document?

10. Shaoli Hyatt earns a salary of \$215 a week, plus a \$15 commission for each encyclopedia she sells. Relate her total pay for one week (y) to the number of encyclopedias she sells during the week (x). How many encyclopedias must she sell to receive \$350 for one week?

Use a graph to solve.

11. The velocity of a model rocket is 3 km/min at 1 s after takeoff. The velocity decreases to 2 km/min at 2.5 s after takeoff. When the rocket reaches its maximum height, the velocity will be 0. Assume that the decrease in velocity is constant. How long will it take the rocket to reach its maximum height?

Review Exercises

Solve.

1. $3x + 4 > 8$

2. $5y - 10 < 0$

3. $7 + 3y \geq -4y$

4. $2(8x + 3) < -2$

5. $6(2y + 7) \leq 42$

6. $-3\left(9x - \frac{2}{3}\right) > -7$

7. $4(9x + 10) \geq 4$

8. $5(4y + 9) \leq 15$

9. $12\left(\frac{x}{6} - \frac{5}{6}\right) > 72$

Calculator Key-In

Use a calculator to find the product.

$$1^2 = \underline{\ ?\ }$$
$$11^2 = \underline{\ ?\ }$$
$$111^2 = \underline{\ ?\ }$$
$$1111^2 = \underline{\ ?\ }$$

Use the pattern to predict the products $11{,}111^2$, $111{,}111^2$, $1{,}111{,}111^2$, $11{,}111{,}111^2$, and $111{,}111{,}111^2$.

8-6 Graphing Inequalities

When we graph a linear equation such as

$$y = x + 1$$

we see that the graph separates the coordinate plane into three sets of points:

(1) those above the line, such as $(-4, 5)$,

(2) those below the line, such as $(3, 1)$, and

(3) those on the line, such as $(2, 3)$.

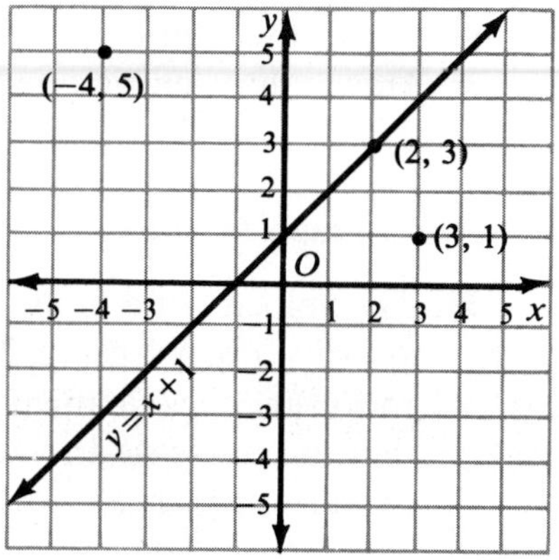

The region *above* the line is the graph of the set of solutions of the inequality

$$y > x + 1.$$

The region *below* the line is the graph of the set of solutions of the inequality

$$y < x + 1.$$

The line $y = x + 1$ forms the **boundary line** of the graphs of the inequalities $y > x + 1$ and $y < x + 1$. For any inequality we can get the boundary line by replacing the inequality symbol with the "equals" symbol.

Since the graph of an inequality consists of all the points above or below a boundary line, we use shading to indicate the region. If the boundary line is part of the graph, it is drawn with a solid line. If the boundary line is not part of the graph, use a dashed line.

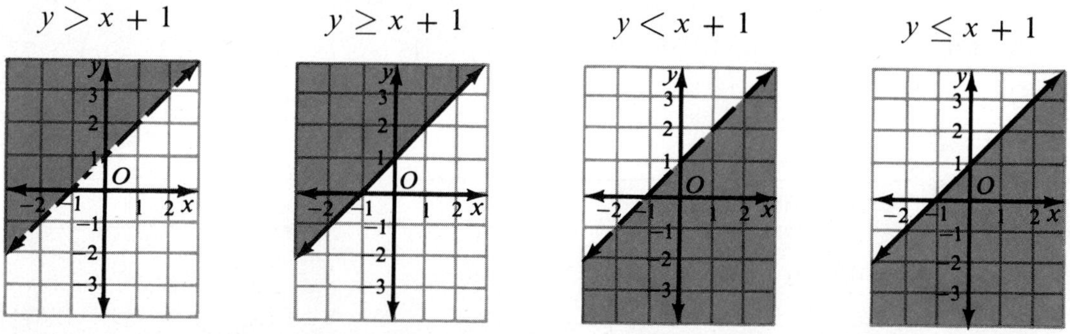

To check whether the shading is correct, choose a point in the shaded region. Then substitute its coordinates for x and y in the inequality. If the coordinates satisfy the inequality, then the shading is correct.

Any set of ordered pairs is a **relation.** Each of the open sentences

$y = x + 1$, $y > x + 1$, $y \geq x + 1$, $y < x + 1$, and $y \leq x + 1$ defines a relation. The equation $y = x + 1$ is a special kind of relation because it defines a function. Not all relations are functions. Recall that for a function, every value of x has only one corresponding value of y. Notice in the shaded region of each graph above, more than one value of y may be associated with each value of x. For example, the following ordered pairs all satisfy the inequalities $y > x + 1$ and $y \geq x + 1$:

$$(-2, 0), (-2, 1), (-2, 2), (-2, 3)$$

Therefore, the relation defined by the inequalities $y > x + 1$ and $y \geq x + 1$ is not a function.

EXAMPLE 1 Graph $y - x < 4$.

Solution First transform $y - x < 4$ into an equivalent inequality with y alone on one side.

$$y < 4 + x$$

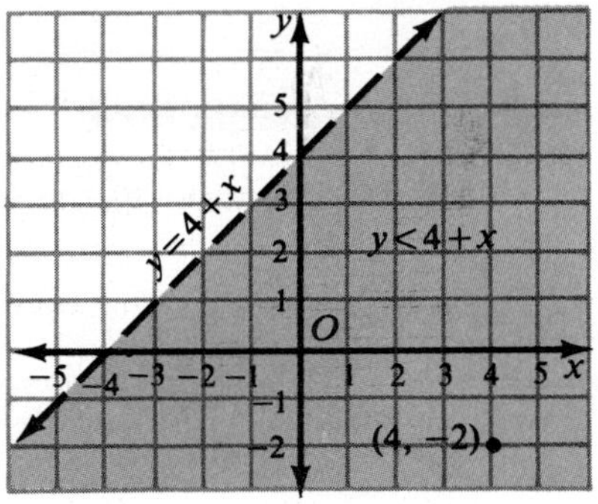

Then locate the boundary line by graphing

$$y = 4 + x.$$

Use a dashed line to draw the boundary line, and shade the region below.

Check: Use (4, −2).

$$y - x < 4$$
$$-2 - 4 \overset{?}{<} 4$$
$$-6 < 4 \quad \checkmark$$

EXAMPLE 2 Graph $x \geq -7$.

Solution Locate the boundary line by graphing

$$x = -7.$$

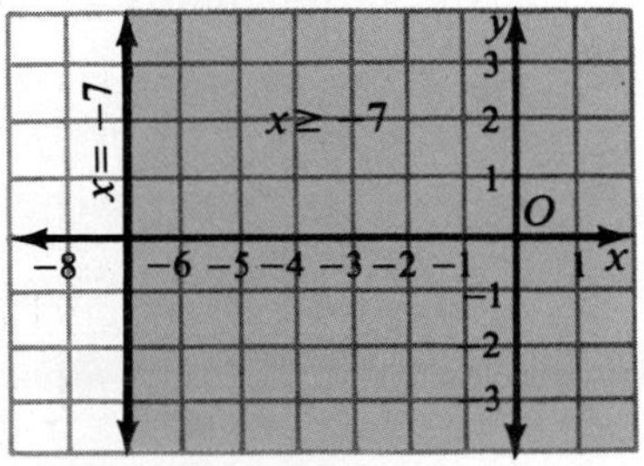

Use a solid line to draw the boundary. Shade the region to the right since all values of x greater than -7 lie to the right of the boundary line.

Class Exercises

Transform the inequality into an equivalent inequality with y alone on one side. State the equation of the boundary line.

1. $4x + y < 8$ **2.** $y - 9x < 2$ **3.** $4y + 2x > 10$

4. $6x - y > 0$ **5.** $3 \leq 5x + y$ **6.** $9y \geq 18$

State whether each point belongs to the graph of the given inequality.

7. $y \leq x + 2$ $(0, 1), (3, 6)$ **8.** $-x + 2y \geq 0$ $(4, 4), (-2, 1)$

9. $x \leq -7$ $(-4, -10), (-8, 0)$ **10.** $5 \leq -x + y$ $(-6, -5), (2, 7)$

11. $0 \geq x + y - 5$ $(2, 1), (4, 1)$ **12.** $y \geq 3$ $(9, 4), (0, 8)$

Written Exercises

State the equation of the boundary line.

A **1.** $3x + y > -6$ **2.** $x + y \geq 2$ **3.** $x - y \leq 2$

4. $2y - 4 > 0$ **5.** $-x \geq y - 3$ **6.** $2y - 6x < 0$

Graph the inequality.

7. $x + y \geq 9$ **8.** $y > -3x + 3$ **9.** $-2x + y \geq 2$

10. $x + 6y \leq -5$ **11.** $4x + 2y \geq 8$ **12.** $3y - x < -3$

13. $y \geq 2x + 5$ **14.** $x + 2y \leq 6$ **15.** $3y - 4 > 2x - 5$

B **16.** $3(x - y) > 6$ **17.** $y \leq 8$ **18.** $6x + 2y + 3 < 2x - 1$

19. $4x + 3y \leq x - 3$ **20.** $3y - 6 > 0$ **21.** $x \leq -3$

22. $y > 0$ **23.** $2(x + y) < 6x + 10$ **24.** $3y - 6 \geq 3(x + 2y)$

Write an inequality for the graph shown.

25.

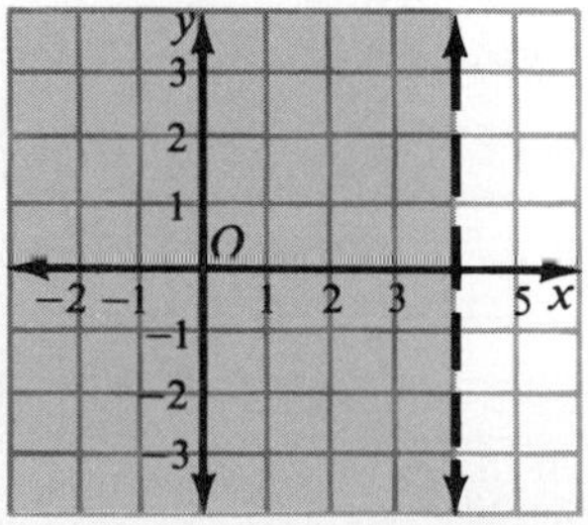

26.

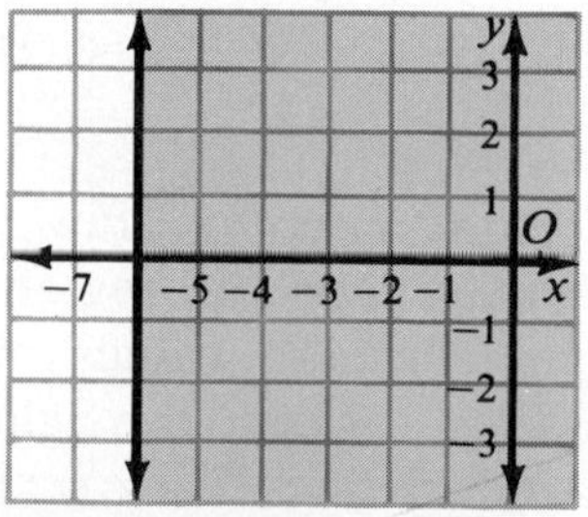

27.

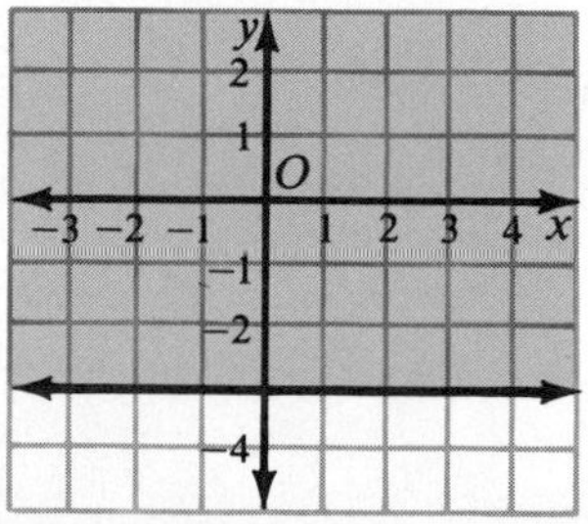

Graph the solutions of each system of inequalities.

EXAMPLE $y \geq -3 + x$
$y \leq 2 - x$

Solution First graph $y \geq -3 + x$. Use blue to shade the region. Then graph $y \leq 2 - x$. Use gray to shade the region.

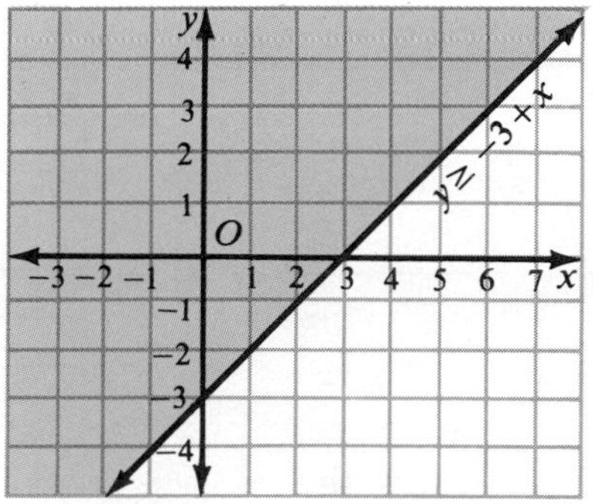

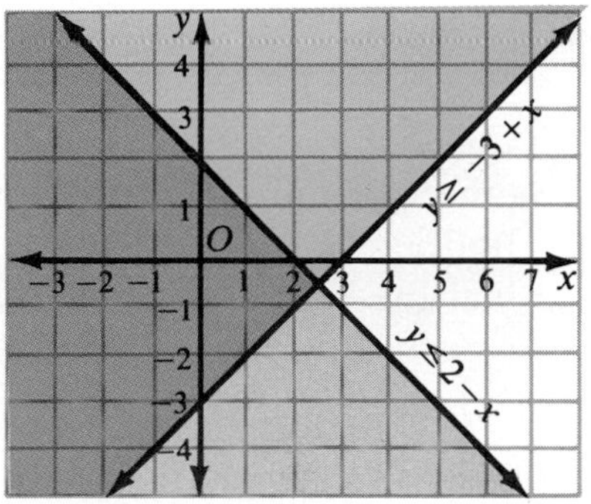

The graph of the solutions of the system is the region where the blue and gray shading overlap.

C **28.** $y \geq -4$
$x \leq 2$

29. $y > 5 - x$
$y \geq x + 5$

30. $x \leq 9 - y$
$y < x + 3$

31. $x \geq -6$
$x < 3$

Self-Test B

Use a graph to solve the system. Do the lines intersect or coincide, or are they parallel? **[8-4]**

1. $x + y = 6$
$y - x = -2$

2. $x + 2y = 6$
$6y + 3x = 18$

3. $2x + y = 3$
$-2x - y = 2$

Use a graph to solve.

4. When Fritz enrolled in a speed-reading class, he read about 250 words per minute. Two weeks later, his reading speed was about 750 words per minute. If his reading speed increases steadily, how many weeks after enrollment will it take Fritz to read about 1250 words per minute? **[8-5]**

Graph each inequality. **[8-6]**

5. $x + y \leq 10$

6. $3y - x > 9$

7. $x - 5y \geq 5$

Self-Test answers and Extra Practice are at the back of the book.

The Computer and Linear Equations

For a science project, Nina watered 6 identical lima bean gardens by different amounts. The crop yields were as recorded below.

Water applied daily in cm	0.5	1.0	1.5	2.0	2.5	3.0
Yield of lima beans in kg	1.6	1.8	2.0	2.4	2.6	2.8

Can Nina use these data to predict crop yields for other amounts of daily watering? If we plot her findings as shown on the graph at the right, we see that the points are very nearly in line.

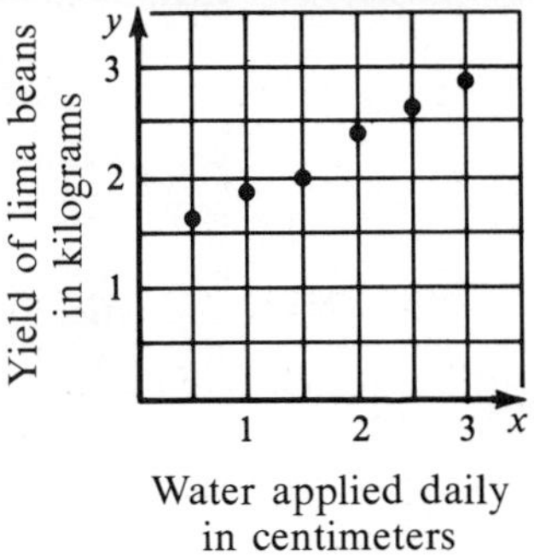

The computer program below gives the equation of the line that best fits the points on the graph. Notice how the coordinates of the points are entered in line 40.

```
10  DIM L(50)
20  PRINT "NUMBER OF POINTS ON GRAPH IS";
30  INPUT N
40  DATA .5,1.6,1,1.8,1.5,2,2,2.4,2.5,2.6,3,2.8
50  FOR I = 1 TO N
60  READ X,Y
70  LET A = A + X
80  LET B = B + Y
90  LET C = C + X * X
100  LET D = D + X * Y
110  NEXT I
120  LET Q = N * C - A * A
130  LET R =  INT (100 * (N * D - A * B) / Q + .5) / 100
140  LET S =  INT (100 * (B * C - A * D) / Q + .5) / 100
145  PRINT
150  PRINT "EQUATION OF BEST FITTING LINE IS"
155  PRINT " Y = ";R;"X";
160  IF S >  = 0 THEN 190
170  PRINT S
180  STOP
190  PRINT " ";"+ ";S
200  END
```

1. RUN the program to find the equation of the best fitting line for Nina's data.

2. Draw the graph of the equation.

3. Use the graph to predict the yield if Nina applied 3.3 cm of water daily.

Use the computer program to find the equation of the best fitting line for the data given in each chart. Then graph the equation and use the graph to answer the question.

4. The chart below shows the distance a spring stretches when different masses are hung from it.

Mass in kg	0.3	0.6	0.9	1.2	1.5	1.8
Stretch in cm	2.1	4.9	6.0	7.1	8.9	10.8

About how much stretch would a 1 kg mass produce?

5. The chart below shows temperature changes as a cold front approached.

Time in hours from 1st reading	0	1	2	3	4
Temperature in °C	21	17	14	12	7

a. Estimate the temperature 1.5 hours from the first reading.

b. If the temperature continues to decrease steadily, about how many hours will it take to reach 0°C?

6. The chart below shows the profit earned by a bookstore on the sale of a bestseller.

No. sold	3	4	7	9	11
Profit	$13.50	$18.00	$31.50	$40.50	$49.50

How many sales will it take to earn a profit of at least $80?

7. The chart below shows the cost of college education for the past 5 years.

Year	1	2	3	4	5
Cost (in thousands)	$7.8	$8.6	$9.4	$9.9	$10.1

Predict the cost of college education for the next two years.

Chapter Review

True or false?

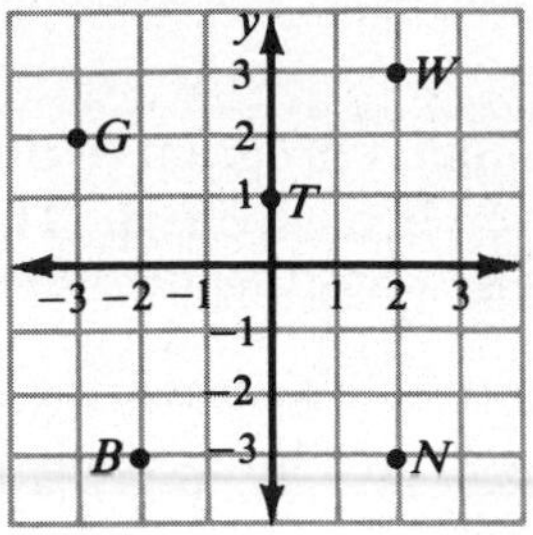

1. The coordinates of point G are (3, 2). **[8-1]**

2. The abscissa of point W is 2.

3. The ordinate of point T is 1.

4. Point B is associated with the ordered pair $(2, -3)$.

Match each equation with an ordered pair that satisfies the equation.

5. $2y - 7x = 4$ **A.** $(-18, 1)$ **[8-2]**

6. $10x + \frac{5}{9}y = 0$ **B.** (9, 2)

7. $-2x + 9y = 0$ **C.** (2, 9)

8. $y - \frac{1}{3}x = 7$ **D.** $(1, -18)$

Graph the equation on a coordinate plane. Use a separate set of axes for each equation.

9. $x + y = 0$ **10.** $2y - 3x = -6$ **11.** $y - 2x = 2$ **[8-3]**

Use a graph to solve the system of equations. Match the system with the word that describes its graphs.

12. $y + x = -3$; $2y - 3x = 4$ **13.** $y - 3x = -6$; $y - 3x = 3$ **14.** $5y - 2x = 4$; $15y - 6x = 12$ **[8-4]**

A. intersect **B.** coincide **C.** parallel

Complete.

15. A basic property of a straight line is that its slope remains __?__. **[8-5]**

16. The slope of a line is the ratio of the change in the __?__-coordinate to the change in the __?__-coordinate when moving from one point on the line to another.

17. The boundary line for the graph of $y > x + 6$ is a __?__ line. **[8-6]**

18. If the boundary line is part of the graph of an inequality, it is drawn with a __?__ line.

Chapter Test

Give the coordinates of the point. **[8-1]**

1. I 2. M 3. E 4. R

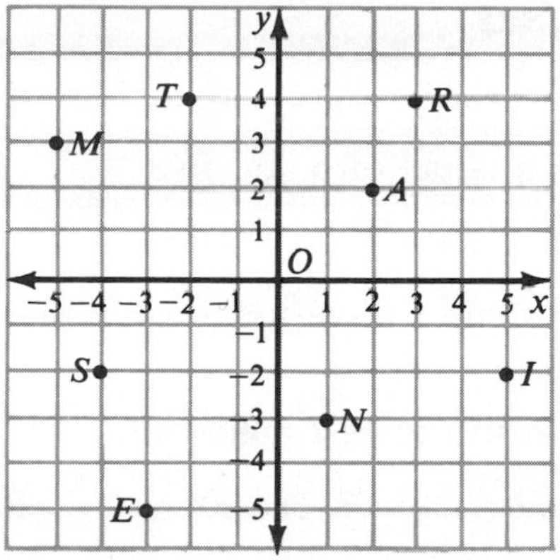

Name the point for the ordered pair.

5. $(-2, 4)$ 6. $(1, -3)$

7. $(-4, -2)$ 8. $(5, -2)$

a. Solve the equation for y in terms of x.
b. Find solutions of the equation for the given values of x: $-3, 0, 4$.

9. $y + 7x = 23$ 10. $2y - 4x = 1$ 11. $3y - 6x = 0$ **[8-2]**

Graph the equation on a coordinate plane. Use a separate set of axes for each equation.

12. $y - 3x = 7$ 13. $4y - x = 8$ 14. $2y + x = -10$ **[8-3]**

Use a graph to solve the system. Do the lines intersect or coincide, or are they parallel?

15. $x - 2y = 0$
$2x + y = 5$
16. $3x - y = -4$
$3x - y = 3$
17. $5x + y = 2$
$10x + 2y = 4$ **[8-4]**

Use a graph to solve the problem.

18. One hour after the start of an experiment, the temperature of a solution was $-15°C$. Three hours later it was $-6°C$. If the temperature continues to rise steadily, about how many hours will it take for the temperature to reach $0°C$? **[8-5]**

19. It takes the window washers 24 min to get ready and 4 min to wash a 6 m by 6 m window.
   a. Write an equation relating the total time (y) required on the job to the number of windows (x) to be washed.
   b. Graph the equation.
   c. About how many 6 m by 6 m windows can they wash in 2 h?

a. State the equation of the boundary line.
b. Graph the inequality.

20. $y \geq 2x + 1$ 21. $x + y > -4$ 22. $y - 3x < 0$ **[8-6]**

Cumulative Review (Chapters 1–8)

Exercises

Write a variable expression for the word phrase.

1. The product of b and five

2. Eight times a number x

3. Twelve less than the sum of y and z

4. A number q divided by seven

5. The sum of three times a number p and seven

Round to the nearest hundredth.

6. 46.871 **7.** 288.005 **8.** 0.7826 **9.** 100.758 **10.** 33.663

Perform the indicated operation.

11. $-8.709 + 13.6001$

12. $7615.7 - 333.61$

13. $606.08 + (-51.99)$

14. $272.65 - (-0.88)$

15. 37.61×0.08

16. $1.5798 \div 0.03$

17. -11.56×36.77

18. $72.5 \div 5$

19. $6.7 \times (-1.22)$

20. $-\frac{1}{3} + \frac{4}{5}$

21. $\frac{4}{7} \times \left(-\frac{3}{8}\right)$

22. $6\frac{1}{2} \div \left(-2\frac{1}{2}\right)$

23. $\frac{7}{8} - \left(-\frac{1}{4}\right)$

24. $3\frac{1}{2} - 1\frac{7}{8}$

25. $-3\frac{4}{5} \times 1\frac{3}{10}$

Write an equation or inequality for the word sentence and solve.

26. The sum of x and three is seven.

27. A number t is the product of negative three fourths and one fifth.

28. The quotient of negative eight divided by w is seven.

29. The sum of x and twelve is greater than the product of x and 2.

Find the circumference of the circle described. Use $\pi \approx 3.14$.

30. diameter = 28 cm

31. radius = 3.3 m

32. diameter = 88.5 km

Solve the proportion.

33. $\frac{n}{4.8} = \frac{0.4}{1.2}$

34. $\frac{1.5}{n} = \frac{1}{4}$

35. $\frac{13}{14} = \frac{39}{n}$

36. $\frac{1.2}{2.0} = \frac{n}{3.0}$

Tell whether the ordered pair is a solution of the given equation.

$2x + y = 15$ **37.** (0, 12) **38.** (−5, 25) **39.** (5, 5) **40.** (4, 13)

Problems

Problem Solving Reminders

Here are some reminders that may help you solve some of the problems on this page.

- Sometimes more than one method can be used to solve.
- Consider whether making a sketch will help.
- When rounding an answer to division, consider whether it is reasonable to round up or round down.

Solve.

1. Bill Murphy earns \$4.85 an hour working in a day care center. Last week he worked from 1:00 P.M. to 4:30 P.M. on Monday through Friday. How much did he earn?

2. "I feel like I ran a mile," gasped Marge. If Marge ran 5 times around a circular track with a diameter of 210 ft, did she really run a mile? (*Hint:* 5280 ft = 1 mi)

3. Light travels at a speed of 297,600 km/s. If the circumference of Earth is about 39,800 km, about how many times could light travel around Earth in 1 s?

4. Michael Woolsey bought \$5671 worth of stock. The commission rate was \$28 plus 0.6% of the dollar amount. How much was the commission?

5. A car dealer is expecting a price increase of between $2\frac{1}{2}$% and 5% over the price of last year's models. If a certain car sold for \$9560 last year, what is the least it can be expected to sell for this year? the most?

6. Myra Daley was given an advance of \$18,000 on royalties expected from a book she wrote. If the selling price of the book is \$15.95 and her royalty rate is 5%, how many books must be sold before her royalties exceed her advance?

7. A baby that weighed 7 lb 6 oz at birth weighed 10 lb 10 oz at 6 weeks of age. To the nearest tenth of a percent, what was the percent of increase?

8. It took Thomas 25 min longer to do his math homework than to do his French homework. He spent a total of 2.25 h on both subjects. How much time did he spend on math?

9. If a microwave oven uses 1.5 kilowatt hours (kW·h) of electricity in 15 min, how much electricity does it use in 5 min?

9

Areas and Volumes

Many geometric figures are symmetric with regard to a point or a line. If you imagine the petals of the flower in the photograph rotated about its center, you will recognize an illustration of point symmetry. Starfish and snowflakes are other examples of objects in nature with point symmetry. Butterflies, trees, and human beings are examples of objects with line symmetry that occur in nature. Line or point symmetry can also be found in some letters of the English alphabet and other objects created by people.

In this chapter, you will learn how to determine whether figures are symmetric. You will also learn how to use symmetry in finding the areas of figures.

Career Note

Designing floral arrangements requires good color sense, a knowledge of flower care and handling, and a creative eye. Designers are usually expected to work from a customer's order that may specify color and type of flower, the occasion for the arrangement, and the amount of money to be spent.

9-1 Areas of Rectangles and Triangles

By the **area** of a polygon, we mean the measure of the part of the plane that the polygon encloses. We can find the area of the rectangle at the right by counting the unit squares it contains. The area is 12 cm^2. The same result can be found by multiplying the length of the rectangle by the width of the rectangle, as shown below.

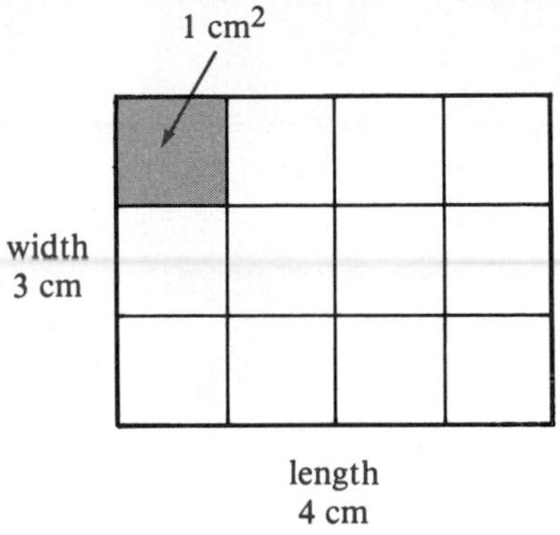

$$\text{Area} = 4 \times 3 = 12\ (\text{cm}^2).$$

This example suggests a formula for finding the area of any rectangle.

Formula

Area of rectangle = length × width

$$A = lw$$

When a rectangle is a square, all sides have equal measures. We usually use the simpler formula $A = s^2$, where s is the measure of a side.

To find a formula for the area of a triangle, choose any side to be the **base.** The word *base* is also used for the length of the base. The **height** of the triangle is the perpendicular distance from the opposite vertex to the base line.

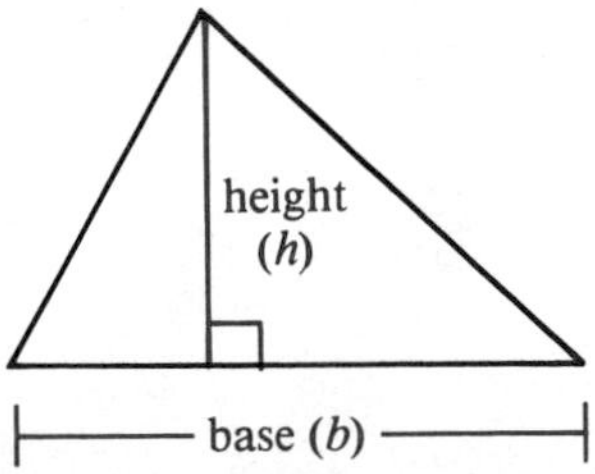

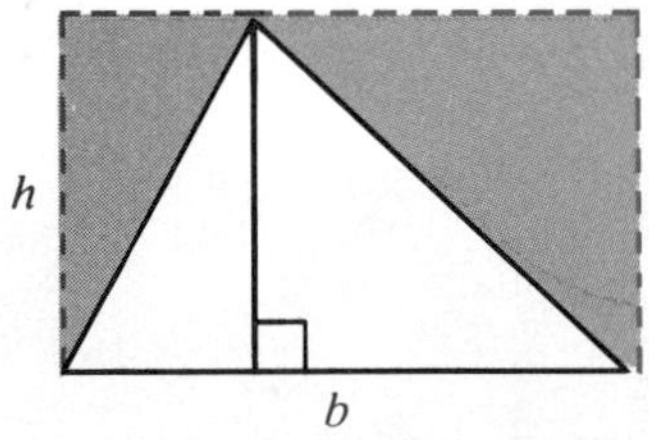

If you were to complete a rectangle around the triangle as shown at the right above, you would find that the areas of the red and blue regions together match exactly the area of the original triangle. Thus the triangle's area is exactly half the rectangle's area, which is bh.

Formula

Area of triangle $= \frac{1}{2} \times$ base $\times$ height

$$A = \frac{1}{2}bh$$

In the first paragraph, we used the square centimeter (cm^2) as the unit of area. In other cases we may use smaller or larger units, for example, the square millimeter (mm^2), square meter (m^2), or square kilometer (km^2). When a unit of length is not specified, we simply measure area in *square units*. We will usually not write the labels *units* and *square units*.

EXAMPLE 1 Find the area of the region pictured.

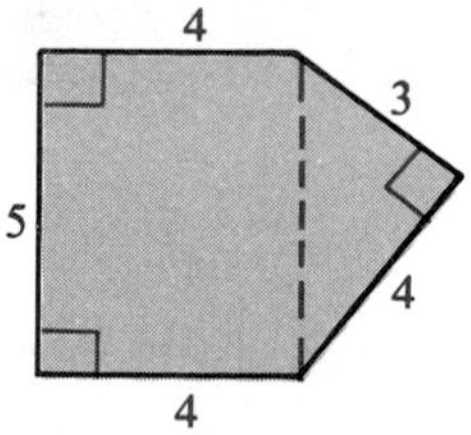

Solution The dashed line divides the region into a 5-by-4 rectangle and a triangle having base 4 and height 3. Notice that in a right triangle, one of the perpendicular sides can be considered the base. The length of the other perpendicular side can be considered the height.

First find the area of the rectangle.

$$A = bh = 5 \times 4 = 20$$

Then find the area of the triangle.

$$A = \frac{1}{2}bh = \frac{1}{2} \times 4 \times 3 = 6$$

Thus the total area is $20 + 6 = 26$ (square units).

To measure plots of land such as farms, the **hectare** (ha) can be used.

$$1 \text{ ha} = 10{,}000 \text{ m}^2 = 0.01 \text{ km}^2$$

EXAMPLE 2 A wheat field is a rectangle 5 km by 2.5 km. Find its area in hectares.

Solution $A = 5 \times 2.5 = 12.5$ (km^2)
Since 1 km^2 = 100 ha, 12.5 km^2 = 1250 ha.
The area of the field is 1250 ha.

Class Exercises

Find the area of the shaded region.

1.

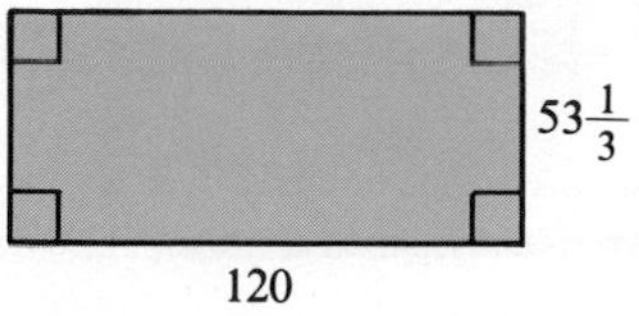

2.

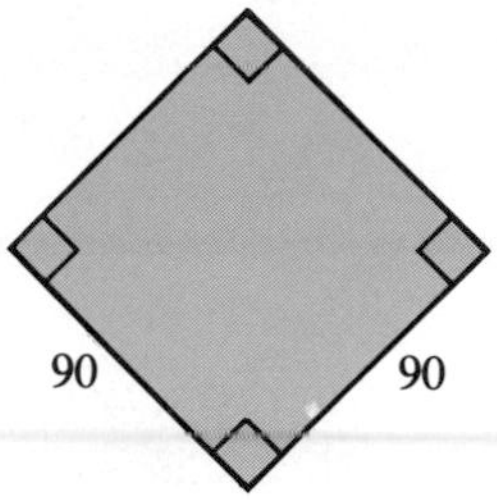

3.

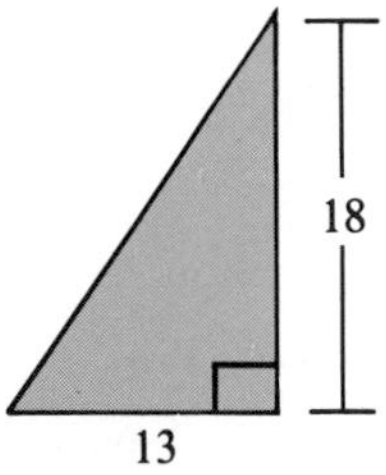

4.

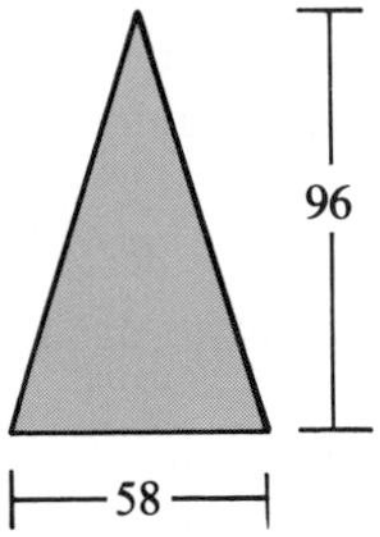

5. Find the perimeters of the shaded regions in Exercises 1 and 2.

6. What is the area of a square whose perimeter is 20 cm?

Complete.

7. 1 m = __?__ cm

1 m^2 = __?__ cm^2

8. 1 km = __?__ m

1 km^2 = __?__ m^2

9. 0.01 km^2 = __?__ ha

1 km^2 = __?__ ha

10. Choose a rectangular wall of your classroom and estimate its area in square meters.

Written Exercises

Find the area of each shaded region.

A

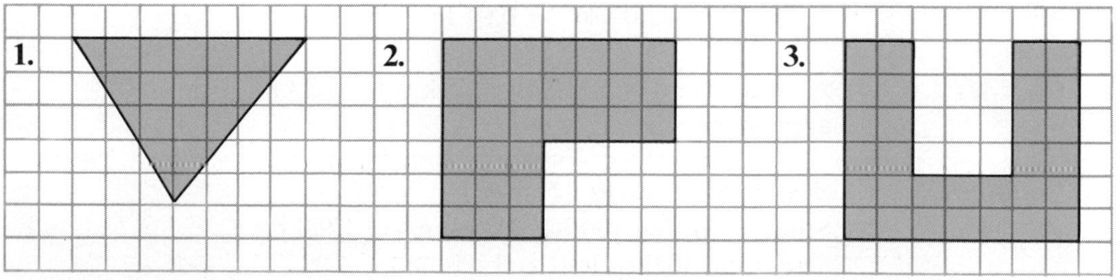

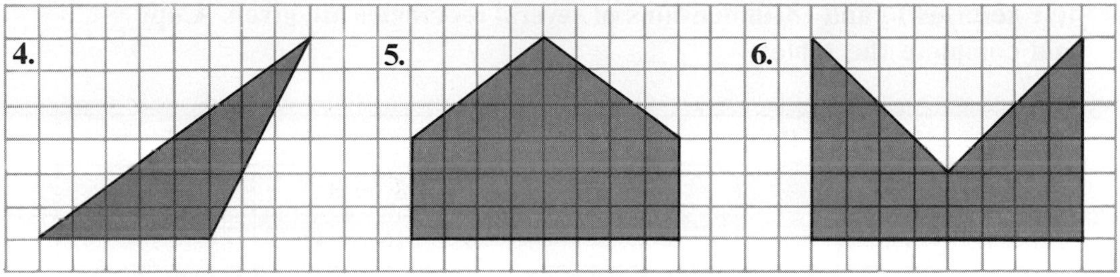

Find the perimeter and the area of the polygon.

7.
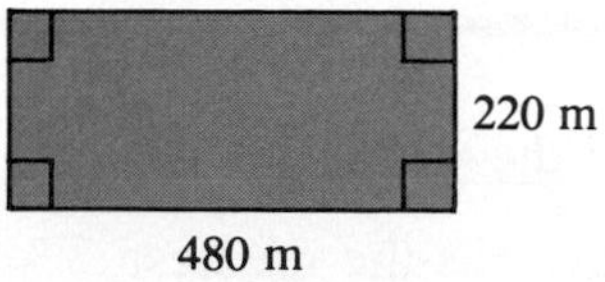

8.
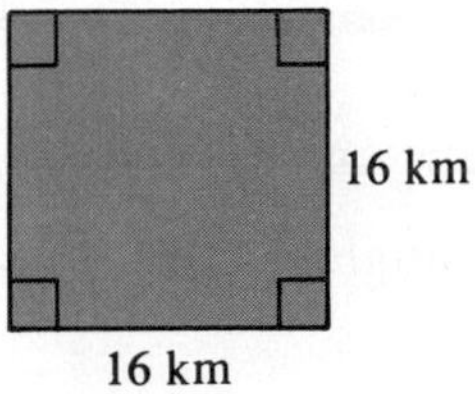

9.
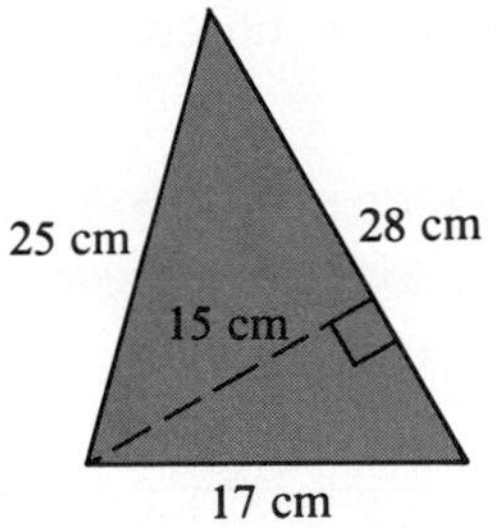

10.
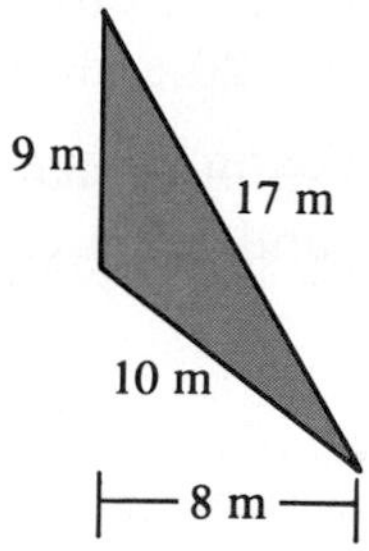

11. How many hectares are in a square field 27 km on a side?

12. How many hectares are in a rectangular field 360 m by 140 m?

13. A 2000 ha field is 2.5 km long. How wide is it?

14. A 36 ha field is 480 m wide. How long is it?

Find the length of the segment printed in red.

15.
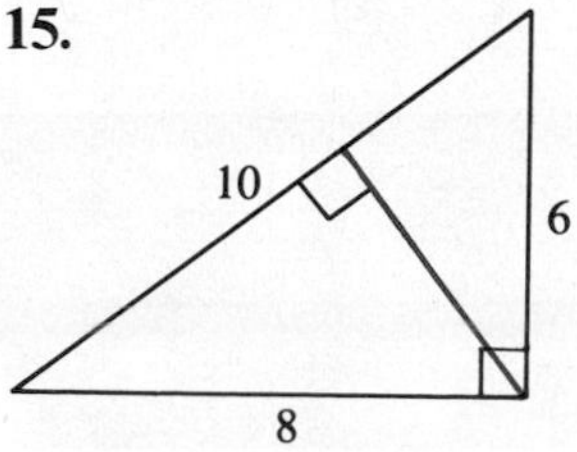

16.
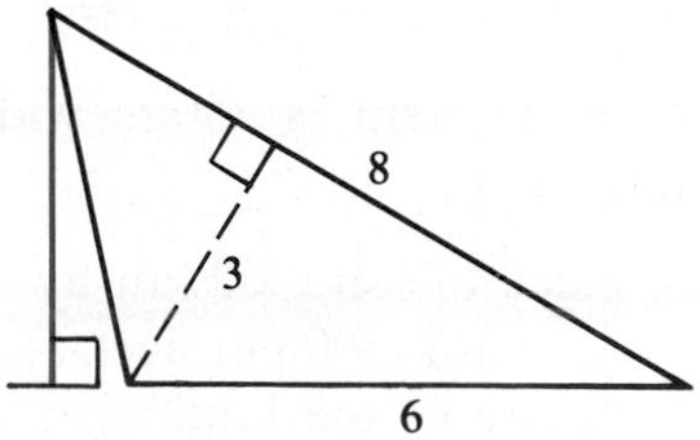

In Exercises 17 and 18, dimensions of several rectangles are given. Copy and complete the tables.

17.

Dimensions	Perimeter	Area
10 by 10	?	?
12 by 8	?	?
18 by 2	?	?
19 by 1	?	?

18.

Dimensions	Perimeter	Area
8 by 8	?	?
16 by 4	?	?
32 by 2	?	?
64 by 1	?	?

Use the evidence of Exercises 17 and 18 to complete these statements.

B **19.** Of all rectangles with a given perimeter, the square has the greatest __?__.

20. Of all rectangles with a given area, the square has the least __?__.

C **21.** Use Exercise 19 or 20 to explain why there can be no rectangle having perimeter 20 and area 36.

22. If the dimensions of a triangle are doubled, the perimeter is multiplied by __?__, and the area is multiplied by __?__.

Problems

A **1.** A particular carpet sells for $7 per square foot. What is the cost of the carpet needed to cover a floor 12 ft by 27 ft?

2. One can of paint will cover 24 m^2. How many cans should you buy to be sure that you have enough to cover a 16 m by 8 m ceiling? (You may have paint left over.)

3. A 21 ha field is 350 m wide. How long is it?

4. A piece of land 1.2 km by 3.6 km is for sale at $1500 per hectare. What is the price of the land?

5. Sixty meters of fencing enclose a square corral. What is the area of the corral?

6. A field 480,000 m^2 is 160 m wide. What length of fencing is needed to enclose it?

7. Find the total area of the sails shown below.

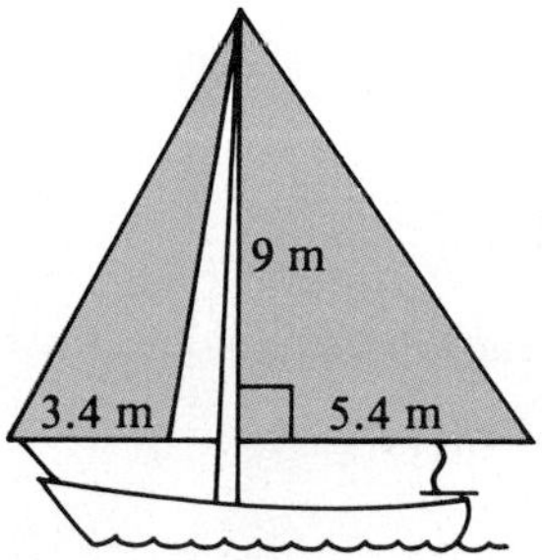

Ex. 7

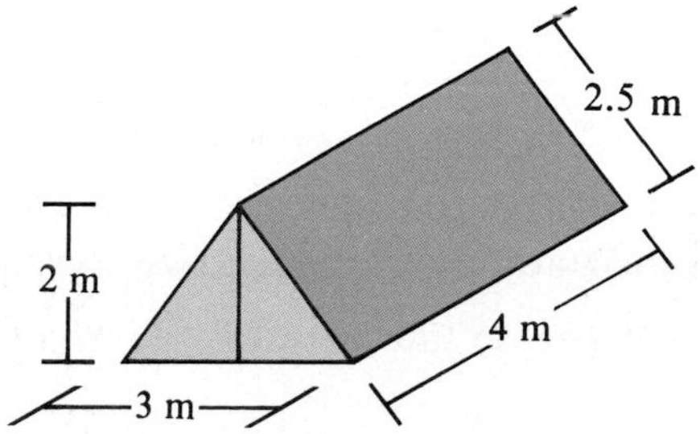

Ex. 8

8. The ends of the tent shown above are mosquito netting costing $3.50 per square meter, and the rest of the tent, including the floor, is canvas costing $15 per square meter. What is the total cost of these materials?

B 9. A brick walk 2 m wide surrounds a rectangular pool that is 3 m by 5 m. Find the area of the walk.

10. How many square vinyl tiles, 20 cm on a side, are needed to cover a floor 6 m by 5 m?

C 11. How many square tiles, 9 in. on a side, are needed to cover a floor 12 ft by 21 ft?

Review Exercises

Evaluate each expression using the given values of the variables.

$a + b$	**1.** $a = 119,\ b = 61$	**2.** $a = 5.7,\ b = 0.65$
$2x + 2y$	**3.** $x = 18,\ y = 26$	**4.** $x = 16.5,\ y = 4.9$
$\frac{1}{2}(c + d)$	**5.** $c = 12,\ d = 22$	**6.** $c = 5.6,\ d = 3.1$
$\frac{1}{2}(x + y)z$	**7.** $x = 4,\ y = 11,\ z = 8$	**8.** $x = 12.3,\ y = 6.44,\ z = 8.2$

9-2 Areas of Quadrilaterals

Either pair of parallel sides of a parallelogram can be taken to be the **bases.** The **height** is the perpendicular distance between the base lines.

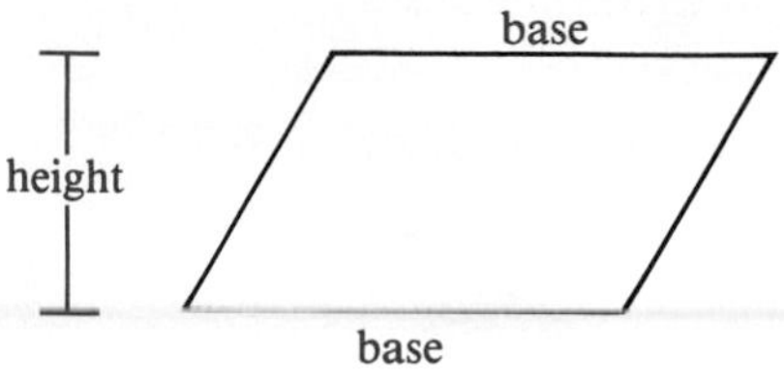

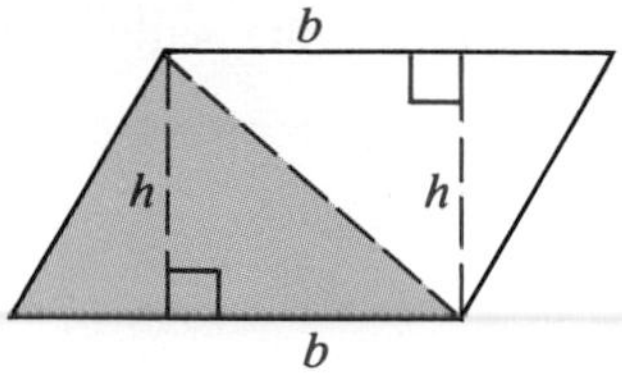

The parallelogram at the right above has base b and height h. A diagonal divides the parallelogram into two congruent triangles, each having area $\frac{1}{2}bh$. Therefore, the area of the parallelogram is two times $\frac{1}{2}bh$, that is, bh.

Formula

Area of parallelogram = base × height

$$A = bh$$

EXAMPLE 1 Find (a) the perimeter and (b) the area of the parallelogram.

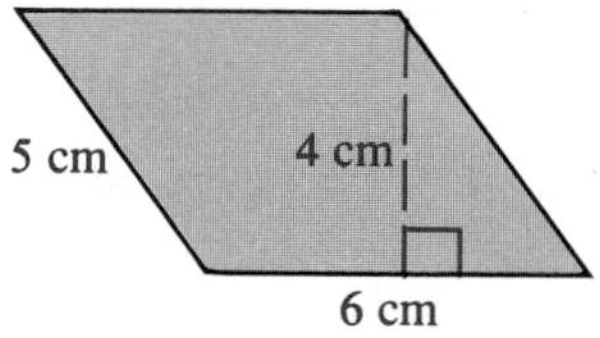

Solution

a. Since opposite sides of a parallelogram are congruent,

$p = (2 \times 5) + (2 \times 6) = 22.$

The perimeter is 22 cm.

b. $A = bh$
$= 6 \times 4 = 24$

The area is 24 cm^2.

The **height** of a trapezoid is the perpendicular distance between its parallel sides, which are called its **bases.** Let us find a formula for the area of a trapezoid having bases b_1 and b_2 and height h. This trapezoid and a congruent copy of it can be put together to form a parallelogram as shown on the next page.

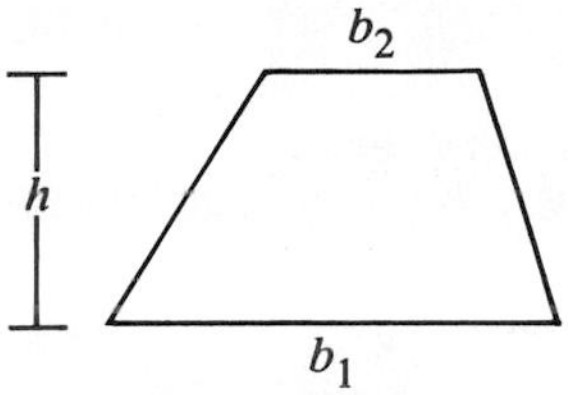

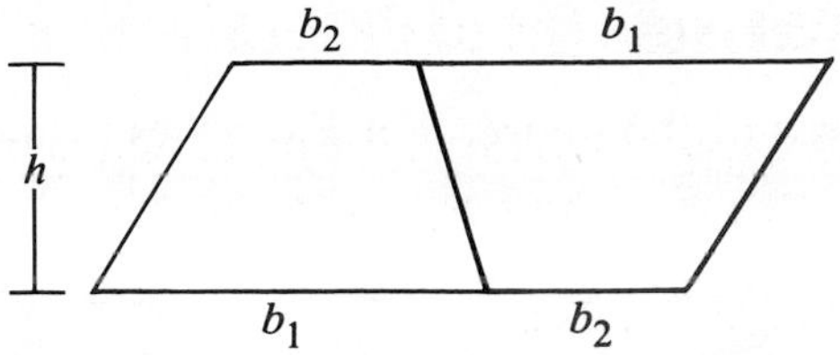

The parallelogram has area $(b_1 + b_2)h$, and this is twice the area of the original trapezoid. Therefore:

Formula

Area of trapezoid $= \frac{1}{2} \times$ (sum of bases) $\times$ height

$$A = \frac{1}{2}(b_1 + b_2)h$$

EXAMPLE 2 Find the area of a trapezoid with height 5 m and bases 2 m and 4 m.

Solution

$$A = \frac{1}{2}(b_1 + b_2)h$$

$$= \frac{1}{2}(2 + 4) \times 5 = 15$$

The area of the trapezoid is 15 m^2.

EXAMPLE 3 Find the area of the quadrilateral $ABCD$.

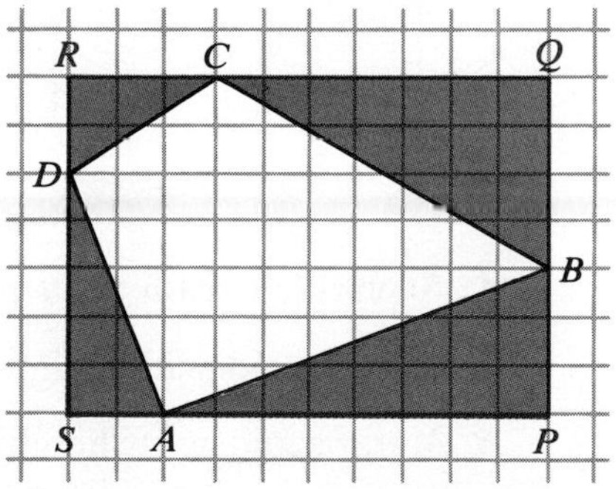

Solution Subtract the areas of the corner triangles from the area of rectangle $PQRS$.

Area $PQRS = 10 \times 7 = 70$

Area $\triangle APB = \frac{1}{2} \times 8 \times 3 = 12$

Area $\triangle BQC = \frac{1}{2} \times 7 \times 4 = 14$

Area $\triangle CRD = \frac{1}{2} \times 3 \times 2 = 3$

Area $\triangle DSA = \frac{1}{2} \times 2 \times 5 = 5$

Area $PQRS$ − areas of triangles $= 70 - (12 + 14 + 3 + 5) = 36$

Class Exercises

Find the area of the figure. For Exercises 5 and 6, give your answers in hectares.

1.

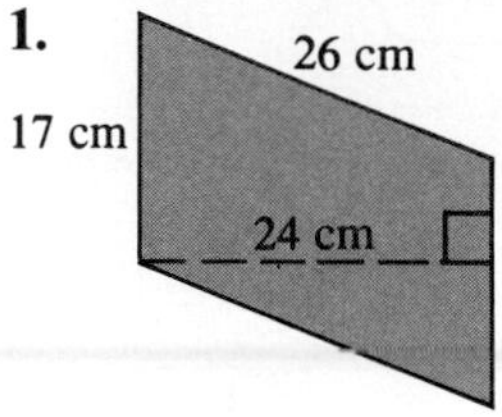

Parallelogram

2.

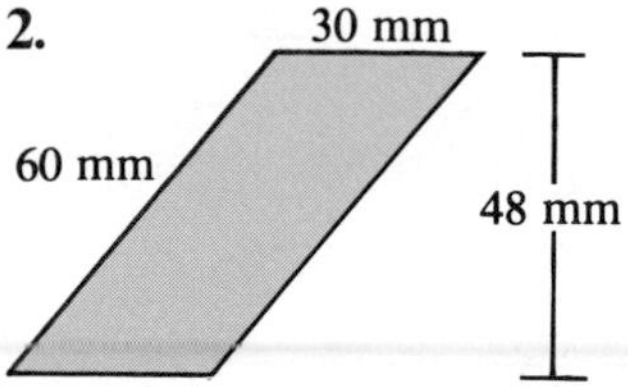

Parallelogram

3.

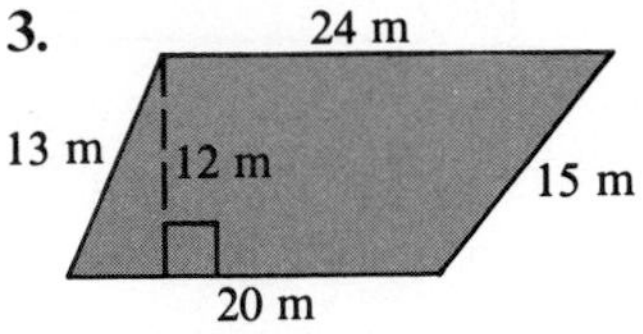

Trapezoid

4.

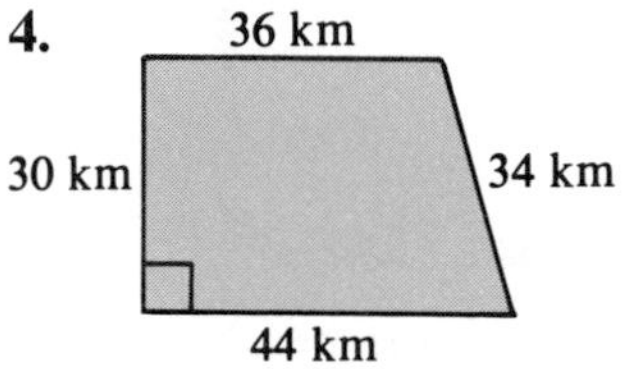

Trapezoid

5.

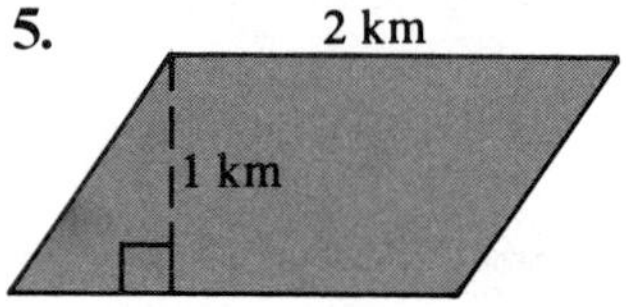

Parallelogram

6.

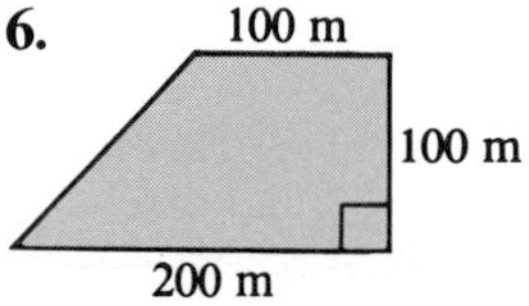

Trapezoid

Written Exercises

Find the area of the trapezoid or parallelogram.

A **1.**

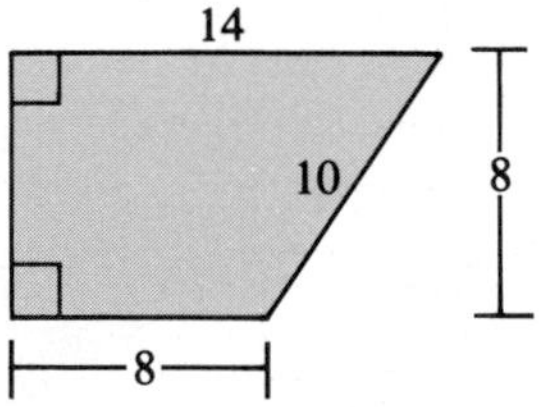

2.

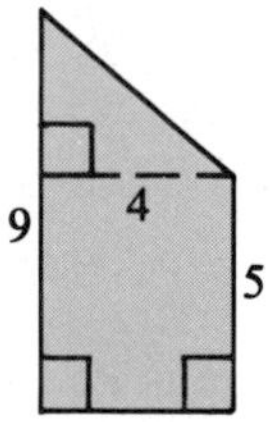

3.

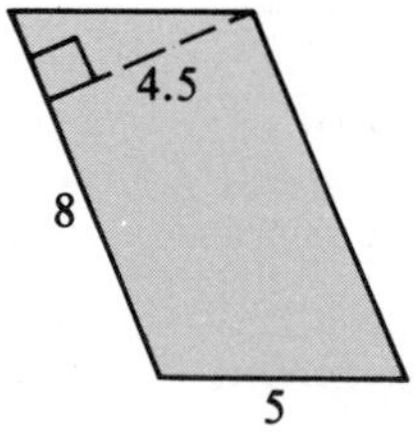

4. A parallelogram with base 15 cm and height 6 cm

5. A trapezoid with height 8 m and bases 18 m and 12 m

6. A trapezoid with height 12 cm and bases 14.5 cm and 5.5 cm

7. A parallelogram with height 5.2 km and base 11.4 km

Exercises 8 and 9 refer to parallelograms. Complete.

8. Area = 360 km^2, base = 15 km, height = __?__

9. Area = 175 cm^2, height = 12.5 cm, base = __?__

Exercises 10 and 11 refer to trapezoids. Complete.

10. Area = 336 m^2, bases = 7 m and 14 m, height = _?_

11. Area = 132 m^2, height = 12 m, one base = 16 m, other base = _?_

12. Gina and Tom found the area of parallelogram *ABCD* in different ways. Who was correct?

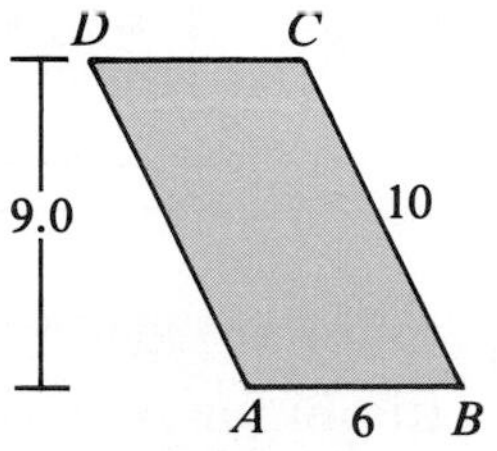

Gina

$A = 6 \times 9.0$

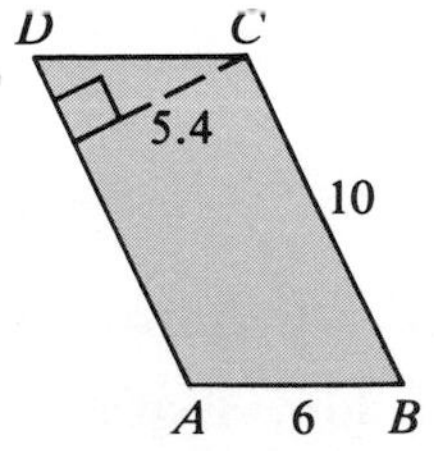

Tom

$A = 10 \times 5.4$

Find the area of each quadrilateral.

B

13.

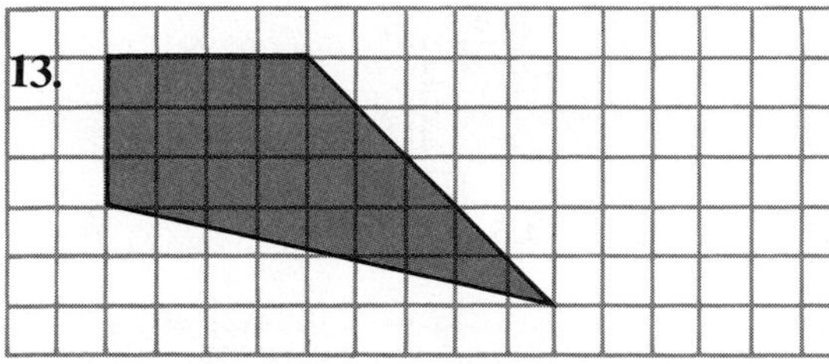

14.

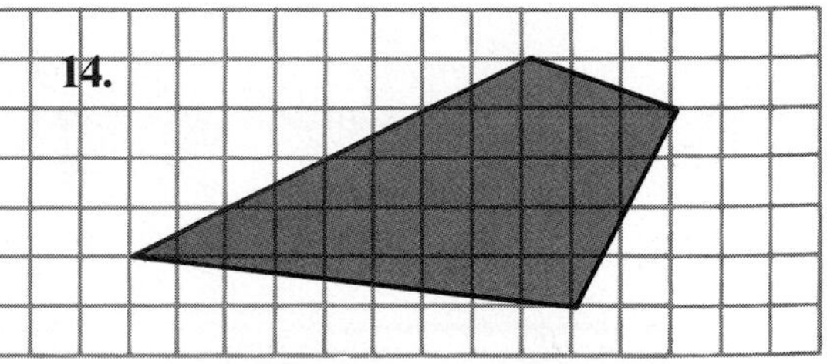

15.

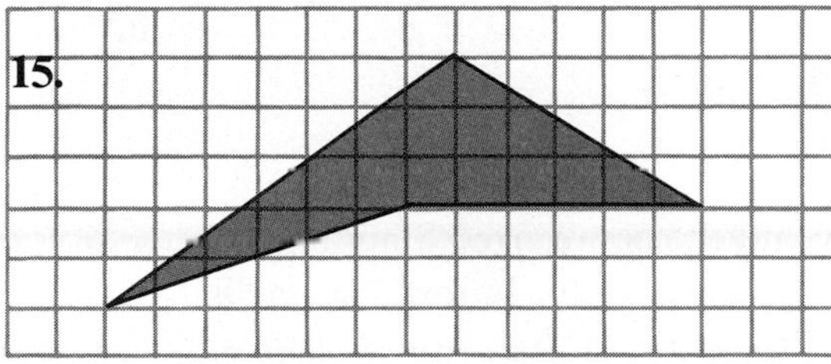

16.

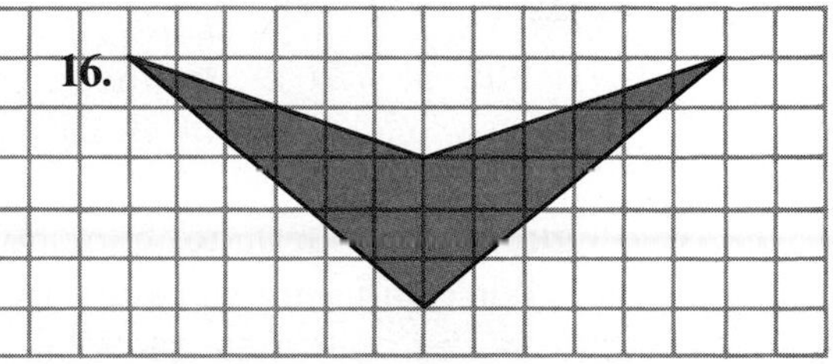

Find the length of the segment printed in red in the parallelogram.

17.

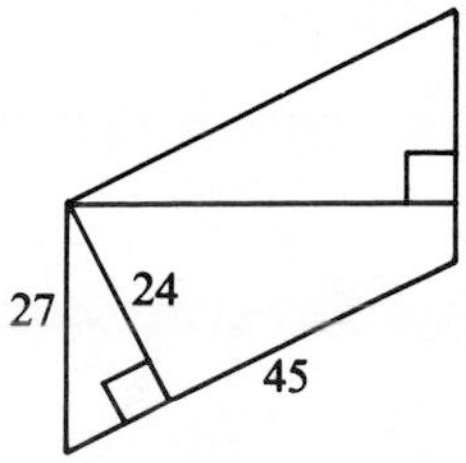

18.

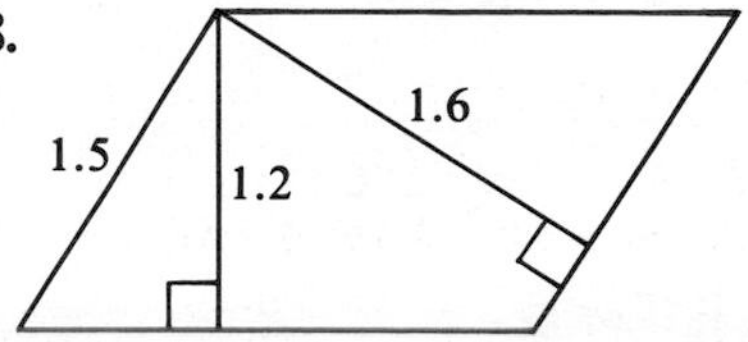

19. The diagonals of a rhombus are perpendicular and bisect each other. Find the area of a rhombus whose diagonals are 8 cm and 20 cm long.

Find the area of the figure by first dividing it into simpler regions. The figure in Exercise 21 has three pairs of parallel sides.

20.

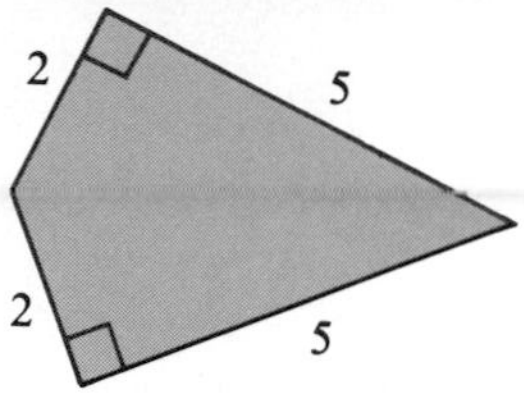

21.

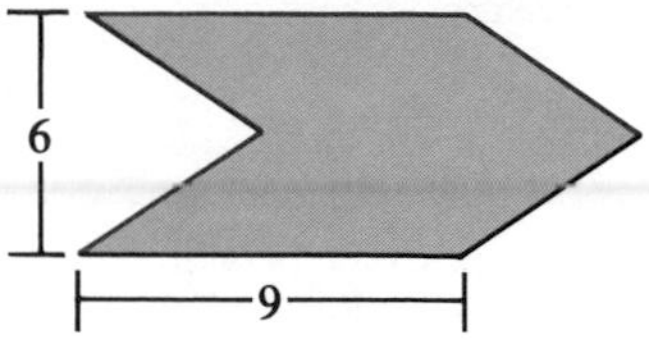

Refer to the diagrams below. Express each ratio in lowest terms.

22. a. $RS:OP$ **b.** $ST:PQ$ **c.** $TR:QO$
d. Perimeter of $\triangle RST$:Perimeter of $\triangle OPQ$
e. Area of $\triangle RST$:Area of $\triangle OPQ$

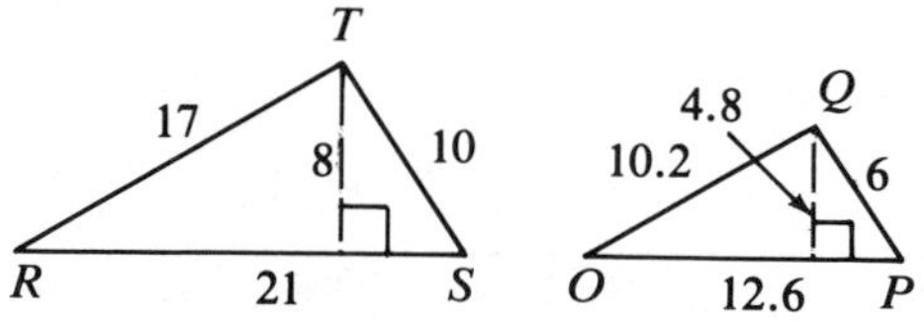

Ex. 22

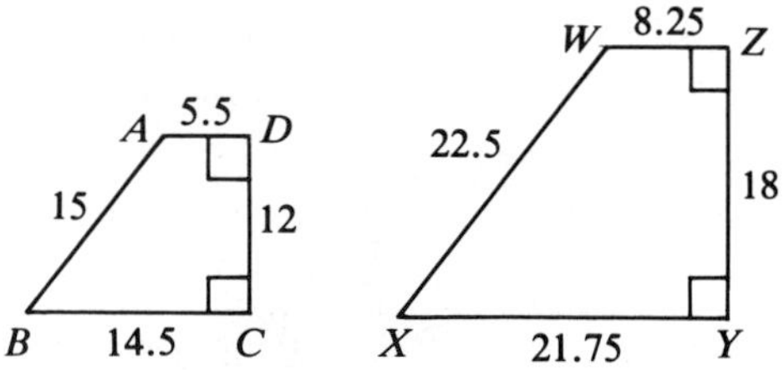

Ex. 23

23. a. $AB:WX$ **b.** $BC:XY$ **c.** $CD:YZ$ **d.** $AD:WZ$
e. Perimeter of $ABCD$:Perimeter of $WXYZ$
f. Area of $ABCD$:Area of $WXYZ$

C 24. Two figures have the same shape but not the same size. The lengths of their corresponding sides are in the ratio given below. What is the ratio of their perimeters? What is the ratio of their areas? (*Hint:* Refer to Exercises 22 and 23.)
a. 2:1 **b.** 3:4

Review Exercises

Complete.

1. $1^2 = \underline{\ ?\ }$ **2.** $5^2 = \underline{\ ?\ }$ **3.** $8^2 = \underline{\ ?\ }$ **4.** $0.3^2 = \underline{\ ?\ }$ **5.** $1.2^2 = \underline{\ ?\ }$

6. $\underline{\ ?\ }^2 = 16$ **7.** $\underline{\ ?\ }^2 = 49$ **8.** $\underline{\ ?\ }^2 = 100$ **9.** $\underline{\ ?\ }^2 = 0.36$ **10.** $\underline{\ ?\ }^2 = 1.21$

9-3 Areas of Circles

We know that the circumference, C, of a circle of radius r is given by the formula $C = 2\pi r$. Two approximations for the number π are $\pi \approx 3.14$ and $\pi \approx \frac{22}{7}$.

The area of a circle is given by this formula:

> ***Formula***
>
> Area of circle $= \pi \times (\text{radius})^2$
>
> $A = \pi r^2$

EXAMPLE 1 Find the area of the shaded region. Use $\pi \approx 3.14$.

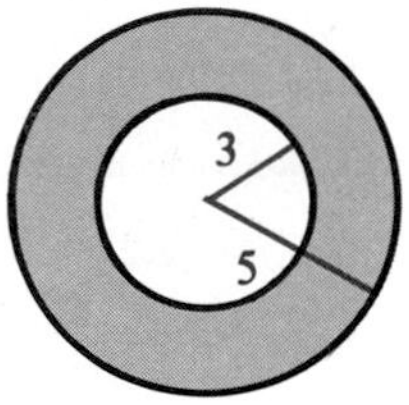

Solution Subtract the area of the small circle from the area of the large circle.

Area of large circle $= \pi \times 5^2$
$\approx 3.14 \times 25 = 78.5$

Area of small circle $= \pi \times 3^2 \approx 3.14 \times 9 = 28.26$

Area of shaded region $\approx 78.5 - 28.26 = 50.24$

Rounded to three digits, the area of the shaded region is approximately 50.2.

EXAMPLE 2 Find the radius of a circle whose area is $201\frac{1}{7}$. Use $\pi \approx \frac{22}{7}$.

Solution Substitute $201\frac{1}{7}$ for A in the formula $A = \pi r^2$.

$$201\frac{1}{7} = \pi r^2$$

$$201\frac{1}{7} \approx \frac{22}{7} \times r^2$$

$$\frac{1408}{7} \times \frac{7}{22} \approx \frac{22}{7} \times \frac{7}{22} \times r^2$$

$$64 \approx r^2$$

Since $8^2 = 64$, $r \approx 8$.

To avoid approximations when working with circles, we often give answers *in terms of* π. Any time we need a decimal answer, we can replace π by 3.14 or some other approximation.

EXAMPLE 3 Find (a) the radius and (b) the circumference of a circle whose area is 49π. Leave your answer in terms of π.

Solution **a.** Substitute 49π for A in the formula for area.

$$A = \pi r^2$$

$$49\pi = \pi r^2$$

$$\frac{49\pi}{\pi} = \frac{\pi r^2}{\pi}$$

$$49 = r^2$$

Since $7^2 = 49$, $r = 7$.

b. Use $r = 7$ in the formula for circumference.

$$\begin{aligned} C &= 2\pi r \\ &= 2\pi \times 7 \\ &= 14\pi \end{aligned}$$

The circumference is 14π.

Class Exercises

1. Find the area of a circle whose radius is 7 cm. Use $\pi \approx \frac{22}{7}$.

2. Find the area of a circle whose diameter is 20 km. Use $\pi \approx 3.14$.

3. A circle has radius 8. What is the area? Use $\pi \approx 3.14$.

4. A circle has diameter 10. What is the area? Use $\pi \approx \frac{22}{7}$.

5. The circumference of a circle is 12π.
a. Find the radius. **b.** Find the area.

6. The circumference of a circle is 2π.
a. Find the radius. **b.** Find the area.

Written Exercises

Find the area of the circle described. Use $\pi \approx \frac{22}{7}$.

A **1.** radius = 21 km **2.** diameter = 21 km

3. diameter = 1.4 cm **4.** radius = 1.4 cm

Find the area of the circle described. Use $\pi \approx 3.14$.

5. radius = 4 m

6. radius = 10 m

7. diameter = 10 cm

8. diameter = 12 cm

9. circumference = 94.2 m

10. circumference = 6.28 m

In Exercises 11 and 12, use $\pi \approx 3.14$.

11. The area of a circle is 314 cm^2. Find the radius.

12. The area of a circle is 12.56 m^2. Find the radius.

The table gives data about circles. Copy and complete it, leaving your answers in terms of π.

B

	13.	**14.**	**15.**	**16.**	**17.**	**18.**
Radius	7	?	?	?	?	?
Diameter	?	18	?	?	?	?
Circumference	?	?	8π	30π	?	?
Area	?	?	?	?	25π	100π

19. If the radius of a circle is doubled, the area is multiplied by __?__.

20. If the radius of a circle is tripled, the area is multiplied by __?__.

Find the area of the shaded region. Leave your answer in terms of π.

21.

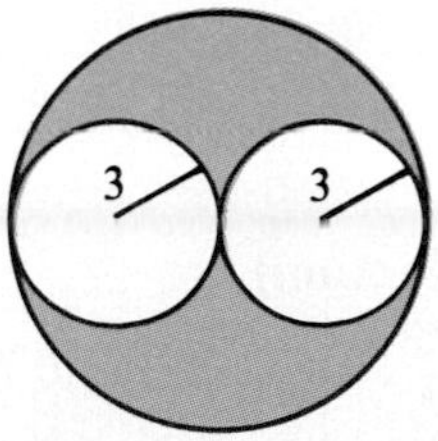

22.

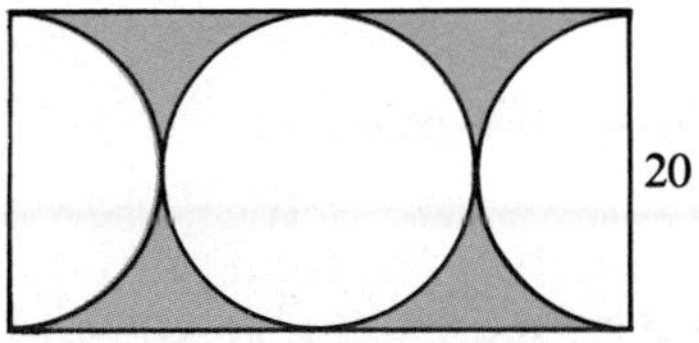

C **23.**

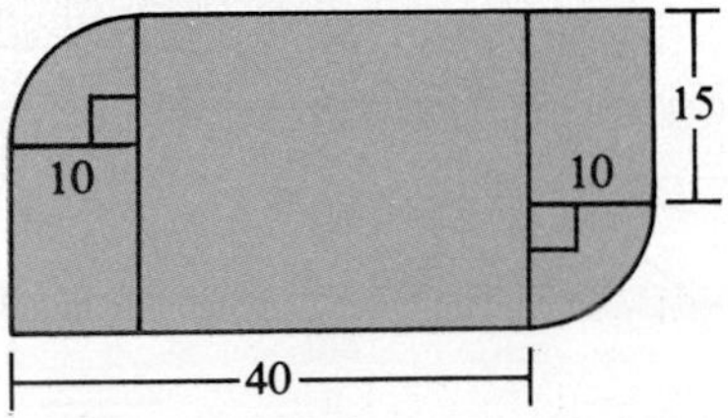

24.

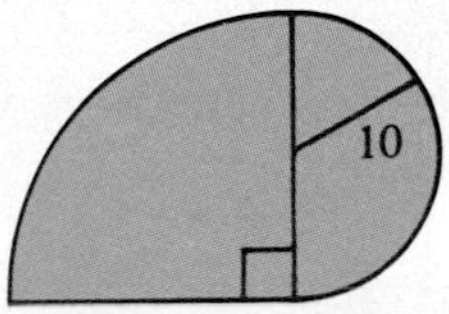

Problems

Solve. Use $\pi \approx 3.14$.

A **1.** A circular pond 12 m in diameter is surrounded by a brick walk 3 m wide. Find the areas of the pond and the walk.

2. The bull's eye of an archery target is 10 cm in diameter, and each ring is 5 cm wide. Find the areas of the first, second, and third rings.

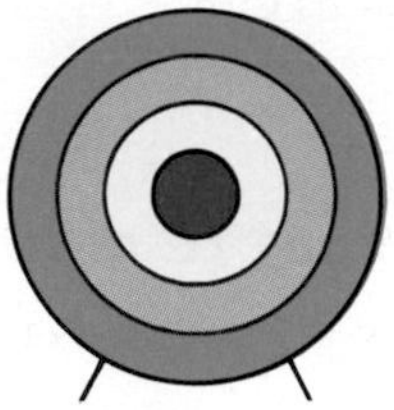

Ex. 2

Problems 3–6 refer to the running track pictured at the right.

B **3.** Find the inside perimeter of the track.

4. Find the outside perimeter of the track.

5. Find the area of the region inside the track.

6. Find the area of the track surface.

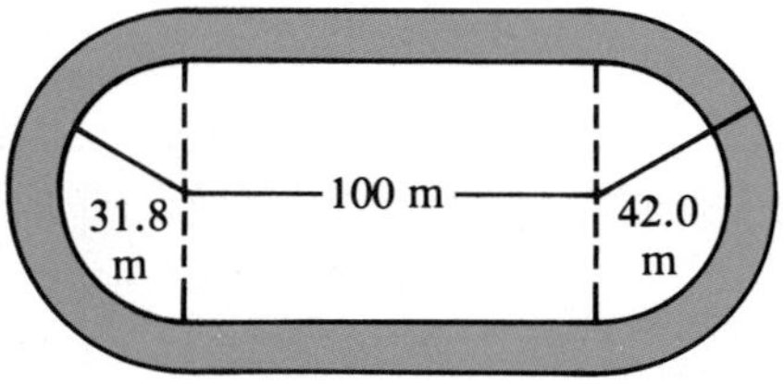

Exs. 3–6

C **7.** A circle is inscribed in a square (four points of the circle are on the square). What percent of the area of the square is outside the circle?

8. A square is inscribed in a circle (all vertices of the square are on the circle). What percent of the area of the circle is outside the square?

Review Exercises

State which of the rigid motions (translation, rotation, or reflection) are needed to match the vertices of the congruent figures.

1. 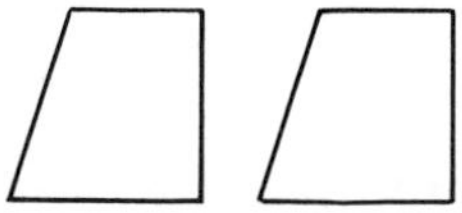

2. 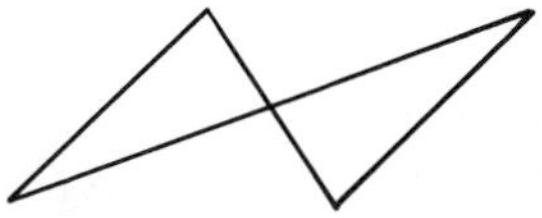

3. 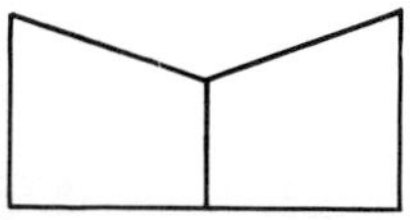

4. 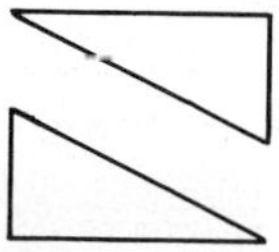

5. 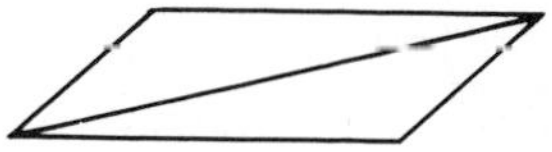

6. 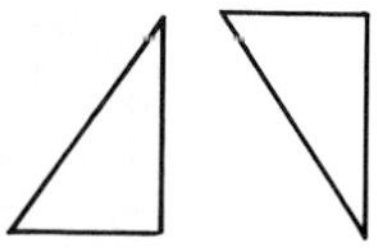

9-4 Areas of Symmetric Figures

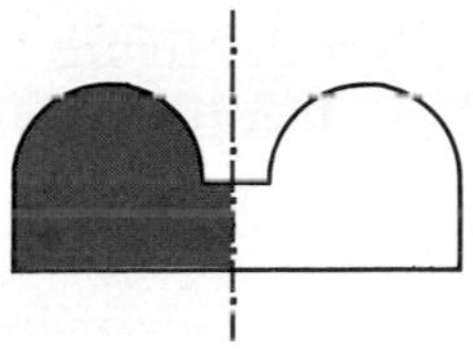

If we could fold the figure at the right along the dot-dash line l, the shaded region would fall exactly on the region that is not shaded. We say that the figure is **symmetric with respect to the line** l and that l is a **line of symmetry.** A figure can have more than one line of symmetry, as illustrated below.

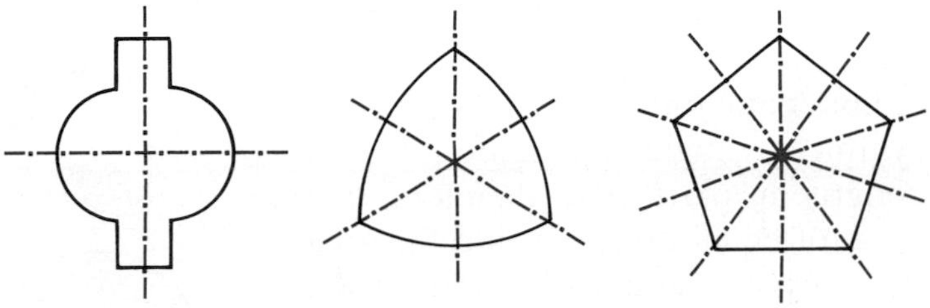

Often we can take advantage of symmetry when finding areas of figures.

EXAMPLE 1 Find the area of the figure pictured at the right. The dot-dash line is a line of symmetry.

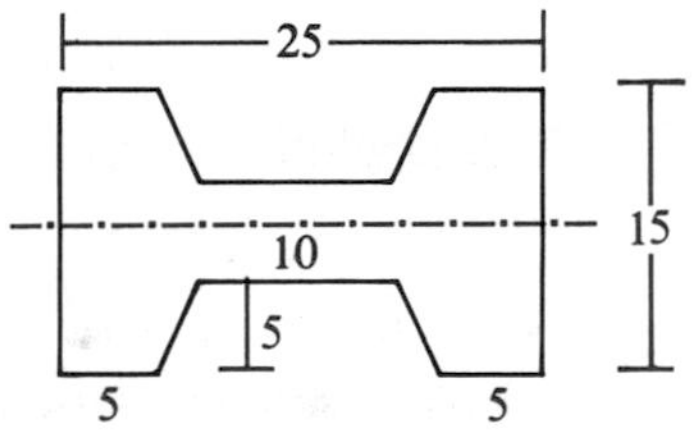

Solution We can think of the region as a rectangle with two trapezoids removed.

First find the area of the rectangle.

$$A = bh = 25 \times 15 = 375$$

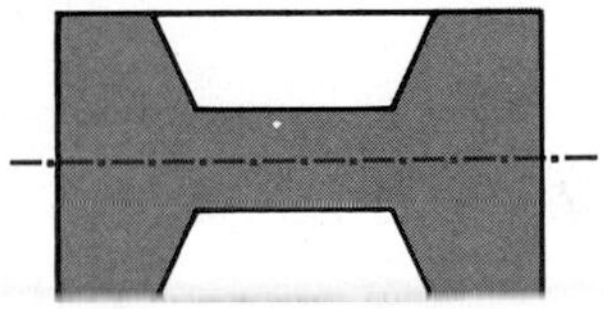

Then find the area of one trapezoid. One base has length 10. The other base has length

$$25 - (5 + 5) = 15.$$

The height is 5.

$$A = \frac{1}{2}(b_1 + b_2)h = \frac{1}{2}(10 + 15)5 = 62.5$$

Because of symmetry, the trapezoids have equal areas. Subtract the areas of the two trapezoids from the area of the rectangle.

$$\text{Area of region} = 375 - (2 \times 62.5) = 250$$

A figure is **symmetric with respect to a point** O if for every point P on the figure, there is an "opposite" point Q on the figure such that O is the midpoint of $\overline{PQ}$.

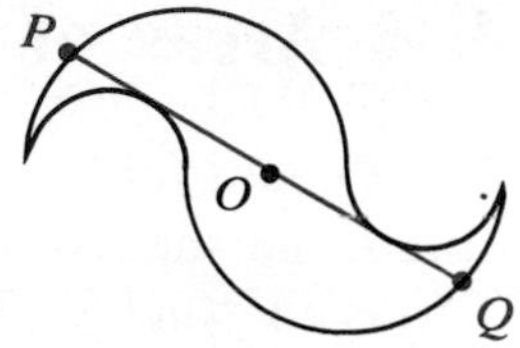

If a figure is symmetric with respect to a point O, then any line through O divides it into two congruent figures.

EXAMPLE 2 The figure at the right is symmetric with respect to point O. Find the area of the shaded region. Use $\pi \approx 3.14$.

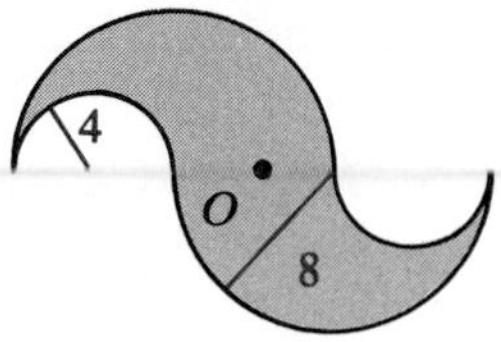

Solution A horizontal line through the point of symmetry divides the figure into two congruent parts and therefore two parts of equal area. To find the area of one part, subtract the area of the small semicircle from the area of the large semicircle. Recall that a semicircle is half of a circle so the area of a semicircle is half the area of a circle.

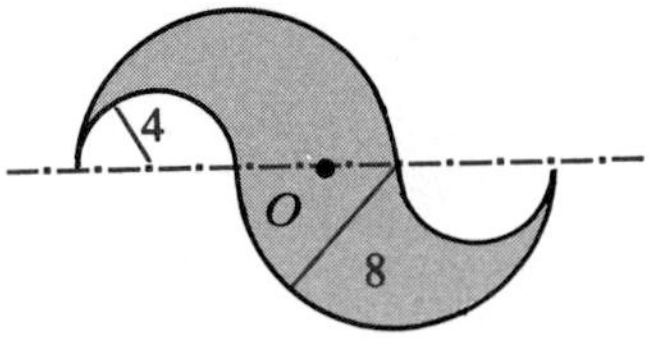

Large semicircle:

$$A = \frac{1}{2}\pi r^2 \approx \frac{1}{2} \times 3.14 \times 8^2 = \frac{1}{2} \times 3.14 \times 64 = 100.48$$

Small semicircle:

$$A = \frac{1}{2}\pi r^2 \approx \frac{1}{2} \times 3.14 \times 4^2 = \frac{1}{2} \times 3.14 \times 16 = 25.12$$

Area of part $\approx 100.48 - 25.12 = 75.36$

To find the area of the entire shaded region, multiply by 2.

$$\text{Area of region} \approx 2 \times 75.36 = 150.72$$

Rounded to three digits, the area is approximately 151.

Class Exercises

1. Draw a square and all of its lines of symmetry. Is it symmetric with respect to a point?

2. Draw an equilateral triangle and all of its lines of symmetry. Is it symmetric with respect to a point?

3. Does a circle have one, two, or infinitely many lines of symmetry? Is it symmetric with respect to a point?

Complete. In each of the two figures below, the red and blue regions are congruent because of symmetry.

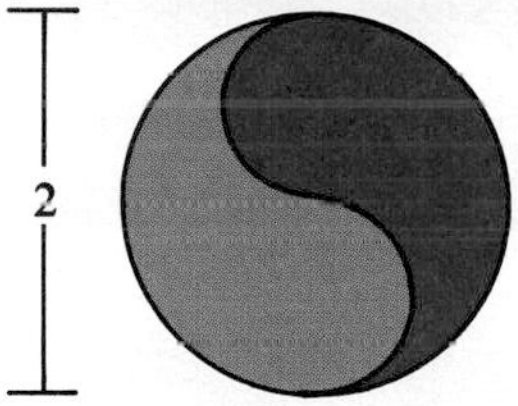

Ex. 4

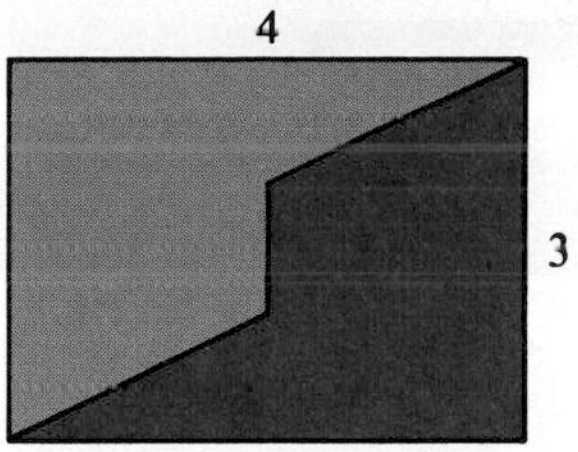

Ex. 5

4. The sum of the areas of the red and blue regions is __?__. Therefore the area of each is __?__.
5. The sum of the areas of the red and blue regions is __?__. Therefore the area of each is __?__.

Written Exercises

Copy the figure. Draw dashed lines to represent all lines of symmetry (if any) and mark each point of symmetry (if any) with a • .

A **1.**

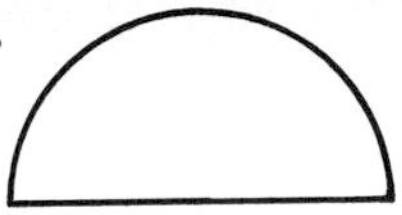

2.

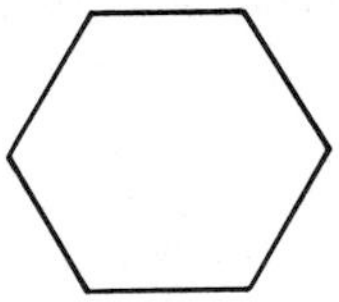

3.

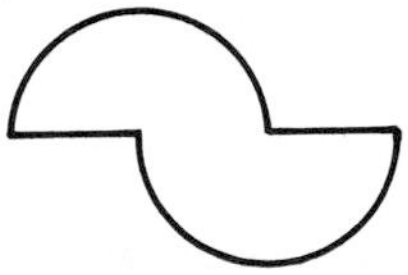

4.

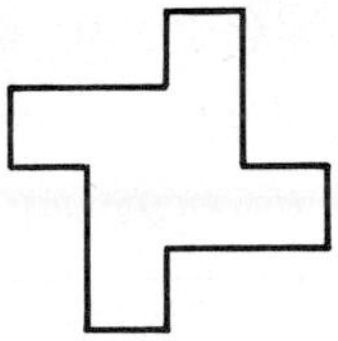

5.

6.

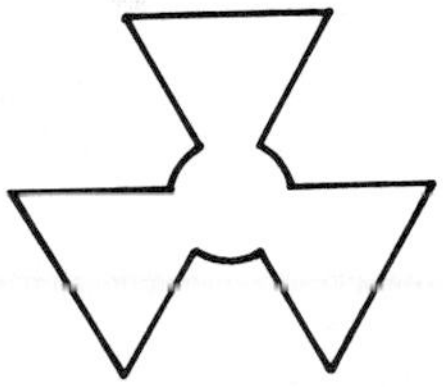

Find the area of the shaded region. Use the fact that the figure has symmetry. Use $\pi \approx 3.14$.

7.

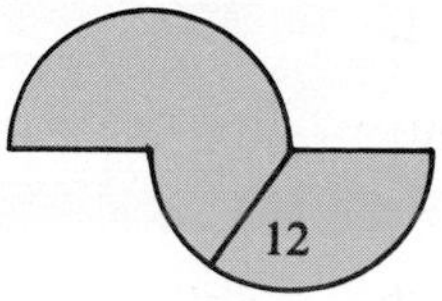

8.

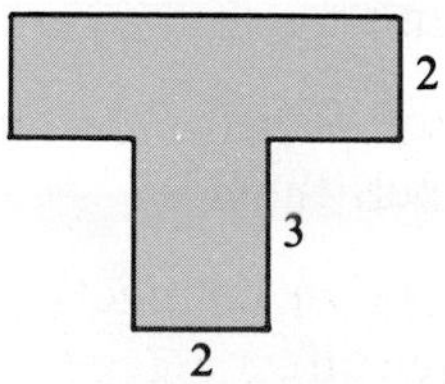

9.

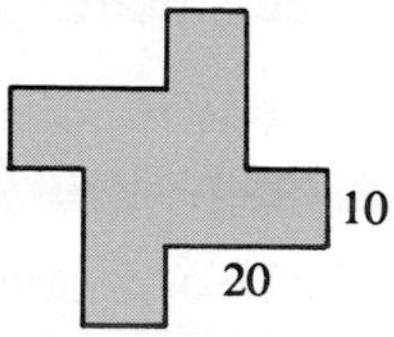

Find the area of the shaded region. Use the fact that the figure has symmetry. Use $\pi \approx 3.14$.

B 10.

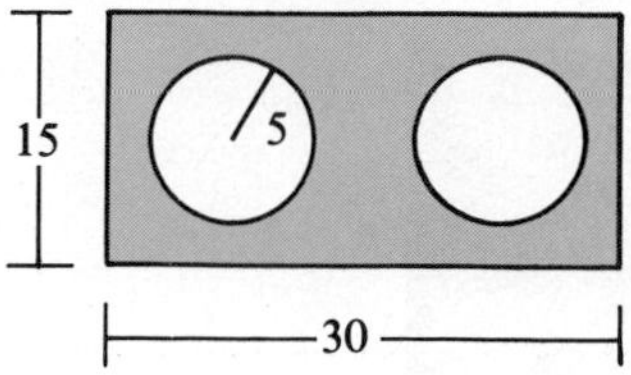

11.

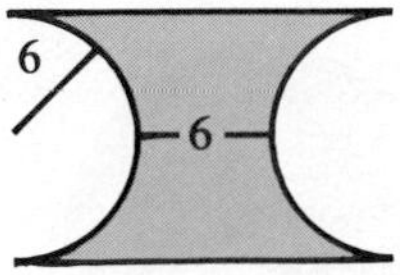

12.

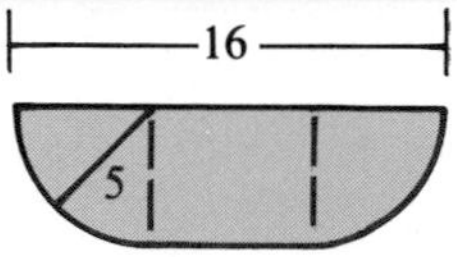

13.

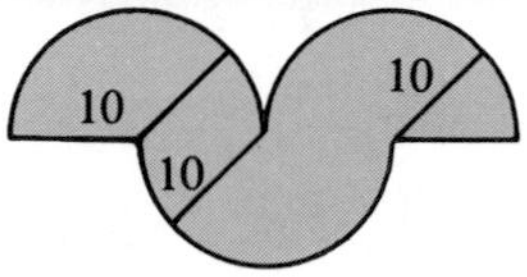

14.

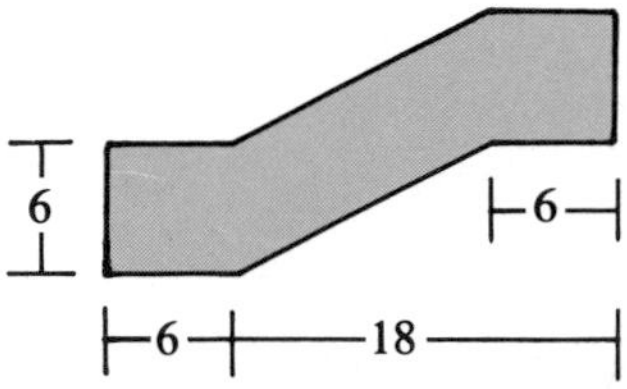

15.

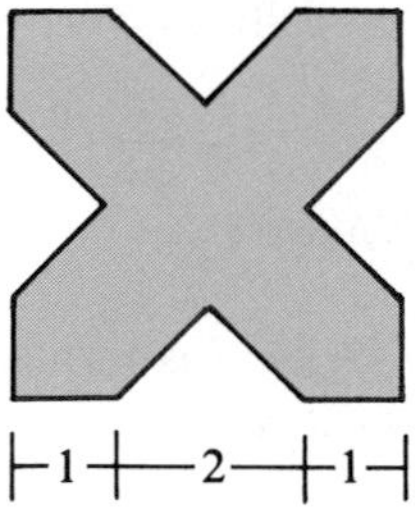

C 16.

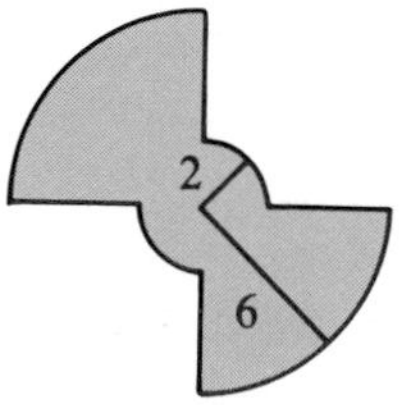

17.

18.

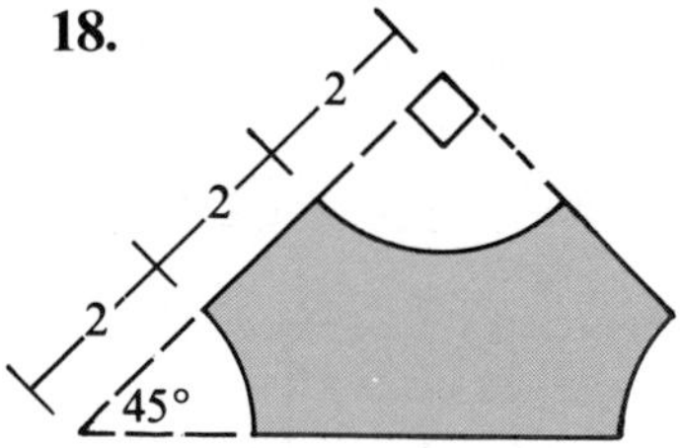

Challenge

Draw a square and then add a congruent square to one of its sides. Add a third congruent square to a side of one of the first two squares. There are exactly two ways (shown) to connect the three squares so that the resulting figures are not congruent.

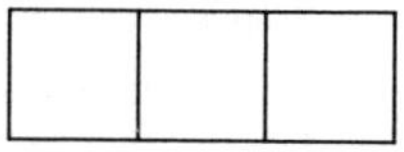

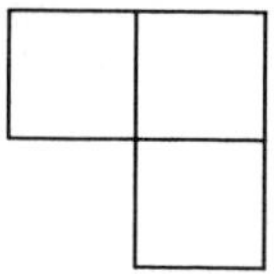

There are exactly five possibilities for connecting four congruent squares. Can you sketch them?

There are twelve possibilities for connecting five congruent squares. Can you sketch them all?

Self-Test A

Find the area of the region pictured.

[9-1]

1.

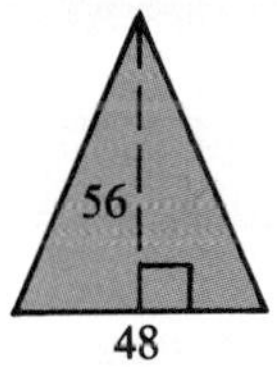

2.

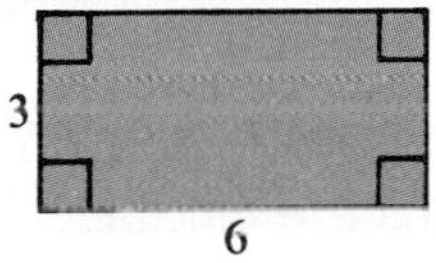

3.

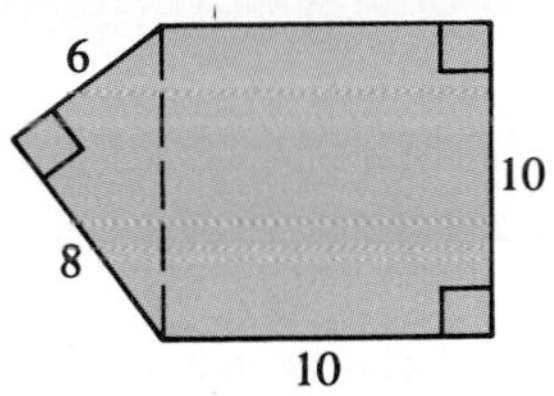

4. The area of a rectangular field is 140 ha. The field is 350 m wide. How long is it?

5. The area of a parallelogram is 120 cm^2. The base is 16 cm. What is the height?

6. The area of a parallelogram is 406 cm^2. The height is 14 cm. What is the base?

Find the area of the region pictured.

[9-2]

7.

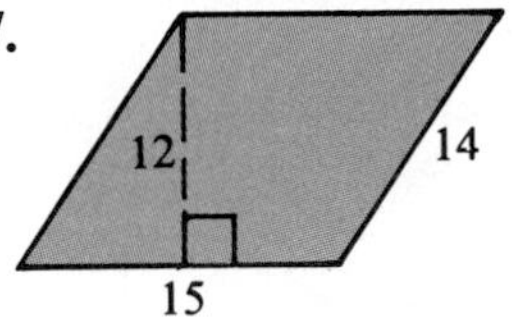

Parallelogram

8.

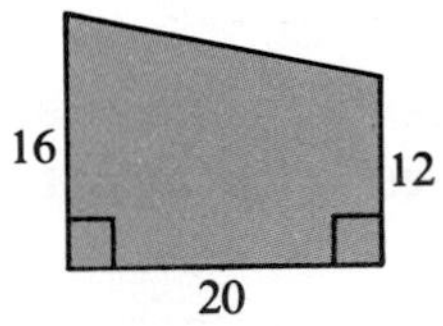

Trapezoid

Find the area of the circle described. Use $\pi \approx 3.14$.

9. radius = 2.5 cm **10.** diameter = 18 m **11.** circumference = 37.68 m **[9-3]**

Find the area of the shaded region. Use the fact that the figure has symmetry. Use $\pi \approx 3.14$.

[9-4]

12.

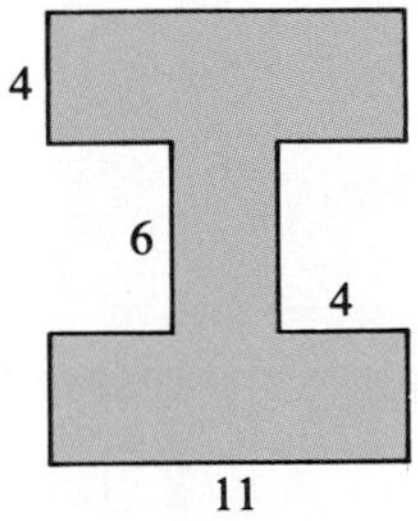

13.

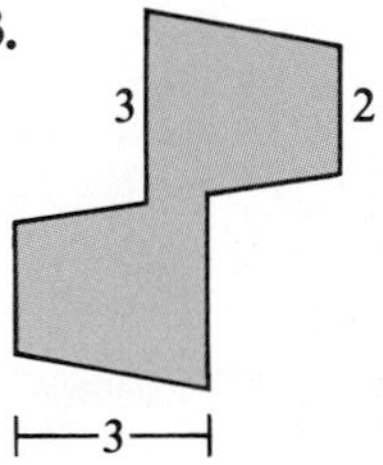

14.

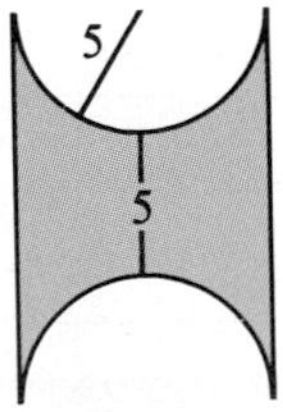

Self-Test answers and Extra Practice are at the back of the book.

9-5 Volumes of Prisms and Cylinders

A **polyhedron** is a figure formed of polygonal parts of planes, called **faces,** that enclose a region of space. A **prism** is a polyhedron that has two congruent faces, called **bases,** that are parallel. The other faces are regions bounded by parallelograms. The bases may also be parallelograms. Prisms are named according to their bases. Unless otherwise stated, we will only consider prisms whose faces are rectangles.

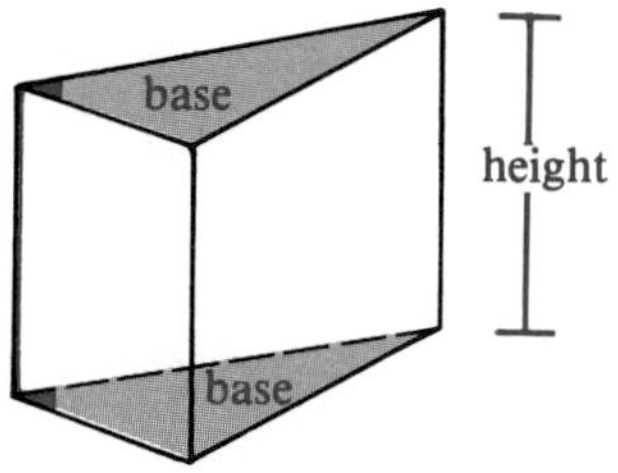

Triangular Prism

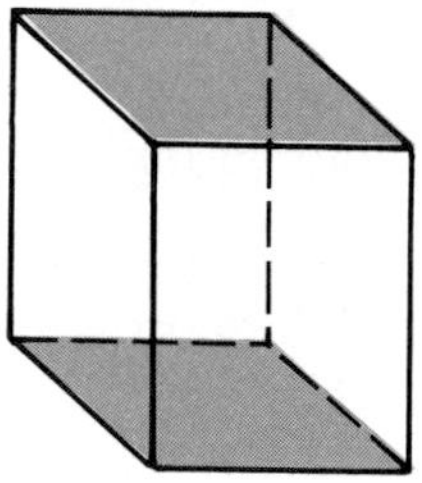

Square Prism

In each figure above, the bases are shaded. The perpendicular distance between the bases is the **height** of the prism.

A polyhedron together with the region inside it is called a **solid.** The measure of the space occupied by a solid is called the **volume** of the solid. The prism at the right, filled with 3 layers of 8 unit cubes, has 24 unit cubes. In this case, each unit cube is a cubic centimeter (cm^3). Thus the volume of the cube is 24 cm^3.

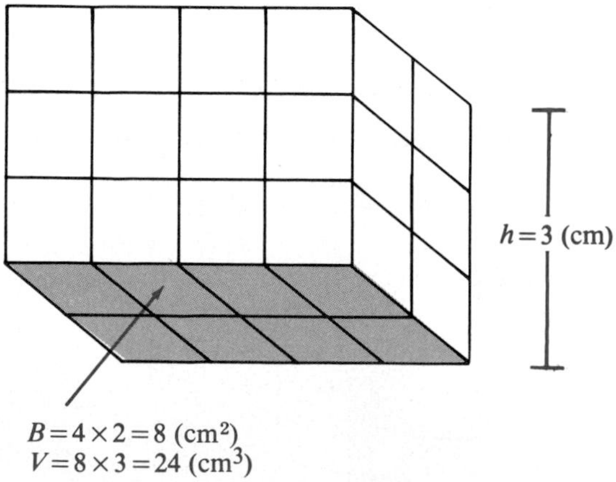

This example suggests a formula for finding the volume of any prism.

Formula

Volume of prism = Base area × height

$$V = Bh$$

EXAMPLE 1 A watering trough is in the form of a trapezoidal prism. Its ends have the dimensions shown. How long is the trough if it holds 12 m^3?

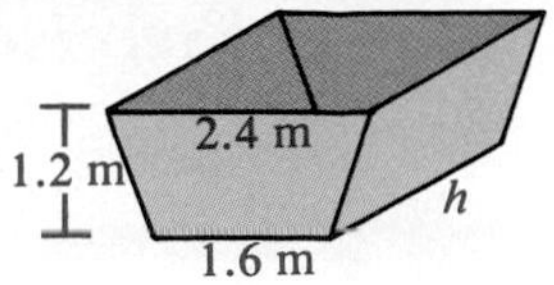

Solution Examine the diagram carefully to determine which regions are the bases. In this diagram, one of the bases is at the front. You know that the volume is 12 m^3. Find the area of the base.

$$B = \frac{1}{2}(1.6 + 2.4) \times 1.2 = 2.4\ (\text{m}^2)$$

Then, use the formula.

$$V = Bh$$
$$12 = 2.4h$$
$$5 = h$$

The length of the trough is 5 m.

A **cylinder** is like a prism except that its bases are circles instead of polygons. The area of the base, B, is πr^2. Thus:

Formula

Volume of cylinder = Base area × height

$$V = \pi r^2 h$$

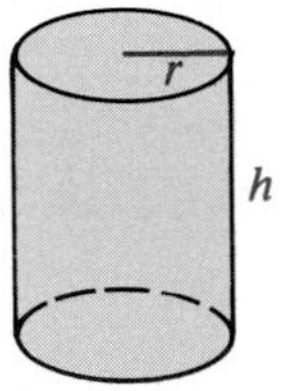

The volume of a container is often called its **capacity.** The capacity of containers of fluids is usually measured in **liters** (L) or **milliliters** (mL).

$$1 \text{ L} = 1000 \text{ cm}^3 \qquad 1 \text{ mL} = 1 \text{ cm}^3$$

It is easy to show that 1 m^3 = 1000 L.

EXAMPLE 2 A cylindrical storage tank 1 m in diameter is 1.2 m high. Find its capacity in liters. Use $\pi \approx 3.14$.

Solution Use the formula $V = \pi r^2 h$. The height is 1.2 m and, because the diameter is 1 m, the radius is 0.5 m.

$$V \approx 3.14 \times (0.5)^2 \times 1.2 = 0.942\ (\text{m}^3)$$

Since 1 m^3 = 1000 L, 0.942 m^3 = 942 L. The capacity of the tank is approximately 942 L.

Class Exercises

Find the volume of the solid. In Exercises 5 and 6, leave your answer in terms of π.

1.

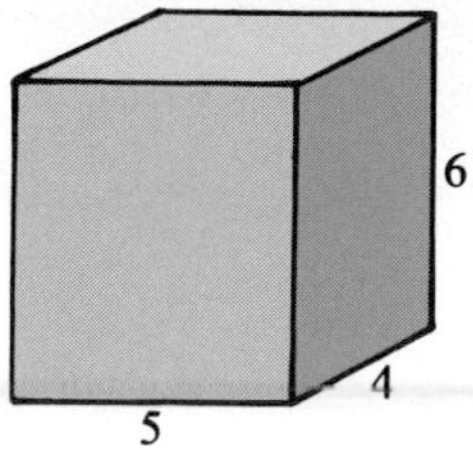

2.

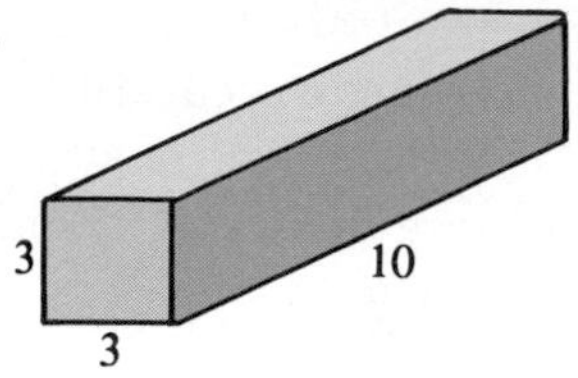

3.

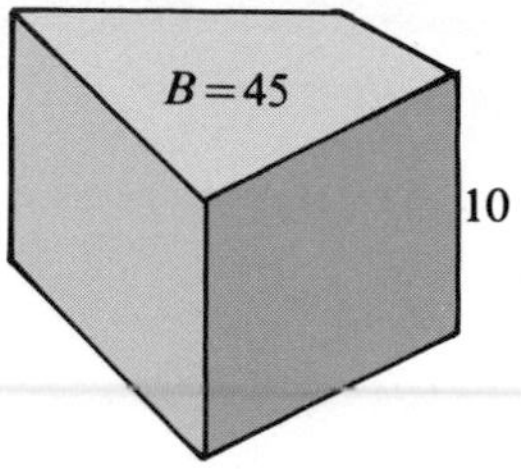

4.

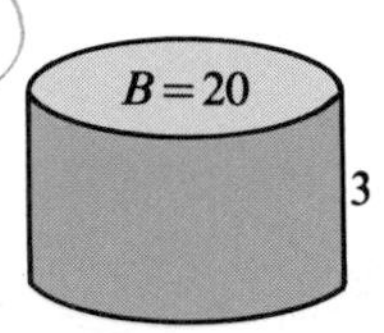

5.

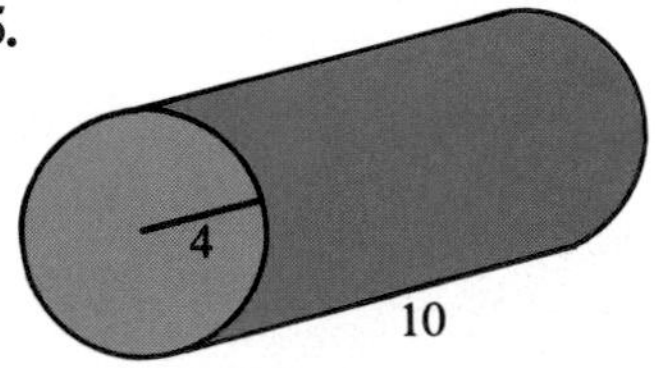

6.

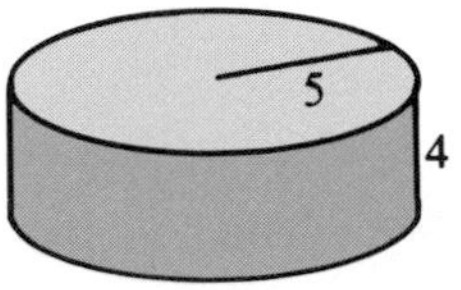

7. a. 1 m = _?_ cm
b. 1 m^3 = _?_ cm^3
c. 1000 L = _?_ cm^3

8. a. 1 cm = _?_ mm
b. 1 cm^3 = _?_ mm^3
c. 1 mL = _?_ mm^3

Written Exercises

In this exercise set, use $\pi \approx 3.14$ unless told to do otherwise. Find the volume of the solid.

A **1.**

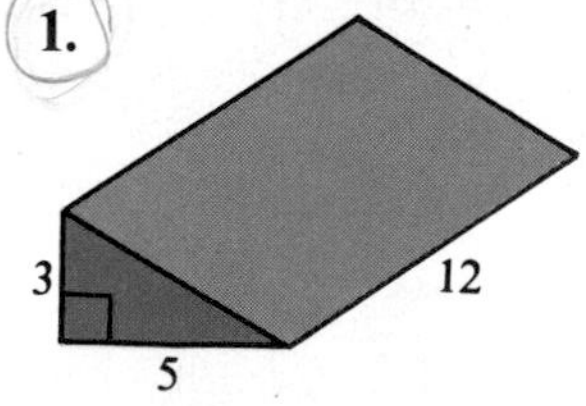

2.

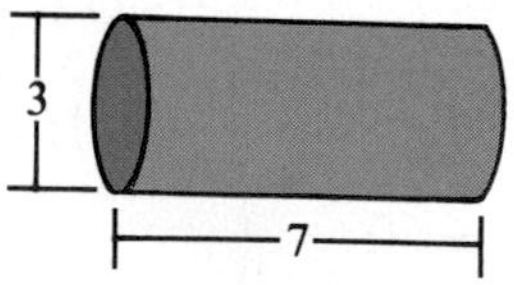

3.

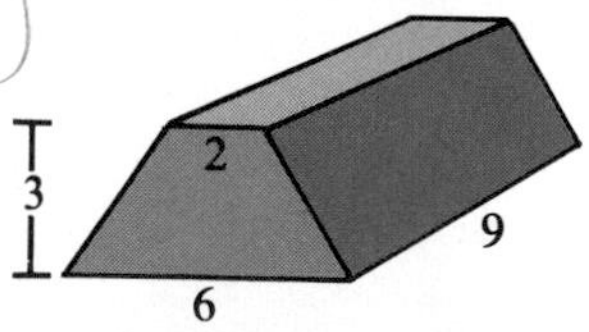

4.

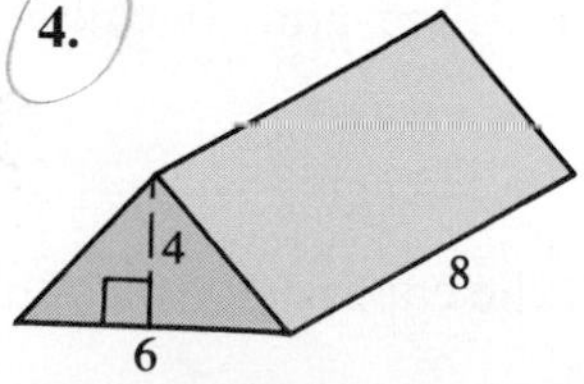

5.

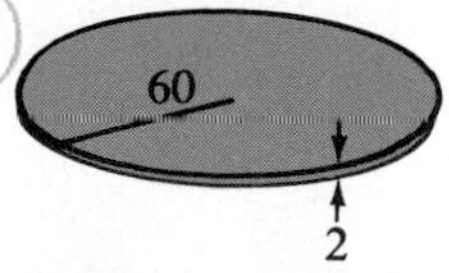

6.

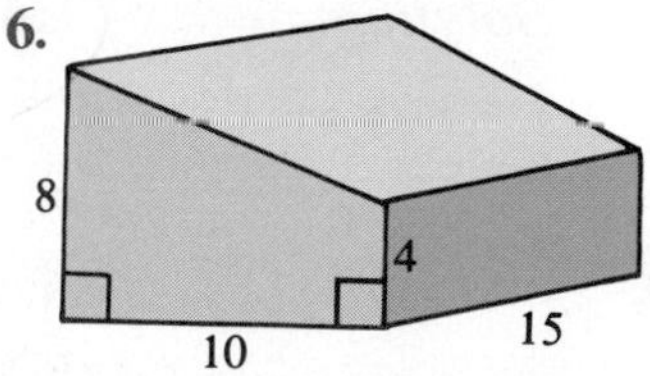

7.

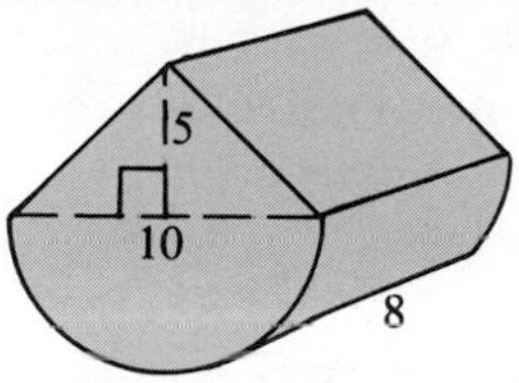

8.

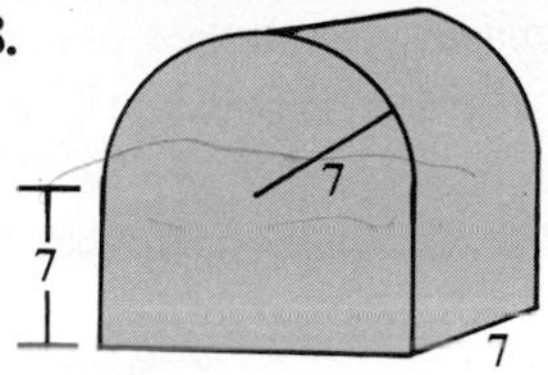

Find the capacity in liters of the prism or cylinder.

9. Square prism: 25 cm by 25 cm by 80 cm
10. Prism: base area = 1.2 m^2, height = 2.3 m
11. Cylinder: base radius = 1.2 m, height = 1.4 m
12. Cylinder: base diameter = 1 m, height = 75 cm

The table below refers to cylinders. Copy and complete it. Leave your answers in terms of π.

B

	13.	14.	15.	16.	17.	18.
Volume	12π	150π	100π	20π	18π	100π
base radius	2	5	?	?	?	?
Base area	?	?	25π	4π	?	?
height	?	?	?	?	2	25

Find the volume of the prism if the pattern were folded.

19.

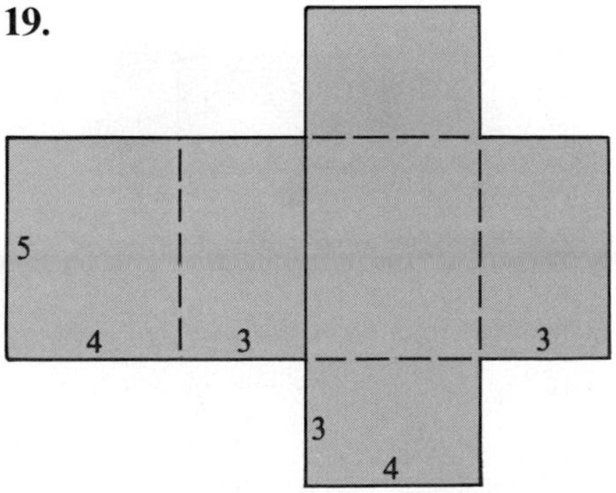

20.

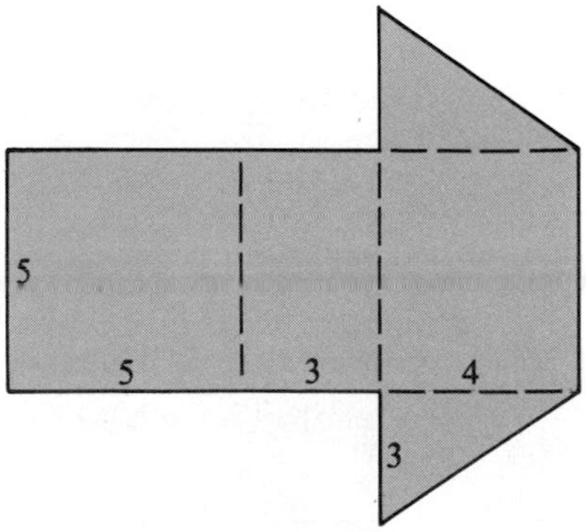

C 21. What happens to the volume of a cylinder if this change is made?
a. The radius is doubled. **b.** The height is halved.
c. The radius is doubled and the height is halved.

22. What happens to the volume of a cylinder if this change is made?
a. The radius is halved. **b.** The height is doubled.
c. The radius is halved and the height is doubled.

In an *oblique prism,* the bases are *not* perpendicular to the other faces. The volume formula $V = Bh$ still applies, where h is the perpendicular distance between the bases. Find the volume of each figure shown in red.

23.

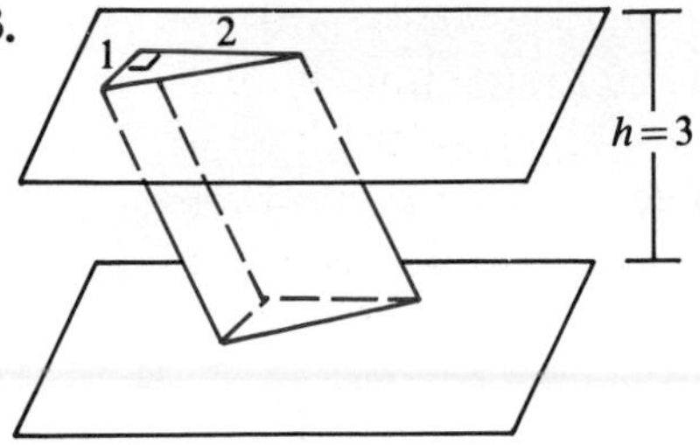

24.

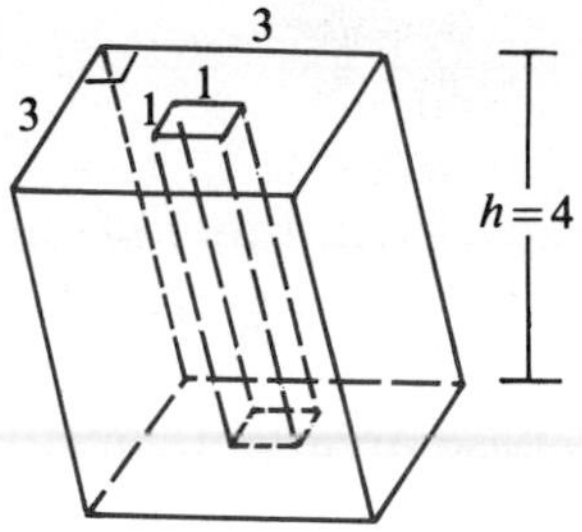

Problems

Solve. Use $\pi \approx 3.14$.

A **1.** Find the capacity in liters of the V-shaped trough shown below.

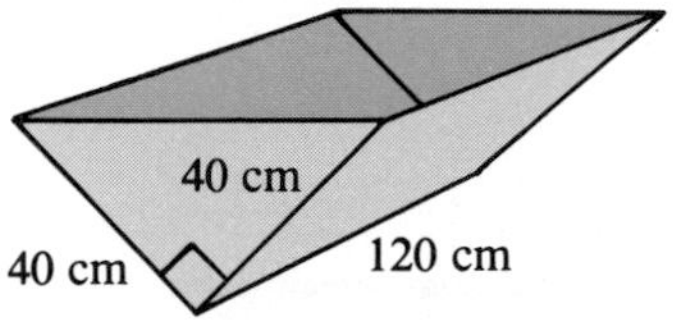

2. Find the capacity in liters of the half-cylinder trough shown below.

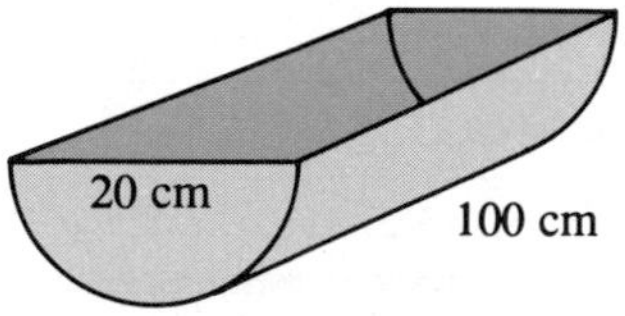

B **3.** Find the volume of metal in the copper pipe shown below.

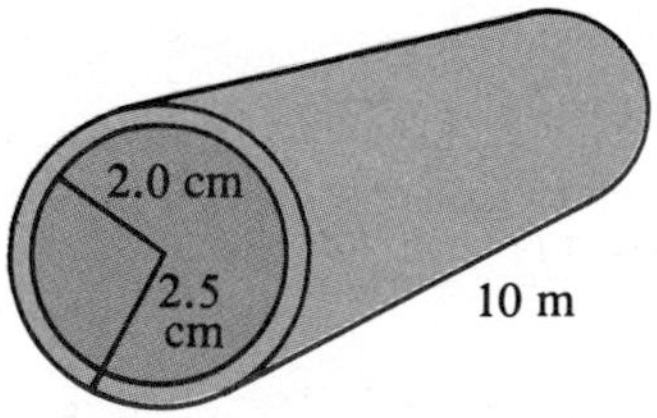

4. Find the volume of concrete in the construction block shown below.

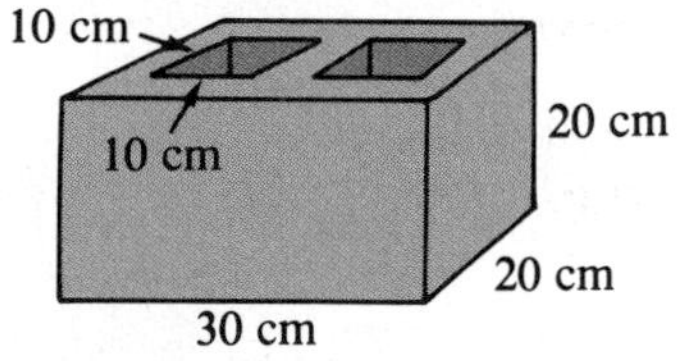

C **5.** A cylindrical water bottle is 28 cm in diameter. How many centimeters does the water level drop when one liter is drawn off?

Review Exercises

Solve for *x*.

1. $x = \frac{1}{3} \times 6.4 \times 15$ **2.** $x = \frac{1}{2}(7.2) \times 3$ **3.** $3.38 = 4x$ **4.** $\frac{1}{3}x = 11$

5. $3.14 \times 20^2 = x$ **6.** $(0.8)^2x = 5.12$ **7.** $314 = 3.14x^2$ **8.** $x^2 = 169$

9-6 Volumes of Pyramids and Cones

If we shrink one base of a prism to a point, we obtain a **pyramid** with that point as its **vertex.** A **cone** is obtained in the same way from a cylinder. In each case, the **height** of the solid is the perpendicular distance from its vertex to its base. As for a prism, the shape of the base of a pyramid determines its name. All other faces of a pyramid are triangles. A cone is like a pyramid except that its base is a circle instead of a polygon.

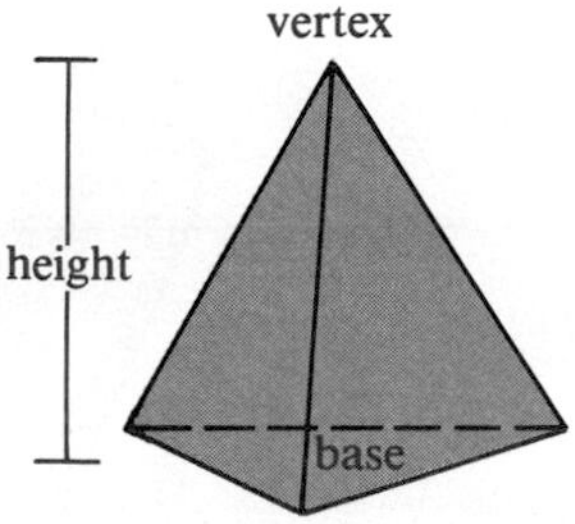

Triangular Pyramid or Tetrahedron

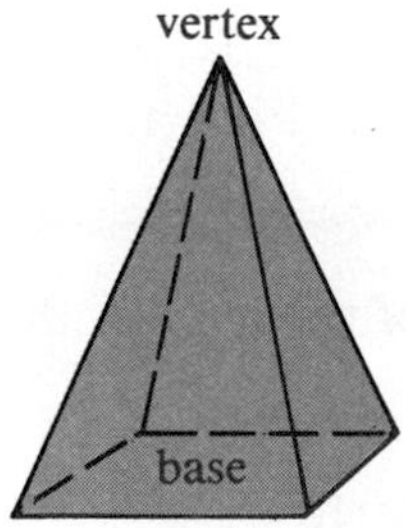

Square Pyramid

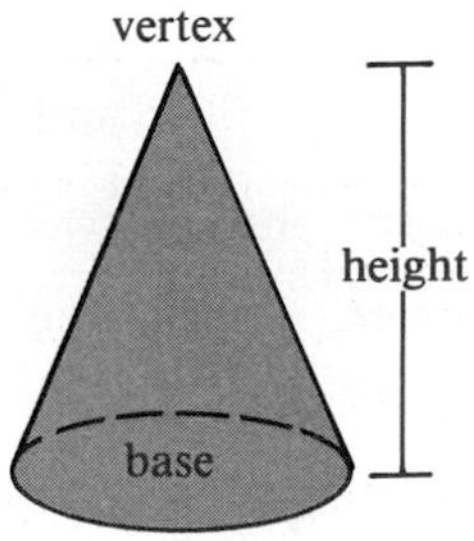

Cone

The volume of a pyramid can be found using this formula:

Formula

$$\text{Volume of pyramid} = \frac{1}{3} \times \text{Base area} \times \text{height}$$

$$V = \frac{1}{3}Bh$$

EXAMPLE 1 Find the volume of the square pyramid shown at the right.

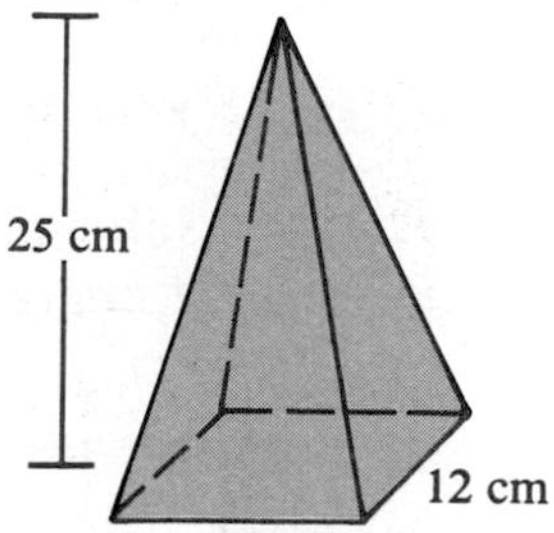

Solution First find the base area. Since the base is a square,

$$B = 12^2 = 144 \text{ (cm}^2\text{)}.$$

Then use the volume formula.

$$V = \frac{1}{3}Bh$$

$$= \frac{1}{3} \times 144 \times 25 = 1200 \text{ (cm}^3\text{)}$$

For a cone, the base area is given by the formula $B = \pi r^2$.

Formula

Volume of cone $= \frac{1}{3} \times$ Base area $\times$ height

$$V = \frac{1}{3}\pi r^2 h$$

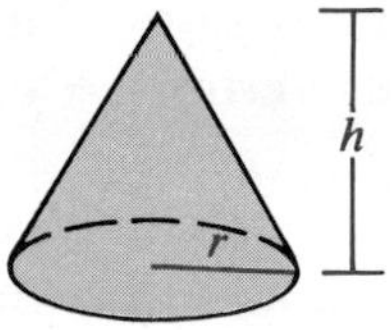

EXAMPLE 2 A conical container is 20 cm across the top and 21 cm deep. Find its capacity in liters. Use $\pi \approx 3.14$.

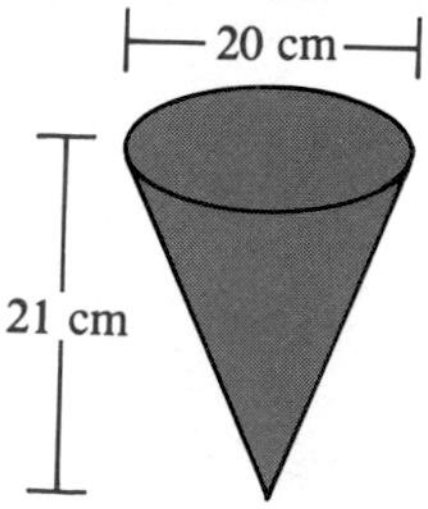

Solution The diameter of the base of the cone is 20 cm, so the radius is 10 cm.

$$V = \frac{1}{3}\pi \times 10^2 \times 21$$

$$\approx \frac{1}{3} \times 3.14 \times 100 \times 21 = 2198$$

Rounding the product to three digits, the volume is approximately 2200 cm^3. Because 1000 cm^3 equals 1 L, the capacity of the conical container is approximately 2.2 L.

Reading Mathematics: *Vocabulary*
Words that we use in everyday speech may have different meanings in mathematics. For example, the everyday word *base* often refers to the part of an object that it is resting on. The geometrical term *base* refers to a particular face of a figure that may appear at the top, the side, or the end of the figure in a drawing. In Example 2, above, the base appears at the top of the container.

Class Exercises

Find the volume of the solid. In Exercise 3, the base is a square. In Exercise 4, leave your answer in terms of π.

1.

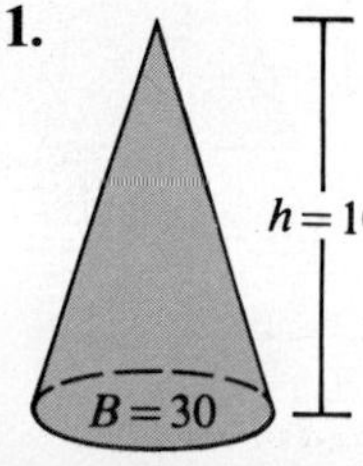

2.

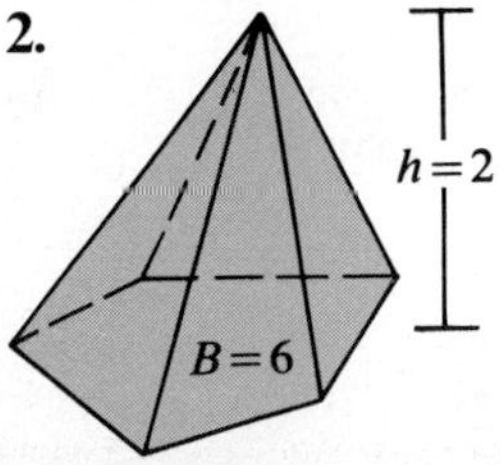

3.

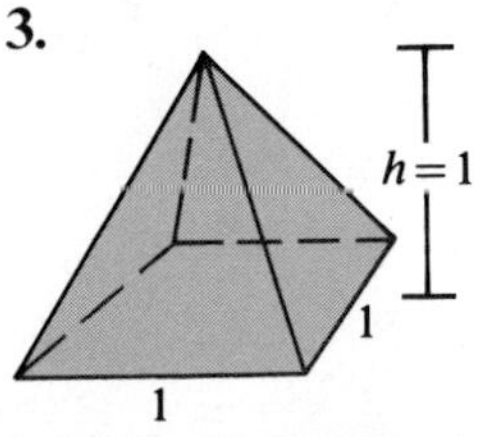

4.

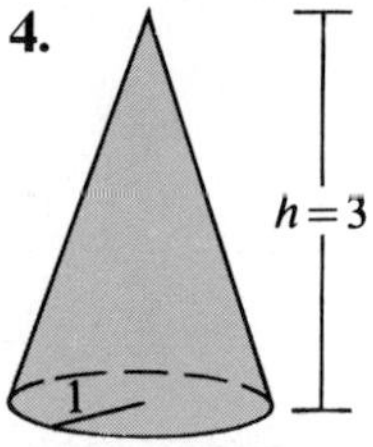

Complete.

5. Except for the base, the shapes of all the faces of a pyramid are __?__.
6. The shapes of all the faces of a tetrahedron are __?__.
7. A cone has base radius 3 and height 6. The volume of the cone is __?__ π.

Written Exercises

For Exercises 1–10, use $\pi \approx 3.14$ when needed. Find the volume of the solid pictured.

A **1.**

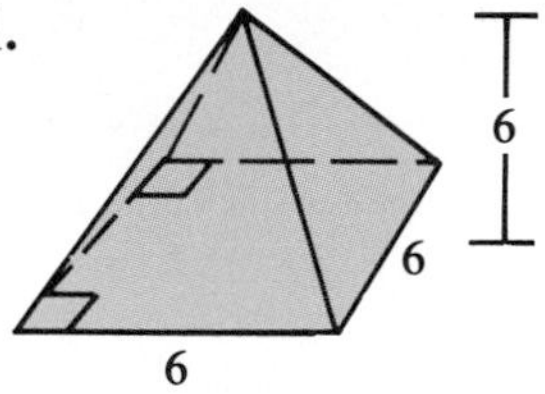

2.

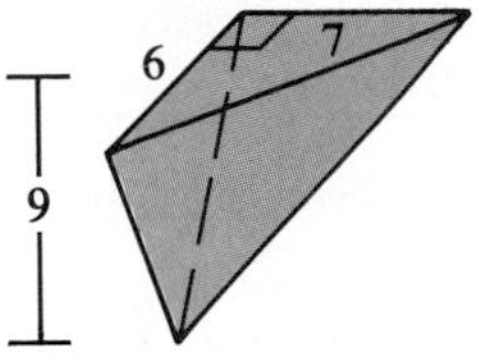

3.

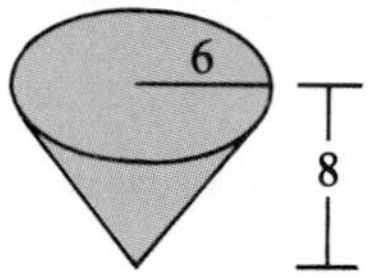

4.

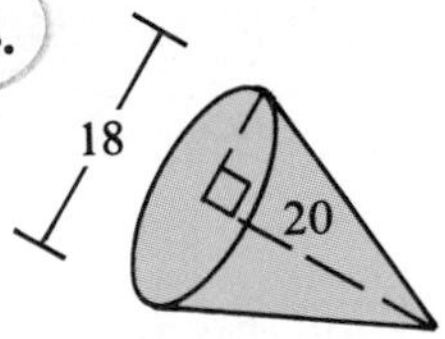

5.

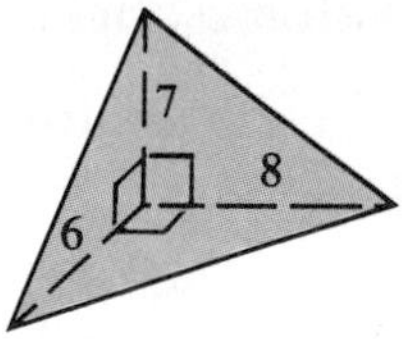

6.

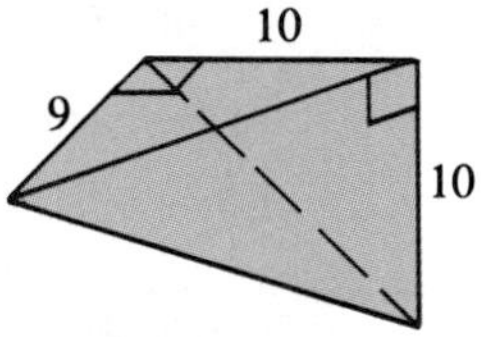

Find the capacity in liters of the cone or pyramid described.

7. A pyramid of height 12 cm having a 5 cm by 8 cm rectangle as base
8. A pyramid having height 10 m and a square base 15 m on a side
9. A cone having base radius 0.8 m and height 1.5 m
10. A cone of height 24 cm and base diameter 11 cm

Copy and complete the table for pyramids.

	11.	**12.**	**13.**	**14.**	**15.**	**16.**
Base area, *B*	5	33	4	13	?	?
height, *h*	6	12	?	?	10	15
Volume, *V*	?	?	8	13	10	20

Copy and complete the table for cones.

B

	17.	18.	19.	20.
radius, r	1	2	?	?
height, h	?	?	4	15
Volume, V	5π	12π	12π	5π

Complete.

C **21.** A cone has volume 6 cm^3. The volume of a cylinder having the same base and same height is __?__ cm^3.

22. A cylinder of height 2 m has the same base and same volume as a cone. The cone's height is __?__ m.

Problems

Solve. Use $\pi \approx 3.14$.

A **1.** The Pyramid of Cheops in Egypt has a square base approximately 230 m on a side. Its original height was approximately 147 m. What was its approximate volume originally?

2. A volcano is in the form of a cone approximately 1.8 km high and 12 km in diameter. Find its volume.

B **3.** Find the volume of this buoy.

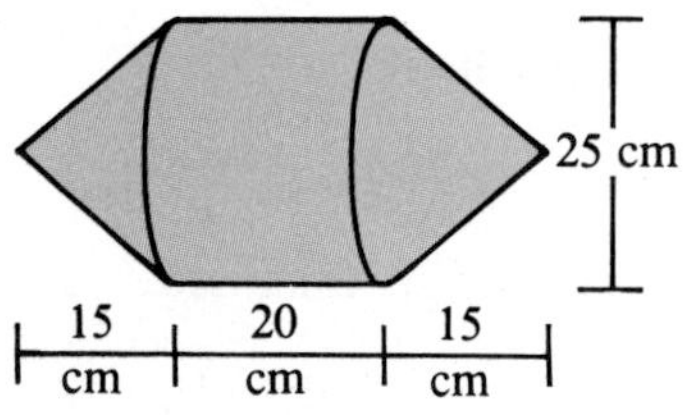

4. Find the volume of this tent. The floor of the tent is square.

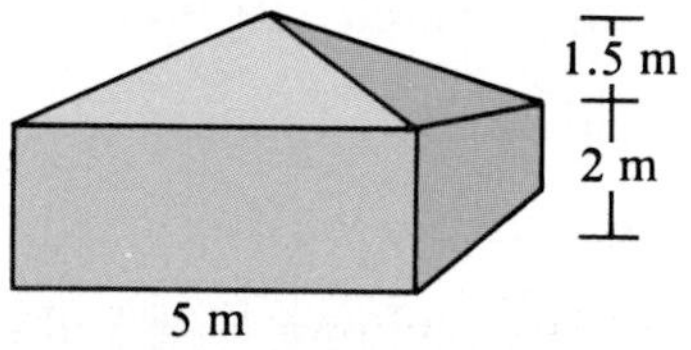

Review Exercises

Find the perimeter of the figure whose sides have the given lengths.

1. rhombus: 9 m per side

2. trapezoid: 4 cm, 4 cm, 5 cm, 7 cm

3. triangle: 35 cm per side

4. parallelogram: 15 m, 7 m, 15 m, 7 m

5. square: 12.8 km per side

6. rectangle: 24.63 km by 37.40 km

7. square: 145.2 km per side

8. triangle: 3.70 m, 12.90 m, 14.85 m

9-7 Surface Areas of Prisms and Cylinders

The **surface area** of every prism and cylinder is made up of its two **bases** and its **lateral surface** as illustrated in the figures below. The lateral surface of a prism is made up of its **lateral faces.** Each lateral face is a rectangle.

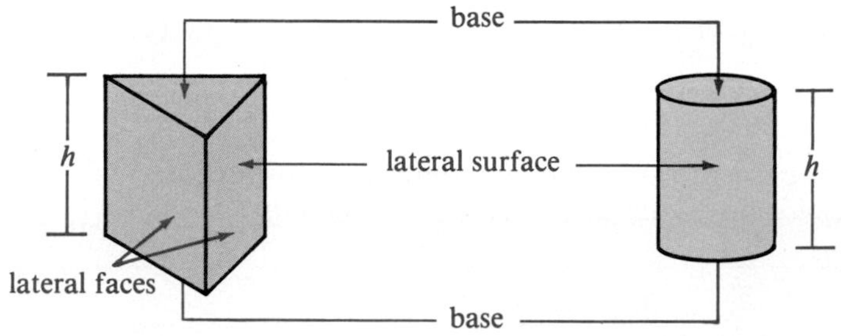

If we were to cut open and flatten out the prism and cylinder shown above, the bases and the lateral surfaces of the figures would look like this:

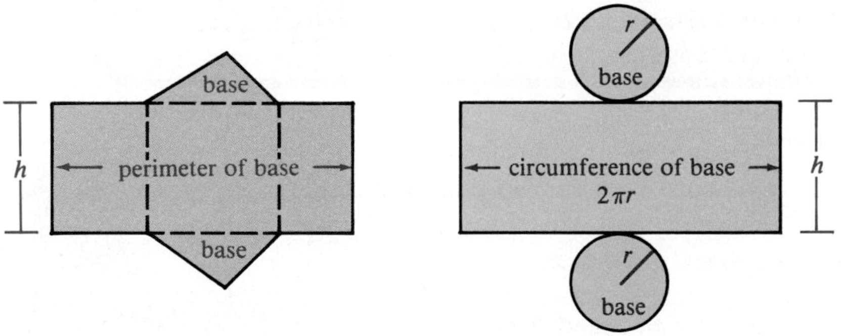

In each of the figures above, the area of the lateral surface, called the **lateral area,** is the product of the perimeter of the base and the height of the figure. To find the **total surface area** of a prism or cylinder, we simply add the area of the two bases to the lateral area of the figure.

Formulas

For a prism or cylinder,

lateral area = perimeter of base × height

total surface area = lateral area + area of bases

EXAMPLE 1 Find (a) the lateral area, (b) the area of the bases, and (c) the total surface area of the prism shown.

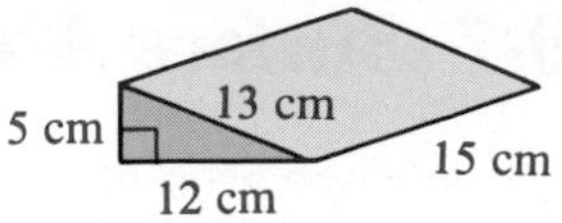

Solution a. perimeter of base $= 5 + 12 + 13 = 30$ (cm)
height $= 15$ cm
lateral area $= 30 \times 15 = 450$ (cm^2)

b. area of bases $= 2 \times \left(\frac{1}{2} \times 12 \times 5\right) = 60$ (cm^2)

c. total surface area $= 450 + 60 = 510$ (cm^2)

In a cylinder of base radius r, the perimeter (circumference) of the base is $2\pi r$. Thus:

Formulas

For a cylinder,

lateral area $= 2\pi rh$

area of bases $= 2\pi r^2$

total surface area $= 2\pi rh + 2\pi r^2$

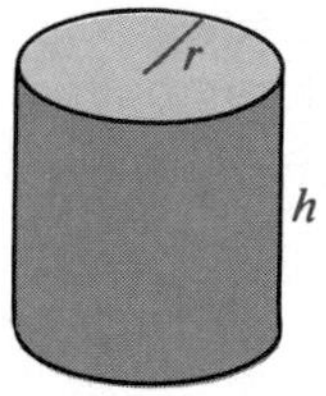

EXAMPLE 2 A can of paint will cover 50 m^2. How many cans are necessary to paint the inside (top, bottom, and sides) of the storage tank shown? Use $\pi \approx 3.14$.

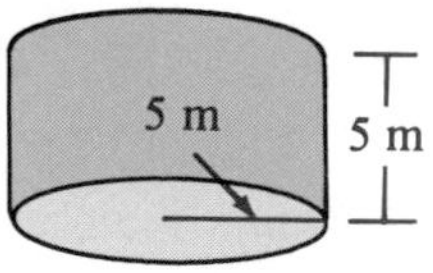

Solution Since $r = 5$ and $h = 5$,

$$\text{total surface area} = (2\pi \times 5 \times 5) + (2\pi \times 5^2)$$
$$\approx (3.14 \times 50) + (3.14 \times 50) = 314$$

The total surface area is approximately 314 m^2.

The number of cans of paint, is $314 \div 50$, or 6.28. Rounding *up* to the nearest whole number, the answer is 7 cans.

Problem Solving Reminder
For problems whose answers are the result of division, take time to consider whether it is reasonable *to round up or round down.* In Example 2, the answer to the division was 6.28 cans of paint. Because paint cannot be purchased in hundredths of a can, the answer was rounded up to the nearest whole number. If the answer had been rounded down, there would not have been enough paint to cover the interior of the tank.

Class Exercises

1. If a prism has hexagonal bases, how many lateral faces does it have? How many faces does it have in all?

Find the lateral area and the total surface area. Use $\pi \approx 3.14$.

2.

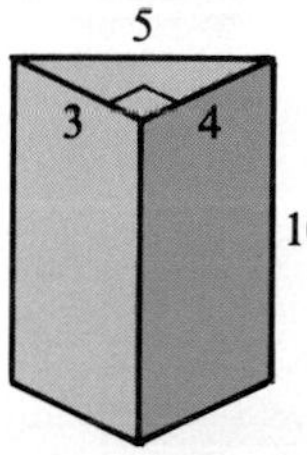

3.

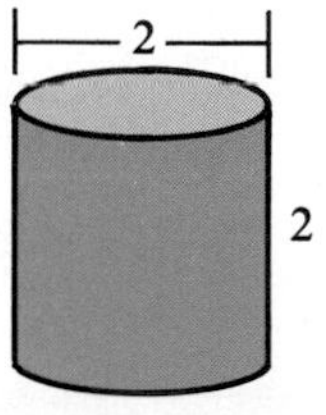

4.

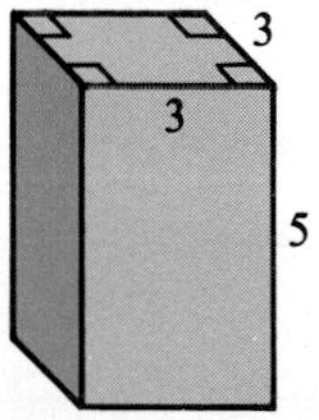

5. If each edge of a cube is one unit long, what is the total surface area in square units?

Written Exercises

Find the total surface area of a rectangular prism having the given dimensions.

A 1. 45 cm by 30 cm by 20 cm

2. 5 cm by 18 cm by 25 cm

3. 2.5 m by 1.6 m by 0.8 m

4. 1.8 m by 0.6 m by 2.0 m

Find (a) the lateral area and (b) the total surface area of the cylinder or prism. Use $\pi \approx 3.14$.

5. A cylinder having base radius 12 cm and height 22 cm

6. A cylinder having base diameter 6 m and height 4.5 m

7.

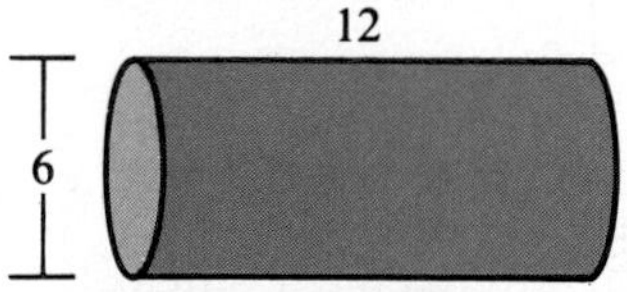

8.

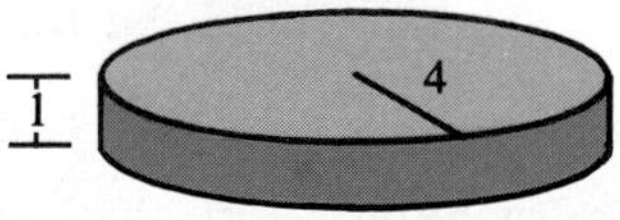

9.

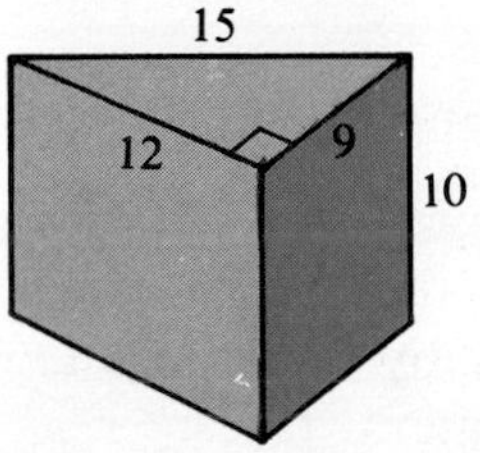

10.

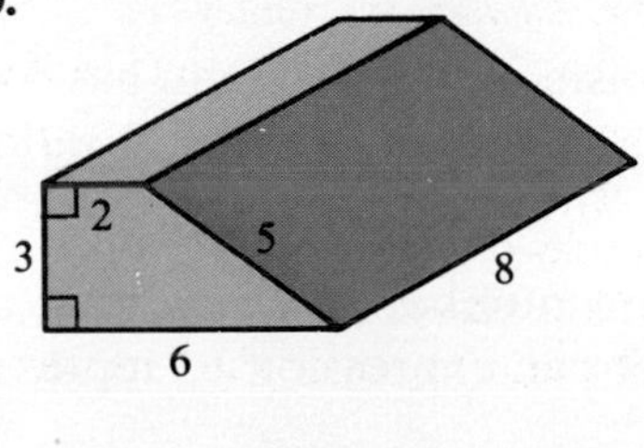

If the patterns below were drawn on cardboard, they could be folded along the dotted lines to form prisms. Find (a) the volume and (b) the total surface area of each.

B 11.

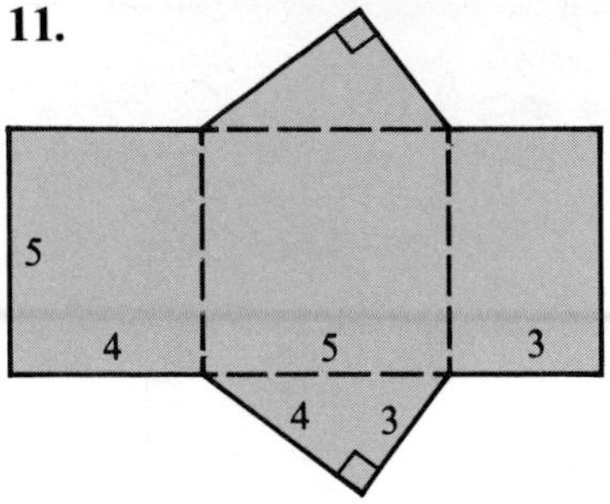

12.

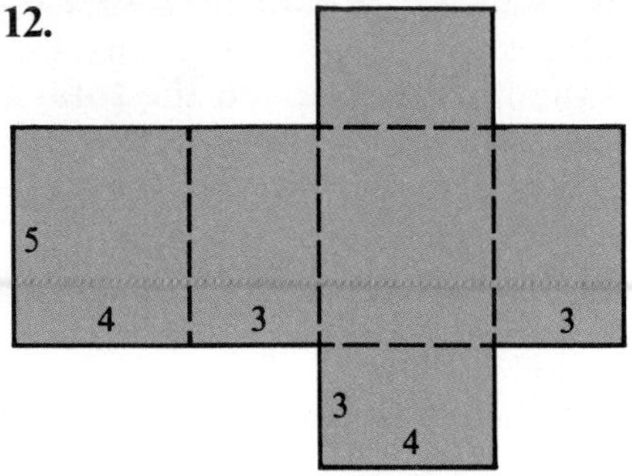

13. Find the length of the edge of a cube whose total area is 150 cm^2.

14. Three faces of a box have a common vertex and their combined area is 20 cm^2. What is the total surface area of the box?

15. One can of varnish will cover 64 m^2 of wood. If you want to put one coat of varnish on each of 24 wooden cubes with the dimensions shown at the right, how many cans of varnish should you buy?

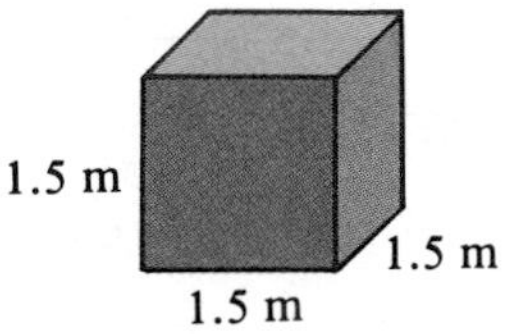

16. You have two cans of red paint, each of which will cover 100 m^2. Which of the two cylinders pictured below can you paint completely using just the paint that you have?

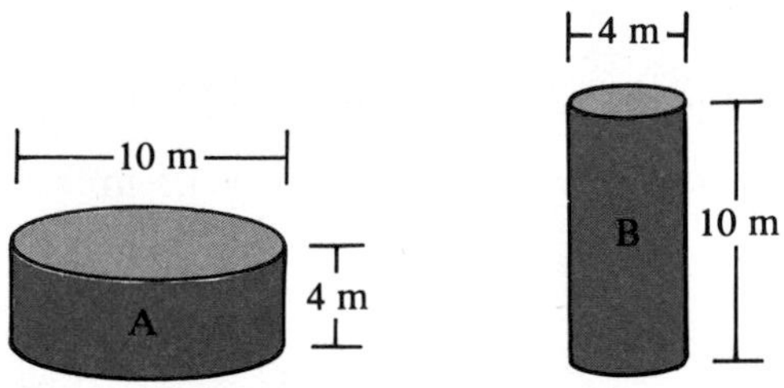

17. A prism of height 3 m has bases that are right triangles with sides 6 m, 8 m, and 10 m. Find the lateral area and the total surface area. (Be sure to draw and label a sketch.)

18. A prism of height 10 cm has bases that are right triangles with sides 5 cm, 12 cm, and 13 cm. Find the lateral area and the surface area. (Be sure to draw and label a sketch.)

19. If the number of faces of a prism is represented by n, write an algebraic expression to represent the number of lateral faces.

C 20. The lateral surface of a cone is made up of many small wedges like the one shown in color. Thinking of the wedge as a triangle of base b and height s, we see that its area is $\frac{1}{2}bs$. When we add all these areas together, we obtain $\frac{1}{2}(2\pi r)s$, or πrs, because the sum of all the b's is $2\pi r$, the circumference of the base. Thus, for a cone:

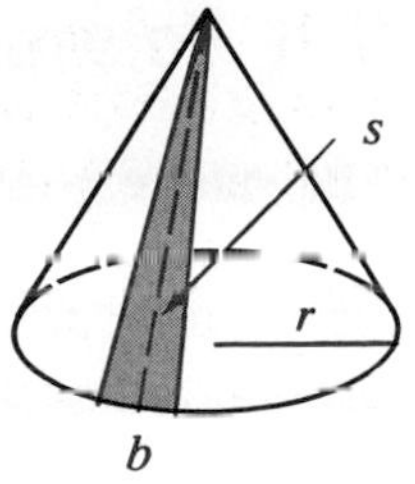

$$\text{lateral area} = \pi rs$$

$$\text{area of base} = \pi r^2$$

$$\text{total surface area} = \pi rs + \pi r^2$$

The length s is called the **slant height** of the cone.

Find the total surface area of each figure.

a.

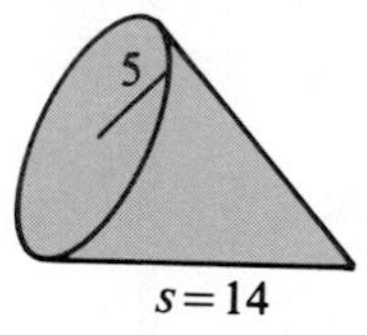

b.

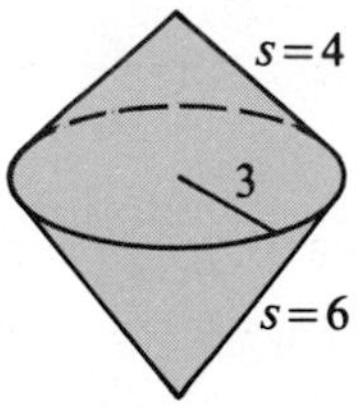

c.

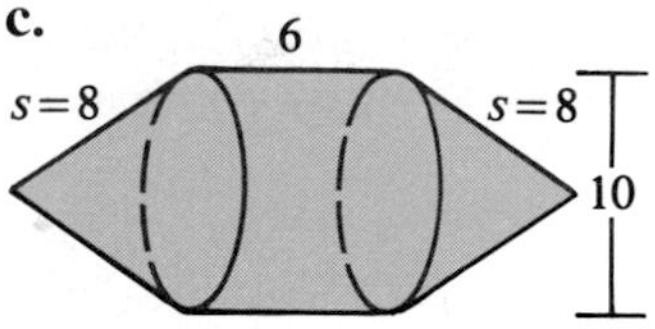

Review Exercises

Find the radius of the circle with the given circumference C or diameter d. Use $\pi \approx 3.14$.

1. $d = 12$ **2.** $C = 62.8$ **3.** $d = 210$ **4.** $C = 83.6$

5. $C = 220$ **6.** $d = 25$ **7.** $d = 76$ **8.** $C = 2.42$

Challenge

1. Copy the square at the right and cut it into four pieces along the dashed lines. Re-form the four pieces into a larger square with a "hollow" square at the center.

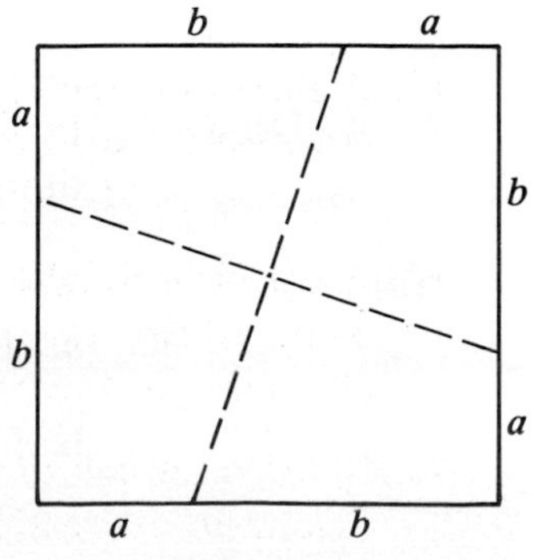

2. Repeat step 1 several times, assigning different values to a and b each time. In each case, what is the area of the "hollow" square?

9-8 Volumes and Surface Areas of Spheres

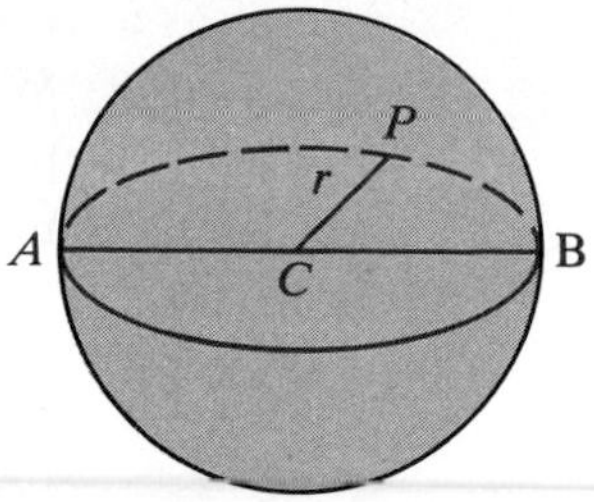

The **sphere** with **radius** r and **center** at C consists of all points at the distance r from point C. The word *radius* also is used for any segment having C as one endpoint and a point of the sphere as another (for example, $\overline{CP}$ in the figure). The word **diameter** is also used in two ways: for a *segment* through C having its endpoints on the sphere (for example, $\overline{AB}$), and for the *length* of such a segment.

The following formulas for the surface area and volume of a sphere can be proved using higher mathematics.

Formulas

For any sphere of radius r,

Area $= 4\pi \times (\text{radius})^2$ Volume $= \frac{4}{3}\pi \times (\text{radius})^3$

$A = 4\pi r^2$ $V = \frac{4}{3}\pi r^3$

The surface area of a sphere is usually referred to simply as the *area* of the sphere.

Reading Mathematics: *Diagrams*

Reading diagrams correctly is an important reading skill in mathematics. When three-dimensional objects are pictured on a two-dimensional page, the lines used to draw congruent segments may be of different lengths. For example, in the drawing above, you understand that all radii of a sphere are congruent and that $CP = CB$. Yet these radii cannot be drawn to be of equal length if the picture is to look realistic.

EXAMPLE 1 Find (a) the surface area and (b) the volume of a sphere having diameter 18. Leave your answer in terms of π.

Solution The radius equals $\frac{1}{2}$ the diameter, so $r = 9$.

a. $A = 4\pi r^2 = 4\pi \times 9^2 = 4\pi \times 81 = 324\pi$

b. $V = \frac{4}{3}\pi r^3 = \frac{4}{3}\pi \times 9^3 = \frac{4}{3}\pi \times 729 = 972\pi$

EXAMPLE 2 The area of a sphere is 1600π cm^2. What is the radius?

Solution Substitute 1600π for A in the formula $A = 4\pi r^2$.

$$1600\pi = 4\pi r^2$$

$$\frac{1600\pi}{4\pi} = \frac{4\pi r^2}{4\pi}$$

$$400 = r^2$$

Since $20^2 = 400$, $r = 20$ cm.

Class Exercises

Complete. In Exercises 1 and 2, give your answers in terms of π.

1. The area of a sphere of radius 1 is __?__, and the volume is __?__.
2. The area of a sphere of radius 2 is __?__, and the volume is __?__.
3. If the radius of a sphere is doubled, the area is multiplied by __?__.
4. If the radius of a sphere is doubled, the volume is multiplied by __?__.
5. If $\overline{AB}$ is a diameter of a sphere having center C, then $\overline{AC}$ and $\overline{BC}$ are __?__ of the sphere.

Complete the following analogies with choice a, b, c, or d.

6. Sphere: Circle = Cube: __?__
   a. Pyramid **b.** Prism **c.** Square **d.** Cylinder
7. Cone: Pyramid = Cylinder: __?__
   a. Sphere **b.** Prism **c.** Circle **d.** Triangle

Written Exercises

Copy and complete the table below. Leave your answers in terms of π.

A

	1.	**2.**	**3.**	**4.**	**5.**	**6.**
radius of sphere	3	5	6	9	10	12
surface area	?	?	?	?	?	?
volume	?	?	?	?	?	?

Half of a sphere is called a *hemisphere*. Solve. Leave your answers in terms of π.

7. Find the volume of a hemisphere of radius 2.
8. Find the area of the curved surface of a hemisphere of radius 8.
9. Find the area of the curved surface of a hemisphere of radius 2.2.
10. Find the volume of a hemisphere of radius 3.3.

Copy and complete the table below. Leave your answers in terms of π.

B

	11.	12.	13.	14.	15.	16.
radius of sphere	3.6	?	?	4.5	?	?
surface area	?	64π	?	?	256π	?
volume	?	?	972π	?	?	288π

Solve. Leave your answers in terms of π.

17. The observatory building shown at the right consists of a cylinder surmounted by a hemisphere. Find its volume.
18. The water tank at the right consists of a cone surmounted by a cylinder surmounted by a hemisphere. Find its volume.

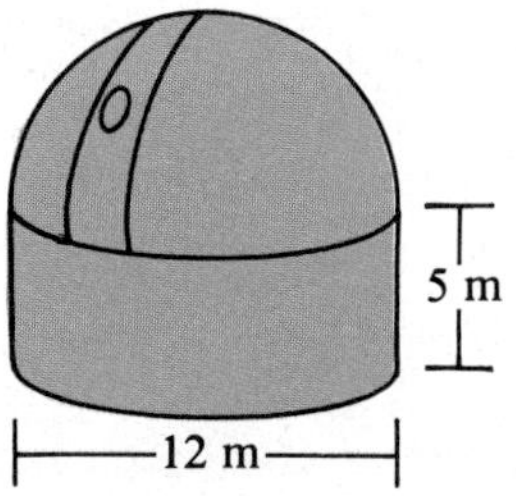

Ex. 17

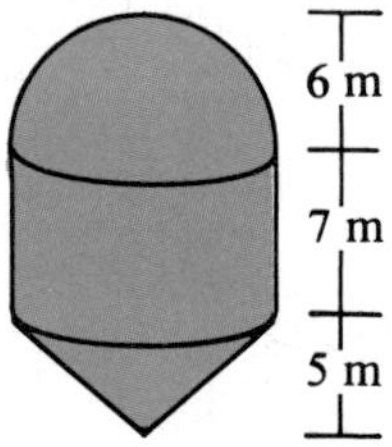

Ex. 18

19. Earth's diameter is about $3\frac{2}{3}$ times that of the moon. How do their volumes compare?
20. The sun's diameter is about 110 times that of Earth. How do their volumes compare?

If a sphere fits snugly inside a cylinder it is said to be *inscribed* in the cylinder. Use the diagram at the right for Exercises 21 and 22.

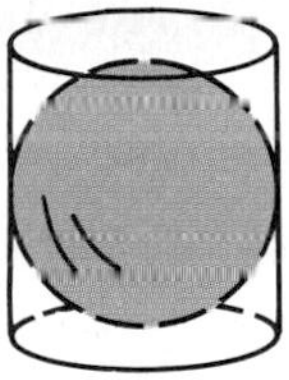

C 21. a. A sphere of radius 4 is inscribed in a cylinder of height 8. What is the ratio of the volume of the sphere to the volume of the cylinder?

b. A sphere of radius 5 is inscribed in a cylinder of height 10. What is the ratio of the volume of the sphere to the volume of the cylinder?

c. A sphere of radius r is inscribed in a cylinder. What is the ratio of the volume of the sphere to the volume of the cylinder?

22. a. A sphere of radius 6 is inscribed in a cylinder of height 12. What is the ratio of the surface area of the sphere to the lateral area of the cylinder?

b. A sphere of radius 7 is inscribed in a cylinder of height 14. What is the ratio of the surface area of the sphere to the lateral area of the cylinder?

c. A sphere of radius r is inscribed in a cylinder. What is the ratio of the surface area of the sphere to the lateral area of the cylinder?

Review Exercises

Simplify these in your head if you can. Write down the answers.

1. 7×0.3	**2.** 4×5.1	**3.** 0.8×0.8	**4.** 23.3×100
5. $3500 \div 1000$	**6.** $10.75 \div 100$	**7.** 300×2.7	**8.** 0.0004×0.2

Calculator Key-In

The surface area of Earth is approximately 510,070,000 km^2. The surface area of Jupiter is approximately 64,017,000,000 km^2. About how many times greater than the surface area of Earth is the surface area of Jupiter?

If you try to enter the numbers as they are shown above on your calculator, you may find it will not accept more than eight digits. Many calculators have a key marked *EXP* that allows you to use scientific notation to express very large (or very small) numbers. For example, you can enter 510,070,000 by thinking of the number as 5.1007×10^8 and entering 5.1007 [EXP] 8. Your calculator may show 5.1007   08.

Try to find a calculator that will accept scientific notation and solve the problem above.

9-9 Mass and Density

The **mass** of an object is a measure of the amount of matter it contains. In the metric system, units of mass are the **gram (g)**, the **kilogram (kg)**, and the **metric ton (t)**.

1 g = mass of 1 cm^3 of water under standard conditions
(Standard conditions are 4°C at sea-level pressure.)

$$1 \text{ kg} = 1000 \text{ g}$$

$$1 \text{ t} = 1000 \text{ kg}$$

The *weight* of an object is the force of gravity acting on it. While the mass of an object remains constant, its weight would be less on a mountaintop or on the moon than at sea level. In a given region, mass and weight are proportional (so that mass can be found by weighing).

The tables below give the masses of unit volumes (1 cm^3) of several substances.

TABLE 1

Substance	Mass of 1 cm^3	Mass of 1 m^3
Pine	0.56 g	0.56 t
Ice	0.92 g	0.92 t
Water	1.00 g	1.00 t
Aluminum	2.70 g	2.70 t
Steel	7.82 g	7.82 t
Gold	19.3 g	19.3 t

TABLE 2

Substance	Mass of 1 cm^3	Mass of 1 L
Helium	0.00018 g	0.00018 kg
Air	0.0012 g	0.0012 kg
Gasoline	0.66 g	0.66 kg
Water	1.00 g	1.00 kg
Milk	1.03 g	1.03 kg
Mercury	13.6 g	13.6 kg

The mass per unit volume of a substance is its **density.** In describing densities we use a slash (/) for the word *per.* For example, the density of gasoline is 0.66 kg/L.

EXAMPLE Find the mass of a block 3 cm by 5 cm by 10 cm made of wood having density 0.8 g/cm^3.

Solution The volume of the block is $3 \times 5 \times 10$, or 150, cm^3.

Since 1 cm^3 of the wood has mass 0.8 g, 150 cm^3 has mass 0.8×150, or 120, g.

The example illustrates the following formula.

Formula

Mass = Density × Volume

In Table 2, the number of grams per cubic centimeter is the same as the number of kilograms per liter. This is because there are 1000 g in a kilogram and 1000 cm^3 in a liter. Similarly in Table 1, the number of grams per cubic centimeter is the same as the number of metric tons per cubic meter.

Class Exercises

Complete.

1. 1 t = __?__ kg
2. 1 kg = __?__ g
3. 1 t = __?__ g
4. 2400 kg = __?__ t
5. 0.62 kg = __?__ g
6. 400 g = __?__ kg

Use the tables in this lesson to give the mass of the following.

7. 2 L of water
8. 10 cm^3 of gasoline
9. 100 cm^3 of milk
10. 4 L of gasoline
11. helium filling a 1000 L tank
12. a cube of ice 2 cm on each edge
13. the block of steel shown

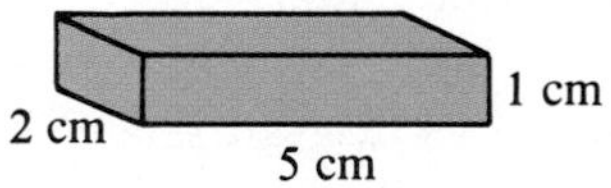

Written Exercises

Complete.

1. 6.3 kg = __?__ g
2. 2500 kg = __?__ t
3. 4.3 t = __?__ kg

Use the tables in this lesson to find the mass of the following.

4. 50 cm^3 of gold
5. 300 cm^3 of aluminum
6. 25 L of gasoline
7. 2.5 L of mercury
8. 500 m^3 of water
9. 500 m^3 of ice
10. 1 m^3 of air
11. 1 m^3 of helium
12. 4 L of milk

In Exercises 13–15, the solid pictured is made of the specified material. Use the tables in this lesson to find the mass of the solid. Use $\pi \approx 3.14$.

13.

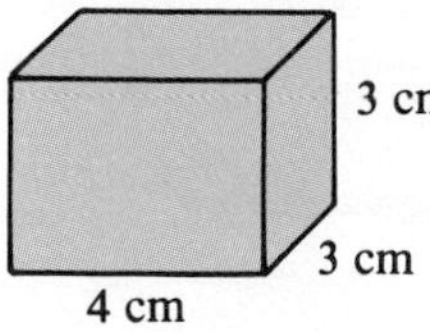

Ice

14.

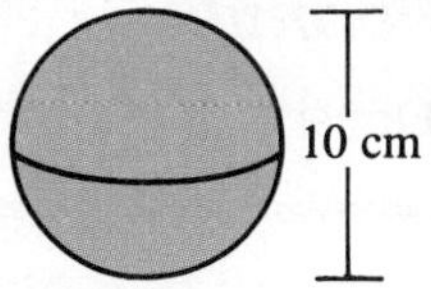

Steel

15.

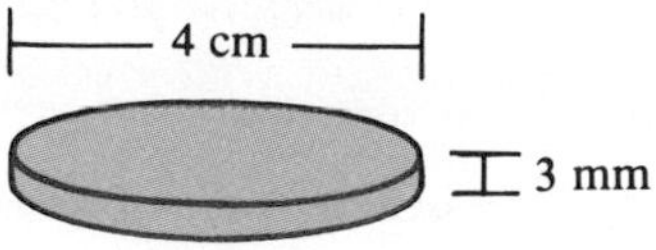

Gold

Use the tables in this lesson to find the mass of the named content of the container pictured. Use $\pi \approx 3.14$.

16.

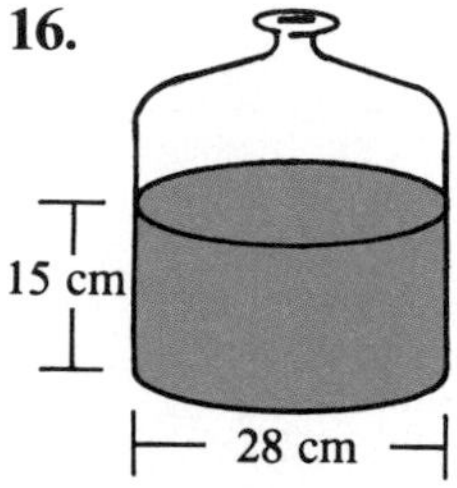

Mercury

17.

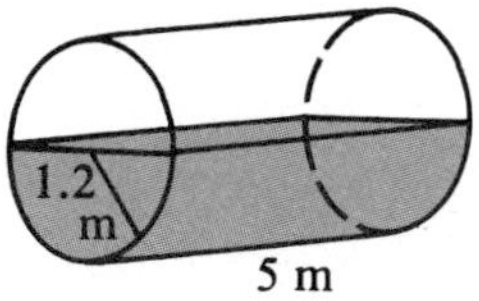

Gasoline

18.

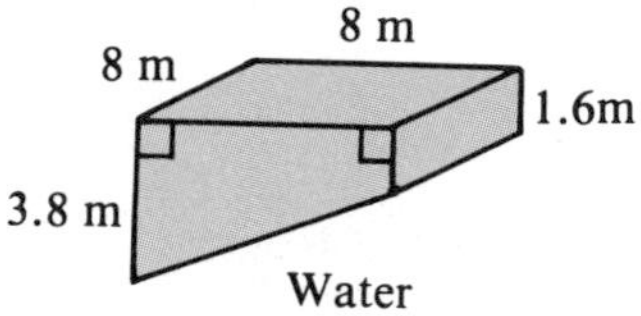

Water

Problems

Solve. Use the tables in this lesson if no density is given. Use $\pi \approx 3.14$.

A **1.** A solid gold bar has dimensions of approximately 17 cm by 9 cm by 4.5 cm. Find its mass in kilograms.

2. A solid pine board has dimensions of approximately 100 cm by 30 cm by 1.5 cm. Find the mass of the board in grams.

3. The optical prism shown at the right is made of glass having density 4.8 g/cm³. Find its mass.

4. A piece of ice is in the form of a half-cylinder 5 cm in radius and 3 cm high. What is its mass?

B **5.** What is the mass in metric tons of the steel I-beam shown at the right?

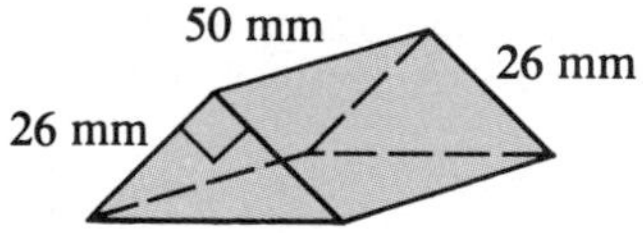

Ex. 3

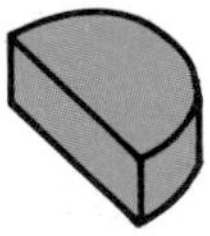

Ex. 4

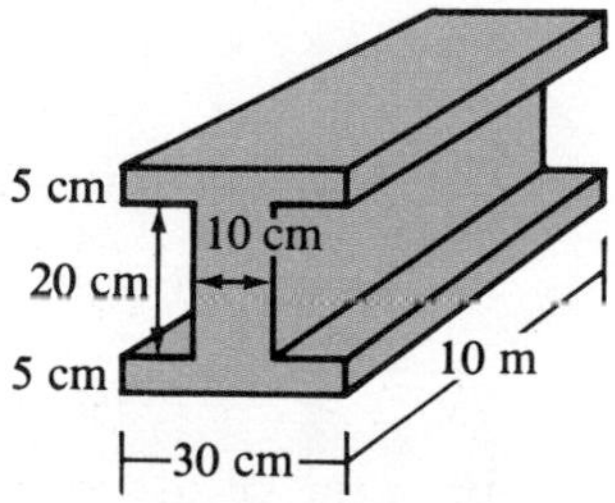

Ex. 5

6. The drawing at the right shows the cross-section of a two-kilometer-long tunnel that is to be dug through a mountain. How many metric tons of earth must be removed if its density is 2.8 t/m^3?

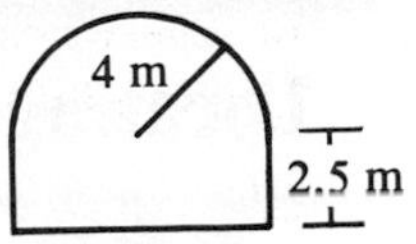

Ex. 6

Self-Test B

Use $\pi \approx 3.14$ unless told to do otherwise.

Complete.

1. Triangular prism: base area = 7.6 m^2, height = 5.5 m, volume = __?__ m^3 [9-5]

2. Cylinder: base diameter = 38 cm, height = 24 cm, volume = __?__ cm^3

3. Square prism: 17 cm by 17 cm by 32 cm, volume = __?__ cm^3, capacity = __?__ L

Find the volume of the solid.

4. A cone with base radius 0.5 m and height 1.2 m [9-6]

5. A pyramid with base of 180 m^2 and height 20 m

6. A square pyramid with base 26 cm on a side and height 48 cm

Find (a) the lateral area and (b) the total surface area of the solid.

7. A rectangular prism with base 4 by 3 and height 7 [9-7]

8. A cylinder with base diameter 10 and height 3

9. A square prism with height 42 and base 18 per side

Find (a) the surface area and (b) the volume of a sphere with the given dimensions. Leave your answers in terms of π.

10. radius = 18 cm

11. diameter = 12 m [9-8]

Find the mass of the solid.

12. A sphere of aluminum with diameter 18 cm, density 2.70 g/cm^3 [9-9]

13. A 4 cm by 4 cm by 20 cm block of pine, density of 0.568 g/cm^3

Self-Test answers and Extra Practice are at the back of the book.

Locating Points on Earth

We can think of Earth as a sphere rotating on an axis that is a diameter with endpoints at the North Pole (N) and South Pole (S). A **great circle** on a sphere is the intersection of the sphere with a plane that contains the center of the sphere. The great circle whose plane is perpendicular to Earth's axis is called the **equator.** The equator divides Earth into the Northern and Southern Hemispheres.

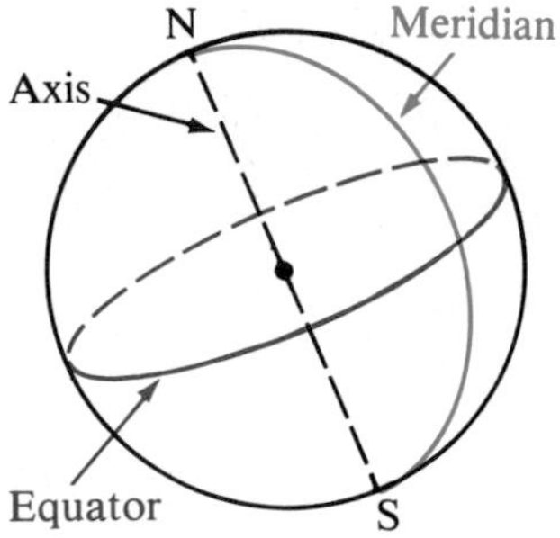

Semicircles with endpoints at the North and South Poles are called **meridians.** The meridian that passes through Greenwich, England, is called the **prime meridian.** The great circle on which the prime meridian lies divides Earth into the Eastern and Western Hemispheres.

The prime meridian and the equator are important parts of a degree-coordinate system that we use to describe the location of points on Earth. A series of circles whose planes are parallel to the equator, called **parallels of latitude,** identify the **latitude** of a point as a number of degrees between 0° and 90° *north* or *south of the equator.* The meridians identify the **longitude** of a point as the number of degrees between 0° and 180° *east* or *west of the prime meridian.*

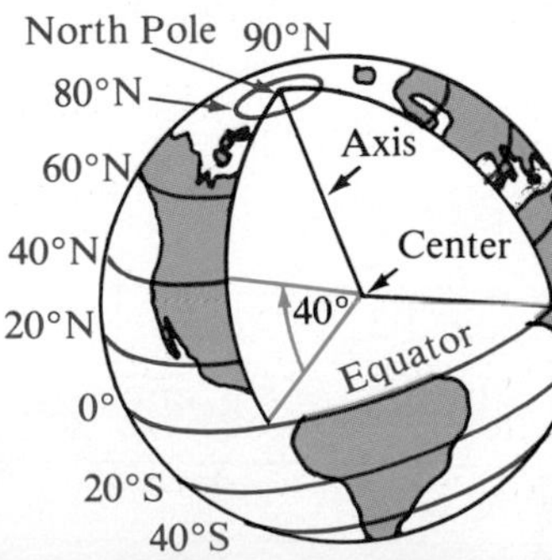

Parallels of Latitude

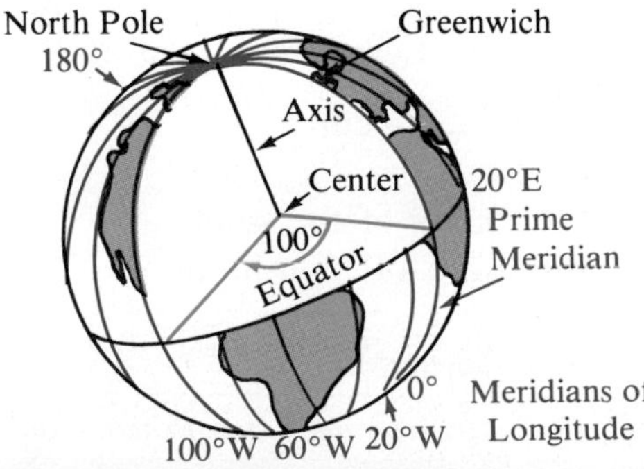

Meridians of Longitude

Thus, each point on the surface of Earth can be assigned an ordered pair of degree-coordinates: (latitude, longitude).

The flat map below, called a **Mercator projection,** shows the meridians and parallels of latitude marked off in 10° intervals as perpendicular lines. Notice that the city of Paris, France, is located at about 48°N, 2°E.

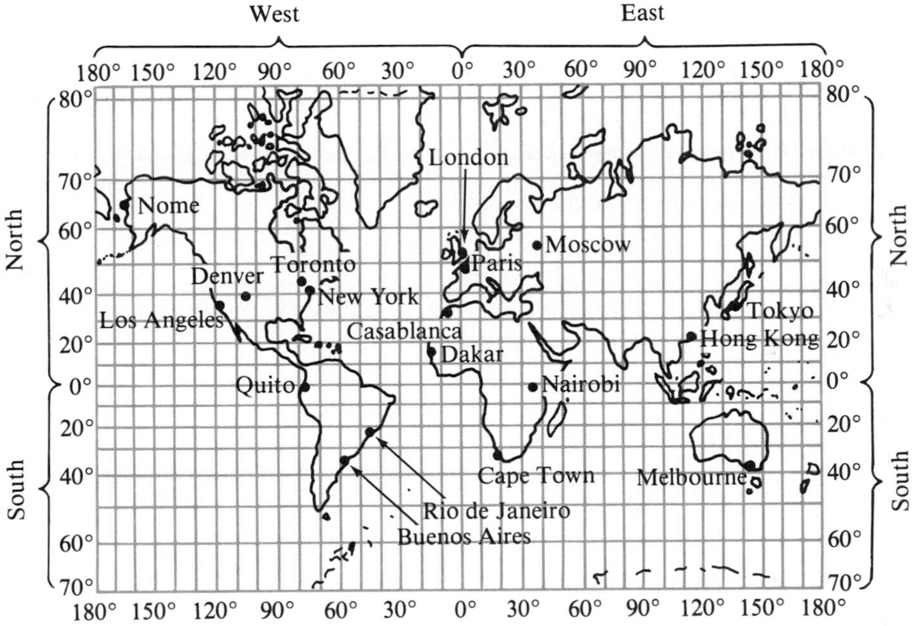

Mercator projection

Use the map above to name the major city at the location specified.

1. 40°N, 74°W **2.** 34°S, 58°W **3.** 23°S, 43°W **4.** 34°S, 18°E

5. 55°N, 37°E **6.** 37°S, 145°E **7.** 33°N, 7°W **8.** 34°N, 118°W

Give the latitude and longitude of the following cities to the nearest 5°.

9. Denver **10.** Nairobi **11.** London **12.** Quito

13. Dakar **14.** Toronto **15.** Nome **16.** Hong Kong

Career Activity

Ancient navigators determined their position by observing the sun and the stars. Modern navigators use much more sophisticated methods. If you were a navigator today what are some of the instruments and methods you might use?

Chapter Review

True or false?

1. A triangle with base 26 cm and height 36 cm has area 936 cm^2. [9-1]

2. A rectangular field that is 7 km by 12.8 km has area 8960 ha.

3. A parallelogram with area 308 cm^2 and height 14 cm has base 22 cm. [9-2]

4. A trapezoid with bases 23 m and 37 m and height 25 m has area 1500 m^2.

5. A circle with diameter 24 has area 576 π. [9-3]

6. A semicircle with radius 18 has area 162 π.

7. A figure cannot have more than one line of symmetry. [9-4]

8. If a figure is symmetric with respect to a point, then any line drawn through the point of symmetry divides the figure into two parts of equal area.

Complete. Use $\pi \approx 3.14$ when needed.

9. A rectangular prism has a base 12 cm by 14 cm and height 23 cm. Its volume is __?__. [9-5]

10. A cylinder has base radius 4 cm and height 15 cm. Its capacity is __?__ liters.

11. A cone with base diameter 6 and height 4.8 has volume __?__. [9-6]

12. A pyramid with base area 160 cm^2 and height 24 cm has volume __?__.

13. A cylinder with base radius 7 and height 12 has lateral area __?__ π and surface area __?__ π. [9-7]

14. A prism has height 16. Its bases are triangles with base 15, height 12, and remaining side 18. Its total surface area is __?__.

15. A sphere with radius 24 has surface area __?__ π and volume __?__ π. [9-8]

16. A sphere with radius 32 has surface area __?__ π and volume __?__ π.

17. A rectangular storage tank has dimensions 14 m by 6 m by 4 m. It is filled with helium of density 0.00018 kg/L. The mass of the helium is __?__. [9-9]

Chapter Test

Find the area of the region pictured or described. Leave your answers in terms of π when applicable. For Exercises 7 and 8, use the fact that the figures have symmetry.

1. Triangle: base = 56, height = 30 [9-1]

2. Rectangle: sides of 14 m and 23 m

3. Trapezoid: bases 10.5 and 20, height = 15 [9-2]

4. Parallelogram: base = 34, height = 26

5. Circle: radius = 11 m

6. Circle: Circumference = 12π [9-3]

7. [9-4]

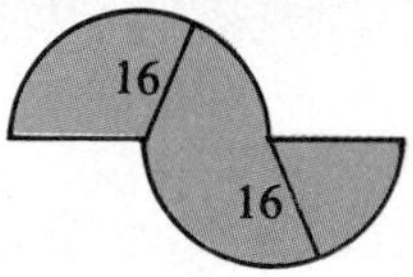

8.

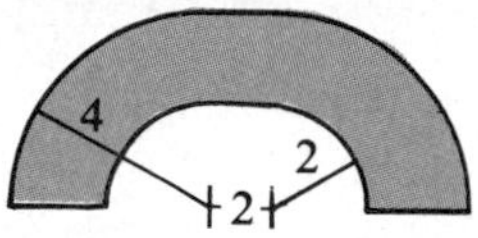

Find the volume. Use $\pi \approx 3.14$.

9. Cylinder: base radius = 7.2 m, height = 5.8 m [9-5]

10. Prism: base area = 45 cm^2, height = 33 cm

11. Cone: base diameter = 6 cm, height = 14 cm [9-6]

12. Pyramid: square base 17 cm on a side, height = 21 cm

Find (a) the lateral area and (b) the total surface area of each. Use $\pi \approx 3.14$.

13.

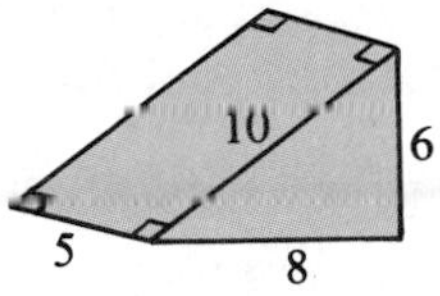

14. [9-7]

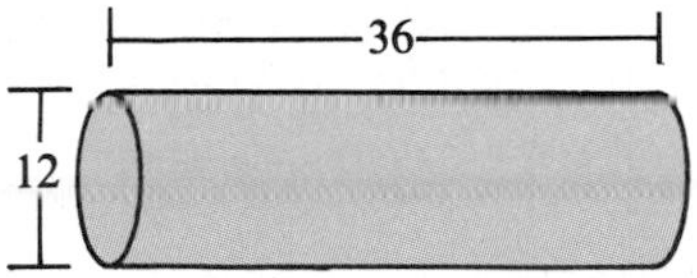

Find (a) the surface area and (b) the volume of a sphere with the given dimensions. Leave your answer in terms of π.

15. diameter = 18 cm

16. radius = 45 m [9-8]

17. Find the mass of a sphere with diameter 20 cm and density 8.9 g/cm^3. Use $\pi \approx 3.14$. [9-9]

18. Find the mass of a cube 9 cm on each edge with density 0.56 g/cm^3.

Cumulative Review (Chapters 1–9)

Exercises

Evaluate the expression if $a = 0.5$, $b = 5$, and $c = 2$.

1. abc **2.** $a + b + c$ **3.** $b \div a$ **4.** $3a - 3b$

5. ab^2 **6.** $c^2 + b^3$ **7.** $6(a^2 - c^2)$ **8.** $10a - \frac{b}{c}$

Evaluate the expression if $x = \frac{1}{3}$, $y = 2\frac{3}{4}$, and $z = -\frac{3}{5}$.

9. $x + y$ **10.** xz **11.** $3x + z$ **12.** $5z - x$

13. $x + 4y - 10z$ **14.** $6x + 8y + z$ **15.** $20z - (-y)$ **16.** $12x \div z$

Solve.

17. $15n + 7 > 52$ **18.** $6 - 2x < 21$ **19.** $38 \geq x - 2$

20. $\frac{n}{8} > 3$ **21.** $27 \leq 3x$ **22.** $3b + 5 < 56$

23. $4x + 7 = 35$ **24.** $-y + 10 = 26$ **25.** $\frac{3w}{7} = 9$

26. Find the measure of each angle of an equilateral triangle.

27. The measure of one angle in an isosceles triangle is 90°. Find the measures of the other angles.

28. An equilateral triangle has perimeter 37.5 cm. Find the length of each side.

29. What is 18% of 45? **30.** 8 is what percent of 4000?

31. 6.48 is what percent of 27? **32.** 105 is 42% of what number?

33. 316 is 0.5% of what number? **34.** What is $34\frac{1}{2}$% of 1100?

Solve the equation for y in terms of x.

35. $4x + y = 18$ **36.** $x + 2y = 15$ **37.** $6x - 6y = 50$

38. $\frac{x}{2} + y = 17$ **39.** $xy = 20$ **40.** $x^2 + y = 100$

Find the area of the circle described. Leave your answer in terms of π.

41. radius 14 cm **42.** diameter 46 mm **43.** radius 125 km

44. diameter 286 m **45.** radius 1805 cm **46.** diameter 305.6 m

Find the surface area and volume for the sphere described. Leave your answer in terms of π.

47. radius 8 **48.** radius 15 **49.** radius 36

Problems

Problem Solving Reminders

Here are some reminders that may help you solve some of the problems on this page.

- Determine what information is necessary to solve the problem.
- Consider whether drawing a sketch will help.
- If more than one method can be used to solve a problem, use one method to solve and one to check.

Solve.

1. The Aleutian Trench in the Pacific Ocean is 8100 m deep. Each story of an average skyscraper is about 4.2 m high. How many stories would a skyscraper as tall as the Aleutian Trench have? Round your answer to the nearest whole number.

2. Beryl's Bike Repair Shop occupies an area that is 25 ft long and 35 ft wide. Beryl pays a monthly fee of $1.75 per square foot for rent. What is her monthly rent?

3. A rancher bought 15 fence sections at $58 each to complete one side of a corral. If the length of the side is 375 m and each section is the same length, what is the length of a section?

4. George had 15 flat tires last year. The cost of repairing each tire was $6.35 plus 5% tax. How much did George spend on tire repairs for the year?

5. A boat salesperson receives a commission of 4.5% of sales. What would be the commission on sales of $135,000?

6. Gus is canning tomato sauce. He has 20 jars that have a diameter of 9 cm and height of 9 cm. If he must leave one centimeter of air space at the top of each jar, what volume of sauce can a jar hold? Use $\pi \approx 3.14$ and round the answer to three digits.

7. The cost of an average basket of groceries rose from $78.80 in April to $82.74 in June. What was the percent of increase?

8. A roll of 36-exposure film costs $5.85. Processing for color prints costs $.42 per print. What is the total cost for film and processing of 36 prints?

10

Square Roots and Right Triangles

Suppose that the string attached to a kite, like the one shown in the photograph, was held nearly taut. Suppose also that you knew the length of the kite string and the angle that the string made with the ground. You could then find the height of the kite by using a ratio from trigonometry.

Trigonometric ratios can be used to determine angles and distances, both large and small. A method known as trigonometric parallax, for example, can be used to measure distances as great as those from Earth to stars neighboring our solar system. Trigonometry can also be used to describe certain phenomenon such as the passage of light through transparent objects.

In this chapter, you will extend your knowledge of triangles and learn about trigonometric ratios. You will study some methods for finding angles and lengths.

Career Note

The job of surveyor is a career in which knowledge of right triangles and trigonometry plays an important role. Surveyors are responsible for establishing legal land boundaries. About half of their time is spent on location measuring sites and collecting data for maps and charts. The remaining part of their time is spent preparing reports, drawing maps, and planning future surveys.

10-1 Square Roots

Recall that we can write $b \times b$ as b^2 and call it the *square* of b. The **square root** of b^2 is the factor b. A given number a has b as a square root if

$$b^2 = a.$$

Thus 9 has 3 as a square root because $3^2 = 9$.

Every positive number has two square roots, and these are opposites of each other. For example, the square roots of 25 are 5 and -5 because

$$5^2 = 5 \times 5 = 25 \quad \text{and} \quad (-5)^2 = (-5) \times (-5) = 25.$$

The only square root of 0 is 0 because $b \times b = 0$ only when $b = 0$.

In this chapter we will work mostly with positive square roots. We use $\sqrt{a}$ to denote the *positive* square root of a. Thus $\sqrt{25} = 5$, not -5. A symbol such as $2\sqrt{25}$ means *2 times the positive square root of 25.* The negative square root of 25 is $-\sqrt{25}$, or -5.

Negative numbers have no real-number square roots because no real number has a square that is negative.

If $\sqrt{a}$ is an integer, we call a a **perfect square.** For example, 36 is a perfect square because $\sqrt{36}$ is the integer 6. Also, 144 is a perfect square because $\sqrt{144} = 12$.

If a is not a perfect square, we can estimate $\sqrt{a}$ by finding the two consecutive integers between which the square root lies. In the process, we use the fact that the smaller of two positive numbers has the smaller positive square root.

EXAMPLE Between which two consecutive integers does $\sqrt{40}$ lie?

Solution 40 lies between the consecutive perfect squares 36 and 49.

$$\begin{aligned} 36 &< 40 < 49 \\ \sqrt{36} &< \sqrt{40} < \sqrt{49} \\ \text{Thus} \quad 6 &< \sqrt{40} < 7. \end{aligned}$$

Class Exercises

Read each symbol.

1. $\sqrt{7}$ **2.** $3\sqrt{10}$ **3.** $-\sqrt{81}$ **4.** $\sqrt{64}$ **5.** $2\sqrt{14}$

If the given symbol names an integer, state the integer. If not, name the two consecutive integers between which the number lies.

6. $\sqrt{16}$ 7. $-\sqrt{36}$ 8. $\sqrt{21}$ 9. $\sqrt{70}$ 10. $\sqrt{50}$

11. $-\sqrt{49}$ 12. $\sqrt{81}$ 13. $\sqrt{69}$ 14. $\sqrt{144}$ 15. $\sqrt{169}$

Written Exercises

If the given symbol names an integer, state the integer. If not, name the two consecutive integers between which the number lies.

A 1. $\sqrt{43}$ 2. $\sqrt{64}$ 3. $-\sqrt{16}$ 4. $\sqrt{24}$ 5. $\sqrt{1}$

6. $\sqrt{0}$ 7. $-\sqrt{6^2}$ 8. $\sqrt{13}$ 9. $\sqrt{54}$ 10. $\sqrt{9}$

11. $\sqrt{30}$ 12. $\sqrt{48}$ 13. $\sqrt{15}$ 14. $\sqrt{8^2}$ 15. $\sqrt{2}$

16. $\sqrt{25} + \sqrt{16}$ 17. $\sqrt{100} - \sqrt{49}$ 18. $\sqrt{144} + \sqrt{25}$

19. $\sqrt{79 - 61}$ 20. $-\sqrt{66 - 2}$ 21. $\sqrt{100 - 19}$

Replace the _?_ with <, >, or = to make a true statement.

EXAMPLE $\sqrt{9} + \sqrt{25}$ _?_ $\sqrt{9 + 25}$

Solution $\sqrt{9} + \sqrt{25} = 3 + 5 = 8;\ \sqrt{9 + 25} = \sqrt{34} < 8.$
Thus $\sqrt{9} + \sqrt{25} > \sqrt{9 + 25}$.

B 22. $\sqrt{9} + \sqrt{16}$ _?_ $\sqrt{9 + 16}$ 23. $\sqrt{16} + \sqrt{4}$ _?_ $\sqrt{16 + 4}$

24. $\sqrt{16} - \sqrt{9}$ _?_ $\sqrt{16 - 9}$ 25. $\sqrt{25} - \sqrt{9}$ _?_ $\sqrt{25 - 9}$

26. $\sqrt{4} \times \sqrt{9}$ _?_ $\sqrt{4 \times 9}$ 27. $\sqrt{25} \times \sqrt{4}$ _?_ $\sqrt{25 \times 4}$

28. $2\sqrt{2}$ _?_ $\sqrt{2 \times 2}$ 29. $3\sqrt{12}$ _?_ $\sqrt{3 \times 12}$

Evaluate the expression.

C 30. $(\sqrt{25})^2$ 31. $(\sqrt{81})^2$ 32. $(\sqrt{49})^2$ 33. $(\sqrt{11})^2$ 34. $(\sqrt{2})^2$

Review Exercises

Divide. Round to the nearest hundredth.

1. $44 \div 6.7$ 2. $35 \div 5.9$ 3. $72 \div 8.3$ 4. $96 \div 9.5$

5. $147 \div 12.3$ 6. $230 \div 14.7$ 7. $0.0165 \div 0.13$ 8. $0.68 \div 0.81$

10-2 Approximating Square Roots

To get a close approximation of a square root, we can use the *divide-and-average* method. This method is based on the fact that

$$\text{if } \sqrt{a} = b, \text{ then } a = b \times b \text{ and } \tfrac{a}{b} = b.$$

In other words, when we divide a number a by its square root b, the quotient is b. When we use an estimate for b that is *less* than b for a divisor, the quotient is then *greater* than b. The average of the divisor and quotient can be used as a new estimate for b.

EXAMPLE 1 Approximate $\sqrt{55}$ to the tenths' place.

Solution

Step 1 To estimate $\sqrt{55}$, first find the two integers between which $\sqrt{55}$ lies.

$$\begin{aligned} 49 &< 55 < 64 \\ \sqrt{49} &< \sqrt{55} < \sqrt{64} \\ 7 &< \sqrt{55} < 8 \end{aligned}$$

Since 55 is closer to 49 than to 64, you might try 7.3 as an estimate of $\sqrt{55}$.

Step 2 Divide 55 by the estimate, 7.3. Compute to one more place than you want in the final answer.

$$\begin{array}{r} 7.53 \\ 7.3\overline{)55.0\,00} \\ 51\,1 \\ \hline 3\,9\,0 \\ 3\,6\,5 \\ \hline 2\,50 \\ 2\,19 \\ \hline 31 \end{array}$$

Step 3 Average the divisor and quotient.

$$\frac{7.3 + 7.53}{2} \approx 7.42$$

Use the average as the next estimate and repeat Steps 2 and 3 until your divisor and quotient agree in the tenths' place.

In this case, use 7.42 as your next estimate and divide.

$$\begin{array}{r} 7.41 \\ 7.42\overline{)55.00\,00} \\ 51\,94 \\ \hline 3\,06\,0 \\ 2\,96\,8 \\ \hline 9\,20 \\ 7\,42 \\ \hline 1\,78 \end{array}$$

As you can see, $\sqrt{55} \approx 7.4$ to the tenths' place.

We can approximate $\sqrt{55}$ to whatever decimal place we wish by repeating the steps shown in Example 1 on the previous page. Because $\sqrt{55}$ is a nonterminating, nonrepeating decimal, we say that $\sqrt{55}$ is an **irrational number.** Together, irrational and rational numbers form the set of **real numbers.** Other irrational numbers are discussed on page 133.

To find the square root of a number that is not an integer by the divide-and-average method, we use the same steps as in Example 1. The first step, finding the two integers between which a square root lies, is shown below.

EXAMPLE 2 Complete the first step in estimating each square root.

a. $\sqrt{12.3}$ **b.** $\sqrt{0.7}$

Solution The first step in estimating a square root is to find the two integers between which it lies.

a.
$$9 < 12.3 < 16$$
$$\sqrt{9} < \sqrt{12.3} < \sqrt{16}$$
$$3 < \sqrt{12.3} < 4$$

b.
$$0 < 0.7 < 1$$
$$\sqrt{0} < \sqrt{0.7} < \sqrt{1}$$
$$0 < \sqrt{0.7} < 1$$

Class Exercises

Give the first digit of the square root.

1. $\sqrt{7}$ **2.** $\sqrt{11}$ **3.** $\sqrt{30}$ **4.** $\sqrt{50}$ **5.** $\sqrt{94}$

Give the next estimate for the square root of the dividend.

EXAMPLE $3.8\overline{)15.000}$ with quotient 3.95

Solution $\dfrac{3.8 + 3.95}{2} \approx 3.88$

Thus 3.88 is the next estimate.

6. $2\overline{)4.8}$ with quotient 2.4 **7.** $3\overline{)11}$ with quotient 3.7 **8.** $5\overline{)28.5}$ with quotient 5.7 **9.** $4.3\overline{)21.000}$ with quotient 4.88

10. $14\overline{)225}$ with quotient 16 **11.** $0.7\overline{)0.53}$ with quotient 0.76 **12.** $0.6\overline{)0.3}$ with quotient 0.5 **13.** $0.9\overline{)0.83}$ with quotient 0.92

Written Exercises

Approximate to the tenths' place.

A

1. $\sqrt{11}$
2. $\sqrt{13}$
3. $\sqrt{33}$
4. $\sqrt{23}$
5. $\sqrt{8}$
6. $\sqrt{5}$
7. $\sqrt{26}$
8. $\sqrt{42}$
9. $\sqrt{57}$
10. $\sqrt{75}$
11. $\sqrt{91}$
12. $\sqrt{69}$
13. $\sqrt{5.7}$
14. $\sqrt{7.5}$
15. $\sqrt{9.1}$
16. $\sqrt{6.9}$
17. $\sqrt{8.2}$
18. $\sqrt{4.6}$
19. $\sqrt{3.5}$
20. $\sqrt{1.6}$

B

21. $\sqrt{152}$
22. $\sqrt{285}$
23. $\sqrt{705}$
24. $\sqrt{328}$
25. $\sqrt{15.2}$
26. $\sqrt{28.5}$
27. $\sqrt{70.5}$
28. $\sqrt{32.4}$
29. $\sqrt{0.4}$
30. $\sqrt{0.6}$
31. $\sqrt{0.05}$
32. $\sqrt{0.21}$

Approximate to the hundredths' place.

33. $\sqrt{2}$
34. $\sqrt{3}$
35. $\sqrt{5}$
36. $\sqrt{10}$

Review Exercises

Simplify.

1. $4(11 - 2) + 3(2) + 2(5 + 3)$
2. $5(81 \div 9) - 36 + 11$
3. $7.3 + (9.14 - 6.91) - 2.81$
4. $11.32 - 67(8.01 - 7.92)$
5. $3.617 + 0.7(5.301 - 4.911)$
6. $14.95 + 5(3.2 + 14) - 90.84$
7. $(72 - 65) + 11(8.76 - 0.89)$
8. $5.143 + 0.3(8.914 - 7.126)$

Calculator Key-In

On many calculators there is a square root key. If you have access to such a calculator, use it to complete the exercises below.

1. a. $\sqrt{1}$ b. $\sqrt{100}$ c. $\sqrt{10,000}$
2. a. $\sqrt{7}$ b. $\sqrt{700}$ c. $\sqrt{70,000}$
3. a. $\sqrt{70}$ b. $\sqrt{7000}$ c. $\sqrt{700,000}$
4. a. $\sqrt{0.08}$ b. $\sqrt{8}$ c. $\sqrt{800}$
5. a. $\sqrt{0.54}$ b. $\sqrt{54}$ c. $\sqrt{5400}$

10-3 Using a Square-Root Table

Part of the Table of Square Roots on page 498 is shown below. Square roots of integers are given to the nearest thousandth.

Number	Positive Square Root	Number	Positive Square Root	Number	Positive Square Root	Number	Positive Square Root
N	$\sqrt{N}$	N	$\sqrt{N}$	N	$\sqrt{N}$	N	$\sqrt{N}$
1	1	**26**	5.099	**51**	7.141	**76**	8.718
2	1.414	**27**	5.196	**52**	7.211	**77**	8.775
3	1.732	**28**	5.292	**53**	7.280	**78**	8.832
4	2	**29**	5.385	**54**	7.348	**79**	8.888

We can use the table to approximate the square roots of integers from 1 to 100. For example, to find $\sqrt{78}$, first locate 78 under a column headed "Number." Then read off the value beside 78 in the "Square Root" column.

$$\sqrt{78} \approx 8.832$$

Reading Mathematics: *Tables*
Some tables may have many columns of information. When you are reading a table, use a ruler to help guide your eyes across the page or down a column. This way you can be sure to find the correct entry.

To find an approximate square root of a number that lies between two entries in the column headed "Number," we can use a process called **interpolation.** The interpolation process may cause an error in the last digit of the approximation.

EXAMPLE 1 Approximate $\sqrt{3.8}$ by interpolation.

Solution On a number line $\sqrt{3.8}$ lies between $\sqrt{3}$ and $\sqrt{4}$. We can assume that $\sqrt{3.8}$ is about 0.8 of the distance between $\sqrt{3}$ and $\sqrt{4}$.

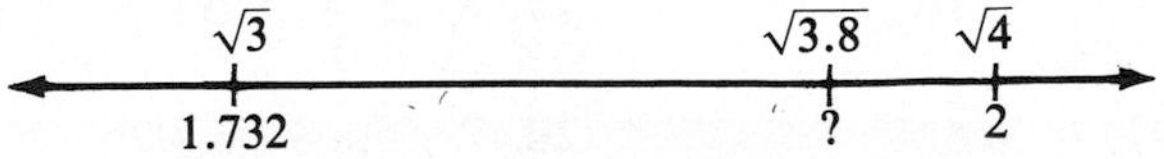

$$\begin{aligned}\sqrt{3.8} &\approx \sqrt{3} + 0.8(\sqrt{4} - \sqrt{3})\\ &\approx 1.732 + 0.8(2.000 - 1.732)\\ &\approx 1.732 + 0.2144 = 1.9464\end{aligned}$$

Thus, rounded to the thousandths' place, $\sqrt{3.8} = 1.946$.

EXAMPLE 2 The area of a square display room is 71 m^2. Find the length of a side to the nearest hundredth of a meter.

Solution Recall that the formula for the area of a square is $A = s^2$.

$$s^2 = 71$$
$$s = \sqrt{71}$$

Using the table on page 498, we see that $\sqrt{71} = 8.426$.
To the nearest hundredth of a meter, the length of a side is 8.43 m.

Class Exercises

Use the table on page 498 to find the approximate square root.

1. $\sqrt{39}$ **2.** $\sqrt{83}$ **3.** $\sqrt{20}$ **4.** $\sqrt{95}$ **5.** $\sqrt{34}$

6. $\sqrt{49}$ **7.** $\sqrt{11}$ **8.** $\sqrt{52}$ **9.** $10\sqrt{87}$ **10.** $\frac{1}{10}\sqrt{22}$

Find two decimals in the table on page 498 between which the square root lies.

11. $\sqrt{54.3}$ **12.** $\sqrt{1.7}$ **13.** $\sqrt{60.7}$ **14.** $\sqrt{4.5}$ **15.** $\sqrt{28.6}$

Written Exercises

For Exercises 1–37, refer to the table on page 498.

Approximate the square root to the nearest hundredth.

A **1.** $\sqrt{65}$ **2.** $\sqrt{31}$ **3.** $\sqrt{56}$ **4.** $\sqrt{13}$ **5.** $\sqrt{97}$

6. $10\sqrt{37}$ **7.** $10\sqrt{41}$ **8.** $\frac{1}{10}\sqrt{83}$ **9.** $\frac{1}{10}\sqrt{75}$ **10.** $\frac{1}{10}\sqrt{24}$

11. $3\sqrt{55}$ **12.** $2\sqrt{30}$ **13.** $6\sqrt{19}$ **14.** $4\sqrt{18}$ **15.** $7\sqrt{72}$

B **16.** $\sqrt{39} + \sqrt{16}$ **17.** $\sqrt{28} + \sqrt{53}$ **18.** $\sqrt{71} - \sqrt{25}$

19. $\sqrt{91} - \sqrt{84}$ **20.** $2\sqrt{56} - \sqrt{4}$ **21.** $\sqrt{37} - 2\sqrt{8}$

Approximate the square root to the nearest hundredth by interpolation.

22. $\sqrt{13.2}$ **23.** $\sqrt{5.9}$ **24.** $\sqrt{14.7}$ **25.** $\sqrt{81.6}$ **26.** $\sqrt{24.3}$

27. $\sqrt{8.7}$ **28.** $\sqrt{69.2}$ **29.** $\sqrt{50.9}$ **30.** $5\sqrt{84.4}$ **31.** $3\sqrt{81.9}$

Approximate the square root to the nearest hundredth.

32. $\sqrt{700}$ (*Hint:* $\sqrt{100 \times 7} = \sqrt{100} \times \sqrt{7} = 10\sqrt{7}$) 33. $\sqrt{500}$ 34. $\sqrt{1100}$

35. $\sqrt{380}$ (*Hint:* $\sqrt{100 \times 3.8} = \sqrt{100 \times 3.8} = 10\sqrt{3.8}$) 36. $\sqrt{420}$ 37. $\sqrt{3470}$

Problems

Solve.

A 1. The area of a square is 85 m^2. Find the length of a side to the nearest hundredth of a meter.

2. A square floor has an area of 32 m^2. Find the length of a side to the nearest tenth of a meter.

3. The area of a square room measures 225 ft^2. How much will it cost to put molding around the ceiling at $.35 per foot?

B 4. An isosceles right triangle has an area of 13.5 cm^2. Find the length of the equal sides to the nearest tenth of a centimeter.

5. A circle has an area of 47.1 cm^2. Find its radius to the nearest hundredth of a centimeter. (Use $\pi \approx 3.14$.)

6. The height of a parallelogram is half the length of its base. The parallelogram has an area of 67 cm^2. Find the height to the nearest tenth of a centimeter.

C 7. The total surface area of a cube is 210 m^2. Find the length of an edge to the nearest hundredth of a meter.

8. One base of a trapezoid is three times as long as the other base. The height of the trapezoid is the same as the shorter base. The trapezoid has an area of 83 cm^2. Find the height to the nearest tenth of a centimeter.

Review Exercises

Write the value of the product.

1. 0.9^2 2. 0.05^2 3. 0.06^2 4. 0.7^2 5. 3.7^2 6. 1.9^2 7. 24.3^2 8. 5.03^2

10-4 The Pythagorean Theorem

The longest side of a right triangle is opposite the right angle and is called the **hypotenuse.** The two shorter sides are called **legs.**

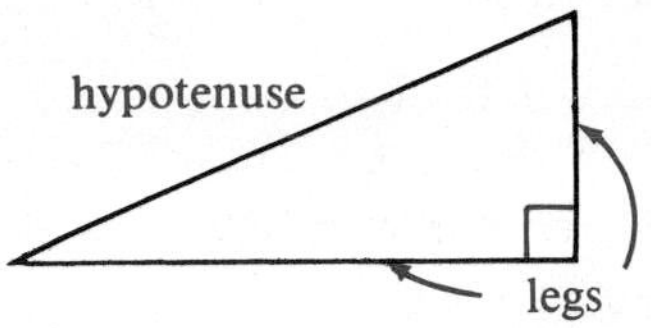

About 2500 years ago, the Greek mathematician Pythagoras proved the following useful fact about right triangles.

The Pythagorean Theorem

If the hypotenuse of a right triangle has length c, and the legs have lengths a and b, then

$$c^2 = a^2 + b^2.$$

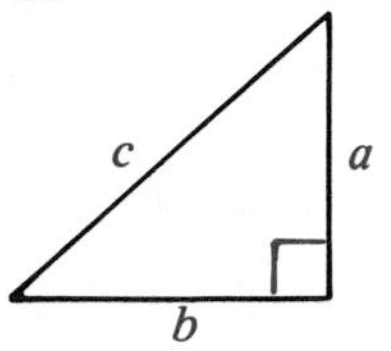

The figure at the right illustrates the Pythagorean theorem. We see that the area of the square on the hypotenuse equals the sum of the areas of the squares on the legs:

$$25 = 9 + 16,$$

$$\text{or } 5^2 = 3^2 + 4^2.$$

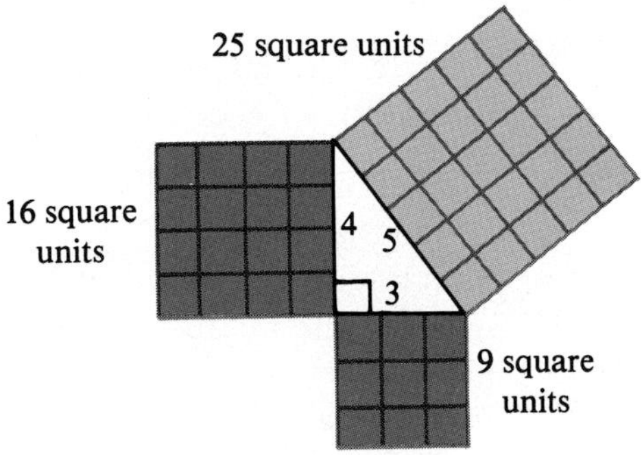

The converse of the Pythagorean theorem is also true. It can be used to test whether a triangle is a right triangle.

Converse of the Pythagorean Theorem

If the sides of a triangle have lengths a, b, and c, such that $c^2 = a^2 + b^2$, then the triangle is a right triangle.

EXAMPLE 1 Is the triangle with sides of the given lengths a right triangle?

a. 4, 5, 7 **b.** 5, 12, 13

Solution **a.** $4^2 = 16$, $5^2 = 25$, $7^2 = 49$

No, since $16 + 25 \neq 49$. The triangle with sides of lengths 4, 5, and 7 *cannot* be a right triangle.

b. $5^2 = 25,\ 12^2 = 144,\ 13^2 = 169$
Yes, since $25 + 144 = 169$. The triangle with sides of lengths 5, 12, and 13 is a right triangle.

Sometimes it may be necessary to solve for the length of a missing side of a right triangle. The example below illustrates the steps involved.

EXAMPLE 2 For right triangle ABC, find the length of the missing side to the nearest hundredth. Use the table on page 498.

a. $a = 3,\ b = 7$ **b.** $a = 4,\ c = 9$

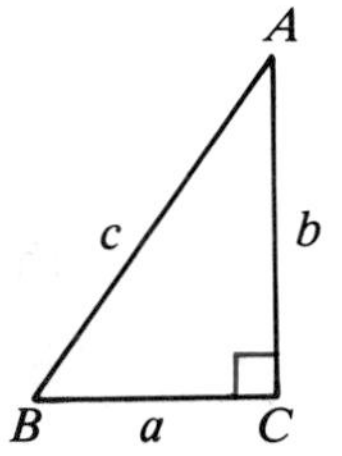

Solution Using the equation $c^2 = a^2 + b^2$:

a.
$$\begin{aligned} c^2 &= 3^2 + 7^2 \\ &= 9 + 49 = 58 \\ c &= \sqrt{58} \\ c &\approx 7.62 \end{aligned}$$

b.
$$\begin{aligned} 9^2 &= 4^2 + b^2 \\ 9^2 - 4^2 &= b^2 \\ 81 - 16 &= b^2 \\ 65 &= b^2 \\ \sqrt{65} &= b \\ b &\approx 8.06 \end{aligned}$$

Class Exercises

Without actually counting them, tell how many unit squares there are in the shaded square.

1.

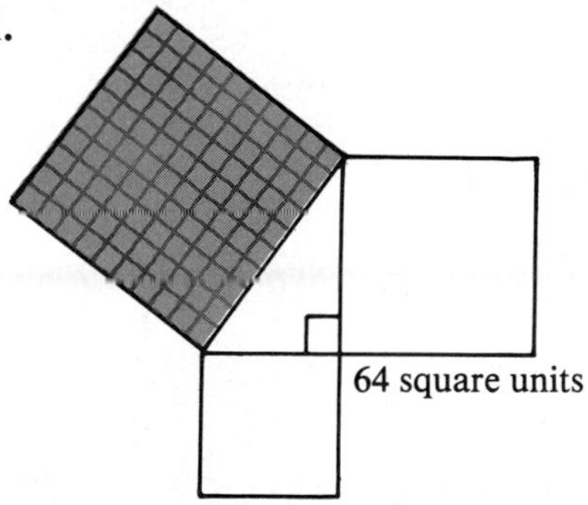

2.

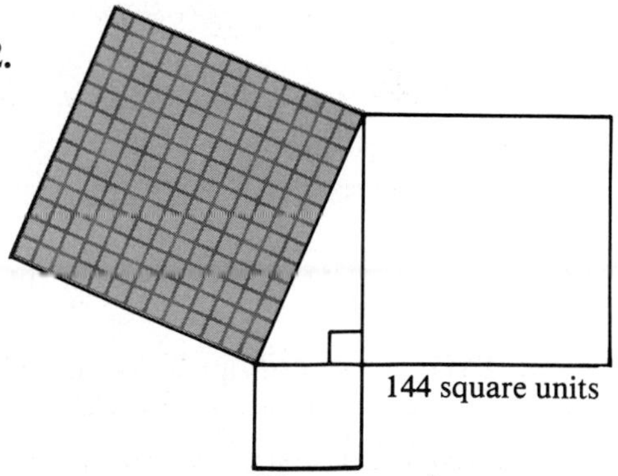

Replace _?_ with = or ≠ to make a true statement.

3. 6^2 _?_ $4^2 + 5^2$ **4.** 5^2 _?_ $3^2 + 4^2$ **5.** 10^2 _?_ $6^2 + 8^2$

The lengths of the sides of a triangle are given. Is it a right triangle?

6. 3, 4, 5 **7.** 7, 24, 25 **8.** 5, 10, 12 **9.** 10, 24, 26

Written Exercises

Find the area of the square.

A **1.**

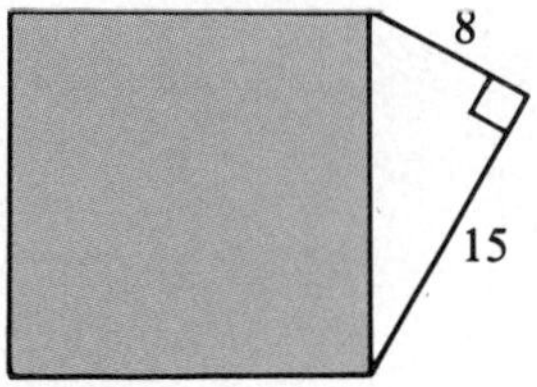

2.

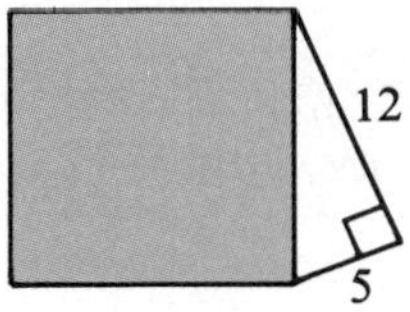

3.

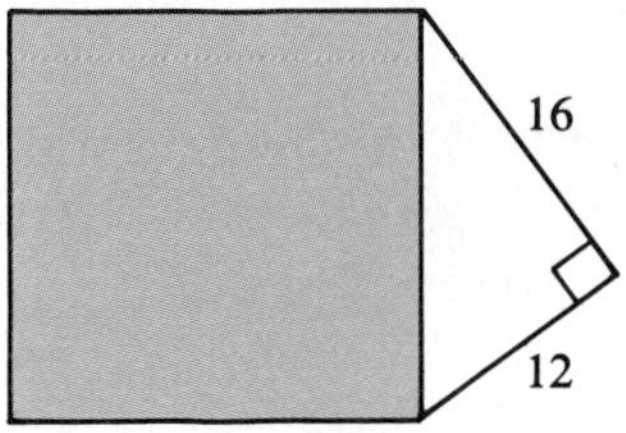

Is the triangle with sides of the given lengths a right triangle?

4. 6, 8, 10

5. 8, 15, 17

6. 16 cm, 30 cm, 34 cm

7. 9 m, 12 m, 15 m

8. 1.5 mm, 2.0 mm, 2.5 mm

9. 0.6 km, 0.8 km, 1.0 km

10. 9 m, 21 m, 23 m

11. 20 cm, 21 cm, 29 cm

12. 9 km, 40 km, 41 km

13. 8 m, 37 m, 39 m

A right triangle has sides of lengths *a*, *b*, and *c*, with *c* the length of the hypotenuse. Find the length of the missing side. If necessary, use the table on page 498 for the square root values and round answers to the nearest hundredth.

B **14.** $a = 2,\ b = 1$ **15.** $a = 8,\ b = 6$ **16.** $a = 4,\ c = 9$ **17.** $b = 5,\ c = 6$

18. $a = 5,\ b = 12$ **19.** $a = 9,\ b = 7$ **20.** $b = 11,\ c = 19$ **21.** $a = 24,\ c = 74$

A **Pythagorean Triple** consists of three positive integers a, b, and c that satisfy the equation $a^2 + b^2 = c^2$. You can find as many Pythagorean Triples as you wish by substituting positive integers for m and n (such that $m > n$) in the following expressions for a, b, and c.

$$a = m^2 - n^2 \qquad b = 2mn \qquad c = m^2 + n^2$$

Find Pythagorean Triples using the given values of *m* and *n*.

C **22.** $m = 5,\ n = 1$ **23.** $m = 6,\ n = 3$ **24.** $m = 4,\ n = 2$

Problems

Solve. Give your answer to the nearest tenth.

A **1.** A plane flies 90 km due east and then 60 km due north. How far is it then from its starting point?

2. The foot of a 6 m ladder is 2.5 m from the base of a wall. How high up the wall does the ladder reach?

3. The figure shows two cables bracing a television tower. What is the distance between the points where the cables touch the ground?

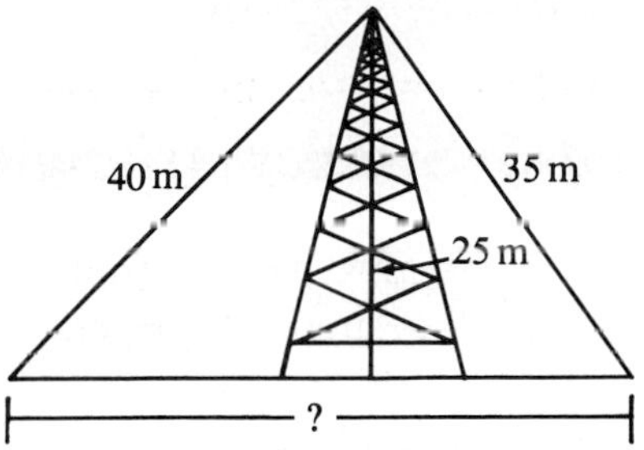

4. Find the length of a diagonal of a 10 cm by 10 cm square.

B 5. A square has diagonals 10 cm long. Find the length of a side.

6. The diagonals of a rhombus are perpendicular and bisect each other. Find the length of a side of a rhombus whose diagonals have lengths 12 m and 18 m.

C 7. Find the length of a diagonal of a 10 by 10 by 10 cube. (*Hint:* First find AQ using right triangle PQA. Then find the required length AB using right triangle AQB.)

8. Find the length of a diagonal of a box having dimensions 2 by 3 by 6. (See the *Hint* for Problem 7.)

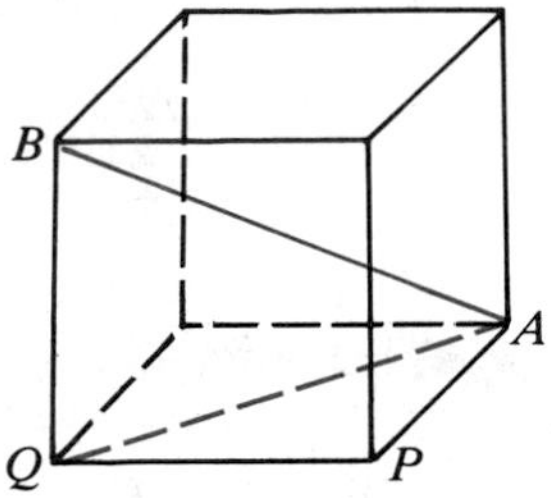

Self-Test A

If the given symbol names an integer, state the integer. If not, name the two consecutive integers between which the number lies.

1. $\sqrt{56}$ 2. $-\sqrt{81}$ 3. $\sqrt{9} + \sqrt{25}$ 4. $\sqrt{106 - 57}$ **[10-1]**

5. Use the divide-and-average method to approximate $\sqrt{86.4}$ to the nearest tenth. **[10-2]**

Use the table on page 498 and interpolation to approximate each square root to the nearest tenth.

6. $\sqrt{18}$ 7. $\sqrt{50}$ 8. $\sqrt{9.8}$ 9. $\sqrt{5.6}$ **[10-3]**

A right triangle has sides of lengths a, b, and c, with c the length of the hypotenuse. Find the length of the missing side.

10. $a = 3$, $b = 4$ 11. $b = 96$, $c = 100$ 12. $c = 20$, $a = 12$ **[10-4]**

Self-Test answers and Extra Practice are at the back of the book.

10-5 Similar Triangles

As you know, we say that two figures are congruent when they are identical in both shape and size. When two figures have the same shape, but do not necessarily have the same size, we say that the figures are **similar.**

For two *triangles* to be similar it is enough that the measures of their corresponding angles are equal.

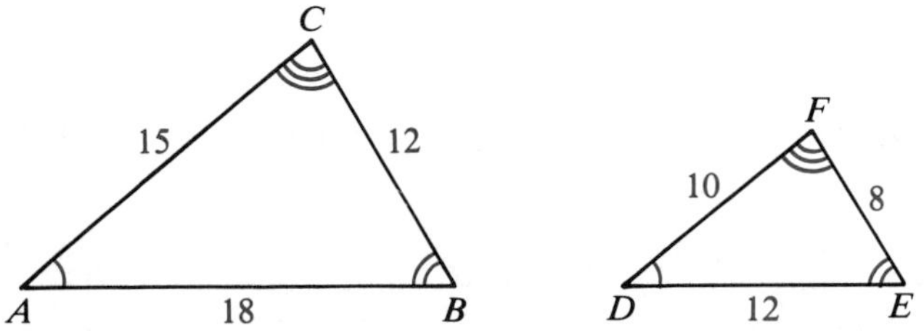

To indicate that the triangles shown above are similar, we can write the following.

$$\triangle ABC \sim \triangle DEF$$

The symbol $\sim$ means *is similar to.* Note that when we write expressions such as the one above, we list corresponding vertices in the same order.

In triangles ABC and DEF, we see that the lengths of the corresponding sides have the same ratio:

$$\frac{AB}{DE} = \frac{18}{12} = \frac{3}{2} \qquad \frac{BC}{EF} = \frac{12}{8} = \frac{3}{2} \qquad \frac{CA}{FD} = \frac{15}{10} = \frac{3}{2}$$

Therefore,

$$\frac{AB}{DE} = \frac{BC}{EF} = \frac{CA}{FD}.$$

Because the ratios are equal, we say that the lengths of the corresponding sides are *proportional.*

In general, we can say the following.

For two similar triangles,

corresponding angles are congruent

and

lengths of corresponding sides are proportional.

EXAMPLE 1 If $\triangle RUN \sim \triangle JOG$, find the lengths marked x and y.

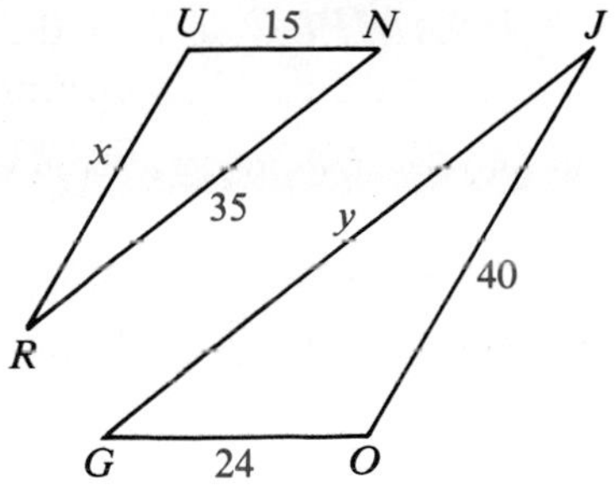

Solution Since the corresponding vertices are listed in the same order, we know the following.

$$\angle R \cong \angle J$$

$$\angle U \cong \angle O$$

$$\angle N \cong \angle G$$

$$\frac{RU}{JO} = \frac{UN}{OG} = \frac{NR}{GJ}$$

Substituting the values that are given in the diagram, we obtain

$$\frac{x}{40} = \frac{15}{24} = \frac{35}{y}.$$

Therefore, we can set up one proportion involving x and another involving y.

$$\frac{x}{40} = \frac{15}{24} \qquad \frac{15}{24} = \frac{35}{y}$$

$$24x = 15 \times 40 \qquad 15y = 35 \times 24$$

$$x = \frac{15 \times 40}{24} \qquad y = \frac{35 \times 24}{15}$$

$$x = \frac{600}{24} = 25 \qquad y = \frac{840}{15} = 56$$

The length of x is 25 and the length of y is 56.

In the two *right triangles* shown at the right, the measures of two acute angles are equal. Since all right angles have equal measure, 90°, the two remaining acute angles must also have equal measure. (Recall that the sum of the angle measures of any triangle is 180°.) Thus the two right triangles are similar.

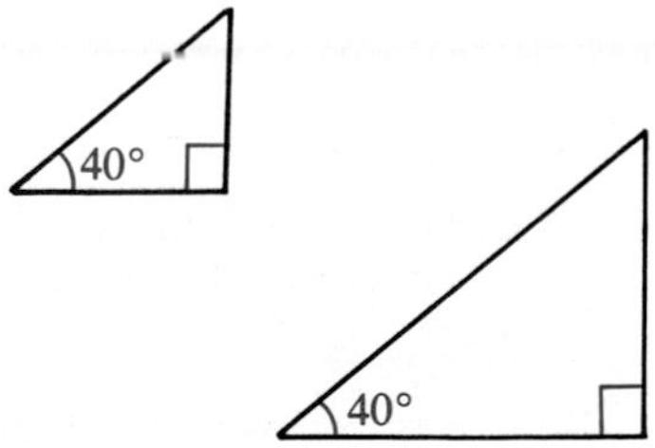

If an acute angle of one *right* triangle is congruent to an angle of a second *right* triangle, then the triangles are similar.

EXAMPLE 2 At the same time a tree on level ground casts a shadow 48 m long, a 2 m pole casts a shadow 5 m long. Find the height, h, of the tree.

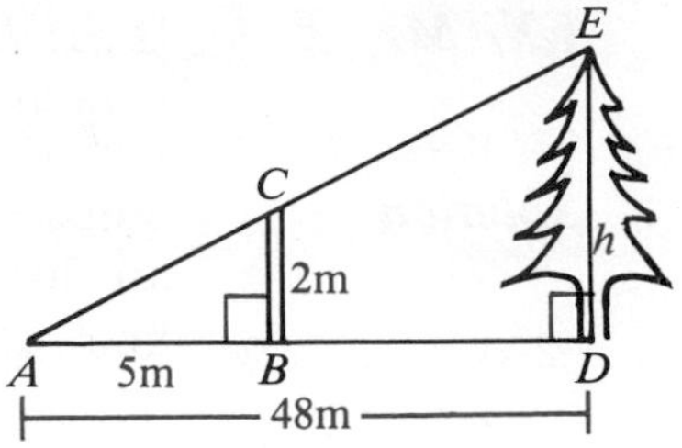

Solution In the diagram, right triangles ABC and ADE share acute $\angle A$ and thus are similar. Since $\frac{AD}{AB} = \frac{DE}{BC} = \frac{EA}{CA}$, we can set up a proportion to solve for h.

$$\frac{h}{2} = \frac{48}{5}$$
$$5h = 48 \times 2$$
$$h = \frac{48 \times 2}{5} = 19.2$$

The height of the tree is 19.2 m.

Reading Mathematics: *Diagrams*
To help you read a diagram that has overlapping triangles, you can redraw the diagram, pulling apart the individual triangles. For example, $\triangle ADE$ above can be separated as shown below.

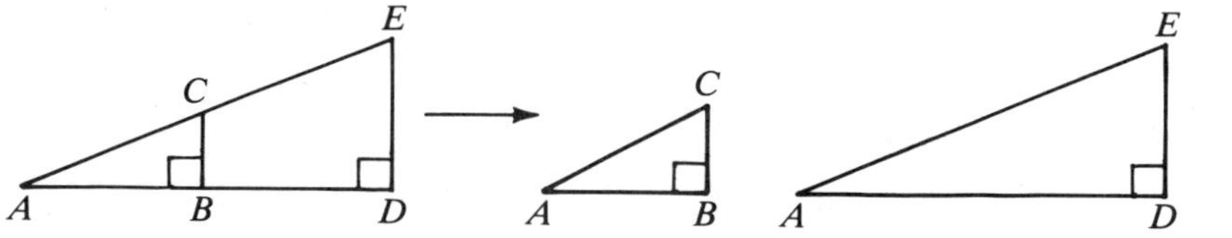

Class Exercises

In Exercises 1–4, $\triangle LOG \sim \triangle RIT$.

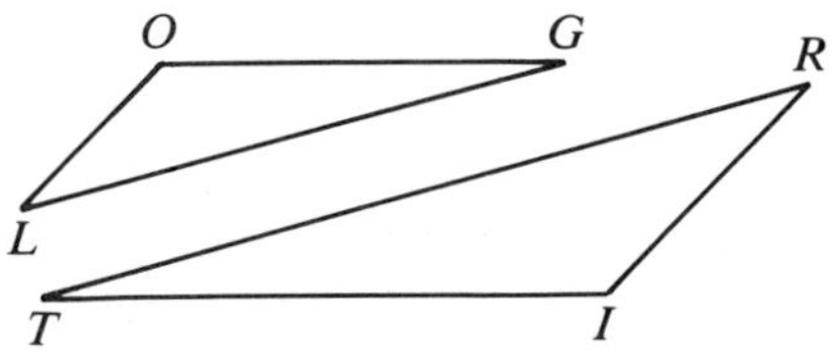

1. Name all pairs of corresponding angles.
2. Name all pairs of corresponding sides.
3. $\frac{OL}{IR} = \frac{OG}{?}$
4. $\frac{LG}{?} = \frac{GO}{TI}$

True or false?

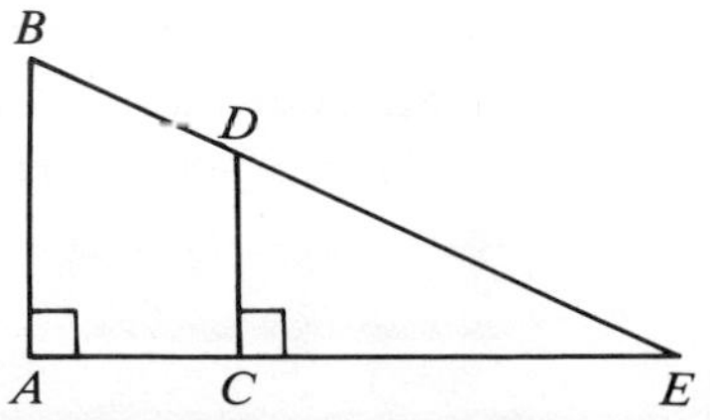

5. $\triangle BAE$ and $\triangle DCE$ are right triangles.
6. $m\angle ABE = m\angle CDE$
7. $\triangle BAE \sim \triangle DCE$
8. $\frac{CE}{AE} = \frac{BA}{DE}$
9. $\frac{BA}{DC} = \frac{BE}{DE}$

Written Exercises

Exercises 1–5 refer to the diagram at the right. $\triangle ABC \sim \triangle PQR$.

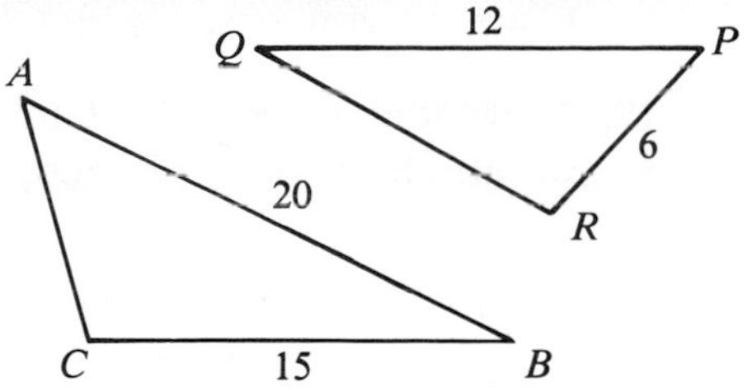

A **1.** $\frac{PR}{AC} = \frac{?}{CB}$

2. $\frac{BA}{?} = \frac{CB}{RQ}$

3. Find the length of $\overline{RQ}$.

4. Find the length of $\overline{AC}$.

5. $m\angle A = 47°$ and $m\angle Q = 29°$, $m\angle C = \underline{\ ?\ }°$.

Exercises 6–10 refer to the diagram at the right. $\triangle AED \sim \triangle ACB$.

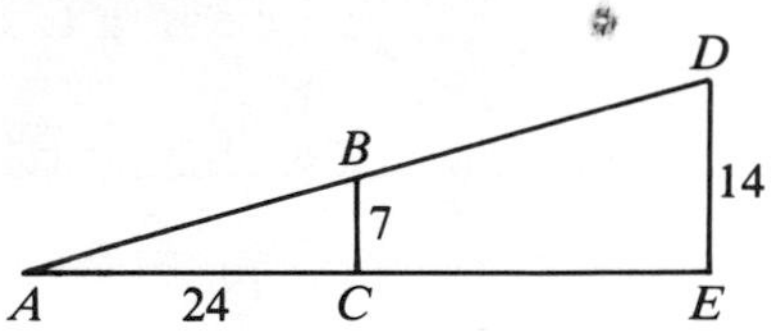

6. The length of $\overline{AE} = \underline{\ ?\ }$.

7. The length of $\overline{AB} = \underline{\ ?\ }$.

8. The length of $\overline{AD} = \underline{\ ?\ }$.

9. If $m\angle A = 25°$, then $m\angle ABC = \underline{\ ?\ }°$ and $m\angle ADE = \underline{\ ?\ }°$.

10. If $\frac{BC}{DE} = \frac{1}{2}$, then $\frac{AB}{AD} = \underline{\ ?\ }$.

Find the lengths marked *x* and *y*.

11. $\triangle MAB \sim \triangle SRO$

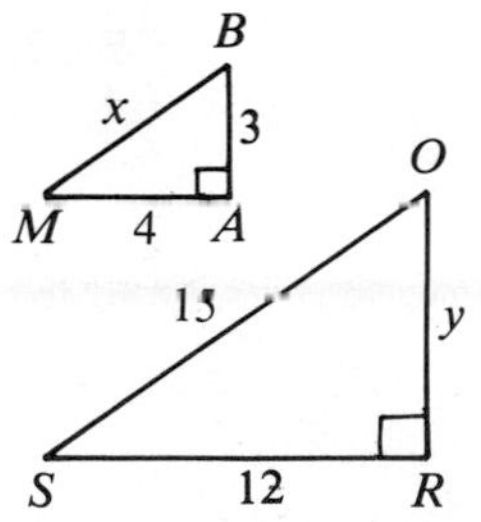

12. $\triangle DIP \sim \triangle MON$

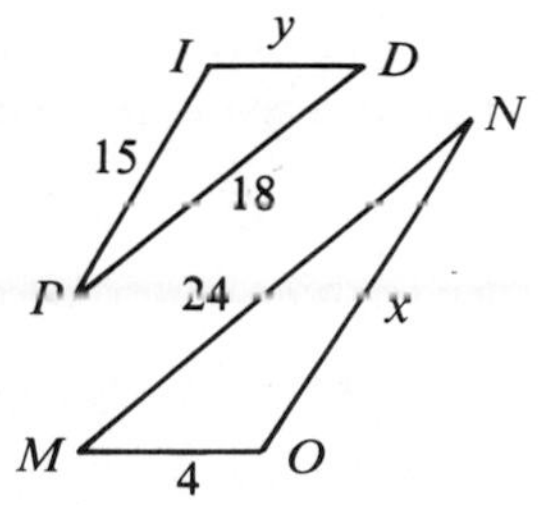

13. $\triangle RST \sim \triangle RUV$

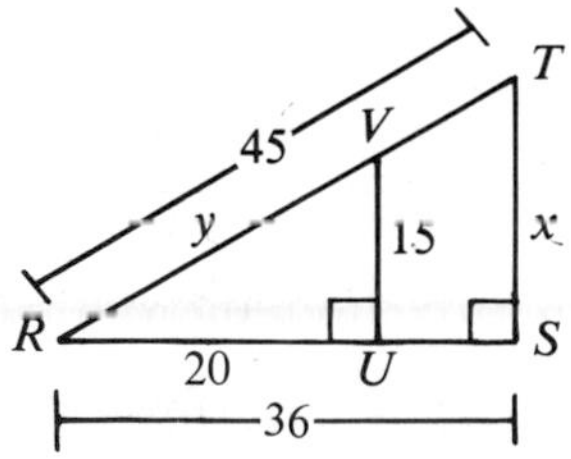

B **14.** $\triangle GEM \sim \triangle TIM$

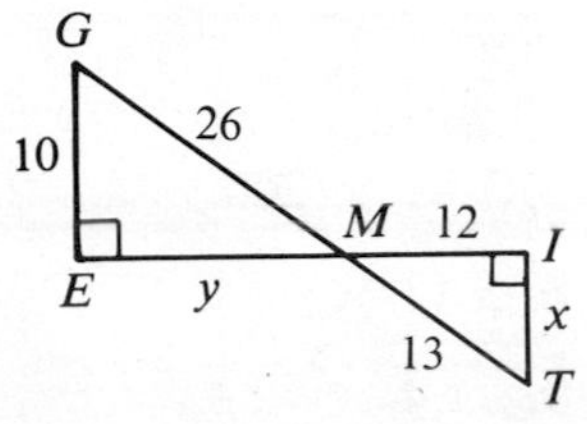

15. $\triangle PAR \sim \triangle PBT$

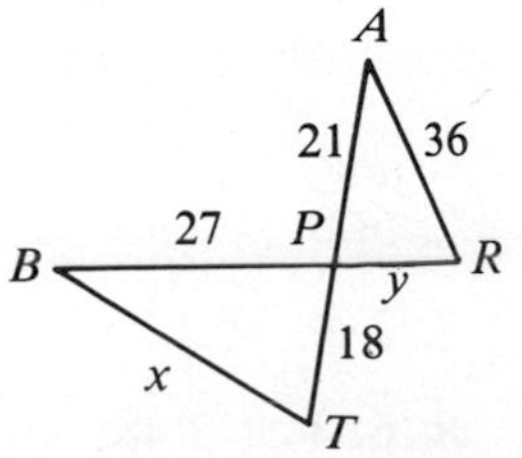

16. $\triangle ART \sim \triangle ABC$

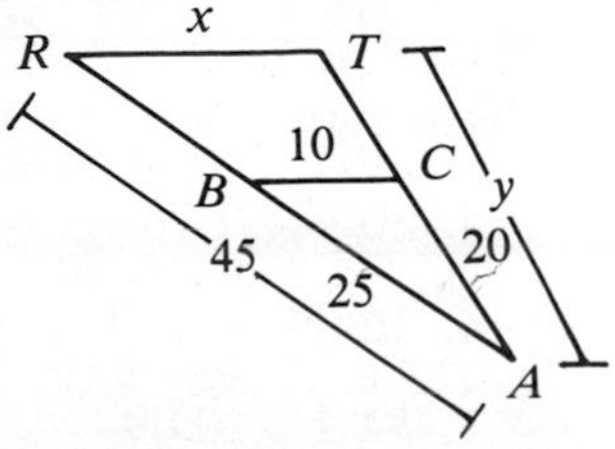

17. One day Jessica, who is 150 cm tall, cast a shadow that was 200 cm long while her father's shadow was 240 cm long. How tall is her father?

18. A person 1.8 m tall standing 7 m from a streetlight casts a shadow 3 m long. How high is the light?

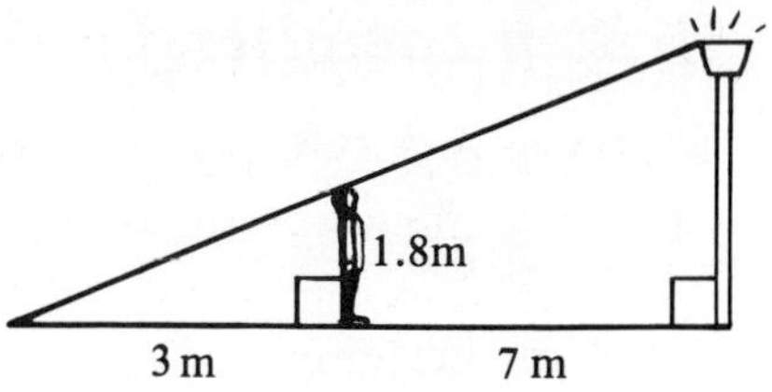

Ex. 18

19. Find (a) the perimeter and (b) the area of the shaded trapezoid in the figure at the left below.

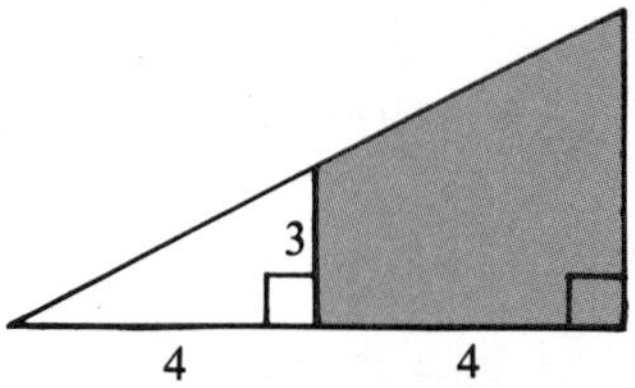

Ex. 19

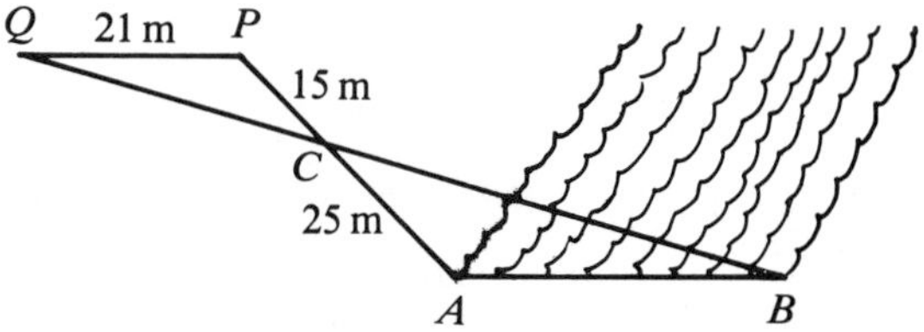

Ex. 20

20. To find the distance AB across a river, surveyors laid off $\overline{PQ}$ parallel to $\overline{AB}$ and created 2 similar triangles. They made the measurements shown in the figure at the right above. Find the length of $\overline{AB}$.

Exercises 21–22 refer to the diagram at the right.

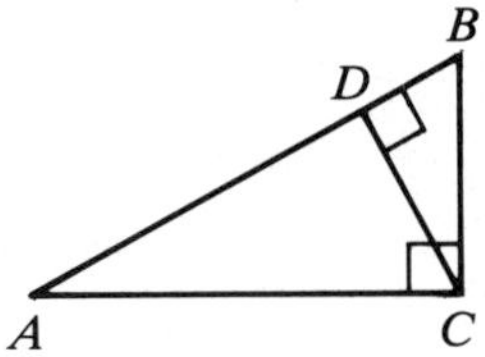

Ex. 21, 22

C 21. Explain why $\triangle ADC \sim \triangle ACB$.

22. Explain why $\triangle ADC \sim \triangle CDB$.

23. If $\triangle MNO \sim \triangle PQR$ and $\triangle PQR \sim \triangle STU$, is $\triangle MNO \sim \triangle STU$? Explain your answer.

24. If $\triangle MNO \cong \triangle PQR$, is $\triangle MNO \sim \triangle PQR$? Explain your answer.

25. If $\triangle MNO \sim \triangle PQR$, is $\triangle MNO \cong \triangle PQR$? Explain your answer.

Review Exercises

Multiply.

1. 300×1.73
2. 500×3.9
3. 7.81×200
4. 16.34×120
5. 2.18×1.03
6. 3.17×6.01
7. 54.2×0.09
8. 683×2.48
9. 71.4×52.4

10-6 Special Right Triangles

In an *isosceles right triangle* the two acute angles are congruent. Since the sum of the measures of these two angles is 90°, each angle measures 45°. For this reason, an isosceles right triangle is often called a **45° right triangle.**

In the diagram each leg is 1 unit long. If the hypotenuse is c units long, by the Pythagorean theorem we know that $c^2 = 1^2 + 1^2 = 2$ and thus

$$c = \sqrt{2}.$$

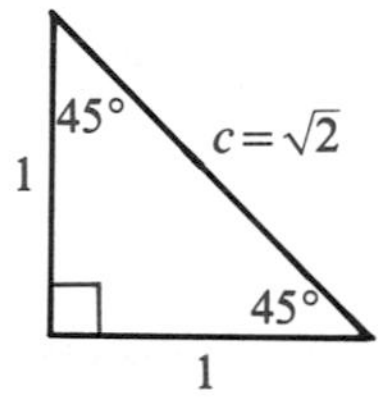

Every 45° right triangle is similar to the one shown. Since corresponding sides of similar triangles are proportional, we have the following property.

> If each leg of a 45° right triangle is a units long, then the hypotenuse is $a\sqrt{2}$ units long.

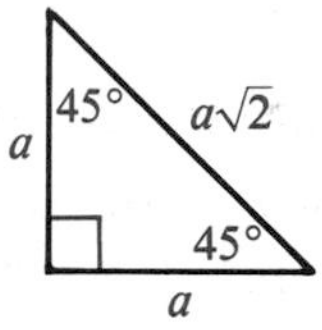

EXAMPLE 1 A square park measures 200 m on each edge. Find the length, d, of a path extending diagonally from one corner to the opposite corner. Use $\sqrt{2} \approx 1.414$.

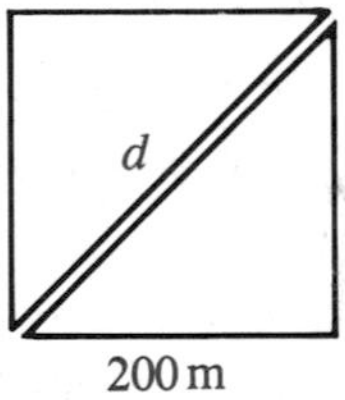

Solution Since the park is square, we can apply the property of 45° right triangles to solve for d. We use the fact that d is the hypotenuse of the right triangle and that each side measures 200 m.

$$d = 200\sqrt{2} \approx 200 \times 1.414 = 282.8$$

Thus the path measures approximately 282.8 m.

A **30°-60° right triangle,** such as $\triangle ACB$, may be thought of as half an equilateral triangle. If hypotenuse $\overline{AB}$ is 2 units long, then the shorter leg $\overline{AC}$ (half of $\overline{AD}$) is 1 unit long. To find BC, we use the Pythagorean theorem:

$$(AC)^2 + (BC)^2 = (AB)^2$$
$$1^2 + (BC)^2 = 2^2$$
$$(BC)^2 = 2^2 - 1^2 = 3$$
$$BC = \sqrt{3}$$

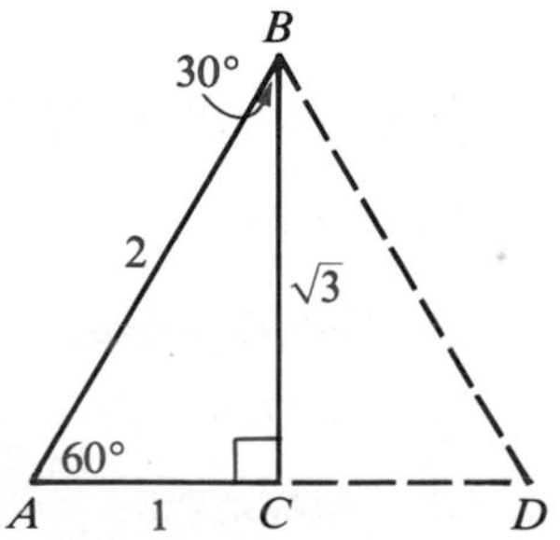

Every 30°–60° right triangle is similar to the one above, and since corresponding sides of similar triangles are proportional, we have the following property.

If the shorter leg of a 30°–60° right triangle is a units long, then the longer leg is $a\sqrt{3}$ units long, and the hypotenuse is $2a$ units long.

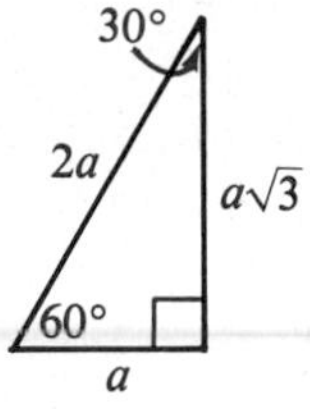

EXAMPLE 2 The hypotenuse of a 30°–60° right triangle is 8 cm long. Find the lengths of the legs.

Solution Using the 30°–60° right triangle property, we know that

$$2a = 8,\ a = 4,\ \text{and}\ a\sqrt{3} = 4\sqrt{3}.$$

Thus the lengths of the legs are 4 cm and $4\sqrt{3}$ cm.

The symbol $\sqrt{\ }$ is called the **radical sign.** An expression such as $\sqrt{3}$ or $\sqrt{x}$ is called a **radical.** We often leave answers *in terms of radicals* with the radical in the numerator. To rewrite expressions such as $\frac{6}{\sqrt{3}}$ so that the radical appears in the numerator, we may use the fact that $\sqrt{x} \times \sqrt{x} = x$.

EXAMPLE 3 Rewrite $\frac{6}{\sqrt{3}}$ in lowest terms with the radical in the numerator.

Solution If we multiply the numerator and denominator by $\sqrt{3}$, we will find an equivalent fraction with the radical in the numerator.

$$\frac{6}{\sqrt{3}} = \frac{6 \times \sqrt{3}}{\sqrt{3} \times \sqrt{3}}$$

$$= \frac{6\sqrt{3}}{3}$$

$$= 2\sqrt{3}$$

Thus, $2\sqrt{3}$ is equivalent to $\frac{6}{\sqrt{3}}$ in lowest terms with the radical in the numerator.

Class Exercises

Rewrite the expression in lowest terms with the radical in the numerator.

1. $\frac{1}{\sqrt{3}}$ 2. $\frac{2}{\sqrt{3}}$ 3. $\frac{2}{\sqrt{2}}$ 4. $\frac{6}{\sqrt{2}}$ 5. $\frac{1}{\sqrt{x}}$ 6. $\frac{x}{\sqrt{x}}$

Find the lengths marked x and y in the triangle. Give your answer in terms of radicals when radicals occur.

7.
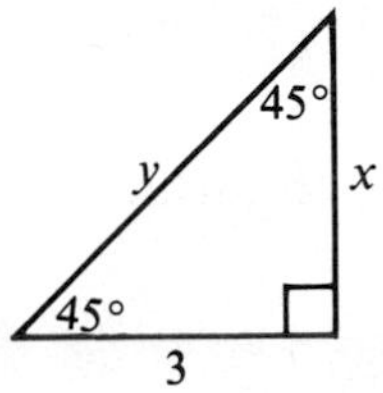

8.
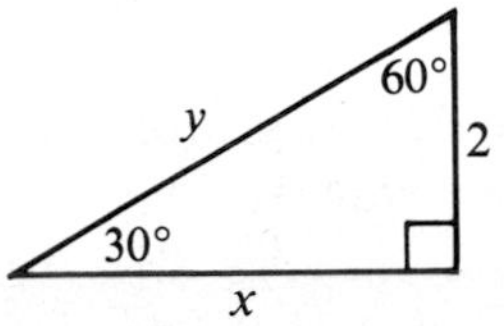

9.
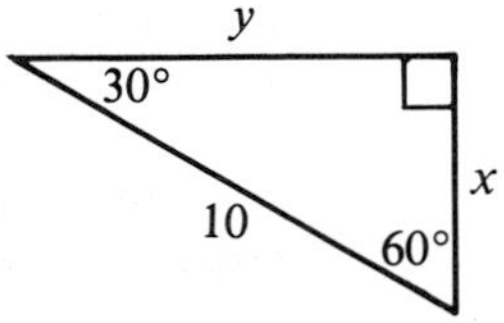

10.
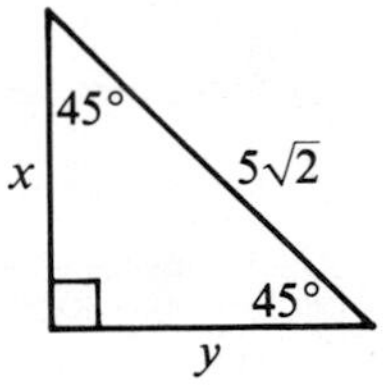

11.
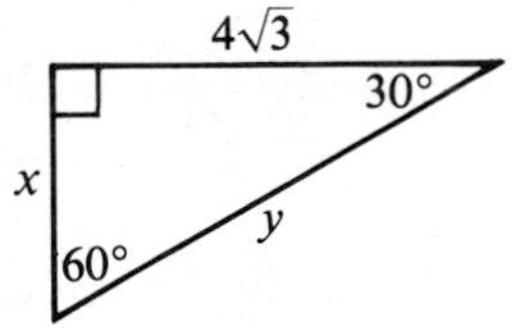

12.
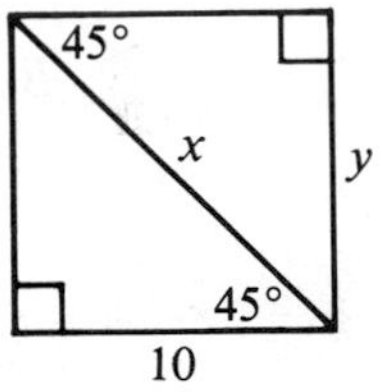

Written Exercises

Rewrite the expression in lowest terms with the radical in the numerator.

A 1. $\frac{6}{\sqrt{10}}$ 2. $\frac{12}{\sqrt{13}}$ 3. $\frac{3}{\sqrt{3}}$ 4. $\frac{1}{\sqrt{2}}$ 5. $\frac{2}{\sqrt{x}}$ 6. $\frac{3x}{\sqrt{x}}$

Approximate the lengths marked x and y to the nearest tenth.
Use $\sqrt{2} \approx 1.414$ and $\sqrt{3} \approx 1.732$.

7.
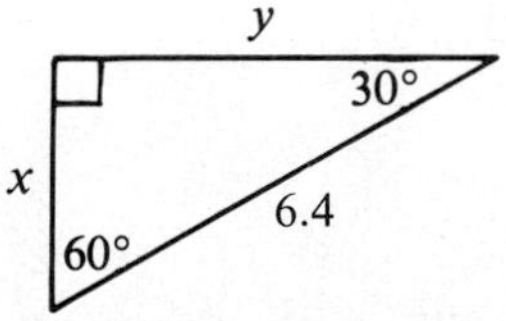

8.
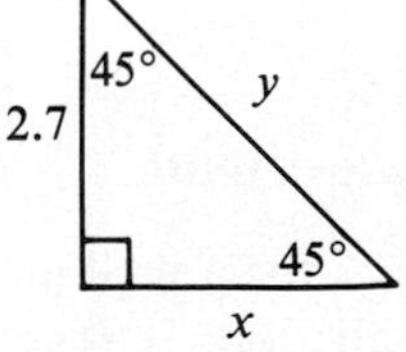

9.
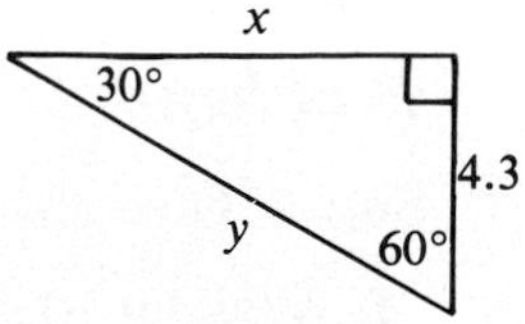

10.
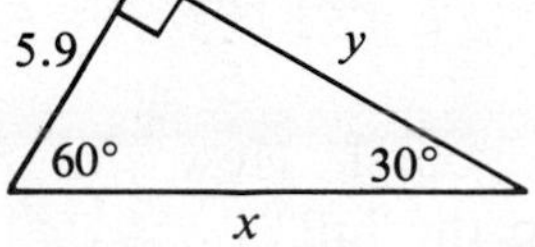

11.
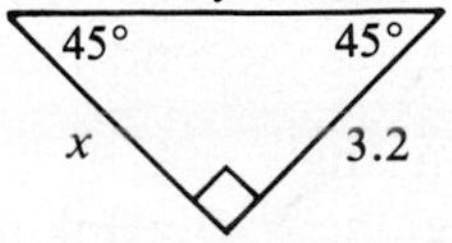

12.
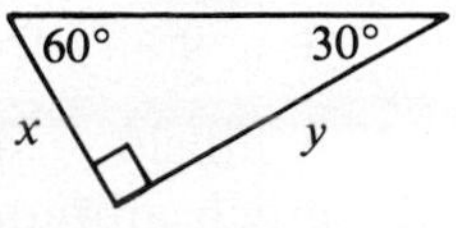

In Exercises 13–16, give answers in terms of radicals with the radical in the numerator.

B **13.** The hypotenuse of an isosceles right triangle has length 4. How long is each leg?

14. The hypotenuse of a 45° right triangle has length 10. How long is each leg?

15. The longer leg of a 30°–60° right triangle has length 15. How long are the other sides?

16. The side opposite the 60° angle of a right triangle has length 3. How long are the other sides?

In Exercises 17–22, $\angle C$ is a right angle in $\triangle ABC$. Find the length of the missing side to the nearest tenth.

17. $AC = 2,\ BC = 5$

18. $AB = 18,\ AC = 9$

19. $AB = 6\sqrt{2},\ AC = 6$

20. $AC = CB = x$

C **21.** $\frac{1}{2}BA = CA = y$

22. $2BC = BA = z$

Approximate the lengths marked x and y to the nearest tenth.

23.

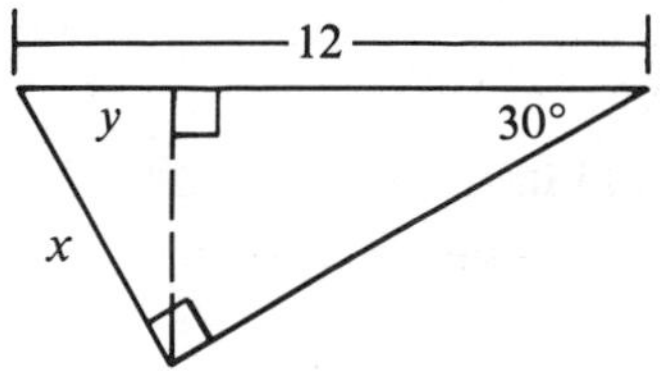

24.

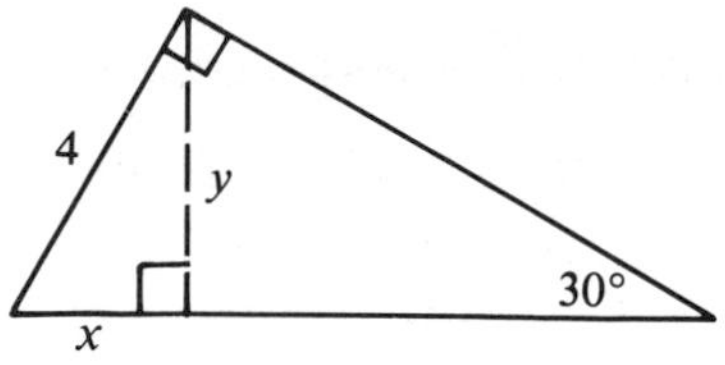

Problems

Solve. Give answers to the nearest tenth.

A **1.** A ladder 10 m long resting against a wall makes a 60° angle with the ground. How far up the wall does it reach?

2. A baseball diamond is a square 90 ft on each side. How far is it diagonally from home plate to second base?

3. A hillside is inclined at an angle of 30° with the horizontal. How much altitude has Mary gained after hiking 40 m up the hill?

4. The diagram on the right shows the roof of a house. Find the dimensions marked x and y.

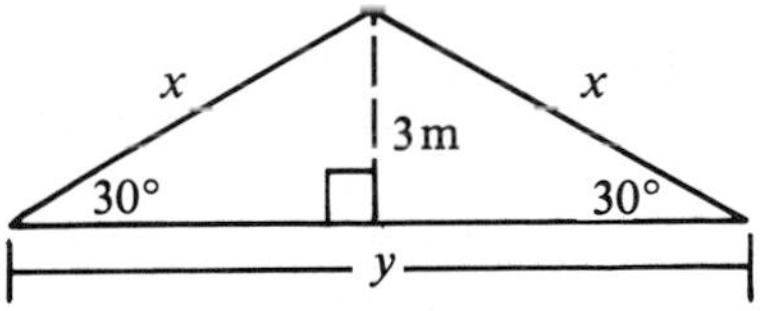

B 5. A checkerboard has 8 squares on each side. If one side of a square is 5 cm long, how far is it from one corner of the board to the opposite corner?

6. Find the height of an equilateral triangle with sides 12 cm long.

7. Find the perimeters of the two squares shown in the diagram.

8. An equilateral triangle has sides 10 units long. Find (a) the height and (b) the area.

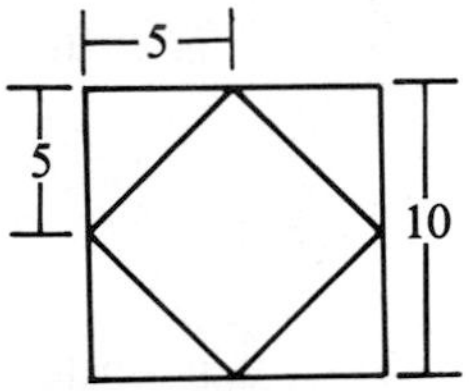

Prob. 7

C 9. An equilateral triangle has sides r units long. Find both (a) the height and (b) the area in terms of r.

10. The area of a square pan is 900 cm^2. What is the length of a diagonal of the pan?

11. A 10 m pole is supported in a vertical position by three 6 m guy wires. If one end of each wire is fastened to the ground at a 60° angle, how high on the pole is the other end fastened?

12. A rhombus has angles of 60° and 120°. Each side of the rhombus is 8 cm long. What are the lengths of the diagonals? (*Hint:* The diagonals bisect the angles of the rhombus.)

Review Exercises

Write the fraction as a decimal. Use a bar to show a repeating decimal.

1. $\frac{5}{4}$ **2.** $\frac{3}{5}$ **3.** $\frac{2}{9}$ **4.** $\frac{7}{12}$ **5.** $\frac{11}{10}$ **6.** $\frac{3}{16}$ **7.** $\frac{1}{6}$ **8.** $\frac{4}{11}$

10-7 Trigonometric Ratios

Since each of the three triangles in the diagram below contains $\angle A$ and a right angle, the triangles are *similar* and their sides are *proportional.* Thus, the ratios written below for the smallest triangle apply to all three triangles.

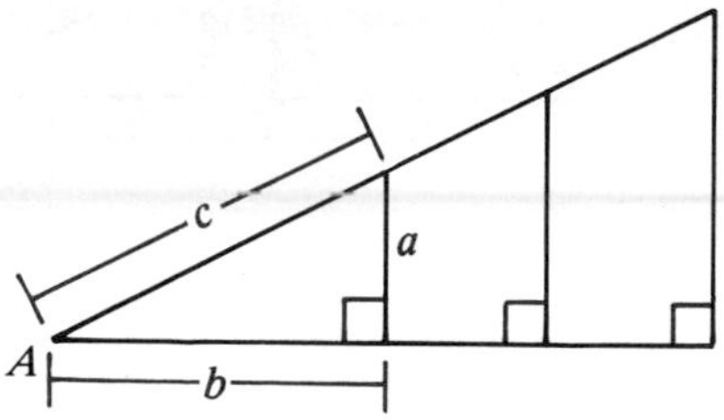

$$\frac{\text{length of side opposite } \angle A}{\text{length of hypotenuse}} = \frac{a}{c}$$

$$\frac{\text{length of side adjacent to } \angle A}{\text{length of hypotenuse}} = \frac{b}{c}$$

$$\frac{\text{length of side opposite } \angle A}{\text{length of side adjacent to } \angle A} = \frac{a}{b}$$

These ratios, called the **trigonometric ratios,** are so useful that each has been given a special name.

$\frac{a}{c}$ is called the **sine** of $\angle A$, or **sin *A*.**

$\frac{b}{c}$ is called the **cosine** of $\angle A$, or **cos *A*.**

$\frac{a}{b}$ is called the **tangent** of $\angle A$, or **tan *A*.**

It is important to understand that each trigonometric ratio depends only on the measure of $\angle A$ and *not* on the size of the right triangle.

The following shortened forms of the definitions may help you remember the trigonometric ratios.

$$\sin A = \frac{\text{opposite}}{\text{hypotenuse}}$$

$$\cos A = \frac{\text{adjacent}}{\text{hypotenuse}}$$

$$\tan A = \frac{\text{opposite}}{\text{adjacent}}$$

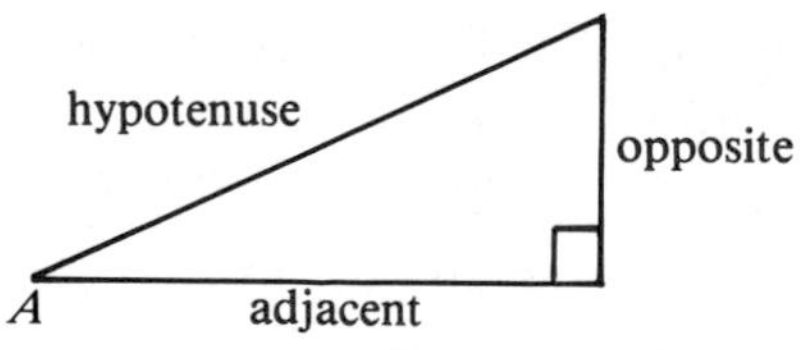

EXAMPLE 1 For $\angle A$ find the value of each trigonometric ratio in lowest terms.

a. sin *A* **b.** cos *A* **c.** tan *A*

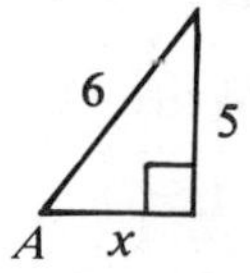

Solution To find the value of the trigonometric ratios for $\angle A$, first find the value of x. By the Pythagorean theorem:

$$x^2 + 5^2 = 6^2$$
$$x^2 + 25 = 36$$
$$x^2 = 36 - 25$$
$$x^2 = 11$$
$$x = \sqrt{11}$$

a. $\sin A = \dfrac{\text{opposite}}{\text{hypotenuse}} = \dfrac{5}{6}$

b. $\cos A = \dfrac{\text{adjacent}}{\text{hypotenuse}} = \dfrac{\sqrt{11}}{6}$

c. $\tan A = \dfrac{\text{opposite}}{\text{adjacent}} = \dfrac{5}{\sqrt{11}} = \dfrac{5 \times \sqrt{11}}{\sqrt{11} \times \sqrt{11}} = \dfrac{5\sqrt{11}}{11}$

EXAMPLE 2 Find the sine, cosine, and tangent of a 30° angle to the nearest thousandth.

Solution To find the values of these trigonometric ratios, first draw a 30°-60° right triangle. Let the shorter leg be 1 unit long and write in the lengths of the other sides according to the property of 30°-60° triangles that you learned in the previous lesson.

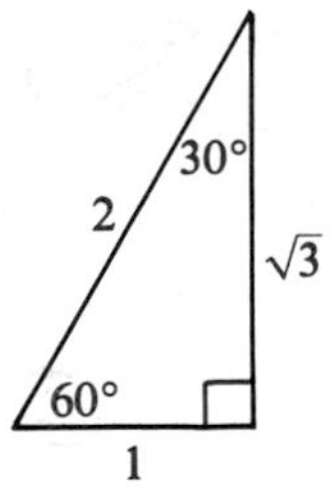

$$\sin 30° = \frac{1}{2} = 0.500$$

$$\cos 30° = \frac{\sqrt{3}}{2} \approx 0.866$$

$$\tan 30° = \frac{1}{\sqrt{3}} = \frac{\sqrt{3}}{3} \approx 0.577$$

Class Exercises

Find the value of the trigonometric ratio.

1. $\sin A$ **2.** $\cos A$

3. $\tan A$ **4.** $\sin B$

5. $\cos B$ **6.** $\tan B$

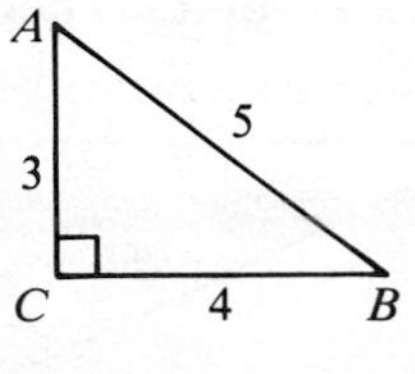

Find the value of the trigonometric ratio.

7. sin P
8. cos P
9. tan P
10. sin R
11. cos R
12. tan R

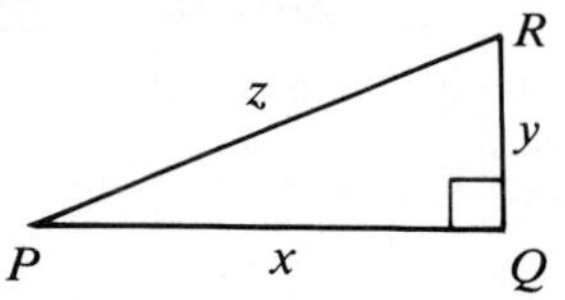

Written Exercises

Give the value of the sine, cosine, and tangent of $\angle A$ and $\angle B$. Give all ratios in lowest terms.

A 1.

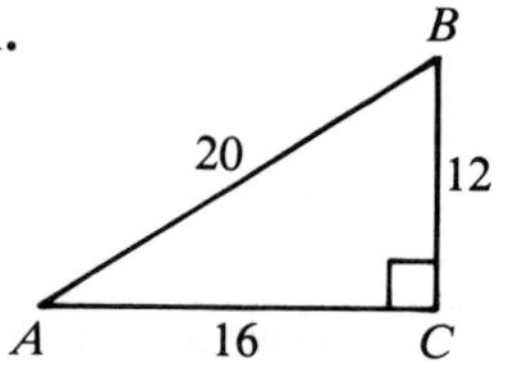

2.

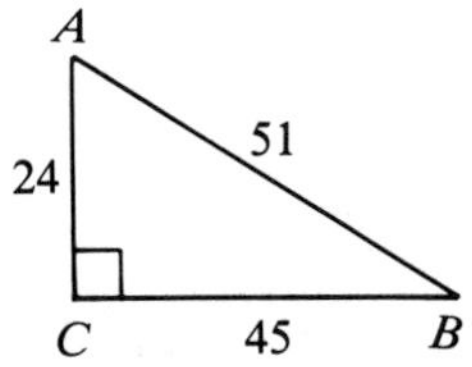

3.

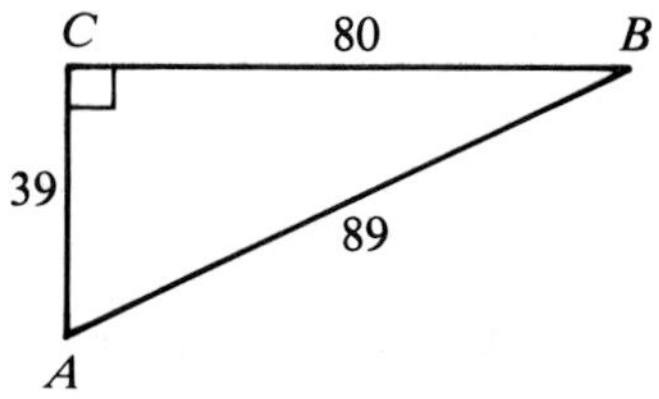

4.

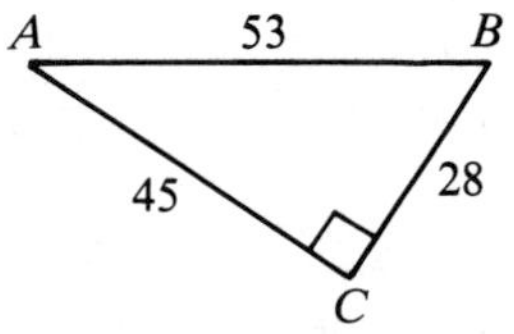

5.

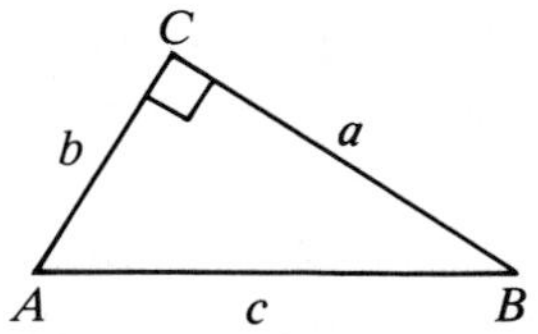

6.

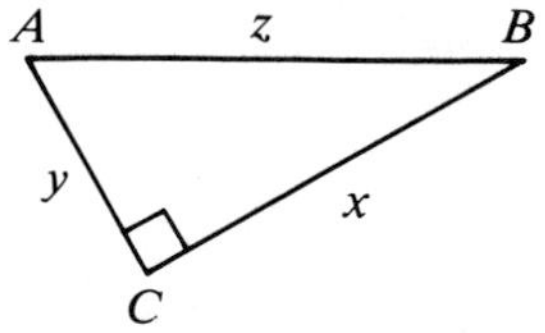

B **In Exercises 7–12, give all ratios in lowest terms and with the radical in the numerator.**

Find the value of x. Then find tan A.

7.

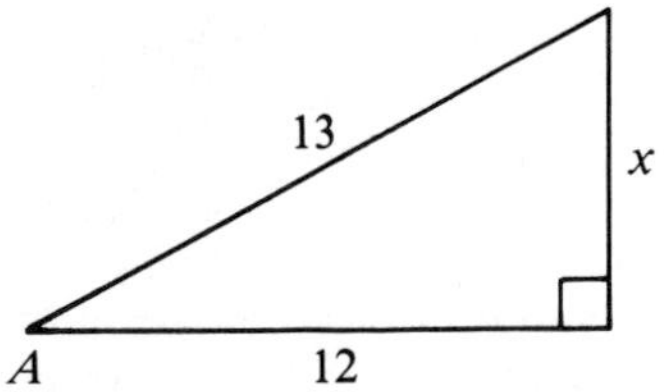

8.

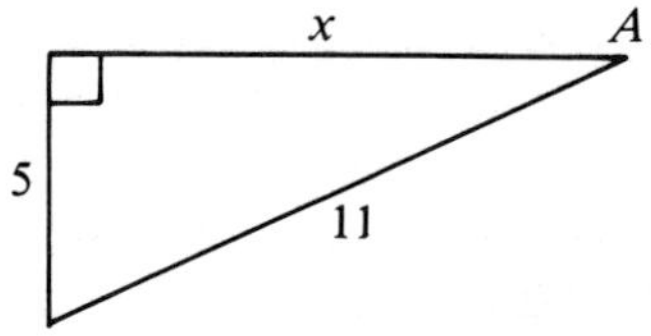

Find the value of x. Then find sin A.

9.

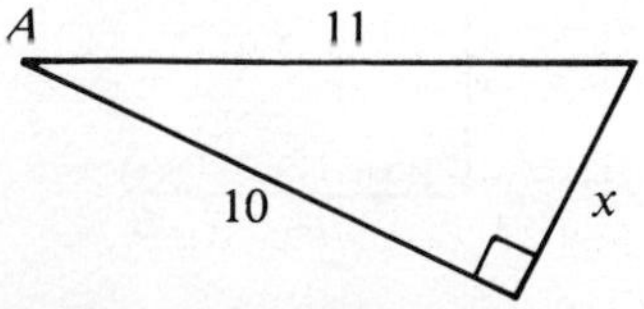

10.

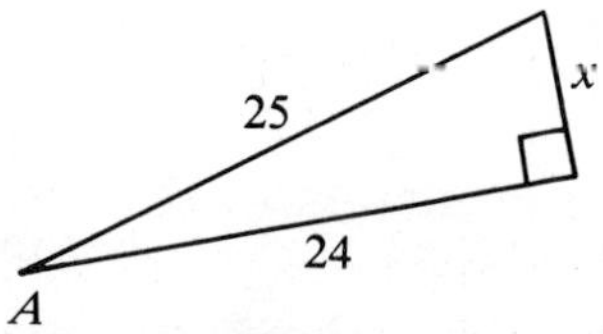

Find the value of x. Then find $\cos A$.

11. 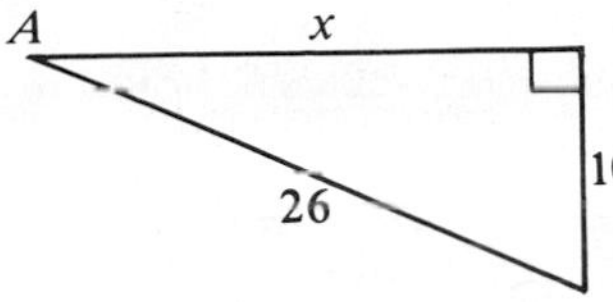

12. 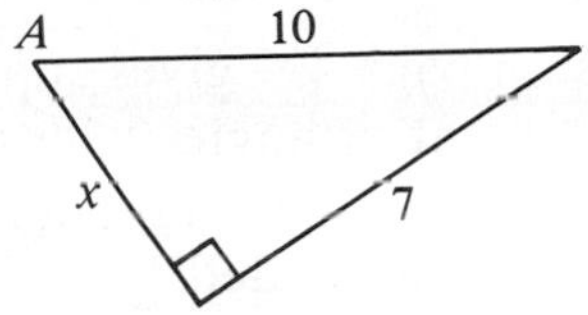

Find the sine, cosine, and tangent. Write the answer both as a fraction and as a decimal to the nearest thousandth. (*Hint:* See Example 2.)

13. a. $\sin 60°$ **b.** $\cos 60°$ **c.** $\tan 60°$

14. a. $\sin 45°$ **b.** $\cos 45°$ **c.** $\tan 45°$

Give answers to the nearest tenth.

C **15.** $\sin 67° = 0.9205$

a. $x =$ _?_

b. $y =$ _?_

c. $\sin 23° =$ _?_

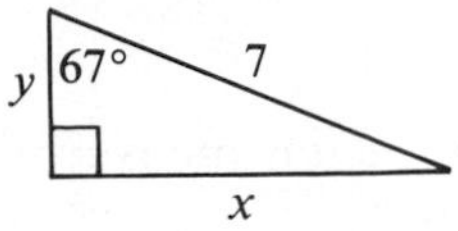

16. $\tan 40° = 0.8391$

a. $m =$ _?_

b. $n =$ _?_

c. $\cos 50° =$ _?_

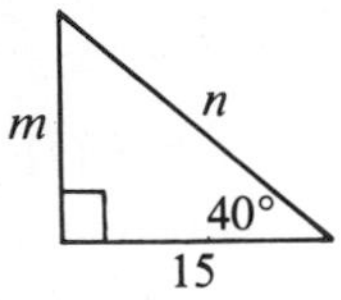

17. $\cos 65° = 0.4226$

a. $e =$ _?_

b. $f =$ _?_

c. $\tan 25° =$ _?_

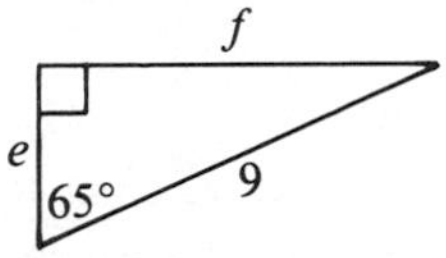

Review Exercises

Select the number that is closest to the one given.

1. 0.3765
a. 0.3774 **b.** 0.3759

2. 8.1443
a. 8.1430 **b.** 8.1451

3. 0.9004
a. 0.9019 **b.** 0.8954

4. 1.8040
a. 1.829 **b.** 1.788

5. 0.2126
a. 0.2666 **b.** 0.1986

6. 11.4301
a. 12.0801 **b.** 10.6801

7. 0.1758
a. 0.1744 **b.** 0.1764

8. 3.2709
a. 3.2712 **b.** 3.2705

Challenge

Leslie is considering two job offers. Alloid Metals pays an hourly wage of \$7.30. Acme Steel Company pays an annual salary of \$14,040. Both jobs have a 40-hour work week. Which job offers a better salary?

10-8 Solving Right Triangles

The table on page 499 gives approximate values of the sine, the cosine, and the tangent of angles with measure 1°, 2°, 3°, . . . , 90°. To find sin 45°, look down the column headed "Angle" to 45°. To the right of it in the column headed "Sine," you see that sin 45° $\approx$ 0.7071.

The values in the table on page 499 are, in general, accurate to only four decimal places. However, in computational work with sine, cosine, and tangent, it is customary to use = instead of $\approx$. In this lesson, we will write *sin 45° = 0.7071* instead of *sin 45° $\approx$ 0.7071.*

We can use the values in the table to **solve right triangles,** that is, to find approximate measures of all the sides and all the angles of any right triangle.

EXAMPLE 1 Solve $\triangle ABC$ by finding each measure.

a. c to the nearest tenth

b. $m\angle A$

c. $m\angle B$

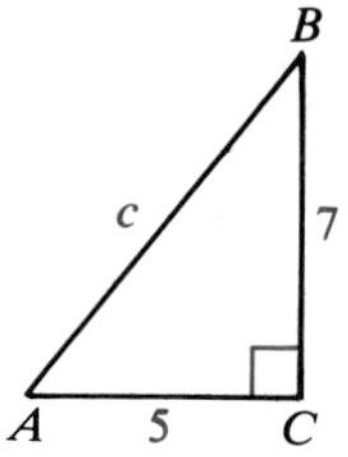

Solution

a. The diagram indicates that $\angle C$ is a right triangle, therefore by the Pythagorean theorem:

$$c^2 = 7^2 + 5^2 = 74$$
$$c = \sqrt{74} = 8.6$$

To the nearest tenth, $c = 8.6$.

b. $\tan A = \frac{7}{5} = 1.4$

In the tangent column in the table, the closest entry to 1.4 is 1.3764, for angle measure 54°. Thus, to the nearest degree, $m\angle A = 54°$.

c. $m\angle A + m\angle B + m\angle C = 180°$

$$54° + m\angle B + 90° = 180°$$
$$m\angle B = 180° - 90° - 54°$$
$$m\angle B = 36°$$

Problem Solving Reminder

To solve some problems, you might need to *use previously obtained solutions* in order to complete the answer. In Example 1, it was convenient to use the $m\angle A$ found in part b to solve for the $m\angle B$.

EXAMPLE 2 Solve $\triangle ABC$ by finding each measure.

a. $m\angle B$

b. a to the nearest tenth

c. b to the nearest tenth

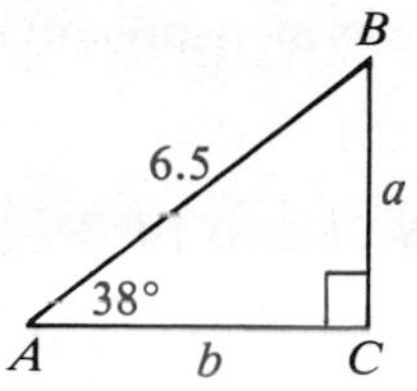

Solution

a. $m\angle A + m\angle B + m\angle C = 180°$

$38° + m\angle B + 90° = 180°$

$m\angle B = 180° - 90° - 38° = 52°$

b. $\sin 38° = \frac{a}{6.5}$

$a = \sin 38° \times 6.5$

$= 0.6157 \times 6.5 = 4.00205$

To the nearest tenth, $a = 4.0$.

c. $\cos 38° = \frac{b}{6.5}$

$b = \cos 38° \times 6.5$

$= 0.7880 \times 6.5 = 5.122$

To the nearest tenth, $b = 5.1$.

Class Exercises

State whether you would use the sine, cosine, or tangent ratio to find x in each diagram.

1.

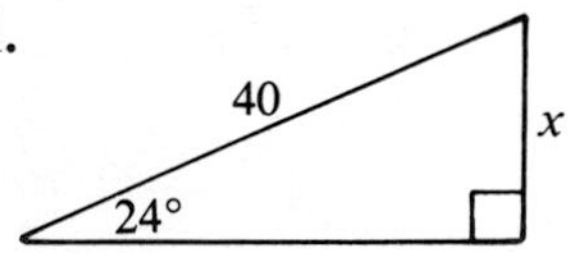

2.

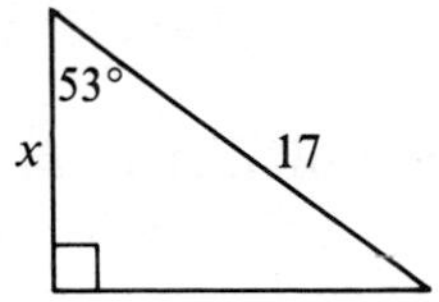

3.

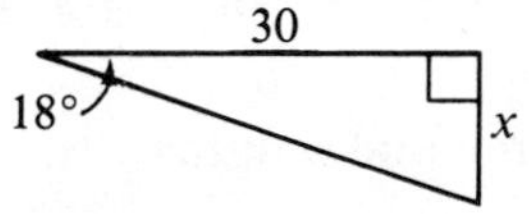

4.

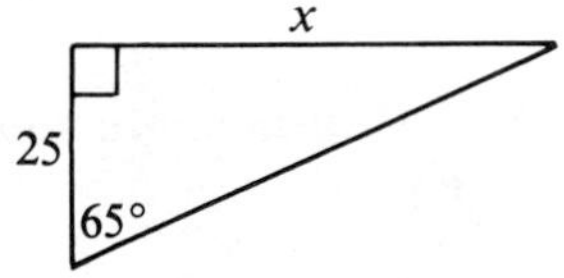

For Exercises 5–18, use the table on page 499.

Find a value for the trigonometric ratio.

5. $\cos 8°$ **6.** $\sin 67°$ **7.** $\tan 36°$ **8.** $\tan 82°$

9. $\sin 15°$ **10.** $\cos 75°$ **11.** $\cos 20°$ **12.** $\sin 70°$

Find the measure of $\angle A$ to the nearest degree.

13. $\sin A = 0.4$ **14.** $\tan A = 1.6$ **15.** $\cos A = 0.85$

16. $\cos A = 0.19$ **17.** $\tan A = 0.819$ **18.** $\sin A = 0.208$

Written Exercises

For Exercises 1–40, use the tables on page 498 and page 499.

Find $\sin A$, $\cos A$, and $\tan A$ for the given measure of $\angle A$.

A **1.** 25° **2.** 76° **3.** 88° **4.** 11° **5.** 39° **6.** 42°

7. 74° **8.** 13° **9.** 40° **10.** 52° **11.** 65° **12.** 81°

Find the measure of $\angle A$ to the nearest degree.

13. $\sin A = 0.9877$ **14.** $\cos A = 0.9205$ **15.** $\tan A = 0.0175$

16. $\cos A = 0.8572$ **17.** $\tan A = 4.0108$ **18.** $\sin A = 0.2250$

Find the measure of the angle to the nearest degree or the length of the side to the nearest whole number.

19. m$\angle A$

21. m$\angle B$

23. t

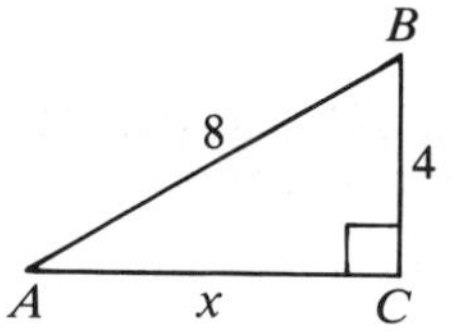

20. x

22. m$\angle L$

24. u

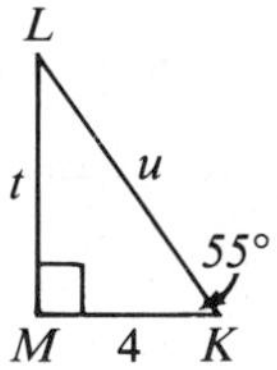

Find the measure of $\angle A$ to the nearest degree.

B **25.** $\sin A = 0.8483$ **26.** $\cos A = 0.2758$ **27.** $\tan A = 0.4560$

28. $\sin A = 0.6559$ **29.** $\tan A = 2.7500$ **30.** $\cos A = 0.5148$

Solve $\triangle ABC$. Round angle measures to the nearest degree and lengths to the nearest tenth.

31. $a = 5$, $b = 8$ **32.** $a = 4$, $b = 7$

33. m$\angle A = 72°$, $c = 10$ **34.** m$\angle B = 26°$, $c = 8$

35. $b = 4$, $c = 9$ **36.** $a = 5$, $c = 7$

37. m$\angle B = 20°$, $b = 15$ **38.** m$\angle A = 80°$, $a = 9$

39. m$\angle A = 58°$, $b = 12$ **40.** m$\angle B = 39°$, $a = 20$

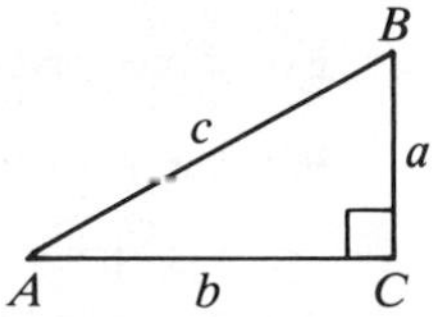

Problems

Give angle measures to the nearest degree and lengths to the nearest tenth.

A 1. How tall is the tree in the diagram below?

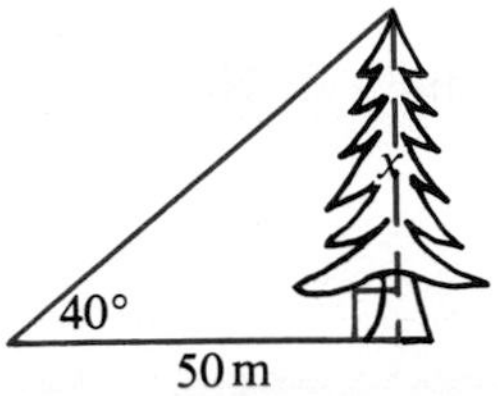

2. How tall is the flagpole in the diagram below?

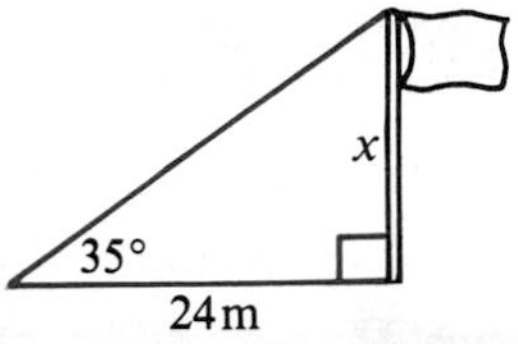

3. In the diagram below, the road rises 20 m for every 100 m traveled horizontally. What angle does it make with the horizontal?

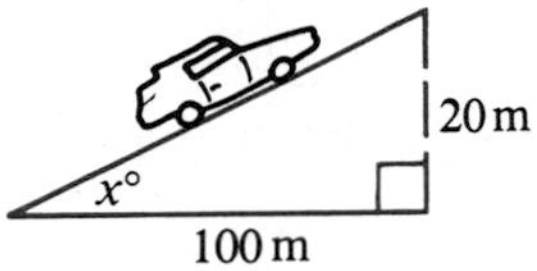

4. What angle does the rope make with the horizontal in the diagram below?

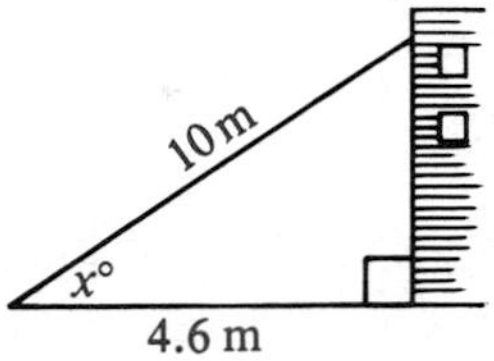

B 5. **a.** How tall is the building in the diagram below?

b. How tall is the antenna?

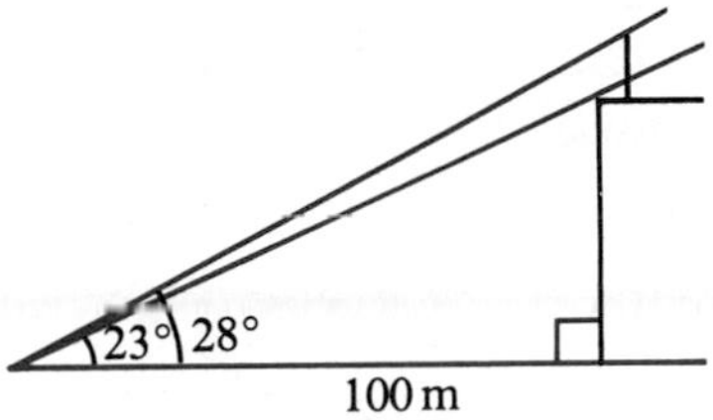

6. What is the height of the child in the diagram below?

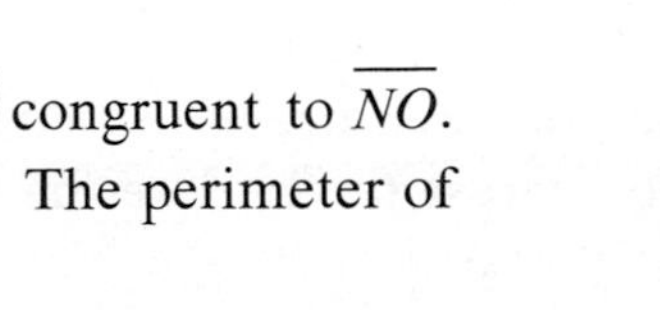

7. In $\triangle ABC$, $\overline{AC}$ is 8 cm long. The length of the altitude to $\overline{AB}$ is 5 cm. Find the measure of $\angle A$.

8. Triangle MNO is an isosceles triangle with $\overline{MO}$ congruent to $\overline{NO}$. The third side of the triangle, $\overline{MN}$, is 36 cm long. The perimeter of the triangle is 96 cm.

a. Find the lengths of $\overline{MO}$ and $\overline{NO}$.

b. The altitude from O to $\overline{MN}$ bisects $\overline{MN}$. Find the measure of $\angle OMN$.

Give angle measures to the nearest degree and lengths to the nearest tenth.

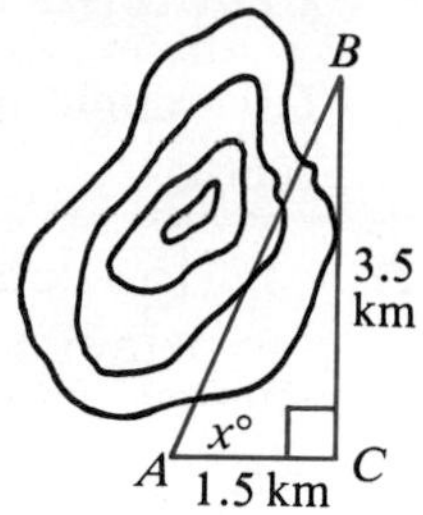

9. A surveyor is determining the direction in which tunnel $\overline{AB}$ is to be dug through a mountain. She locates point C so that $\angle C$ is a right angle, the length of $\overline{AC}$ is 1.5 km, and the length of $\overline{BC}$ is 3.5 km. Find the measure of $\angle A$.

C **10.** In $\triangle RST$, the measure of $\angle S$ is 142°. The length of $\overline{RS}$ is 10. Find the length of the altitude from vertex R.

Self-Test B

Exercises 1–4 refer to the diagram below. Complete. [10-5]

1. $\triangle TOY$ _?_ $\triangle TIN$

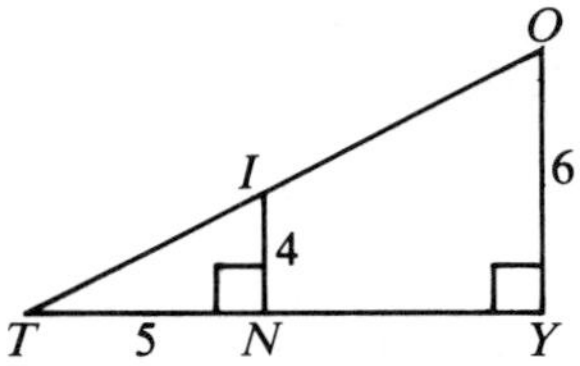

2. $\frac{TI}{TO} = \frac{IN}{OY} = \frac{?}{?}$

3. $TY =$ _?_

4. m$\angle TIN$ _?_ m$\angle TOY$

In Exercises 5 and 6, give answers in terms of radicals with the radical in the numerator.

5. The hypotenuse of a 45° right triangle is 6.2 cm long. What is the length of each leg? [10-6]

6. The longer leg of a 30°–60° right triangle has length 12. What are the lengths of the shorter leg and the hypotenuse?

Exercises 7–13 refer to the diagram at the right.

Complete in terms of *p*, *q*, and *r*. [10-7]

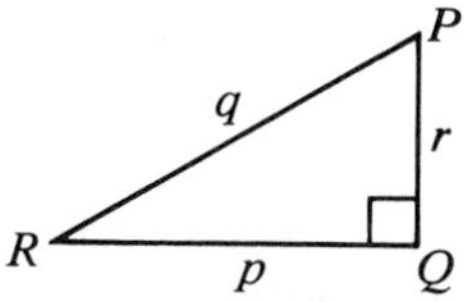

7. $\sin P =$ _?_ 8. $\cos P =$ _?_

9. $\tan P =$ _?_

Find the measure of the angles to the nearest degree and the lengths to the nearest tenth. Use the tables on page 498 and page 499. [10-8]

10. $r = 3,\ q = 6$ 11. m$\angle P = 78°$, $r = 5$

12. m$\angle R = 23°$, $p = 8$ 13. m$\angle R = 57°$, $q = 24$

Self-Test answers and Extra Practice are at the back of the book.

Computer Byte

The following program produces a Pythagorean Triple using any counting number greater than 2.

```
10  PRINT "INPUT THE DESIRED NUMBER";
20  INPUT N
30  IF N * (N - 1) * (N - 2) < > 0 THEN 60
40  PRINT "THERE IS NO SUCH TRIPLE."
50  GOTO 150
60  IF INT (N / 2) < > N / 2 THEN 120
70  IF N = 4 THEN 110
80  LET N = N / 2
90  LET C = C + 1
100  GOTO 60
110  LET N = 3
120  PRINT "A PYTHAGOREAN TRIPLE IS:"
130  LET B = INT (N ↑ 2 / 2)
140  PRINT 2 ↑ C * N,2 ↑ C * B,2 ↑ C * (B + 1)
150  END
```

1. Use the program to find a triple with the number 3. Does it give you the triple you had expected?
2. Use the program to find a triple with the number 4. Does it give you the triple you had expected?
3. Now try 5. Is the output what you had expected?
4. Input each of these numbers to produce Pythagorean Triples:

   6, 7, 8, 11, 17, 24, 101

   Check three of your answers by multiplying.
5. Try 1 or 2 in the program. Can you explain why this output is true?

Challenge

Trace the two squares as they are shown at the right. Can you draw one line that will divide each of the squares into two parts of equal area?

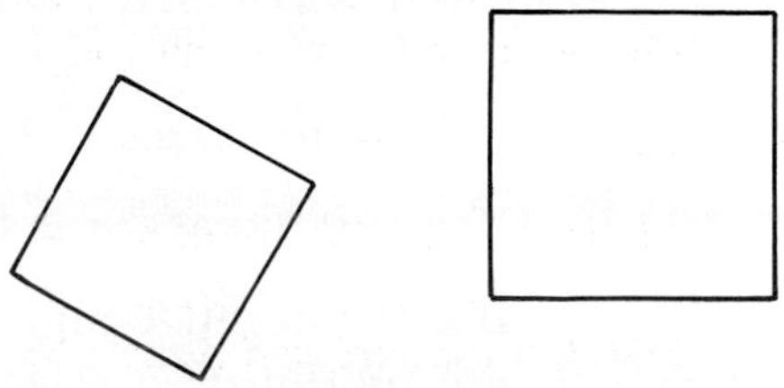

Other Roots and Fractions as Exponents

As you learned earlier, $\sqrt{49} = 7$ because $7^2 = 49$. Recall that we chose 7 and not -7 since 7 is the positive square root of 49.

We can extend the idea of square roots to other roots. The fourth root of 16, denoted $\sqrt[4]{16}$, is 2 since $2^4 = 16$. In general,

> For any positive *even* integer n, and positive integer c,
>
> $$\sqrt[n]{a} = c, \text{ if } c^n = a.$$

The third root, or cube root, of a number may be positive or negative depending on the sign of the number.

For example, $\sqrt[3]{64} = 4$ because $4^3 = 64$

and $\sqrt[3]{-27} = -3$ because $(-3)^3 = -27$.

In general,

> For any positive *odd* integer n, and any integers a and c,
>
> $$\sqrt[n]{a} = c, \text{ if } c^n = a.$$

The following cases will complete our discussion of roots.

If $a = 0$, then $\sqrt[n]{a} = 0$ because $a^n = 0^n = 0$.

If a is a negative number and n is *even*, there is no real nth root of a.

Recall that you add exponents when multiplying powers of the same base.

$$9^1 \times 9^2 = 9^{1+2} = 9^3$$

When this rule is applied to fractional exponents, we have

$$9^{\frac{1}{2}} \times 9^{\frac{1}{2}} = 9^{\frac{1}{2}+\frac{1}{2}} = 9^1 = 9.$$

This example suggests that we define $9^{\frac{1}{2}}$ as $\sqrt{9}$, since $(\sqrt{9})^2 = 9$.

In general,

$$a^{\frac{1}{n}} = \sqrt[n]{a}.$$

Find the root. If the root does not exist, explain why.

1. $\sqrt[3]{27}$ **2.** $\sqrt[6]{0}$ **3.** $\sqrt[4]{16}$ **4.** $\sqrt[3]{1000}$

5. $\sqrt[3]{64}$ **6.** $\sqrt[3]{-27}$ **7.** $\sqrt{-49}$ **8.** $\sqrt[4]{-16}$

9. $\sqrt[3]{-1000}$ **10.** $\sqrt[5]{-32}$ **11.** $\sqrt[3]{125}$ **12.** $\sqrt[7]{-1}$

Write the expression without exponents.

13. $36^{\frac{1}{2}}$ **14.** $27^{\frac{1}{3}}$ **15.** $64^{\frac{1}{3}}$ **16.** $64^{\frac{1}{6}}$ **17.** $16^{\frac{1}{4}}$ **18.** $1000^{\frac{1}{3}}$ **19.** $81^{\frac{1}{4}}$

Calculator Activity

Most scientific calculators have a [$\sqrt[x]{y}$] key that can be used to approximate roots that are not integers. For example, to obtain $\sqrt[4]{7}$, enter [7] [$\sqrt[x]{y}$] [4] [=] to get 1.6265766. On some calculators, the [$\sqrt[x]{y}$] key may be a second function. In this case, push the [2nd F] key to activate the root function.

Other calculators have a [y^x] and a [$1/x$] key. In this case, we can obtain $\sqrt[4]{7}$ by calculating $7^{\frac{1}{4}}$ in the following way.

[7] [y^x] [4] [$1/x$] [=]

This is $\frac{1}{4}$.

Use a calculator to approximate the following.

1. $\sqrt[3]{10}$ **2.** $\sqrt[3]{4}$ **3.** $\sqrt[5]{50}$ **4.** $\sqrt[4]{44}$ **5.** $5^{\frac{1}{4}}$ **6.** $11^{\frac{1}{3}}$

7. The volume of a sphere is related to its radius by the formula $V = \frac{4}{3}\pi r^3$. Use the formula to find the radius of a balloon that has a volume of 3500 ft^3. Use $\pi \approx 3.14$.

Chapter Review

Complete.

1. A positive number has exactly __?__ different square root(s). **[10-1]**
2. $\sqrt{169}$ is 13, therefore 169 is a __?__ square.
3. If 5.2 is used as an estimate for $\sqrt{28.6}$ in the divide-and-average method, the next estimate will be __?__. **[10-2]**
4. Using the divide-and-average method, $\sqrt{53} =$ __?__ to the nearest tenth.
5. In the table on page 498, $\sqrt{24.6}$ lies between __?__ and __?__. **[10-3]**
6. Using interpolation and the table on page 498, $\sqrt{5.7} =$ __?__ to the nearest hundredth.

True or false?

7. The Pythagorean theorem applies to all triangles. **[10-4]**
8. The hypotenuse is the longest side of a right triangle and is opposite the right angle.
9. The measure of the diagonal of a 5 cm by 5 cm square is 50 cm.

Exercises 10–12 refer to the diagram below. $\triangle ABC \sim \triangle DEF$. Complete.

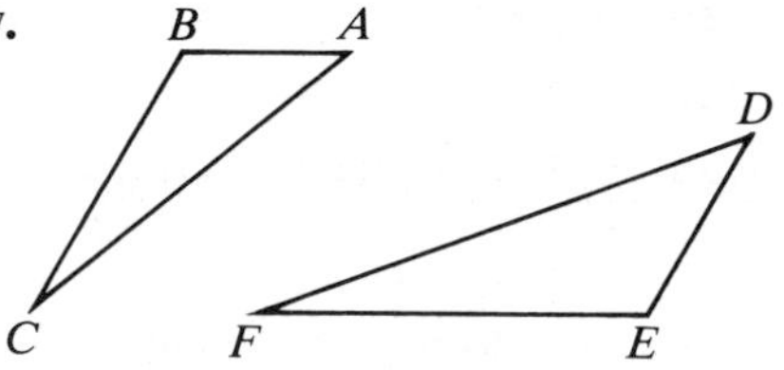

10. $\frac{BA}{?} = \frac{AC}{DF}$ **[10-5]**

11. $\angle C \cong \angle$ __?__

12. $\overline{BC}$ corresponds to __?__.

13. An isosceles right triangle is also called a __?__° right triangle. **[10-6]**
14. An equilateral triangle with sides 16 cm long has an altitude of __?__ cm.
15. The legs of an isosceles right triangle are 7 cm long. The length of the hypotenuse is __?__ cm long.

Exercises 16–21 refer to the diagram at the right. Match. **[10-7]** **[10-8]**

16. sin F
17. cos F
18. tan N
19. y
20. x
21. m $\angle N$

A. $\frac{x}{7}$
B. cos 42° × 7
C. $\frac{y}{7}$
D. sin 42° × 7
E. $\frac{x}{y}$
F. 48°

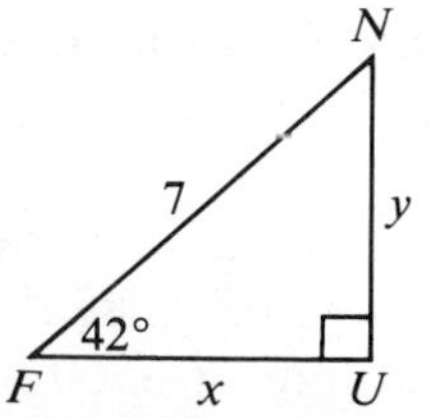

Chapter Test

If the given symbol names an integer, state the integer. If not, name the two consecutive integers between which the number lies.

1. $\sqrt{16}$ **2.** $-\sqrt{144}$ **3.** $\sqrt{169} - \sqrt{121}$ **4.** $\sqrt{38 + 43}$ **[10-1]**

Solve. Give your answer to the nearest tenth.

5. Use the divide-and-average method to approximate $\sqrt{13.7}$. **[10-2]**

6. Using interpolation and the table on page 498, $\sqrt{12.6} \approx$ __?__. **[10-3]**

7. The area of a square deck is 65.6 m^2. Find the length of the side.

Is the triangle with sides of the given lengths a right triangle?

8. 6, 8, 10 **9.** 7, 11, 19 **10.** 8, 15, 17 **[10-4]**

Exercises 11–13 refer to the diagram at the right.
$\triangle MNO \sim \triangle XYZ$.

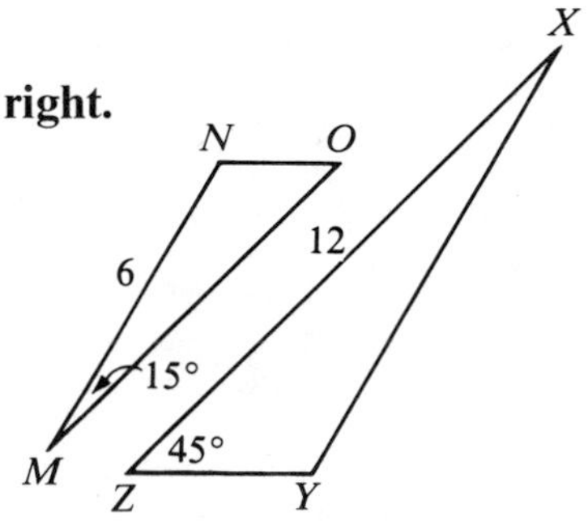

11. If $\frac{MN}{XY} = \frac{3}{4}$, then $\frac{NO}{YZ} =$ __?__. **[10-5]**

12. Find the length of $\overline{MO}$.

13. Find the measure of $\angle N$.

Give answers in terms of radicals with the radical in the numerator.

14. In a 30°–60° right triangle, the shorter leg has length 5. How long is (a) the longer leg and (b) the hypotenuse? **[10-6]**

15. The hypotenuse of a 45° right triangle has a length of 36. How long is each leg?

Exercises 16–19 refer to the diagram at the right. Find a value for the trigonometric ratio.

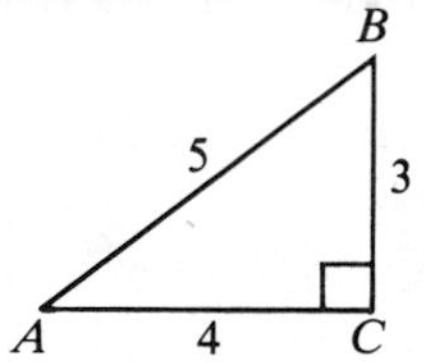

16. $\cos A$ **17.** $\tan A$ **18.** $\cos B$ **19.** $\sin B$ **[10-7]**

$\triangle KLM$ is an isosceles triangle with $\overline{KL} \cong \overline{LM}$. The third side, $\overline{KM}$, is 42 cm long. The perimeter of $\triangle KLM$ is 112 cm.

20. Find the lengths of $\overline{KL}$ and $\overline{LM}$. **21.** Find the height of $\triangle KLM$. **[10-8]**

22. Find $m\angle K$ and $m\angle M$ to the nearest degree. Use the table on page 499.

Cumulative Review (Chapters 1–10)

Exercises

Simplify the expression.

1. $(8 + 2) \div (3 \times 9)$ **2.** $15 \div 8 + 7 \div 9$ **3.** $[48(2 + 5) - 6] \times 10$

4. $-26 - 7 + 9 \times 3$ **5.** $2(10 + 5) \div (-3 - 6)$ **6.** $[(7 - 5)(3 \times 5)] - 5$

Name the property illustrated.

7. $57.89 + 0 = 0 + 57.89$ **8.** $46 \times 8 = (40 \times 8) + (6 \times 8)$

9. $(36 \times 20)15 = 36(20 \times 15)$ **10.** $88 \times 59 = 59 \times 88$

11. $(5 \times 175) + (8 \times 175) = 13(175)$ **12.** $7861 \times 1 = 7861$

Evaluate the expression when $a = 10$, $b = -10$, and $c = 0.5$.

13. ab **14.** ac **15.** $a + b$ **16.** $a - b$ **17.** $2ab$

18. b^2 **19.** ac^2 **20.** a^2c **21.** $\frac{b}{a}$ **22.** $\frac{ab}{c}$

Replace __?__ with <, >, or = to make a true statement.

23. $\frac{1}{2}$ __?__ $\frac{3}{8}$ **24.** $\frac{1}{5}$ __?__ $\frac{2}{8}$ **25.** $-\frac{4}{5}$ __?__ $\frac{3}{4}$ **26.** $-\frac{1}{3}$ __?__ $-\frac{7}{9}$

Solve the equation.

27. $12 + a = 50$ **28.** $x - 27 = 56$ **29.** $43m = 107.5$

30. $\frac{n}{38.6} = 15$ **31.** $z + \frac{2}{3} = 8$ **32.** $w - \frac{1}{5} = 12$

Find the perimeter of the given polygon.

33. square: sides of 2.9 ft **34.** triangle: 7.11 in., 8.11 in., 12.45 in.

Complete the proportion.

35. $\frac{n}{15} = \frac{12}{45}$ **36.** $\frac{6}{7} = \frac{n}{35}$ **37.** $\frac{8}{n} = \frac{32}{40}$ **38.** $\frac{3}{5} = \frac{24}{n}$

Graph each equation on a separate coordinate plane.

39. $x + 2y = 7$ **40.** $2x + 2y = 9$ **41.** $x + \frac{1}{5}y = 1$

Find the volume of a cylinder with the given dimensions. Leave your answer in terms of π.

42. radius: 7 height: 12 **43.** radius: 2.3 height: 10.5

Rewrite the expression in lowest terms with the radical in the numerator.

44. $\frac{4}{\sqrt{10}}$ **45.** $\frac{5}{\sqrt{2}}$ **46.** $\frac{18}{\sqrt{37}}$ **47.** $\frac{2n}{\sqrt{n}}$ **48.** $\frac{6m}{\sqrt{m}}$

Problems

Problem Solving Reminders
Here are some problem solving reminders that may help you solve some of the problems on this page.
- Sometimes more than one method can be used to solve.
- Supply additional information if necessary.
- Check your results with the facts given in the problem.

Solve.

1. Evan is a parking lot attendant at the Lonestar Garage. When counting his tips from Monday he discovered he had 12 more quarters than dimes and 3 fewer nickels than quarters. If Evan earned a total of $19.45 in tips, how many of each type of coin did he have?

2. A regular pentagon has a perimeter of 378.5 m. Find the length of each side.

3. A discount store has an automatic markdown policy. Every 7 days, the price of an item is marked down 25% until the item is sold or 4 weeks have elapsed. If the first price of an item is $40 on September 17, what will the price be on October 1?

4. A window washer uses a vinegar and water solution in the ratio of one-half cup of vinegar to three cups of water. How much vinegar will be in two gallons of solution?

5. Lavender soap is sold in boxes of 3 bars for $6.50. To the nearest cent, what is the cost of one bar?

6. Bertha Magnuson had purchased 2500 shares of ABC stock for $3.50 per share. When she sold the stock, its value had gone down to $\frac{5}{8}$ of the purchase price per share. How much did Bertha lose?

7. The area of a square table is 1936 in.^2. What will be the dimensions of a square tablecloth that drops 4 in. over each side of the table?

8. Mary has $300 to spend on new boots and a winter coat. She expects to spend $\frac{2}{5}$ as much for boots as for a coat. What is the most she can spend on boots?

11
Probability

The force of hurricane winds is dramatized in this photograph taken at Palm Beach, Florida. Winds from these tropical storms range from 116 to 320 km/h. In the southeastern area of the United States, the hurricane season lasts from June through October. September is the month in which hurricanes are most probable.

These storms develop over the ocean and get their energy from the water beneath them. As they approach land, their energy and wind velocity diminish quickly. Then they are reclassified as heavy rain storms. Though the number of hurricanes varies from year to year, the average number of hurricanes in the Atlantic region is seven per year.

In this chapter, you will learn about the probability or chance that a certain event will happen and how to calculate that probability.

Career Note

Meteorologists use sophisticated tracking equipment plus historical climatic patterns to predict the weather. A career in meteorology, the science dealing with weather and weather conditions, is an interesting one. Colleges offer programs that will give the necessary scientific background. A knowledge of mathematics is basic.

11-1 Permutations

After school, Vilma plans to go to the music store and then to the pool. She can take any one of 3 routes from school to the music store and then take either of 2 routes from the store to the pool. In how many different ways can Vilma go from school to the pool?

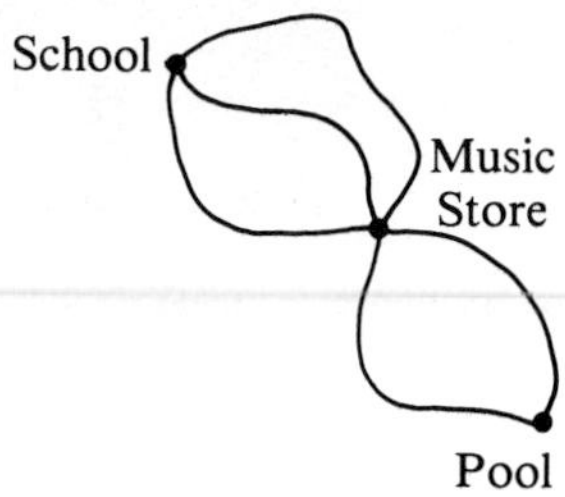

To answer, consider that for each route Vilma can take from school to the music store, she has a choice of either of 2 routes to continue from there. Thus, she has a choice of 3×2, or 6, possible different ways to go from school to the pool.

This example illustrates a general counting principle:

> If there are m ways to do one thing and n ways to do another, then there are $m \times n$ ways to do both things.

In mathematics, an arrangement of a group of things in a particular order is called a **permutation.** The counting principle can help you count the number of different permutations of any group of items.

EXAMPLE 1 In how many different ways can you arrange the three cards shown at the right if you arrange them side by side in a row?

Solution Notice that there are 3 possibilities for the first card: A, B, or C. After the first card is selected, there are 2 possibilities for the second card. After the first and second cards have been selected, there is just 1 possibility for the third card.
Applying the counting principle, there are $3 \times 2 \times 1$, or 6, possible ways to arrange the three cards.

To check, list the permutations: A B C, A C B, B A C, B C A, C A B, C B A

Notice that the number of permutations of 3 things is $3 \times 2 \times 1$. We can write 3! (read *3 factorial*) to represent the expression $3 \times 2 \times 1$. In general, the number of permutations of n things is

$$n \times (n-1) \times (n-2) \times \cdots \times 3 \times 2 \times 1.$$

We can write this expression as $n!$.

If we let ${}_nP_n$ represent the number of permutations of a group of n things when using all n things, we can write the following formula.

Formula

For the number of permutations of n things taken n at a time,

$$ {}_nP_n = n \times (n-1) \times (n-2) \times \cdots \times 3 \times 2 \times 1 = n! $$

EXAMPLE 2 How many four-digit whole numbers can you write using the digits 1, 2, 3, and 4 if no digit appears more than once in each number?

Solution You need to find the number of permutations of 4 things taken 4 at a time.
Using the formula,

$$ {}_4P_4 = 4! = 4 \times 3 \times 2 \times 1 = 24. $$

Therefore, 24 four-digit whole numbers can be written using the given digits.

Sometimes we work with arrangements that involve just a portion of the group at one time.

EXAMPLE 3 This year, 7 dogs are entered in the collie competition at the annual Ridgedale Kennel Club show. In how many different ways can first, second, and third prizes be awarded in the competition?

Solution You want to find the number of permutations of 7 things taken 3 at a time. There are 7 choices for first prize, 6 for second, and 5 for third. Thus,

$$ 7 \times 6 \times 5 = 210. $$

There are 210 possible ways to award the prizes.

If we let ${}_nP_r$ represent the number of permutations of n objects taken r at a time, we can write the following formula.

Formula

For the number of permutations of n things taken r at a time, we use the following formula carried out to r factors:

$$ {}_nP_r = n \times (n-1) \times (n-2) \times \cdots $$

Using the formula in Example 3 above, we find ${}_7P_3 = 7 \times 6 \times 5 = 210$.

Class Exercises

Find the value of each.

1. 4! **2.** 3! **3.** 2! **4.** 1!

5. ${}_5P_5$ **6.** ${}_3P_3$ **7.** ${}_5P_4$ **8.** ${}_6P_3$

Solve.

9. In wrapping a gift, you have a choice of 3 different boxes and 4 different wrapping papers. In how many different ways can you wrap the gift?

10. There are 3 roads from Craig to Hartsdale, 2 roads from Hartsdale to Lee, and 4 roads from Lee to Trumbull. In how many different ways can you travel from Craig to Trumbull by way of Hartsdale and Lee?

Use the formula to answer. Then list all of the permutations to check.

11. In how many different ways can you arrange the letters in the word CAR?

12. In how many different ways can you arrange the 4 cards shown at the right if you take 3 at a time and arrange them side by side?

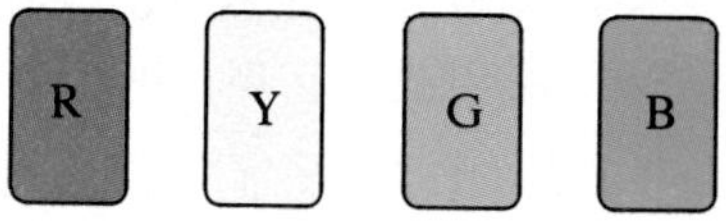

Written Exercises

Find the value of each.

A **1.** 5! **2.** 6! **3.** 7! **4.** 8!

5. ${}_6P_6$ **6.** ${}_7P_7$ **7.** ${}_8P_8$ **8.** ${}_5P_5$

9. ${}_6P_4$ **10.** ${}_8P_4$ **11.** ${}_{43}P_3$ **12.** ${}_{23}P_2$

Problems

Exercises 1–4 refer to the map at the right. Tell how many different ways you can travel from one city to the other.

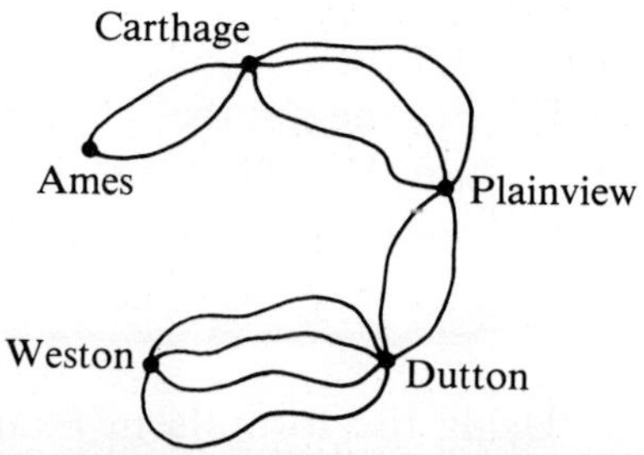

A **1.** Ames to Plainview **2.** Carthage to Dutton

3. Carthage to Weston **4.** Ames to Dutton

5. A furniture store sells couches that are available in 3 different styles, 7 different colors, and 2 different sizes. How many different couches are available?

6. How many different sandwiches can you make using one kind of bread, one kind of meat, and one kind of cheese with these choices?

Bread: white, rye, whole wheat
Cheese: Swiss, cheddar
Meat: turkey, chicken, roast beef

Use a formula to solve. List the permutations to check your answer.

7. In how many different ways can you arrange the 4 books shown side by side on a shelf?

8. In how many different ways can Carla, Dean, and Ellen be seated in a row of 3 chairs?

9. How many different two-digit whole numbers can you make with the digits 1, 3, 5, and 7 if no digit appears more than once in each number?

10. In how many different ways can you arrange the letters in the word RING if you take the letters 3 at a time?

Solve.

B 11. In how many different ways can 7 books be arranged side by side on a shelf?

12. In how many different ways can 6 students stand in a row of 6?

13. In how many different ways can you arrange the letters in the word ANSWER if you take the letters 5 at a time?

14. How many different four-digit numbers can you make using the digits 1, 2, 3, 5, 7, 8, and 9 if no digit appears more than once in a number?

Using the digits 1, 2, 4, 5, 7, and 8, how many different three-digit numbers can you form according to each of the following rules?

C 15. Each digit may be repeated any number of times in a number.

16. The numbers are even numbers and no digit appears more than once in a number.

17. There is a 5 in the ones' place and no digit appears more than once in a number.

18. In how many different ways can you arrange the letters in the word ROOT? (*Hint:* Notice that two of the letters are indistinguishable.)

19. In how many different ways can you arrange the letters in the word NOON?

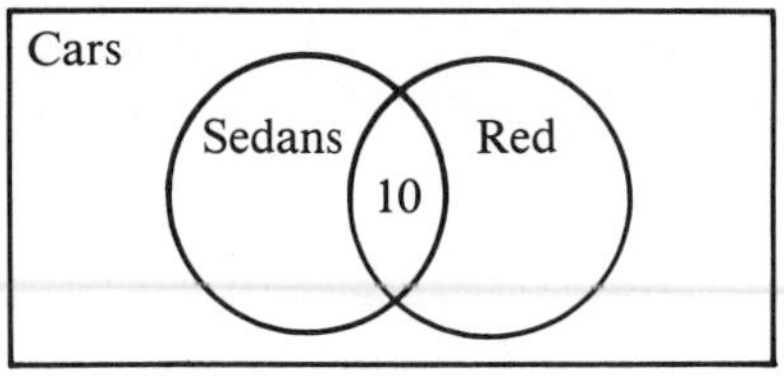

The diagram at the right, called a **Venn diagram,** illustrates the following statement.

> Of 100 cars, 35 are sedans, 25 are red, and 10 are red sedans.

The rectangular region represents the number of cars. One circular region represents the number of sedans; the other represents the number of red cars. The overlapping portion of the two circular regions represents the number of cars that are red and sedans. The number of red cars that are not sedans is 25 − 10, or 15.

Draw a Venn diagram to illustrate the statement. Then answer the questions.

20. Of 240 knit caps, 110 are striped, 65 are blue, and 45 are striped and blue.

a. How many are striped but not blue?
b. How many are blue but not striped?
c. How many are striped or blue (striped, or blue, or both)?
d. How many are neither striped nor blue?

Review Exercises

Simplify.

1. $\frac{70}{5} \times \frac{1}{2}$ **2.** $\frac{15}{12} \times \frac{36}{60}$ **3.** $\frac{21}{5} \times \frac{10}{14}$ **4.** $\frac{27}{51} \times \frac{17}{3}$

5. $\frac{9 \times 8}{3 \times 2}$ **6.** $\frac{7 \times 6}{4 \times 3}$ **7.** $\frac{11 \times 10 \times 9}{3 \times 2 \times 1}$ **8.** $\frac{23 \times 22 \times 21 \times 20}{4 \times 3 \times 2 \times 1}$

Challenge

You and a friend have decided to jog through Peachtree Park. The park has five entrance gates and several paths as shown in the diagram at the right. To jog along all of the paths without covering any path more than once, through which gate would you enter?

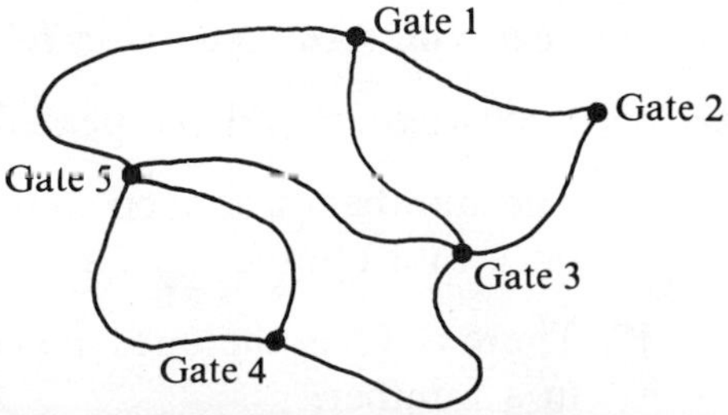

11-2 Combinations

Sometimes we select groups of objects from a larger group without regard to the order of the objects selected. Such groups in which the order is not considered are called **combinations.**

Suppose there is a group of 4 students—Jon, Lin, Meg, and Ray—who wish to go to the computer center today. If only 3 of them may go today, what are the possible combinations of these students who may be selected to go? To find any one combination, just leave out 1 student from the group of 4. The possible combinations are listed below.

Jon, Lin, Meg   Jon, Lin, Ray   Jon, Meg, Ray   Lin, Meg, Ray

The number of groups of 3 students that can be selected from a group of 4 students is 4.

Here is another way to approach the problem.

[number of groups of 3 students you can select from 4]	×	[number of ways of arranging 3 students in a group]	=	[number of ways of arranging 3 out of 4 students]
N	×	${}_3P_3$	=	${}_4P_3$

Solving for N, we find that

$$N = \frac{{}_4P_3}{{}_3P_3} = \frac{4 \times 3 \times 2}{3 \times 2 \times 1} = 4.$$

This formula gives us the same answer that we found by showing and counting the number of combinations of 3 students that may be selected from a group of 4 students.

EXAMPLE 1 How many combinations of 4 cards can be chosen from the cards shown at the right?

Solution Use the formula to find the number of combinations of 6 cards taken 4 at a time.

$$N = \frac{{}_6P_4}{{}_4P_4} = \frac{\overset{3}{\cancel{6}} \times 5 \times \overset{1}{\cancel{4}} \times \overset{1}{\cancel{3}}}{\underset{1}{\cancel{4}} \times \underset{1}{\cancel{3}} \times \underset{1}{\cancel{2}} \times 1} = \frac{15}{1} = 15$$

List the combinations to check.

A B C D	A B D E	A C D E	A D E F	B C E F
A B C E	A B D F	A C D F	B C D E	B D E F
A B C F	A B E F	A C E F	B C D F	C D E F

In general, if we let ${}_nC_r$ represent the number of combinations of n things taken r at a time, we can use the following formula.

Formula

For the number of combinations of n things taken r at a time,

$${}_nC_r = \frac{{}_nP_r}{{}_rP_r} = \frac{n \times (n-1) \times \cdots \text{ (to } r \text{ factors)}}{r!}$$

EXAMPLE 2 Four of 7 students who have volunteered will be chosen to hand out programs at the drama club performance. How many combinations of these students can be selected?

Solution We wish to find the number of combinations of 7 students taken 4 at a time.

Using the formula, we find

$${}_7C_4 = \frac{{}_7P_4}{{}_4P_4} = \frac{7 \times \overset{1}{\cancel{6}} \times 5 \times \overset{1}{\cancel{4}}}{\underset{1}{\cancel{4}} \times \underset{1}{\cancel{3}} \times \underset{1}{\cancel{2}} \times 1} = \frac{35}{1} = 35.$$

Class Exercises

Find the value of each.

1. ${}_5C_3$ **2.** ${}_5C_4$ **3.** ${}_6C_2$ **4.** ${}_7C_2$ **5.** ${}_8C_4$ **6.** ${}_8C_6$ **7.** ${}_{12}C_3$ **8.** ${}_{20}C_2$

Use the formula to solve. List the combinations to check your answer.

9. How many combinations of 2 cards can be chosen from the cards shown at the right?

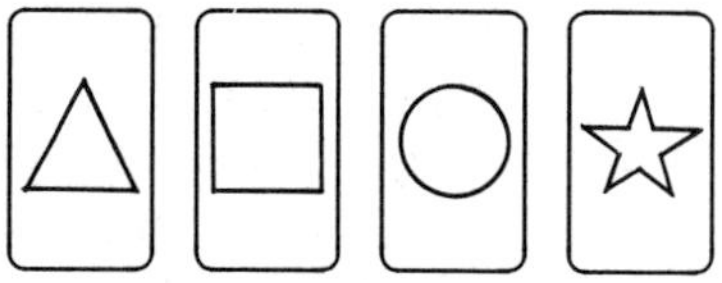

10. How many combinations of 3 letters can be chosen from the letters A, B, C, D, and E?

Problems

A **1.** How many combinations of 4 books can you choose from 6 books?

2. How many groups of 3 types of plants can be selected from 6 types?

3. How many straight lines can be formed by connecting any 2 of 6 points, no 3 of which are on a straight line?

4. How many groups of 4 fabrics can be selected from 7 fabrics?

B 5. How many ways can a class of 21 students select 2 of its members as class representatives for student government?

6. The school photographer wants to photograph 3 students from a club with 14 members. How many combinations can be made?

7. Kristen must answer 5 of 10 questions on her quiz. How many combinations of questions are possible?

8. Philip wishes to check 2 books out of his school library. If the library contains 800 books, in how many ways might Philip make his choice of books?

9. You have a total of 4 coins: a penny, a nickel, a dime, and a quarter. How many different amounts of money can you form using the given number of these coins?
a. 1 coin **b.** 2 coins **c.** 3 coins **d.** 4 coins **e.** one or more coins

10. There are three books left in the sale rack: a book about sailing, a cookbook, and a book about baseball. How many combinations can be formed using the given number of these books?
a. 1 book **b.** 2 books **c.** 3 books **d.** one or more books

C 11. In how many ways can a five-member committee of 3 seniors and 2 juniors be selected from a group of 14 seniors and 8 juniors? (*Hint:* Find the number of combinations of each type and determine their product.)

12. A basketball squad has 17 members. The coach has designated 3 members to play center, 6 to play guard, and 8 to play forward. How many ways can the coach select a starting team of 1 center, 2 guards, and 2 forwards? (*Hint:* See the hint in Exercise 11.)

Review Exercises

Explain the meaning of each term.

1. factor 2. multiple 3. even number 4. odd number
5. cube 6. at least one 7. at most one 8. exactly one

11-3 The Probability of an Event

In a simple game, the five cards shown are turned face down and mixed so that all choices are *equally likely.*

You then draw a card. If the card is a heart, you win a prize. To find your chance of winning, notice that there are 5 possible **outcomes.** Notice, too, that 2 of the outcomes are hearts. We say that 2 of the outcomes **favor** the event of drawing a heart. The **probability,** or chance, of drawing a heart is $\frac{2}{5}$. If we let H stand for the event of drawing a heart, we may write $P(H) = \frac{2}{5}$. This statement is read as *the probability of event H is* $\frac{2}{5}$.

In general we have the following:

Formula

The probability of an event E is

$$P(E) = \frac{\text{number of outcomes favoring event } E}{\text{number of possible outcomes}}$$

for equally likely outcomes.

When all outcomes are equally likely, as in drawing one of the cards in the game described above, we say that the outcomes occur *at random,* or *randomly.*

In this chapter, we shall often refer to *experiments* such as drawing cards, drawing marbles from a bag, or rolling game cubes. We shall always assume that the outcomes of these experiments occur at random. When we refer to spinners like the one shown at the right, we shall always assume that the pointer stops at random but not on a division line.

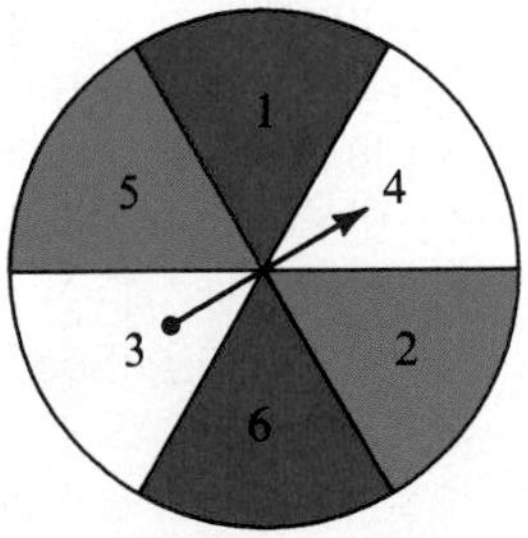

Often it is helpful to list all possible outcomes of an experiment. We could show the possible outcomes for the spinner shown above by using letters to represent the colors and by writing the following:

$R1$	$B2$	$W3$
$R6$	$B5$	$W4$

EXAMPLE 1 Find the probability that the pointer of the spinner shown on the preceding page stops on a wedge of the type described.

a. even-numbered **b.** odd-numbered
c. red **d.** not red
e. even-numbered *and* red **f.** green
g. not green

Solution The number of possible outcomes is 6.

a. $P(\text{even-numbered}) = \frac{3}{6} = \frac{1}{2}$

b. $P(\text{odd-numbered}) = \frac{3}{6} = \frac{1}{2}$

c. $P(\text{red}) = \frac{2}{6} = \frac{1}{3}$

d. $P(\text{not red}) = \frac{4}{6} = \frac{2}{3}$

e. $P(\text{even-numbered and red}) = \frac{1}{6}$

f. $P(\text{green}) = \frac{0}{6} = 0$

g. $P(\text{not green}) = \frac{6}{6} = 1$

The events in parts (f) and (g) of the example illustrate these facts:

> The probability of an impossible event is 0.
> The probability of a certain event is 1.

Sometimes it is useful to picture the possible outcomes of an experiment. Consider the experiment of rolling the two game cubes that are shown at the right. One cube is blue, one cube is red. The numbers 1 through 6 are printed on each cube, one number per face. An outcome can be represented by an ordered pair of numbers. The array at the right shows the 36 possible outcomes when the two cubes are rolled. The encircled dot stands for the outcome of a 5 on the top face of the red cube and a 3 on the top face of the blue cube, or the ordered pair (5, 3).

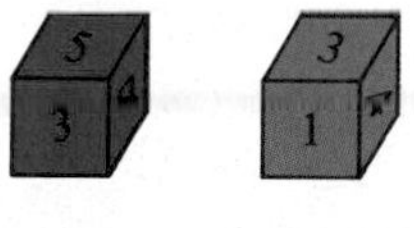

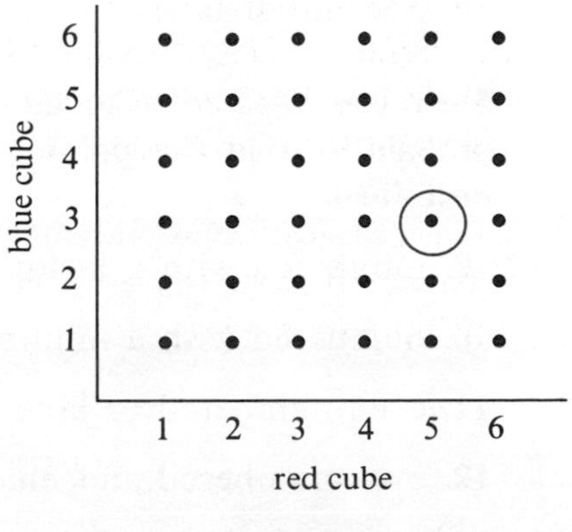

EXAMPLE 2 Two game cubes are rolled.

a. Find the probability that one cube *or* the other cube shows a 5 (that is, that the number 5 is on the top face of either or both cubes).

b. Find the probability that the sum of the top faces is 5.

Solution First, make a sketch to show the possible outcomes. Then circle the event.

a.

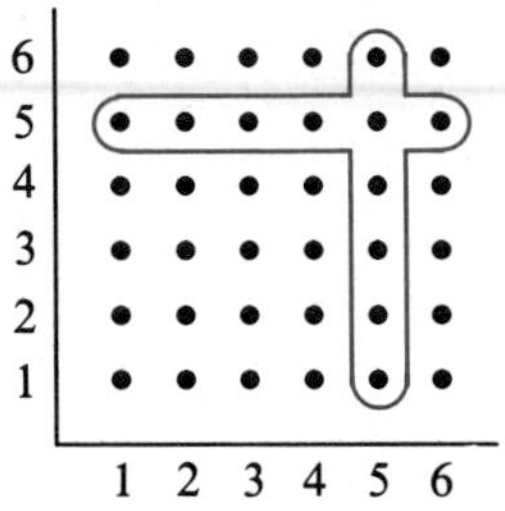

$P(\text{a } 5) = \frac{11}{36}$

b.

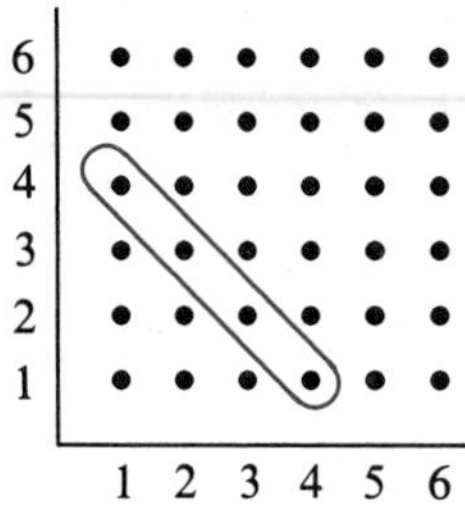

$P(\text{sum} = 5) = \frac{4}{36} = \frac{1}{9}$

Problem Solving Reminder

Sometimes *making a sketch* can help you solve a problem. In Example 2, above, picturing an outcome as the graph of an ordered pair simplifies the problem.

Class Exercises

Two red, one white, and three blue marbles are put into a bag. Find each probability for a marble chosen at random.

1. P(red) **2.** P(white) **3.** P(blue) **4.** P(green)

5. P(not green) **6.** P(red or white)

7. P(white or blue) **8.** P(red or blue)

Exercises 9–12 refer to the spinner at the right. Find the probability that the pointer stops on a wedge of the type described.

9. numbered with a factor of 6

10. numbered with a multiple of 3

11. even-numbered or blue

12. even-numbered and blue

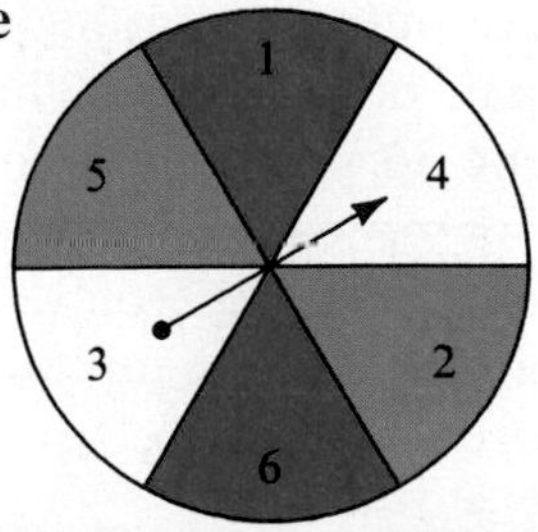

Written Exercises

Find the probability of each roll if you use a single game cube.

A **1.** a 5

2. an odd number

3. a number less than 5

4. a number greater than 3

5. a 7

6. a number less than 7

Each of the 20 cards shown at the right has a letter, a number, and a color. Each card is equally likely to be drawn. Find each probability.

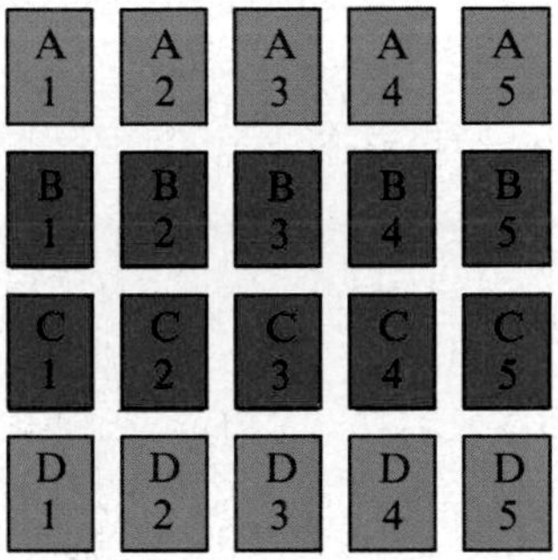

7. $P(\text{C})$

8. $P(\text{A})$

9. $P(1)$

10. $P(2)$

11. $P(\text{red})$

12. $P(\text{blue})$

13. $P(\text{not A})$

14. $P(\text{not D})$

15. $P(1 \text{ or } 2)$

16. $P(1, 2, 3, \text{ or } 4)$

17. $P(\text{neither 1 nor 2})$

18. $P(\text{not 1, or 2, or 3, or 4})$

Exercises 19–28 refer to the spinner below. Find the probability that the pointer stops on a wedge of the type described.

19. red

20. white or blue

21. numbered with a factor of 12

22. even-numbered

23. numbered with a multiple of 3

24. numbered with a multiple of 4

25. odd-numbered or red

26. odd-numbered and red

27. red and a factor of 6

28. blue and a multiple of 5

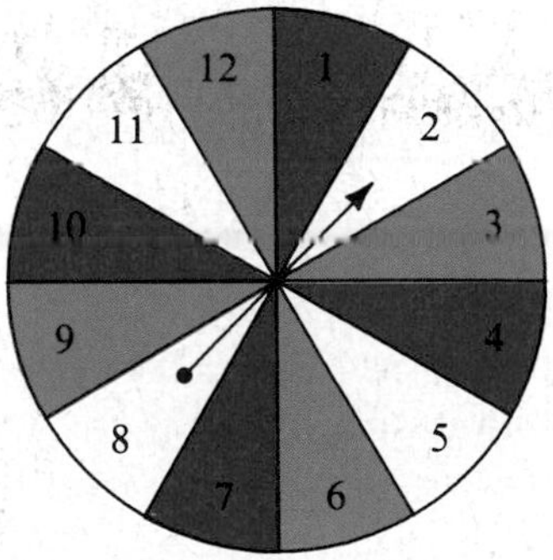

Two game cubes are rolled. Find the probability that this sum shows.

B **29.** 7

30. 12

31. 3

32. 9

33. 7 or 11

34. 2 or 12

35. less than 7

36. 6, 7, or 8

For Exercises 37 and 38, use a *tree diagram* to picture the possible outcomes of the random experiment.

EXAMPLE Two coins are tossed. Find the probability of obtaining at least one head.

Solution Let H stand for heads and T stand for tails.

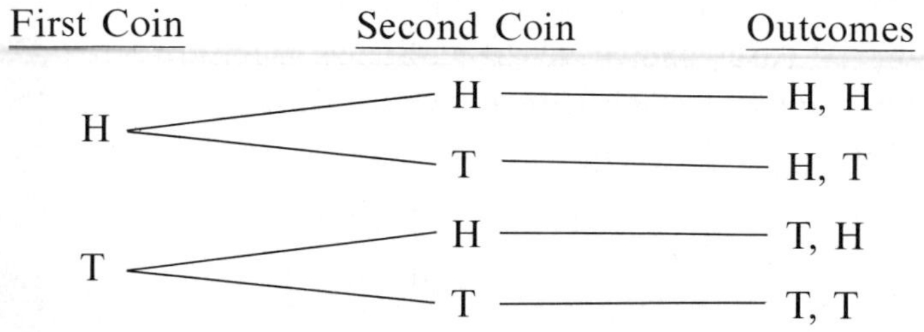

There are 4 possible outcomes. Three of the outcomes have one or more heads.

$$P(\text{at least one H}) = \frac{3}{4}$$

37. You have two bags of marbles, each of which holds one blue marble, one red marble, and one green marble. You choose one marble at random from each bag. Find the probability of obtaining the following.

a. two red marbles **b.** at least one blue marble **c.** no green marbles
d. at most one green marble **e.** exactly one red marble

38. Three coins are tossed. Find the probability of obtaining the following.

a. at least two heads **b.** three heads **c.** no heads
d. at most two tails **e.** exactly one head

C **39.** You have one penny, one nickel, one dime, and one quarter in your pocket. You select two coins at random. What is the probability that you have taken at least 25¢ from your pocket?

Review Exercises

Evaluate each expression using the given values of the variable.

$1 - x$	**1.** $x = 1$	**2.** $x = \frac{1}{2}$	**3.** $x = \frac{2}{3}$	**4.** $x = -1$
$\frac{x}{1 - x}$	**5.** $x = \frac{1}{3}$	**6.** $x = \frac{2}{3}$	**7.** $x = \frac{3}{7}$	**8.** $x = \frac{4}{7}$

11-4 Odds in Favor and Odds Against

EXAMPLE 1 A game is played with the spinner shown at the right. To win the game, the pointer must stop on a wedge that shows a prime number. Find each probability.
a. You win. **b.** You do not win.

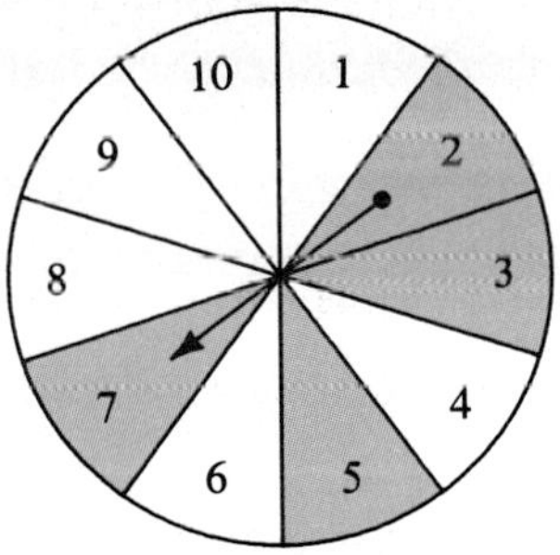

Solution There are 10 possible outcomes.
For you to win, the pointer must stop on 2, 3, 5, or 7. Therefore:

a. $P(\text{win}) = \frac{4}{10} = \frac{2}{5}$

b. $P(\text{not win}) = \frac{6}{10} = \frac{3}{5}$

Example 1 illustrates this general fact:

> If the probability that an event occurs is p, then the probability that the event does not occur is $1 - p$.

In Example 1 there are 4 ways of winning and 6 ways of not winning. We therefore say:

a. The *odds in favor* of winning are 4 to 6, or 2 to 3.

b. The *odds against* winning are 6 to 4, or 3 to 2.

> ### *Formula*
>
> If the probability that an event occurs is p (where $p \neq 0$ and $p \neq 1$), then:
>
> $$\text{Odds in favor of the event} = \frac{p}{1-p}$$
>
> $$\text{Odds against the event} = \frac{1-p}{p}$$

Odds are usually expressed in the form "x to y," where x and y are integers having no common factor.

EXAMPLE 2 Find the odds (a) in favor of and (b) against rolling a sum of 6 with two game cubes.

Solution From the array of possible outcomes, we see that:

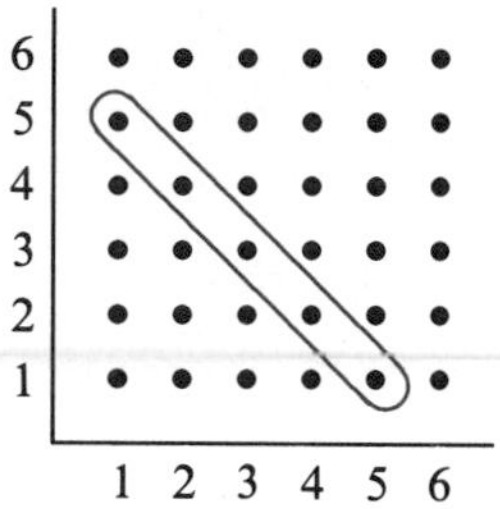

$P(\text{sum} = 6) = \frac{5}{36} = p$

$P(\text{sum} \neq 6) = 1 - p = 1 - \frac{5}{36} = \frac{31}{36}$

a. Odds in favor $= \frac{p}{1-p}$

$$\frac{\frac{5}{36}}{\frac{31}{36}} = \frac{5}{36} \div \frac{31}{36} = \frac{5}{36} \times \frac{36}{31} = \frac{5}{31}$$

Odds in favor are 5 to 31.

b. Odds against are 31 to 5.

EXAMPLE 3 The chance of rain tomorrow is 40%. What are the odds against its raining?

Solution The probability of rain is $p = 40\% = 0.4$.

Odds against rain $= \frac{1-p}{p} = \frac{1-0.4}{0.4} = \frac{0.6}{0.4} = \frac{3}{2}$

Odds against rain are 3 to 2.

Class Exercises

1. The chance of rain tomorrow is 20%. Find the odds against rain.
2. Find the odds against rolling a 4 with one game cube.

Exercises 3–6 refer to the spinner at the right. Find the odds (a) in favor of and (b) against the pointer stopping on a wedge of the type described.

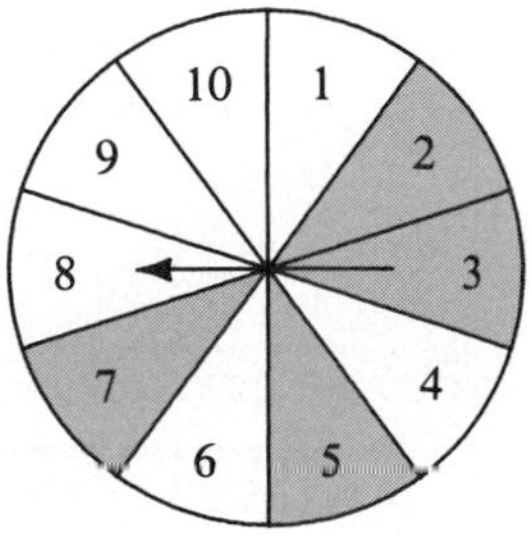

3. an odd number
4. a multiple of 3
5. a factor of 10
6. a number less than 7
7. The odds are 1 to 1 that an event will occur. What is the probability that the event will occur?
8. The probability that an event will occur is $\frac{1}{2}$. What are the odds against the event?

Written Exercises

Exercises 1–6 refer to a bag containing 6 red, 2 white, and 4 blue marbles. Find the odds in favor of drawing a marble of the type described.

A **1.** red

2. white

3. blue

4. white or blue

5. blue or red

6. red or white

7. The chance of rain tomorrow is 60%. What are the odds against rain?

8. The probability of snow next week is 75%. What are the odds in favor of snow?

9. The probability that the Lions football team will win the next game is 0.6. What are the odds that it will win?

10. The Student Union Party has a 30% chance of winning in the next school election. What are the odds against its winning?

In Exercises 11–16 a card has been drawn at random from the 20 cards that are shown. Find the odds against drawing a card of the type described.

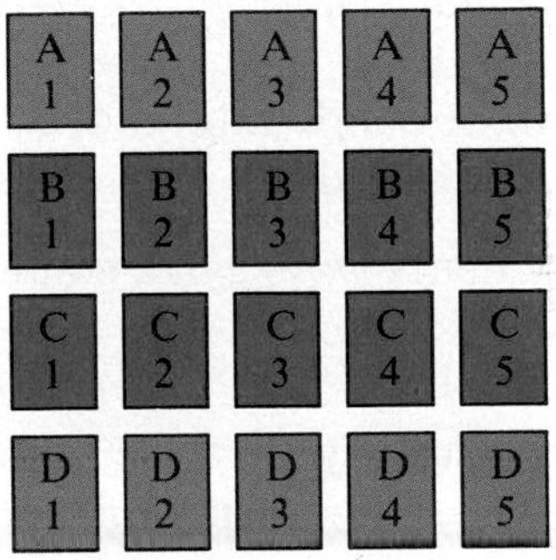

11. an A

12. a blue card

13. a red card

14. a C

15. a 1, 2, or 3

16. B2, B3, B4, or B5

Two game cubes are rolled. Find the odds against obtaining the sum described.

17. 7

18. 11

19. 7 or 11

20. 2 or 12

21. greater than 7

22. less than 6

B **23.** **a.** even **b.** odd

24. **a.** divisible by 3 **b.** not divisible by 3

The two game cubes are rolled again. Find the odds in favor of the event described.

25. Exactly one 5 shows.

26. At least one 5 shows.

27. Two even numbers show.

28. At least one odd number shows.

29. The numbers showing differ by 2.

30. The product of the numbers showing is 6.

C **31.** The odds in favor of the Melodies winning the music competition are 5 to 3. What is the probability that the Melodies will win?

32. The odds in favor of drawing a red marble at random from a bag of marbles are 1 to 8. What is the probability of drawing a red marble?

Self-Test A

1. In how many different ways can you arrange 4 boxes side by side on a shelf? **[11–1]**

2. How many different three-digit numbers can you make with the digits 1, 2, 3, 4, and 5 if no digit appears more than once in each number?

3. How many combinations of 3 letters can be chosen from the letters A, B, C, D, and E? **[11–2]**

4. In how many ways can a committee of 2 people be selected from a group of 15 people?

Find the probability that the pointer on the spinner shown at the right stops on a wedge of the type described.

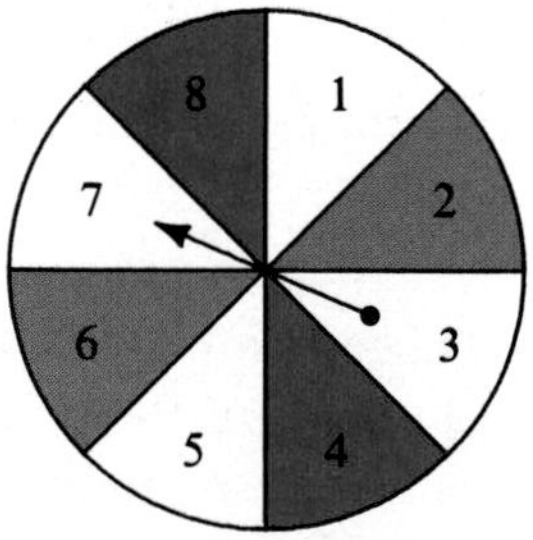

5. 3

6. odd-numbered **[11–3]**

7. red

8. a number less than 9

9. What are the odds in favor of the pointer on the spinner shown stopping on a wedge with a number greater than 6? **[11–4]**

10. What are the odds against the pointer on the spinner shown stopping on a blue wedge?

Self-Test answers and Extra Practice are at the back of the book.

11-5 Mutually Exclusive Events

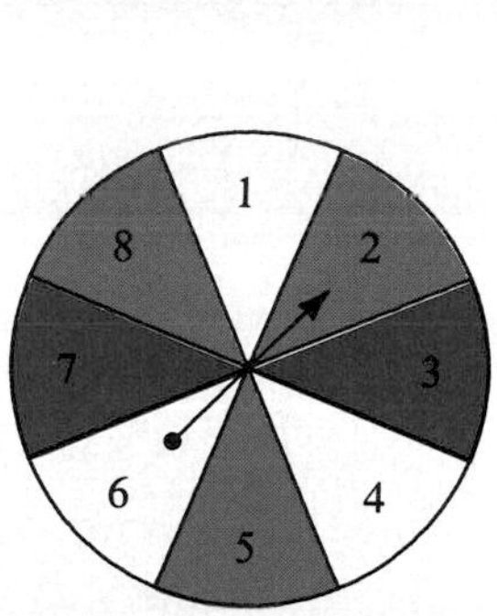

The pointer shown at the right stops at random but not on a division line. Consider the following events.

R: The pointer stops on a red wedge.

B: The pointer stops on a blue wedge.

O: The pointer stops on an odd-numbered wedge.

E: The pointer stops on an even-numbered wedge.

Events R and B cannot both occur at once. Such events are said to be **mutually exclusive.** Notice that events B and E are *not* mutually exclusive because they both occur when the pointer stops on a blue wedge that is even-numbered.

In the spinner above, five of the eight wedges are colored red or blue. Therefore,

$$P(R \text{ or } B) = \tfrac{5}{8}.$$

Notice that

$$P(R) = \tfrac{1}{4},\ P(B) = \tfrac{3}{8},\ \text{and } P(R) + P(B) = \tfrac{1}{4} + \tfrac{3}{8} = \tfrac{5}{8}.$$

Thus, $P(R \text{ or } B) = P(R) + P(B)$.

> If A and B are mutually exclusive events, then
>
> $$P(A \text{ or } B) = P(A) + P(B)$$

EXAMPLE The probability that a randomly chosen car is green is 0.15 and that it is red is 0.25.

a. Find the probability that the next car you see will be red or green.
b. Find the odds against its being red or green.

Solution **a.** The events described are mutually exclusive. Thus,

$$P(\text{red or green}) = P(\text{red}) + P(\text{green}) = 0.25 + 0.15 = 0.40$$

b. Odds against red or green $= \dfrac{1 - 0.40}{0.40} = \dfrac{0.6}{0.4} = \dfrac{3}{2}$

The odds against the next car's being red or green are 3 to 2.

Class Exercises

Are events *A* and *B* mutually exclusive?

1. You take a test.
A: You pass it.
B: You fail it.

2. You take a test.
A: You score less than 9.
B: You score more than 6.

3. Two coins are tossed.
A: Two heads result.
B: Two tails result.

4. Two game cubes are rolled.
A: The sum is 5.
B: A 5 shows on one cube.

5. Two game cubes are rolled.
A: Cubes show the same number.
B: The sum is 7.

6. Two game cubes are rolled.
A: Cubes show the same number.
B: The sum is 8.

A and B are mutually exclusive events. Find $P(A \text{ or } B)$.

7. $P(A) = \frac{1}{4}$, $P(B) = \frac{3}{8}$

8. $P(A) = 0.2$, $P(B) = 0.5$

9. $P(A) = \frac{1}{2}$ and $P(B) = \frac{2}{3}$. Are A and B mutually exclusive events?

Written Exercises

A and B are mutually exclusive events.

A **1.** $P(A) = \frac{1}{5}$, $P(B) = \frac{2}{3}$. Find $P(A \text{ or } B)$.

2. $P(A) = 0.32$, $P(B) = 0.45$. Find $P(A \text{ or } B)$.

3. $P(A) = 0.4$, $P(A \text{ or } B) = 0.7$. Find $P(B)$.

4. $P(B) = \frac{1}{3}$, $P(A \text{ or } B) = \frac{3}{4}$. Find $P(A)$.

In Exercises 5–10, find the probability that the pointer stops on a wedge of the type described.

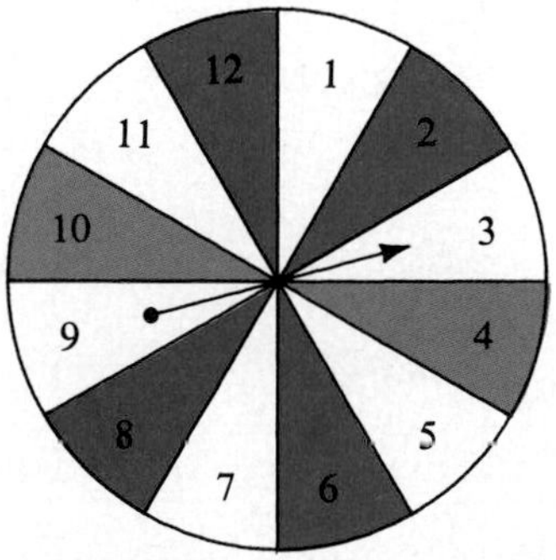

5. a. red **b.** white **c.** red or white

6. a. blue **b.** red **c.** blue or red

7. a. blue **b.** not blue

8. a. white **b.** not white

9. a. odd-numbered **b.** red **c.** odd-numbered or red

10. a. odd-numbered **b.** blue **c.** odd-numbered or blue

Exercises 11–14 refer to the cards at the right. Find the probability that a card drawn at random is of the type described.

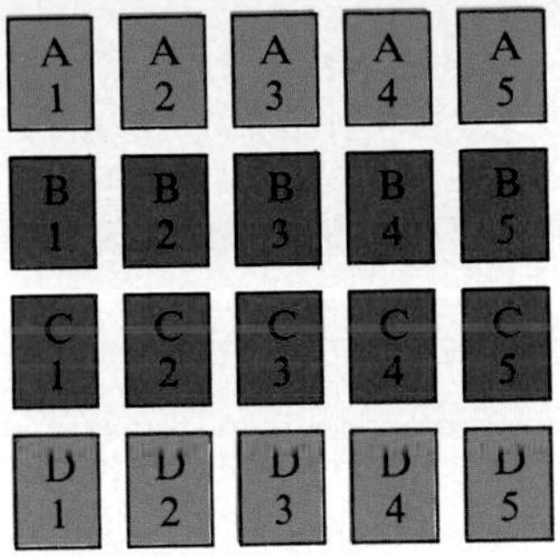

11. **a.** a 5 **b.** less than 3
c. a 5 or less than 3

12. **a.** a 2 **b.** greater than 3
c. a 2 or greater than 3

13. **a.** a D **b.** a red card greater than 2
c. a D or a red card greater than 2

14. **a.** a B **b.** a blue card greater than 3
c. a B or a blue card greater than 3

Two game cubes are rolled. Find the probability of the event described.

B **15.** **a.** The sum is 9. **b.** The roll is a double (for example, [3] [3]).
c. The sum is 9 or a double is rolled.

16. **a.** The sum is 7. **b.** The roll is a double.
c. The sum is 7 or a double is rolled.

17. Joe's batting average (the probability of his getting a hit) is 0.350. What are the odds against his getting a hit?

18. The probability of Jan's team winning the next softball game is 55%. Find the odds that the team will lose.

C **19.** The probability that the next soup ordered will be chicken is 0.45; that it will be tomato is 0.35. What are the odds against its being chicken or tomato?

20. At West High School the probability that a randomly chosen student is a senior is 0.20. The probability that the student is a junior is 0.25. Find the odds against the student's being a junior or senior.

Review Exercises

Solve for x.

1. $x = \frac{1}{5} + \frac{2}{3}$ **2.** $x = \frac{3}{8} + \frac{1}{2} - \frac{1}{4}$ **3.** $\frac{1}{4} + \frac{1}{3} - \frac{1}{12} = x$

4. $x + \frac{7}{8} = \frac{1}{12}$ **5.** $1 = x + \frac{3}{8}$ **6.** $\frac{5}{18} + x = \frac{3}{8} + \frac{7}{15}$

7. $x - 0.2 = 0.9$ **8.** $0.51 + x = 1$ **9.** $0.7 = 0.4 + 0.6 - x$

11-6 "Overlapping" Events

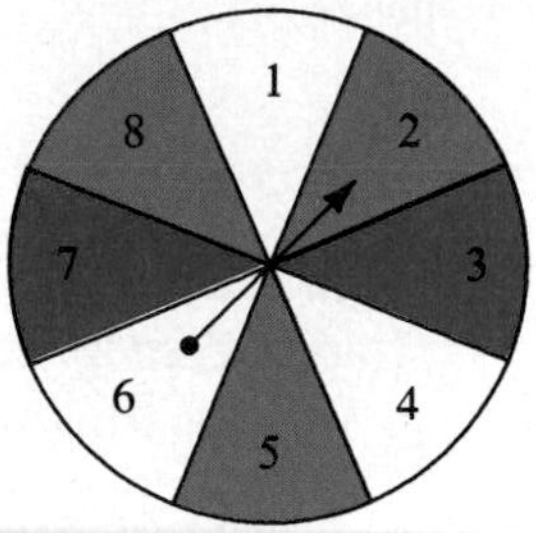

On the spinner at the right, there are 5 wedges that are blue (B) or even-numbered (E) or both. Thus,

$$P(B \text{ or } E) = \tfrac{5}{8}.$$

On the other hand,

$$P(B) + P(E) = \tfrac{3}{8} + \tfrac{1}{2} = \tfrac{7}{8},$$

so that $P(B \text{ or } E) \neq P(B) + P(E)$. This is because events B and E are *not* mutually exclusive. (Both events occur when the pointer stops on a blue wedge numbered 2 or 8; we call this event "B and E.") The rule that covers this "overlapping event" case is this:

> For *any* two events A and B,
>
> $$P(A \text{ or } B) = P(A) + P(B) - P(A \text{ and } B)$$

Applying this formula to the spinner above, we have

$$P(B \text{ or } E) = P(B) + P(E) - P(B \text{ and } E) = \tfrac{3}{8} + \tfrac{1}{2} - \tfrac{1}{4} = \tfrac{5}{8}.$$

EXAMPLE 1 Both dials are spun. Find the probabilities of these events. (In the illustration, 3 and B have come up.)

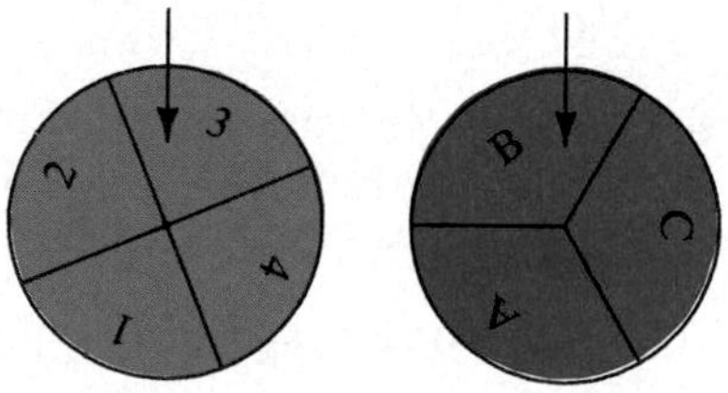

a. 3 comes up.
b. C comes up.
c. 3 and C come up.
d. 3 or C comes up.

Solution From the array of 12 possible outcomes we see that

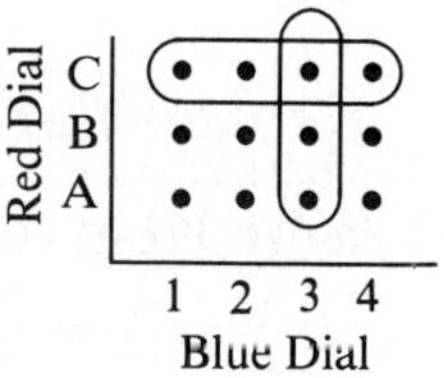

a. $P(3) = \frac{3}{12} = \frac{1}{4}$

b. $P(\text{C}) = \frac{4}{12} = \frac{1}{3}$

c. $P(3 \text{ and C}) = \frac{1}{12}$

d. $P(3 \text{ or C}) = P(3) + P(\text{C}) - P(3 \text{ and C}) = \frac{1}{4} + \frac{1}{3} - \frac{1}{12} = \frac{1}{2}$

Reading Mathematics: ***Vocabulary***

In mathematics *or* means "and/or."

A or B means *A* occurs, or *B* occurs, or both *A* and *B* occur.

A and B means that *both A* and *B* must occur.

EXAMPLE 2 Based on past history, the probability that the Hawks will win the first game of a double header is $\frac{2}{3}$, that they will win the second game is $\frac{1}{2}$, and that they will win both is $\frac{1}{3}$. Find the probability that they will win at least one game.

Solution

$$P(\text{win at least one}) = P(\text{win first}) + P(\text{win second}) - P(\text{win both})$$
$$= \frac{2}{3} + \frac{1}{2} - \frac{1}{3} = \frac{5}{6}$$

EXAMPLE 3 The probability that a randomly chosen marble is red is 0.4, that it is striped is 0.6, and that it is red or striped is 0.7. What is the probability that the marble is red and striped?

Solution

$$\begin{aligned} P(\text{red or striped}) &= P(\text{red}) + P(\text{striped}) - P(\text{red and striped}) \\ 0.7 &= 0.4 + 0.6 - P(\text{red and striped}) \\ 0.7 &= 1.0 - P(\text{red and striped}) \\ P(\text{red and striped}) &= 0.3 \end{aligned}$$

Class Exercises

In Exercises 1–4, find *P*(*A* or *B*).

1. $P(A) = 0.4$, $P(B) = 0.5$, $P(A \text{ and } B) = 0.2$

2. $P(A) = \frac{1}{2}$, $P(B) = \frac{1}{2}$, $P(A \text{ and } B) = \frac{1}{3}$

3. $P(A) = \frac{1}{2}$, $P(B) = \frac{3}{4}$, $P(A \text{ and } B) = \frac{3}{8}$

4. $P(A) = 75\%$, $P(B) = 50\%$, $P(A \text{ and } B) = 30\%$

5. If two events, *A* and *B*, are mutually exclusive, what is the value of *P*(*A* and *B*)? What does the formula at the beginning of this lesson become?

6. Is the following a true statement?

$$P(A \text{ or } B) + P(A \text{ and } B) = P(A) + P(B)$$

Explain.

Written Exercises

Solve.

A 1. $P(A) = 0.35$, $P(B) = 0.55$, $P(A \text{ and } B) = 0.20$. Find $P(A \text{ or } B)$.

2. $P(A) = \frac{3}{8}$, $P(B) = \frac{3}{4}$, $P(A \text{ and } B) = \frac{1}{4}$. Find $P(A \text{ or } B)$.

3. $P(A) = \frac{1}{3}$, $P(B) = \frac{1}{2}$, $P(A \text{ and } B) = \frac{1}{4}$. Find $P(A \text{ or } B)$.

4. $P(A) = 0.45$, $P(B) = 0.75$, $P(A \text{ and } B) = 0.30$. Find $P(A \text{ or } B)$.

5. $P(A) = 0.65$, $P(A \text{ or } B) = 0.85$, $P(A \text{ and } B) = 0.30$. Find $P(B)$.

6. $P(A) = 0.75$, $P(A \text{ or } B) = 0.80$, $P(A \text{ and } B) = 0.15$. Find $P(B)$.

The two dials shown are spun. Find the probabilities of the events described. To answer parts (a), (b), and (c), sketch the array of possible outcomes as in Example 1. Use the formula to answer part (d).

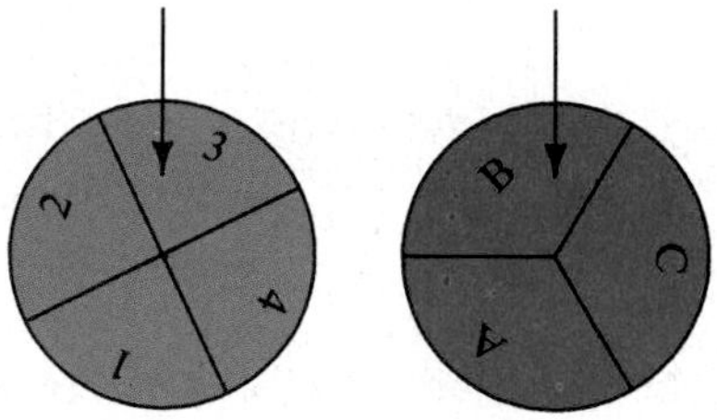

7. **a.** 4 comes up. **b.** B comes up.
   c. 4 and B come up. **d.** 4 or B comes up.

8. **a.** 1 comes up. **b.** A comes up.
   c. 1 and A come up. **d.** 1 or A comes up.

9. **a.** An odd number comes up. **b.** C comes up.
   c. An odd number and C come up. **d.** An odd number or C comes up.

10. **a.** An even number comes up. **b.** A comes up.
    c. An even number and A come up. **d.** An even number or A comes up.

A card is drawn at random from those shown at the right. Find the probability that the card is of the type described.

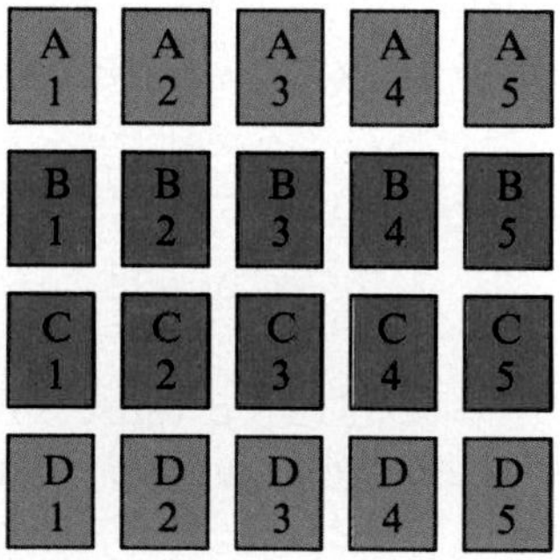

B 11. a C or a number greater than 3

12. a D or a number greater than 2

13. a blue card or a number greater than 3

14. a red card or a number greater than 2

In Exercises 15–18, two game cubes are rolled. Find (a) the probability of the event described and (b) the odds against its occurring.

C 15. The sum is 6 or a double is rolled. 16. The sum is 10 or a double is rolled.

17. The sum is 8 or exactly one 6 shows. **18.** The sum is 7 or exactly one 3 shows.

Problems

A **1.** The chance (probability) of rain tomorrow is 80%, the chance of snow is 40%, and the chance of rain and snow is 30%. What is the chance that it will rain or snow?

2. The probability that a randomly chosen car is a convertible is 0.09, that it is red is 0.25, and that it is a red convertible is 0.03. What is the probability that the next car to come along is red or a convertible?

B **3.** In a certain neighborhood, 60% of the homes receive the *Daily Reporter,* 90% receive the *Daily Reporter* or the *Weekly Times,* and 50% receive the *Daily Reporter* and the *Weekly Times.* Find the probability that a home chosen at random receives the *Weekly Times.*

4. The probability that a randomly chosen adult resident of Bayview City owns a boat is 0.15, that the adult rents an apartment is 0.30, and that the adult owns a boat or rents an apartment is 0.40. Find the probability that the adult owns a boat and rents an apartment.

C **5.** Of 32 marbles in a bag, 18 are green, 9 are spotted, and 11 are neither green nor spotted. What is the probability that a marble chosen at random is green and spotted? Draw a Venn diagram, as on page 400, to illustrate the problem, and then answer the question.

Review Exercises

Write your answer in lowest terms.

1. $\frac{5}{6} \times \frac{1}{6}$ **2.** $\frac{4}{5} \times \frac{2}{7}$ **3.** $\frac{1}{4} \times \frac{2}{3}$ **4.** $\frac{1}{6} \times \frac{1}{2}$

5. $\frac{2}{5} \times \frac{3}{5}$ **6.** $\frac{5}{7} \times \frac{5}{7}$ **7.** $1 - \frac{13}{25}$ **8.** $1 - \frac{11}{21}$

11-7 Independent Events

A coin is tossed and a game cube rolled. Consider these events.

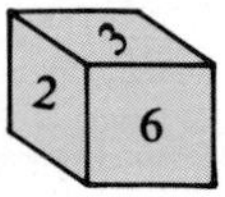

A: The coin shows heads.
B: The cube shows 2, 3, 4, or 5.

Neither of these events has any effect on the other. For example, the probability that *B* will occur is not affected by whether or not *A* occurs. Such events are said to be **independent.** What is $P(A \text{ and } B)$ in the experiment described above? One way to find out is to list the 12 possible outcomes as shown below.

H1 (H2) (H3) (H4) (H5) H6

T1 T2 T3 T4 T5 T6

Notice that 4 of the possible outcomes favor the combined event "*A* and *B*." Thus,

$$P(A \text{ and } B) = \frac{4}{12} = \frac{1}{3}.$$

An easier way to find $P(A \text{ and } B)$ is to use this general principle:

> If *A* and *B* are independent events, then
>
> $$P(A \text{ and } B) = P(A) \times P(B)$$

In the experiment considered above, we know that $P(A) = \frac{1}{2}$ and $P(B) = \frac{4}{6} = \frac{2}{3}$. Thus,

$$P(A \text{ and } B) = P(A) \times P(B)$$
$$= \frac{1}{2} \times \frac{2}{3} = \frac{1}{3}.$$

EXAMPLE A bag contains 2 red and 3 blue marbles. A marble is drawn and replaced. Then a marble is drawn again. Find the probability of each event. (Recall that the marbles are drawn at random.)

a. The first marble is red, and the second one is blue.
b. The first marble is blue, and the second one is red.
c. Both marbles are red.
d. Both marbles are blue.

Solution Because the first marble drawn is replaced, the second-draw events are independent of the first-draw events.

$$P(\text{red}) = \frac{2}{5};\ P(\text{blue}) = \frac{3}{5}$$

a. $P(\text{red, then blue}) = P(\text{red}) \times P(\text{blue}) = \frac{2}{5} \times \frac{3}{5} = \frac{6}{25}$

b. $P(\text{blue, then red}) = P(\text{blue}) \times P(\text{red}) = \frac{3}{5} \times \frac{2}{5} = \frac{6}{25}$

c. $P(\text{red, red}) = P(\text{red}) \times P(\text{red}) = \frac{2}{5} \times \frac{2}{5} = \frac{4}{25}$

d. $P(\text{blue, blue}) = P(\text{blue}) \times P(\text{blue}) = \frac{3}{5} \times \frac{3}{5} = \frac{9}{25}$

The example can be continued to find the probability that the two marbles drawn have the same color and the probability that they have different colors. The events "red, red" and "blue, blue" are mutually exclusive. Therefore,

$$P(\text{same color}) = P(\text{red, red}) + P(\text{blue, blue}) = \frac{4}{25} + \frac{9}{25} = \frac{13}{25}.$$

We can find *P*(different colors) in a similar way by adding the probabilities in parts (a) and (b) of the example.

Class Exercises

Are events *A* and *B* independent? If they are, find the probability that they both occur.

1. A coin is tossed twice.
A: Heads come up on the first toss. *B:* Heads come up on the second toss.

2. A bag contains 1 red marble and 2 blue marbles. A marble is drawn and replaced. Then a marble is drawn again.
A: The first marble is red. *B:* The second marble is red.

3. Same as Exercise 2 except that the first marble is not replaced.

4. A game cube is rolled twice.
A: A 3 comes up on the first roll. *B:* A 5 comes up on the second roll.

5. A red game cube and a green game cube are rolled.
A: A 6 comes up on the red cube. *B:* A 6 comes up on the green cube.

6. One game cube is rolled.
A: An odd number comes up. *B:* A prime number comes up.

Written Exercises

For Exercises 1–16, find the probabilities of the events that are described.

A 1. Two coins are tossed.
A: Both show heads.
B: Both show tails.
C: Exactly one head shows.

2. A game cube is rolled twice.
A: Both rolls come up 6.
B: Neither roll comes up 6.
C: Exactly one 6 comes up.

In Exercises 3 and 4, a marble is drawn and replaced. Then a marble is drawn again.

3. A bag contains 1 red marble and 3 blue marbles.
A: Both marbles are red.
B: Both marbles are blue.
C: Both marbles are the same color.
D: The marbles are different colors.

4. A bag contains 4 red and 2 blue marbles. Events *A*, *B*, *C*, and *D* are the same as in Exercise 3.

5. The two dials pictured at the right are spun.
A: Both dials show a 3.
B: The red dial shows an odd number and the blue dial shows an even number.
C: One dial shows an odd number and the other shows an even number.

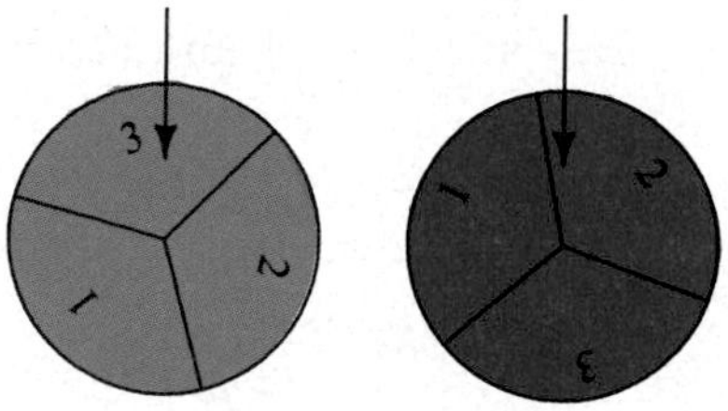

6. Chris and Lee each pick one of the digits, 0, 1, 2, . . . , 9, at random.
A: Lee's digit is 5, and Chris's is 6.
B: Lee's digit is odd, and Chris's is even.
C: One of their digits is odd and the other is even.

In Exercises 7 and 8, a card is drawn at random from those shown at the right and is replaced. Then a card is drawn again.

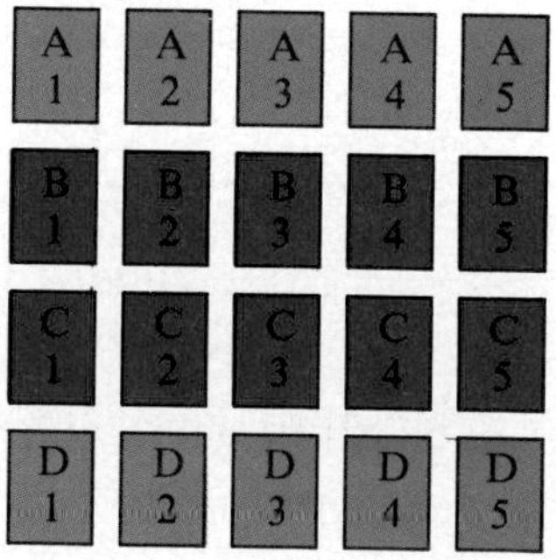

7. *A:* Both cards are C's.
B: Neither card is a C.
C: At least one card is a C.
D: One card is a C and the other is not.

8. *A:* Both cards show numbers greater than 3.
B: Neither card shows a number greater than 3.
C: At least one card shows a number greater than 3.
D: One card shows a number greater than 3 and the other does not.

EXAMPLE A coin is tossed 5 times.
A: Heads come up each time. *B:* No heads come up.

Solution The general principle for finding $P(A \text{ and } B)$ can be extended to more than two independent events.

Therefore,

$$P(A) = \frac{1}{2} \times \frac{1}{2} \times \frac{1}{2} \times \frac{1}{2} \times \frac{1}{2} = \frac{1}{32}$$

$$P(B) = \frac{1}{2} \times \frac{1}{2} \times \frac{1}{2} \times \frac{1}{2} \times \frac{1}{2} = \frac{1}{32}$$

B **9.** Four coins are tossed.
A: Four tails come up.
B: No tails come up.

10. A game cube is rolled three times.
A: All of the rolls come up 6.
B: None of the rolls comes up 6.

11. The probability that the Buffalos will win any given game is 0.6.
A: They win three in a row.
B: They lose three in a row.

12. Amy is taking 4 courses. The probability that she makes an A in any given course is 0.8.
A: She makes no A's.
B: She makes all A's.

13. A coin has been tossed five times and a head has come up each time.
A: A head comes up on the sixth toss.

14. A game cube has been rolled five times and no 6 has come up.
A: A 6 comes up on the sixth roll.

Exercises 15 and 16 refer to the cards in Exercises 7 and 8. Three cards are drawn, each one being replaced before the next one is drawn.

C **15.** *A:* Three C's are drawn.
B: The first card drawn is a C and the others are not.
C: Exactly one C is drawn.

16. *A:* No C's are drawn.
B: The first two cards drawn are C's and the third is not.
C: Exactly two C's are drawn.

Review Exercises

Find the value.

1. ${}_4C_2$ **2.** ${}_4C_3$ **3.** ${}_5C_2$ **4.** ${}_6C_5$

5. ${}_6C_4$ **6.** ${}_7C_3$ **7.** ${}_8C_5$ **8.** ${}_{10}C_3$

11-8 Dependent Events

A bag contains 2 red and 3 blue marbles. One marble is drawn, and then a second marble is drawn. If the first marble drawn is *not* replaced, then the first-draw events and second-draw events are **dependent** events. That is, the result of the first draw affects the result of the second draw.

For example, suppose that the first marble drawn is red and it is not replaced. Now the bag contains 1 red marble and 3 blue marbles, so the probability of obtaining a blue marble on the second draw is $\frac{3}{4}$, not $\frac{3}{5}$.

On the other hand, suppose that the first marble drawn is blue. Then the bag contains 2 red and 2 blue marbles, so the probability of obtaining a blue marble on the second draw is $\frac{2}{4} = \frac{1}{2}$.

We write $P(blue \mid red)$, read *the probability that the second is blue given that the first is red,* to denote the **conditional probability** of drawing a blue marble after a red one has been drawn. Thus, $P(\text{blue} \mid \text{red}) = \frac{3}{4}$, and $P(\text{blue} \mid \text{blue}) = \frac{1}{2}$. We will still use the symbol $P(\text{blue})$ to denote the probability that the *first* marble drawn is blue; thus, $P(\text{blue}) = \frac{3}{5}$.

If we write $P(B \mid A)$ to represent the probability that event B will occur given that event A has occurred, we have the following formula:

> For two events A and B, not necessarily independent,
>
> $$P(A \text{ and } B) = P(A) \times P(B \mid A)$$

EXAMPLE 1 A bag contains 2 red and 3 blue marbles. A marble is drawn and is not replaced. A second marble is drawn. Find the probability of these events.

a. The first marble is red, and the second one is blue.
b. The first marble is blue, and the second one is red.
c. Both marbles are red.
d. Both marbles are blue.
e. They are different colors.

Solution

$P(\text{red}) = \frac{2}{5}$ $\qquad$ $P(\text{blue}) = \frac{3}{5}$

$P(\text{blue} \mid \text{red}) = \frac{3}{4}$ $\qquad$ $P(\text{red} \mid \text{blue}) = \frac{2}{4} = \frac{1}{2}$

$P(\text{red} \mid \text{red}) = \frac{1}{4}$ $\qquad$ $P(\text{blue} \mid \text{blue}) = \frac{2}{4} = \frac{1}{2}$

a. $P(\text{red, then blue}) = P(\text{red}) \times P(\text{blue} \mid \text{red}) = \frac{2}{5} \times \frac{3}{4} = \frac{3}{10}$

b. $P(\text{blue, then red}) = P(\text{blue}) \times P(\text{red} \mid \text{blue}) = \frac{3}{5} \times \frac{1}{2} = \frac{3}{10}$

c. $P(\text{red, red}) = P(\text{red}) \times P(\text{red} \mid \text{red}) = \frac{2}{5} \times \frac{1}{4} = \frac{1}{10}$

d. $P(\text{blue, blue}) = P(\text{blue}) \times P(\text{blue} \mid \text{blue}) = \frac{3}{5} \times \frac{1}{2} = \frac{3}{10}$

e. $P(\text{different colors}) = P(\text{red, then blue}) + P(\text{blue, then red})$

$$= \frac{3}{10} + \frac{3}{10} = \frac{3}{5}$$

Sometimes we can use what we know about combinations to compute probabilities.

EXAMPLE 2 Use combinations to solve Example 1, parts (d) and (e).

Solution

d. Because there are 3 blue marbles in the bag, the number of possible ways of drawing 2 blue marbles is

$$_3C_2 = \frac{3 \times 2}{2 \times 1} = 3.$$

Since the bag contains a total of 5 marbles, the number of possible ways of drawing 2 marbles from the bag is

$$_5C_2 = \frac{5 \times 4}{2 \times 1} = 10.$$

Use the probability formula.

$$P(\text{blue, blue}) = \frac{\text{number of ways of drawing 2 blue marbles}}{\text{number of ways of drawing 2 marbles of any color}}$$

$$= \frac{3}{10}$$

e. Since there are 2 red marbles, there are $_2C_1$, or 2, ways of drawing 1 red marble. For each of these ways, there are $_3C_1$, or 3, ways of drawing 1 blue marble.

Using the counting principle, there are 2×3, or 6, ways of drawing 1 red and 1 blue marble. Therefore, the probability of drawing 1 red and 1 blue marble is

$$P = \frac{\text{number of ways of drawing 1 red and 1 blue marble}}{\text{number of ways of drawing 2 marbles of any color}}$$

$$= \frac{6}{10} = \frac{3}{5}.$$

Class Exercises

A bag contains 5 yellow marbles and 4 green marbles. A marble is drawn and is not replaced. Then a second marble is drawn.

Find $P(B \mid A)$ for events A and B described below.

1. *A:* A yellow marble is drawn. *B:* A green marble is drawn.

2. *A:* A yellow marble is drawn. *B:* A yellow marble is drawn.

3. *A:* A green marble is drawn. *B:* A green marble is drawn.

4. *A:* A green marble is drawn. *B:* A yellow marble is drawn.

Use the formula to find the probability of the events described.

5. The first marble is yellow and the second is green.

6. The first marble is green and the second is yellow.

7. Both marbles are green.

8. They are different colors.

Use combinations to find the probability of the events described.

9. Both marbles are green.

10. They are different colors.

Written Exercises

A bag contains 4 red marbles and 6 blue marbles. A marble is drawn and is not replaced. Then a second marble is drawn.
a. Identify the first and second events.
b. Find *P*(second event | first event).

A **1.** Both marbles are red.

2. Both marbles are blue.

3. The first marble is blue and the second marble is red.

4. The first marble is red and the second marble is blue.

A bag contains 3 orange and 7 green marbles. A marble is drawn and is not replaced. Then a second marble is drawn. Use the formula to find the probability of the events described.

5. Both marbles are orange.

6. Both marbles are green.

7. The first marble is orange and the second is green.

8. The first marble is green and the second is orange.

9. They are different colors.

A bag contains 6 yellow and 5 red marbles. A marble is drawn and is not replaced. Then a second marble is drawn. Use combinations to find the probability of the events described.

B **10.** Both marbles are yellow.

11. Both marbles are red.

12. They are different colors.

Two of the five cards shown are drawn at random at the same time. Find the probability of the events described. (*Hint:* Drawing two at once is the same as drawing one at a time and not replacing the first one drawn.)

13. They are both odd.

14. They are both even.

15. One is even and the other is odd.

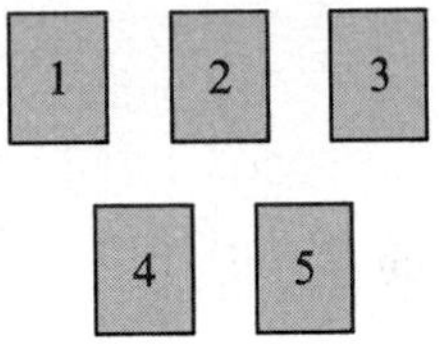

Two letters are chosen at random at the same time from the word TRIANGLE. Find the probability of the events described. (*Hint:* Choosing two at once is the same as choosing one letter and then choosing another from the letters that remain.)

16. Both letters are vowels.

17. Both letters are consonants.

18. One letter is a vowel and one is a consonant.

A bag contains 4 red marbles, 5 blue marbles, and 6 green marbles. Three marbles are drawn one at a time without replacement. Find the probability of the events described.

C **19.** The first marble is green, the second is blue, and the third is red.

20. All three marbles are green.

Review Exercises

Write as a decimal.

1. $\frac{3}{4}$ **2.** $\frac{4}{5}$ **3.** $\frac{7}{8}$ **4.** $\frac{3}{20}$ **5.** $\frac{5}{16}$

6. $\frac{21}{140}$ **7.** $\frac{12}{300}$ **8.** $\frac{180}{250}$ **9.** $\frac{54}{1000}$ **10.** $\frac{1308}{2000}$

11-9 Estimating Probabilities

Experiments such as drawing a card or rolling a game cube are of a special kind. We know all of the possible outcomes and are able to assign an equal probability to each. In many real-life situations, however, we can only estimate probabilities based on experience.

EXAMPLE 1 Up to now Mark has sunk 75 out of 120 free throws. Find the probability that he will succeed in sinking the next free throw he attempts.

Solution We use "past history" to estimate the probability.

$$P(\text{success}) = \frac{\text{number of past successes}}{\text{number of past attempts}} = \frac{75}{120} = \frac{5}{8} = 0.625$$

We say that Mark's *free-throw average* is 0.625.

Often we can use **sampling methods** to estimate probabilities. In such cases, a sample is chosen at random and conclusions are drawn based on an analysis of the sample.

EXAMPLE 2 A factory turns out 5000 digital calculators a day. To control quality, a daily random sample of 200 is taken and tested. Of these, 6 are found to be defective.

a. Find the probability that a randomly chosen calculator will be defective.

b. How many calculators in a day's output are likely to be defective?

Solution

a. We assume that the random sample is representative of the day's output.

$$P(\text{defective}) = \frac{\text{number defective in a sample}}{\text{number in sample}} = \frac{6}{200} = 0.03$$

b. It is possible that only 6 of the entire output of 5000 calculators are defective, but this is very unlikely. We assume that the following proportion is close to the actual situation:

$$\frac{\text{number defective}}{\text{total number}} = \frac{\text{number defective in sample}}{\text{number in sample}}$$

Thus, $$\frac{\text{number defective}}{5000} = 0.03$$

$$\text{number defective} = 0.03 \times 5000 = 150$$

In a day's output, 150 calculators are likely to be defective.

Note that a random sample was specified in Example 2. If the sample were not random, the information obtained from the sample would not be as reliable. For instance, if the sample consisted of the first 200 calculators made that day, the results could be biased by machinery that needed adjustment.

In general, the larger the size of a random sample, the more reliable it is. But the reliability of a large sample must be balanced against the cost and time involved in taking it.

Class Exercises

1. Sarah has been at bat 30 times this season and has hit safely 9 times. Estimate the probability that she will hit safely the next time she is at bat.
2. Thus far this season, 18 of the junior varsity team's 25 free-throw attempts have been successful. Estimate the probability that the next free-throw is successful.
3. In the last 50 years it has snowed on Valentine's Day 15 times. Estimate the probability that it will snow on next Valentine's Day.
4. A quarterback has completed 9 of the last 15 passes he has thrown. Estimate the probability that he will complete his next pass.
5. A weather announcer predicted correctly 990 times out of 1000. Estimate the probability that her next prediction will be correct.

Problems

Estimate the probabilities for these problems.

One thousand golf balls, some white, some green, and some yellow, are put into a barrel. As they are drawn out, their colors are tallied. Using the tally shown, find the probability that the next ball will be this color:

green	𝍸 𝍸 𝍸 I
white	𝍸 𝍸 𝍸 𝍸 III
yellow	𝍸 𝍸 I

A
1. green
2. white
3. yellow
4. white or yellow
5. yellow or green
6. green or white
7. Of the 1000 golf balls described above, about how many are white?
8. Of the 1000 golf balls described above, about how many are yellow?

9. It is halfway through the season and José has hit safely 42 times out of 120 times at bat.
   a. What is the probability that he will hit safely on his next time at bat?
   b. About how many hits can he expect to get during his next 40 times at bat?

10. The County Department of Agriculture caught a random sample of 5000 fruit flies. Of these, 40 were harmful to crops.
   a. What is the probability that the next fruit fly caught will be harmful?
   b. Of an estimated 40 billion fruit flies in the county, about how many are harmful?

B 11. Before it can be shipped, a quality-control inspector must approve each shipment of parts made on an assembly line. She cannot give her approval to a shipment if the probability that a randomly chosen part will be defective is greater than 0.5%. When 300 parts were randomly selected from one shipment, 2 were found to be defective. Will the shipment be approved?

12. The Dynamos have completed 15 of their last 24 passes.
   a. What are the odds that the team's next pass will be completed?
   b. About how many of its next five passes can the team expect to complete?

13. A traffic engineer monitoring a freeway interchange found that of 180 cars, 75 continued straight on, 60 took the left-bound exit ramp, and 45 took the right-bound exit ramp.
   a. What are the odds that the next car will go straight? go left? go right?
   b. Of the 40,000 cars that use the freeway daily, about how many go left at this interchange?

14. A recent survey of 250 randomly selected people indicated that 140 read Thursday's edition of the local newspaper. Among the 140, 70% had seen an advertisement for a particular product in the newspaper. What is the probability that a randomly selected person has seen the advertisement in Thursday's newspaper?

C **15.** Testing of a random sample of products from an assembly line resulted in 7 defective products out of 2000. What is the probability that a buyer of the product made by this company will not get a defective product?

16. A certain ballot measure requires a 60% favorable vote to pass. Of a random sample of 500 voters, 291 favored passage, 166 were opposed, and 43 were undecided.

a. On the basis of this sample, is the measure likely to pass? Give a reason for your answer.

b. Assuming that 120,000 people will vote, about how many in the undecided group must support the measure to ensure its passage?

Self-Test B

1. Events A and B are mutually exclusive. $P(A) = \frac{5}{12}$. $P(B) = \frac{1}{6}$. Find $P(A \text{ or } B)$. **[11-5]**

2. Events A and B are mutually exclusive. $P(A) = 0.5$. $P(A \text{ or } B) = 0.7$. Find $P(B)$.

3. $P(A) = 0.45$, $P(A \text{ or } B) = 0.65$, and $P(A \text{ and } B) = 0.3$. Find $P(B)$. **[11-6]**

4. A card is drawn at random from those shown at the right. Find the probability that the card is a C or a number less than 4.

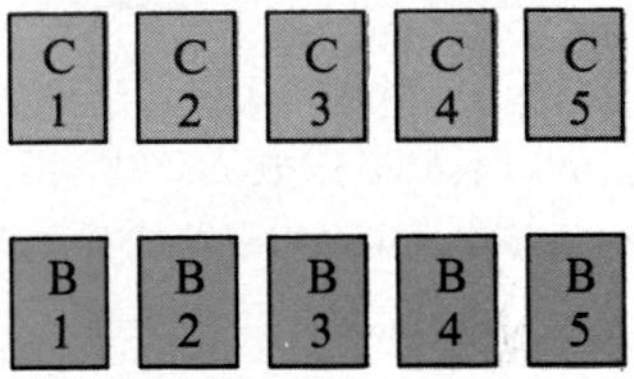

5. A game cube is rolled twice. Find the probability of each event. **[11-7]**

a. Both rolls come up 3.
b. Exactly one 3 comes up.
c. At least one 3 comes up.
d. Neither roll comes up 3.

6. A bag contains 4 red marbles and 5 blue marbles. A marble is drawn at random and is not replaced. Then a second marble is drawn. Find the probability of each event. **[11-8]**

a. The first is red and the second is blue.
b. Both are red.

7. Of a random sample of 275 plants, 11 showed signs of a particular disease. **[11-9]**

a. Estimate the probability that another randomly selected plant will show signs of the disease.

b. Of 1400 plants in the greenhouse, about how many will show signs of the disease?

Self-Test answers and Extra Practice are at the back of the book.

The Computer and Random Experiments

You have learned how to determine the probability of an outcome in a random experiment. Of course, probability does not enable you to know in advance what the outcome of a random experiment will be on a single trial. How well does probability work? A good way to find out is to perform a random experiment many times and to compare the results of the experiment with what your knowledge of probability would lead you to expect.

Consider the random experiment of rolling two number cubes. Let S stand for the sum of the numbers on the top faces of the cubes. The table below shows the sum S for each of the 36 equally likely ways the pair can turn up.

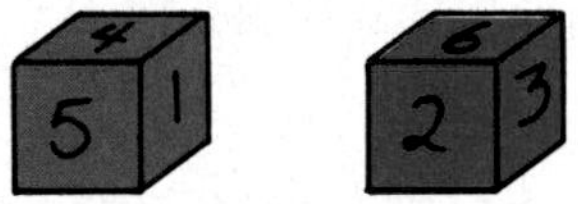

$S = 10$

Red Cube (columns), Blue Cube (rows)

	1	2	3	4	5	6
1	2	3	4	5	6	7
2	3	4	5	6	7	8
3	4	5	6	7	8	9
4	5	6	7	8	9	10
5	6	7	8	9	10	11
6	7	8	9	10	11	12

Sum S for a Pair of Number Cubes

The probability of obtaining a sum of 3 is $\frac{2}{36}$, or $\frac{1}{18}$. The probability of obtaining a sum of 5 is $\frac{4}{36}$, or $\frac{1}{9}$. Based on these probabilities, you would expect that if you were to repeat this experiment several hundred times you would obtain a sum of 5 more frequently than you would obtain a sum of 3.

Of course, it would take you a great deal of time to repeat the experiment several hundred times. The computer, however, can simulate a random experiment, repeat it many times at high speed, and organize the results of the experiment. The BASIC program shown on the next page simulates the experiment of rolling two number cubes and repeats it 300 times. The program also records the sum of the numbers on each trial and prints a bar graph that shows the number of times that each sum occurred.

1. Before you run the program, find the probability of each possible value of S.

2. Run the computer program twice. (Note: Check your computer handbook on the use of the RND function.)
   a. What similarities do you see in the shapes of the two graphs?
   b. Which value of S occurred most often in each graph?
   c. Which value of S occurred least often in each graph?
   d. How do the results of these experiments compare with what you expected based on your answer to Exercise 1? Explain.

```
10  PRINT  TAB( 25);"SUM OF CUBES"
15  PRINT
20  FOR Z = 1 TO 300
25  LET S =  INT (6 *  RND (1)) +  INT (6 *  RND (1)) + 2
30  PRINT S;" ";
35  ON S - 1 GOTO 40,50,60,70,80,90,100,110,120,130,140
40  LET A = A + 1
45  GOTO 145
50  LET B = B + 1
55  GOTO 145
60  LET C = C + 1
65  GOTO 145
70  LET D = D + 1
75  GOTO 145
80  LET E = E + 1
85  GOTO 145
90  LET F = F + 1
95  GOTO 145
100  LET G = G + 1
105  GOTO 145
110  LET H = H + 1
115  GOTO 145
120  LET I = I + 1
125  GOTO 145
130  LET J = J + 1
135  GOTO 145
140  LET K = K + 1
145  NEXT Z
150  PRINT
152  PRINT
155  PRINT  TAB( 25);"BAR GRAPH"
160  PRINT
165  LET L = A
170  GOSUB 280
175  LET L = B
180  GOSUB 280
185  LET L = C
190  GOSUB 280
195  LET L = D
200  GOSUB 280
205  LET L = E
210  GOSUB 280
215  LET L = F
220  GOSUB 280
225  LET L = G
230  GOSUB 280
235  LET L = H
240  GOSUB 280
245  LET L = I
250  GOSUB 280
255  LET L = J
260  GOSUB 280
265  LET L = K
270  GOSUB 280
275  STOP
280  LET M = M + 1
285  PRINT M + 1;
290  FOR N = 1 TO L
295  PRINT  TAB( 4);"*";
300  NEXT N
305  PRINT
310  RETURN
315  END
```

Chapter Review

True or false?

1. You can arrange the letters in the word DRAW in 4 different ways if you take the letters 3 at a time. **[11-1]**
2. A group of 3 people can be selected from 8 people in 56 ways. **[11-2]**
3. The probability of rolling a 4 with a single game cube is $\frac{2}{3}$. **[11-3]**
4. When a single game cube is rolled, the probability that the roll shows a number greater than 3 is $\frac{1}{2}$.
5. If the chance of snow is 30%, the odds against snow are 7 to 1. **[11-4]**
6. The odds in favor of rolling a 2 with a single game cube are 1 to 5.

Complete.

7. If events A and B cannot both occur at the same time, they are said to be __?__ events. **[11-5]**
8. For two mutually exclusive events, the probability of drawing a red card is $\frac{1}{4}$ and the probability of drawing a blue card is $\frac{1}{2}$. The probability of drawing a red card or a blue card is __?__.
9. $P(A) = \frac{1}{2}$, $P(B) = \frac{1}{2}$, and $P(A \text{ and } B) = \frac{1}{6}$. $P(A \text{ or } B) =$ __?__. **[11-6]**
10. If $P(A) = \frac{1}{3}$, $P(A \text{ and } B) = \frac{1}{9}$, and $P(A \text{ or } B) = \frac{5}{9}$, $P(B) =$ __?__.

The dials shown at the right are spun.

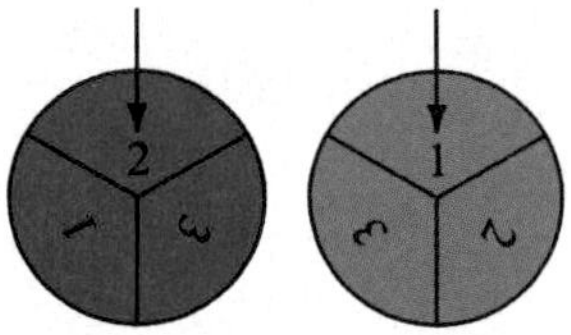

11. The probability that the blue dial shows an even number and the red dial shows an odd number is __?__. **[11-7]**
12. The probability that one dial shows an odd number and one dial shows an even number is __?__.
13. A bag contains 7 red marbles and 5 yellow marbles. A marble is drawn and is not replaced. Then a second marble is drawn. **[11-8]**
    a. The probability that the first is yellow and the second is red is __?__.
    b. The probability that the marbles are different colors is __?__.
14. Of a random sample of 65 cassette holders, 13 were defective. **[11-9]**
    a. The probability that a randomly selected cassette holder is defective is __?__.
    b. Of 2400 produced, about __?__ of the cassette holders are defective.

Chapter Test

1. In how many different ways can 3 people sit in a row of 5 seats? [11-1]

2. How many combinations of 3 colors can you choose from 7 colors? [11-2]

Exercises 3-7 refer to the spinner shown below at the right. Find the probability that the pointer will stop on a wedge of the type described.

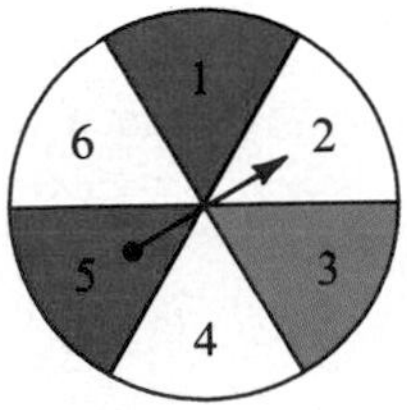

3. blue 4. odd-numbered and red 5. green [11-3]

6. What are the odds in favor of the pointer stopping on a red wedge? [11-4]

7. What are the odds against the pointer stopping on a wedge with a number less than 5?

8. Two game cubes are rolled. Are events A and B mutually exclusive? [11-5]
   A: The sum is 4. B: A 4 shows on one cube.

9. Events A and B are mutually exclusive. $P(A) = \frac{1}{3}$. $P(B) = \frac{5}{12}$. Find $P(A \text{ or } B)$.

10. The two dials are spun. Find each probability. [11-6]

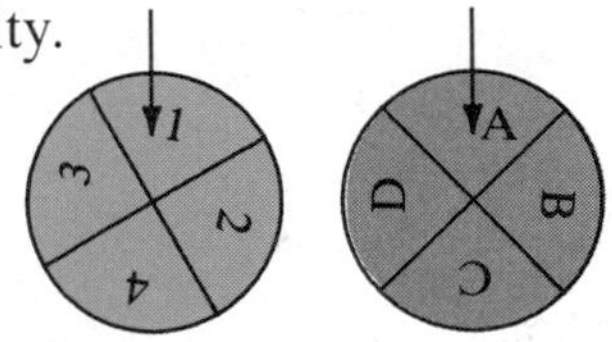

   a. 2 comes up.
   b. B comes up.
   c. 2 and B come up.
   d. 2 or B comes up.

11. $P(A)$ is $\frac{2}{5}$, $P(B)$ is $\frac{1}{2}$, and $P(A \text{ and } B)$ is $\frac{1}{5}$. Find $P(A \text{ or } B)$.

12. A bag contains 3 red marbles and 4 blue marbles. A marble is drawn at random and replaced. Then a second marble is drawn. Find the probability of each event. [11-7]
   a. The first marble is blue and the second is red.
   b. Both marbles are blue.

13. A bag contains 4 green marbles and 2 yellow marbles. A marble is drawn at random and is not replaced. Then a second marble is drawn. Find the probability of each event. [11-8]
   a. The first marble is yellow and the second is green.
   b. Both marbles are green.

14. Of a random sample of 600 tires, 3 were found to be defective. [11-9]
   a. What is the probability that the next tire chosen will be defective?
   b. Of 7000 tires made, about how many are defective?

Cumulative Review (Chapters 1–11)

Exercises

Simplify.

1. $5.4 + (7 \times 6.3)$ **2.** $\frac{16 + 9}{32 + 8}$ **3.** $13(9.2 \div 16)$

4. $4x - y + xy + 3y$ **5.** $2m + 2n - m + n$ **6.** $3p^2(p + 5)$

Perform the indicated operation. Write the answer as a proper fraction in lowest terms or as a mixed number in simple form.

7. $\frac{3}{5} + \frac{4}{7}$ **8.** $\frac{8}{11} - \frac{1}{3}$ **9.** $\frac{3}{4} \times \frac{7}{8}$ **10.** $-1\frac{1}{2} \div -2\frac{1}{2}$

Solve.

11. $6x = -4 + (-18)$ **12.** $-3 - 7 = x + 1$ **13.** $x(4 - 2) = 40$

14. $x + (-9) > -2$ **15.** $4 + (-12) \leq x - 6$ **16.** $11 - x > 0$

Find the radius of a circle with the given circumference. Use $\pi \approx \frac{22}{7}$.

17. $C = 264$ **18.** $C = 343.2$ **19.** $C = 83.6$ **20.** $C = 897.6$

Solve.

21. What is 39% of 120? **22.** What is 125% of 89?

23. What percent of 60 is 12? **24.** What percent of 75 is 35?

25. 18 is 50% of what number? **26.** 35 is 8% of what number?

Use a straight-line graph to complete the ordered pairs, then find the slope.

27. $A(7, 0)$, $B(5, 1)$, $C(-1, ?)$, $D(?, 7)$ **28.** $A(0, 0)$, $B(2, 1)$, $C(4, ?)$, $D(?, 3)$

Find the perimeter and the area of the polygon described.

29. A rectangle with sides 136.5 m and 97.5 m

30. A parallelogram with base 15 cm, one side 7 cm, and height 6 cm

31. A triangle with base 63 m, sides 51 m and 30 m, and height 24 m

Is the triangle with sides of the given lengths a right triangle?

32. 12, 16, 20 **33.** 4, 6, 9 **34.** 9, 12, 15

Find the value of each factorial.

35. 2! **36.** 5! **37.** 3! **38.** 7! **39.** 1!

Problems

Problem Solving Reminders
Here are some problem solving reminders that may help you solve some of the problems on this page.
- Some steps in your plan may not involve operations.
- Consider whether a chart will help to organize information.
- Check by using rounding to find an estimated answer.

Solve.

1. Rosalie has 2 ten-dollar bills. She would like to buy a book for $6.95, some puzzles for a total cost of $12.50, and birthday cards for a total cost of $3.60. Does she have enough money?

2. A faucet leaks at the rate of $\frac{1}{4}$ cup of water per hour. How much water will leak in 24 hours?

3. A Rosebud rocking chair can be purchased for $245.70 in a furniture store or for $189 at a factory store. What is the percent of markup for the furniture store?

4. In order for two elements to combine, the sum of their valence numbers must be 0. One atom of carbon has a valence number of 4, and one atom of fluorine has a valence number of -1. How many atoms of fluorine are needed to combine with 1 atom of carbon?

5. A student from the eighth grade class will be selected at random to represent the Heath School at the governor's conference on schools. If there are 78 boys and 82 girls in the class, what is the probability that a girl will be chosen?

6. Find the area of a rectangular yard that has one side of length 12 m and perimeter 54 m.

7. You can buy whole chickens at Sal's Market for $1.09 per pound. For an additional $.25 per pound, the butcher will cut up the chicken and remove the bones. If chicken is sold in tenths of a pound, how much boneless chicken can be purchased for $7.50?

8. A rectangular painting is 5 ft wide and has an area of 15 ft^2. The frame around the painting is 3 in. wide. What are the dimensions of the framed painting?

12

Statistics

For ecological and other reasons, it is sometimes important to determine the size and geographical location of a group of migrating birds such as those shown in the photograph. A total count of a particular kind of bird obviously poses a difficult problem. By using a sample count, however, only a small part of the bird population needs to be counted. The total number of birds in the entire area can then be estimated from the number in the sampled area.

The simplest method of counting birds and studying migration is direct observation. Because of the disadvantages of this method, more sophisticated methods are being developed and used. These include banding, radio tracking, and radar observation. With the help of computers, this data can be quickly collected and examined.

In this chapter, you will learn some methods for gathering and analyzing data.

Career Note

Statisticians collect, analyze, and interpret numerical results of surveys and experiments. They may use the information that is gathered to determine suitable choices, evaluate a report, or redesign an existing program. Statisticians are usually employed in manufacturing, finance, or government positions. A thorough knowledge of mathematics and a background in economics or natural science is needed.

12-1 Bar Graphs

Everyday life produces masses of numerical facts that we refer to as **data.** Often there is a need to analyze some of these data in order to draw conclusions, and so we organize the data into a table, chart, or graph. This process of organizing and analyzing data is part of the branch of mathematics that is called **statistics.**

When we wish to have a *visual* display of data, we use various kinds of graphs. One type of graph that is used frequently is the **bar graph.** In a bar graph, data are represented by bars that are drawn to an appropriate length using a scale along one of two axes.

EXAMPLE 1 Make a bar graph to illustrate the data in this table.

Coal Production in One Year

Country	Million Metric Tons
China	620
Poland	163
Soviet Union	487
United Kingdom	128
United States	698

Solution Draw perpendicular axes. Mark off regular intervals on the vertical axis. Since all the numbers in the table are hundreds, start at zero and label each interval in increments of 100. Label the horizontal axis with the names of the countries. Then, using the vertical axis as a scale, draw a bar of the appropriate height for each country.

Coal Production in One Year

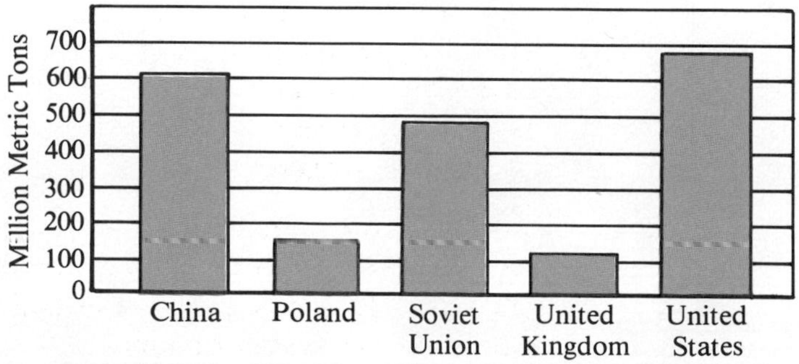

Reading Mathematics: ***Titles and Labels***
A graph must be easy to read to be useful. Therefore, each part of a graph should be clearly identified. In the bar graph for Example 1 on page 440, notice that each bar was labeled along the horizontal axis with the name of the country it represents and that the scale on the vertical axis was labeled *Million Metric Tons*. Notice too that the entire graph was given the title *Coal Production in One Year.*

There are many kinds of bar graphs. In a **double bar graph,** two bars may be used to display two related types of data at the same time. A **legend** is usually placed on the graph to identify the type of data that each bar represents. Example 2, below, illustrates how we interpret a double bar graph.

EXAMPLE 2 Using the double bar graph below, determine the following.

a. The approximate value of United States exports to Africa

b. The approximate value of United States imports from Asia

United States Trade by Geographic Area in One Year

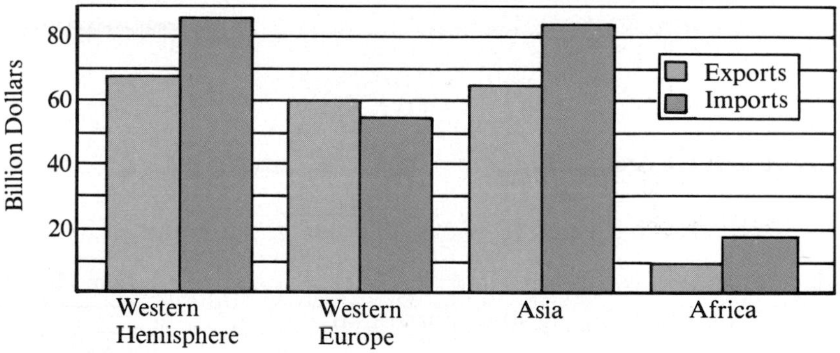

Solution

a. From the colors in the legend on the graph you see that, in each pair of bars on the graph, the bar at the left represents exports. Locate *Africa* on the horizontal axis. The top of the bar at the left of this pair lies at about 10 on the scale of the vertical axis. These numbers represent billion dollars, so we conclude that the value of United States exports to Africa was about 10 billion dollars.

b. The bar at the right of each pair represents imports. For Asia, the top of this bar lies about halfway between 80 and 90 on the vertical scale. Thus the value of United States imports from Asia was about 85 billion dollars.

Class Exercises

Exercises 1–5 refer to the single bar graph.

1. How many categories of imports are displayed?
2. What is represented by the numbers along the horizontal axis?
3. For which category is the amount of United States imports the least? the greatest?
4. What is the approximate amount of United States imports of machinery? of food?
5. The table at the right lists the amounts of United States *exports* for these same categories. Use these data and the data from the graph above to make a *double* bar graph. Title this graph *United States Trade by Category.*

United States Imports by Category

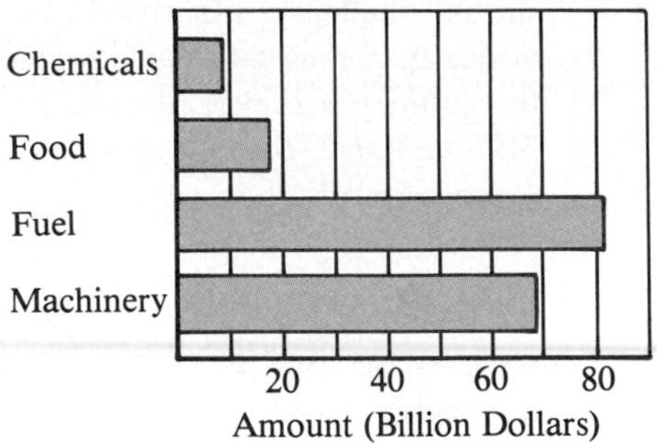

United States Exports

Category	Amount (Billion Dollars)
Chemicals	21
Food	33
Fuel	10
Machinery	96

Written Exercises

Exercises 1–8 refer to the double bar graph below.

A 1. What is represented by the numbers along the horizontal axis?

2. What is represented by the bar at the bottom of each pair?
3. Which job is held by the most sophomores? seniors?
4. Which jobs are held by more seniors than sophomores?
5. For which job is there the greatest difference between sophomores and seniors?

Jobs Held by High School Students

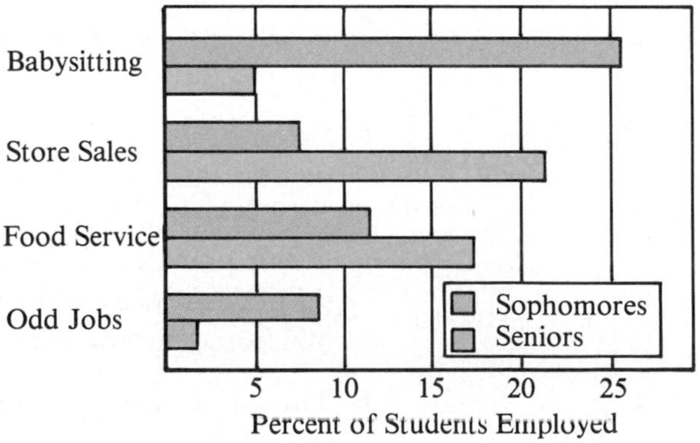

6. About what percent of the sophomores do odd jobs?

Make a bar graph to illustrate the data. For Exercises 7–10, make a single bar graph. For Exercises 11 and 12, make a double bar graph.

7. **Spending by Consumers Younger than 25 Years of Age**

Item	Percent of Spending
Food at Home	28
Food Away from Home	21
Health/Personal Care	5
Housekeeping	3
Transportation/Utilities	31
Other	12

8. **World's Largest Countries**

Country	Area (Million Km^2)
Australia	7.7
Brazil	8.5
Canada	10.0
People's Republic of China	9.6
Soviet Union	22.4
United States	9.4

9. **United States Families**

Family Size	Number of Families (Millions)
1	18.9
2	25.8
3	14.6
4	12.8
5	6.1
6	2.5
7 or more	1.6

10. **Outdoor Recreation**

Activity	Participants (Millions)
Bicycling	79
Camping	88
Downhill Skiing	12
Fishing	91
Hiking	48
Horseback Riding	25
Sailing	19

B **11.** **Family Use of Time on the Microcomputer (Percent)**

Activity	Adult	Teen
Accounting	15	0
Education	15	27
Entertainment	21	53
Programming	7	10
Word Processing	34	8
Work	8	2

12. **New Book Titles Published in One Year (Hundreds)**

Subject	Hardbound	Paperbound
Biography	13.5	5.1
Fiction	18.6	38.0
Juvenile	26.6	4.4
Science	27.8	6.0
Sports	7.4	70.6
Travel	2.5	2.2

The graph at the right is called a **sliding bar graph.** Notice that 0 is at the middle of the horizontal axis and that a scale of numbers extends both to the left and to the right. Graphs such as this are often used to illustrate data concerning gains and losses, highs and lows, and the like.

National League-Eastern Division

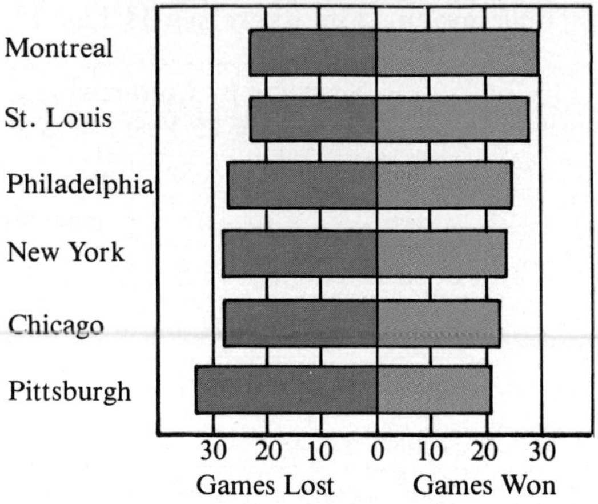

Make a sliding bar graph to illustrate the given data.

C 13.

National League Western Division

Club	Games Won	Games Lost
Houston	33	20
Cincinnati	31	21
San Francisco	29	23
Los Angeles	27	26
Atlanta	25	27
San Diego	18	36

14.

Record Extreme Temperatures (°C)

Continent	Low	High
Antarctica	−88.3	14.4
Asia	−68	53.9
North America	−62.8	56.7
Europe	−45	46
South America	−32.8	48.9
Africa	−23.9	58
Australia	−22	53.1

Review Exercises

Express (a) as a decimal and (b) as a fraction in lowest terms.

1. 18% **2.** 1.25% **3.** 9% **4.** 0.4% **5.** 82.5%

6. $12\frac{1}{2}\%$ **7.** $33\frac{1}{3}\%$ **8.** 0.08% **9.** $25\frac{1}{2}\%$ **10.** $16\frac{2}{3}\%$

Challenge

Replace each $\underline{\ ?\ }$ with +, −, ×, ÷, or = to make a true statement.

1. $\frac{5}{7}\ \underline{\ ?\ }\ \frac{2}{7}\ \underline{\ ?\ }\ \frac{6}{7}\ \underline{\ ?\ }\ \frac{3}{7}$ **2.** $\frac{2}{5}\ \underline{\ ?\ }\ \frac{2}{5}\ \underline{\ ?\ }\ \frac{3}{5}\ \underline{\ ?\ }\ \frac{2}{5}$ **3.** $\frac{2}{3}\ \underline{\ ?\ }\ \frac{2}{3}\ \underline{\ ?\ }\ \frac{7}{9}\ \underline{\ ?\ }\ \frac{1}{3}$

12-2 Line Graphs

When you need to show how data vary over a period of time, it is sometimes better to use a **line graph** than a bar graph. In a line graph the given data are represented by points plotted on a set of coordinate axes, and the points are connected by line segments. The resulting graph clearly displays changes such as increases and decreases and may make it easier to analyze the data.

EXAMPLE 1 Make a line graph to illustrate the data in this table.

School Enrollment in the United States

Year	1960	1965	1970	1975	1980	1985	1990	1995
Students (Millions)	42.2	48.5	51.3	49.8	45.8	43.7	46.1	50.5

Solution Mark off regular intervals on a set of coordinate axes. Label the horizontal axis with the years listed on the table. To choose a scale for the data, notice that the least number is 42.2 and the greatest number is 51.3. Therefore, it is sufficient to label the vertical axis in increments of 2 from 40 to 52. Now consider the data in the table as ordered pairs: (1960, 42.2), (1965, 48.5), (1970, 51.3), and so on. Plot these points on the set of coordinate axes and use line segments to join these points in order from left to right.

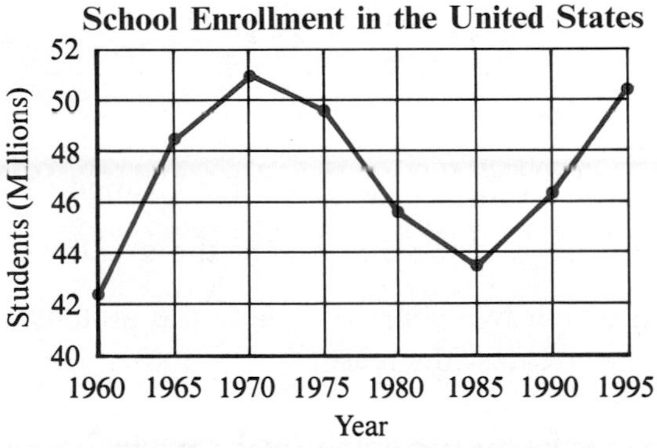

Different types of line graphs are used depending on the purpose of graphing the data. A **double line graph** is often used when the purpose is to make comparisons between two groups of data. Example 2 on the following page illustrates how we interpret double line graphs.

EXAMPLE 2 Using the double line graph below, answer the following.

a. Approximately how great were the rural and urban populations of the United States in 1960?

b. In what year were the rural and urban populations of the United States approximately equal?

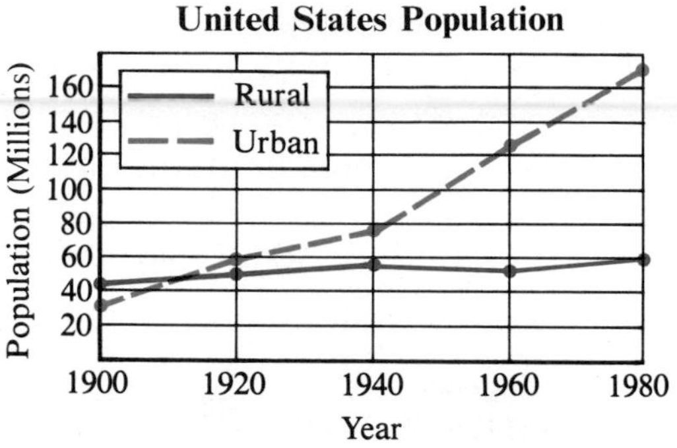

Solution **a.** The solid line represents the rural population and the dashed line represents the urban population. Locate the points along these lines that have 1960 as their horizontal coordinate. Using the vertical coordinates of these points, you see that the rural population was about 50 million and the urban population was about 125 million.

b. The solid and dashed lines intersect at a point with a horizontal coordinate near 1915. Therefore, the rural and urban populations were approximately equal in the year 1915.

Class Exercises

Exercises 1 and 2 refer to the graph for Example 1 on page 445.

1. In which year was the enrollment the greatest? the least?

2. Between which two years was there the greatest increase in enrollment? the greatest decrease?

Exercises 3–5 refer to the graph for Example 2 above.

3. In which year was the urban population about 75 million?

4. About how great were the rural and urban populations in 1920?

5. During what time period was the rural population greater than the urban?

Written Exercises

Exercises 1–4 refer to the graph at the right.

Supermarket Shoppers in One Day

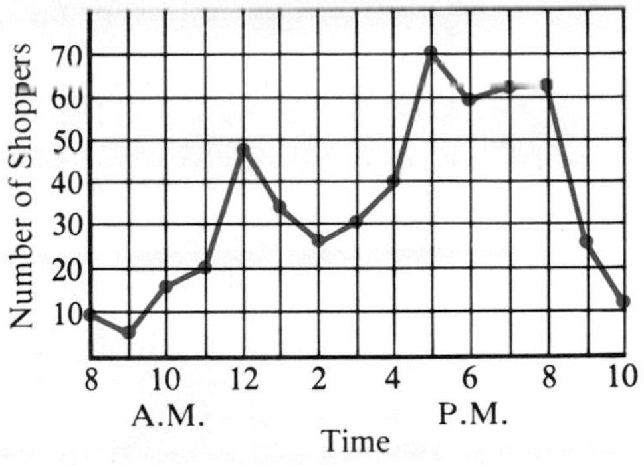

A 1. When was there the greatest number of shoppers?

2. When was there the least number of shoppers?

3. During which period was there the greatest increase in the number of shoppers?

4. During which time period did the number of shoppers remain about the same?

Make a single line graph to illustrate the given data.

5. **United States Population**

Year	1900	1920	1940	1960	1980	2000
Population (Millions)	76	106	132	178	227	268 (estimated)

6. **Reported Volcanic Activity in the World**

Year	1900	1910	1920	1930	1940	1950	1960	1970	1980
Number of Active Volcanoes	27	35	34	40	38	50	45	50	57

7. **Running Practice**

Week	1	2	3	4	5	6	7	8
Time to Run One Mile (Min)	10.0	9.7	9.2	8.8	8.3	8.0	7.5	7.0

8. **Normal Temperatures for Milwaukee, Wisconsin**

Month	J	F	M	A	M	J	J	A	S	O	N	D
Average Temperature (°C)	−7	−5	−1	7	12	18	21	20	16	11	3	−4

Make a double line graph to illustrate the given data.

B **9.** **United States Energy Consumption (Percent of Total)**

Year	1880	1900	1920	1940	1960	1980
Coal	41	71	73	50	23	20
Petroleum and Natural Gas	2	5	16	41	74	72

10. **Money Spent on Recreation in the United States (Million Dollars)**

Year	1940	1950	1960	1970	1980
Motion Pictures	735	1367	956	1536	2899
Spectator Sports	98	223	354	1173	2314

C **11.** Make a *triple* line graph to illustrate the data in this table.

Amount of United States Passenger Traffic (Billion Miles)

Year	Air	Bus	Rail
1940	1	1	24
1950	10	26	32
1960	34	19	22
1970	119	25	11
1980	219	28	12

Review Exercises

Evaluate the expression when $x = -2.8$ and $y = 6.5$.

1. xy **2.** $3x - y$ **3.** $-x + y$ **4.** $5x - (-y)$ **5.** x^2y **6.** $-y^2 - x$

Challenge

A sightseer at Breathless Gorge dropped his sandwich from a gondola. The object fell at the rate of 9.8 meters per second (m/s) after the first second, 19.6 m/s after the second second, and 29.4 m/s after the third second. How fast will the sandwich be falling at 4 s?

12-3 Statistical Measures

Graphing is not the only statistical technique used to analyze numerical data. The *range,* the *mean,* the *median,* and the *mode* are four **statistical measures** that are also used for this purpose. To understand these measures, let's use them to analyze the two sets of test scores shown below at the right.

Class A	Class B
99	100
98	96
98	93
96	88
93	88
93	86
91	84
89	84
87	84
87	80
85	78
85	75
85	75
85	72
83	70
82	69
79	66
78	66
78	65
75	65
73	65
70	63
66	58
63	54
59	51
	47
2077	1922

The **range** of a set of data is the difference between the greatest and the least numbers.

$$\text{range of Class } A = 99 - 59 = 40$$

$$\text{range of Class } B = 100 - 47 = 53$$

The **mean** is the sum of the data in a set divided by the number of items of data. The mean is frequently referred to as the **average.**

$$\text{mean of Class } A = \frac{2077}{25} \approx 83.1$$

$$\text{mean of Class } B = \frac{1922}{26} \approx 73.9$$

When the data are arranged in numerical order, the middle number is called the **median.** If the number of items of data is even, the median is the mean of the *two* middle numbers.

$$\text{median of Class } A = 85$$

$$\text{median of Class } B = \frac{75 + 72}{2} = 73.5$$

The **mode** is the number that occurs most often. A set of data can have more than one mode or no mode.

mode of Class A: 85

modes of Class B: 84, 65

Now let's use these statistical measures to compare the data. For Class A the range of scores was only 40 points, the mean score was 83.1, the median was 85, and the mode was 85. For Class B the range of scores was 53 points, the mean score was only 73.9, the median score was only 73.5, and the modes were 84 and 65. An overall analysis of the data would be that the performance of Class A on this test was better than the performance of Class B.

As you can see, the mean, median, and mode are helpful in locating the "center" of a set of data. For this reason, these measures are often referred to as **measures of central tendency.**

EXAMPLE 1 Find the range, mean, median, and mode of the following set of data. Round to the nearest tenth if necessary.

12, 15, 9, 8, 4, 15, 3, 15, 16, 7, 11, 12

Solution Note that there are twelve items of data in all. Rewrite these numbers in order from greatest to least.

16, 15, 15, 15, 12, 12, 11, 9, 8, 7, 4, 3

Then find the statistical measures.

$$\text{range} = 16 - 3 = 13$$

$$\text{mean} = \frac{16 + 15 + 15 + 15 + 12 + 12 + 11 + 9 + 8 + 7 + 4 + 3}{12}$$

$$= \frac{127}{12} \approx 10.6$$

$$\text{median} = \frac{12 + 11}{2}$$

$$= \frac{23}{2} = 11.5$$

$$\text{mode} = 15$$

EXAMPLE 2 Insert a new number into this set of data so that the mean of the resulting set of data is 17: 12, 15, 21.

Solution Use x to represent the new number. Write and solve an equation.

$$\frac{12 + 15 + 21 + x}{4} = 17$$

$$4\left(\frac{12 + 15 + 21 + x}{4}\right) = 4(17)$$

$$12 + 15 + 21 + x = 68$$

$$48 + x = 68$$

$$48 + x - 48 = 68 - 48$$

$$x = 20$$

The new number is 20.

A statistical measure such as the range, mean, median, or mode is often more simply called a **statistic.**

Class Exercises

Exercises 1–4 refer to the table below.

High Temperatures for June 10

Year	1890	1900	1910	1920	1930	1940	1950	1960	1970	1980
Temperature (°C)	10	16	9	12	16	10	16	21	15	13

1. a. What is the lowest temperature listed?
b. What is the highest temperature listed?
c. What is the range of the temperatures?

2. a. What is the sum of the temperatures?
b. What is the mean of the temperatures?

3. a. List the temperatures in order from lowest to highest. Which two temperatures are at the middle of the list?
b. What is the median of the temperatures?

4. a. Which temperatures occurred more than once?
b. What is the mode of the temperatures?

Written Exercises

Find the range, mean, median, and mode of each of the following sets of data. Round to the nearest tenth if necessary.

A **1.** 12, 10, 8, 4, 3, 3, 2

2. 50, 48, 35, 32, 31, 30

3. 89, 102, 75, 85, 116, 62

4. 83, 118, 143, 99, 194, 210, 153

5. 12.6, 11.0, 10.1, 9.7, 8.9, 8.3

6. 21.6, 30.2, 15.1, 28.8, 19.5

7. 14, −9, −11, 23, 2, 0, −9

8. 4.6, 2.3, 0, −1.2, −3.1, −5.6

9. Points scored by the Basketeers in their most recent games:
98, 100, 96, 101, 99, 98, 101, 101, 100, 102

10. Earned runs allowed by one pitcher in this season's games:
3, 2, 2, 4, 1, 0, 3, 3, 5, 2, 0, 0, 3, 5, 7, 2, 2, 1, 3, 4

Insert a new number into the set of data so that the mean becomes the indicated number.

11. 3, 9, 14; mean = 11

12. 5, 7, 10, 14; mean = 8

13. 6.3, 0.8, 1.2; mean = 4.7

14. −1, 0, 5, −7; mean = −7

Solve.

B **15.** The heights of four of the starting players on the basketball team are 183 cm, 178 cm, 174 cm, and 185 cm. If the mean height of all five starting players is 182 cm, what is the height of the fifth starting player?

16. A student's scores on the first four mathematics tests of the year were 80, 95, 92, and 89. What must the student score on the fifth test so that the mean score for all five tests is 90?

17. Insert another number into the set of data 11, 14, 16, 19 so that the median of the data is not changed.

18. Replace one of the numbers in the set of data 11, 14, 16, 19 so that the median of the data becomes 16.

C **19.** Suppose that each number in a set of data is decreased by 5. How is the median of the data affected?

20. Suppose that each number in a set of data is multiplied by 2. How is the mean of the data affected?

Self-Test A

Exercises 1 and 2 refer to the double bar graph at the right.

Farm Income in One Year

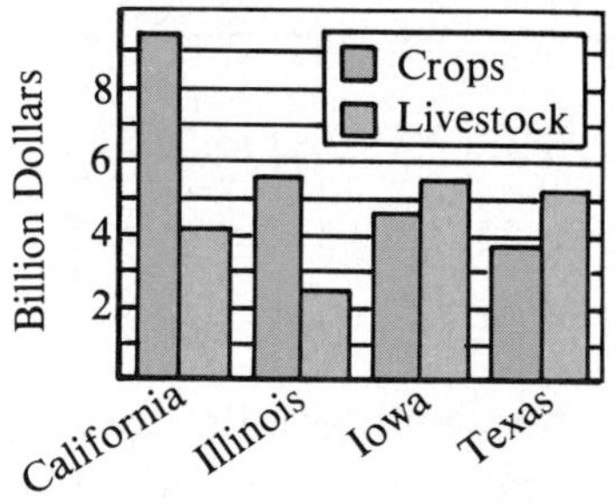

1. Which state had the greatest income from crops and livestock together?

2. About how much was the income from crops in Iowa? [12-1]

3. There were 19 million telephones in the United States in 1940; 39 million in 1950; 66 million in 1960; 105 million in 1970; and 157 million in 1980. Make a line graph to illustrate these data. [12-2]

4. Find the range, mean, median, and mode of the following set of data: 100, 103, 102, 103, 105, 102, 101, 102. [12-3]

5. Insert a new number into this set of data so that the mean of the resulting set of data is 15: 13, 21, 10.

Self-Test answers and Extra Practice are at the back of the book.

12-4 Frequency Distributions

When you need to analyze a large amount of data, a statistic that is often used is **frequency.** The frequency of an item of data is the number of times that the item occurs. A table that pairs each item of data with its frequency is called a **frequency distribution.**

For example, the data below are the weights in kilograms of a group of sixty middle-school students. The table to the right shows the same data listed in a frequency distribution.

41	38	42	39	40	40
43	39	40	41	41	42
44	40	39	40	41	42
41	39	39	39	40	41
42	37	40	39	41	38
42	41	40	39	38	40
38	43	43	41	42	42
39	40	40	42	42	40
44	41	43	42	39	40
41	41	40	43	39	41

Weight x	Frequency f	$x \times f$
37	1	37
38	4	152
39	11	429
40	14	560
41	13	533
42	10	420
43	5	215
44	2	88
Total	60	2434

The numbers in the third column of the table are obtained by multiplying each item by its frequency. Example 1 shows how we use these numbers to compute statistical measures for the given data.

EXAMPLE 1 Find the range, mean, median, and mode of the data above.

Solution The least weight is 37 and the greatest weight is 44. Therefore, the *range* of the weights is $44 - 37 = 7$.

In the third column, 2434 is the total of all 60 weights. Thus,

$$mean = \frac{2434}{60} \approx 40.6.$$

By adding the frequencies of the weights in the table beginning at 37, the least weight, we find that there are exactly 30 weights of 40 kg or less. It follows that the 30th weight in order must be 40, the 31st weight must be 41, and

$$median = \frac{40 + 41}{2} = 40.5.$$

From the frequency column of the table we see that the weight that occurred most often was 40. Therefore, the *mode* is 40.

When a set of data has a very large range, it is usually more convenient to make a frequency distribution by grouping the data into *intervals.*

EXAMPLE 2 The data below are the ages of a group of fifty people who answered a survey. Make a frequency distribution for these data.

27	54	18	22	73	32	48	55	30	35
62	70	45	39	18	33	25	29	65	42
20	55	38	42	36	41	19	24	58	49
37	71	54	22	69	31	43	38	45	64
39	21	71	46	35	67	53	65	42	48

Solution Notice that the ages range from 18 to 73. If you made a table with an entry for *each* age in this range, you would need 56 entries in the table. Therefore, it is probably more efficient to record the data in intervals. Choose seven intervals of ten ages: 10–19, 20–29, 30–39, . . . , 70–79. The table at the right shows the resulting frequency distribution.

Age	Frequency
10–19	3
20–29	8
30–39	12
40–49	11
50–59	6
60–69	6
70–79	4

Class Exercises

The data below represent the scores of a class of 24 students who took a 5-point quiz. Exercises 1 and 2 refer to these data.

5	5	2	4	5	3	3	3	4	2	5	4
3	4	4	3	2	4	4	2	3	2	3	5

1. Complete the frequency distribution shown at the right.

2. Find the following statistics for these data.

a. range

b. mean

c. median

d. mode

Score x	Frequency f	$x \times f$
1	?	?
2	?	?
3	?	?
4	?	?
5	?	?
Total	24	?

Written Exercises

Make a frequency distribution for the given data.

A **1.** 5, 6, 6, 6, 6, 7, 7, 7, 8, 8, 8, 9

2. 6, 6, 7, 7, 7, 7, 9, 9, 9, 10, 10, 10

3. 6, 6, 9, 9, 9, 9, 12, 12, 12, 12, 12, 15

4. 6, 9, 9, 9, 9, 9, 12, 12, 12, 12, 18, 18

5. 10, 8, 8, 6, 8, 2, 4, 4, 6, 4, 10, 2

6. 15, 20, 15, 10, 30, 5, 10, 10, 20, 15, 15, 5

For Exercises 7–10, x represents an item of data and f represents the frequency of the item. Compute the following.

a. range **b.** mean **c.** median **d.** mode

7.

x	f
6	2
7	6
8	7
9	4
10	1

8.

x	f
0	2
3	3
6	5
9	3
12	2

9.

x	f
2	3
4	5
6	4
8	5
10	4
12	4

10.

x	f
4	2
5	6
6	2
7	6
8	3
9	1

Make a frequency distribution for the given data, then use it to compute the range, mean, median, and mode of the data.

11. Numbers of puppies in fourteen litters:

3, 5, 4, 4, 7, 8, 5, 3, 4, 6, 7, 8, 2, 4

12. Numbers of peas in sixteen pods:

6, 5, 2, 9, 12, 6, 5, 6, 11, 9, 6, 4, 7, 8, 10, 6

13. Occupants per car passing through a checkpoint:

2, 1, 1, 4, 3, 1, 2, 2, 6, 1, 1, 4, 2, 5, 1, 4, 4, 2, 4, 2

14. Persons per household surveyed:

3, 2, 2, 3, 6, 1, 2, 1, 4, 3, 5, 2, 2, 4, 2, 1, 1, 5, 3, 2, 3, 5, 2, 4, 2, 4, 1, 4, 3, 2

Complete the frequency distribution for the given data.

15. Distance in kilometers from shoppers' homes to the mall:

18	2	5	12	7	2	13	16
4	4	15	3	10	9	4	2
3	13	17	1	11	5	4	6

Distance (Kilometers)	Frequency
1–3	?
4–6	?
7–9	?
10–12	?
13–15	?
16–18	?

16. Amount in dollars of shoppers' grocery bills:

24	51	14	46	6	37	59	42
27	9	34	12	44	20	25	53
45	31	21	39	5	10	42	37

Amount (Dollars)	Frequency
0–10	?
11–20	?
21–30	?
31–40	?
41–50	?
51–60	?

Make a frequency distribution for the given data.

B **17.** Scores on a mathematics test:
75, 89, 72, 97, 84, 87, 100, 58, 66, 75, 85, 77, 93, 74, 98, 64, 78, 74, 86, 92, 69, 77, 62, 88

18. Students' heights in centimeters:
143, 157, 161, 155, 146, 153, 148, 144, 147, 155, 152, 169, 164, 142, 146, 156, 159, 168, 150, 163

19. The mean of 10 numbers is 15. What is the sum of the numbers?

20. The sum of a set of numbers is 120 and the mean is 10. How many numbers are in this set?

Exercises 21 and 22 refer to a class that consists of 15 girls and 25 boys.

C **21.** On test *A*, the mean of the girls' scores was 80 and the mean of the boys' scores was 70. What was the class mean?

22. On test *B*, the class mean was 80 and the mean of the girls' scores was 75. What was the mean of the boys' scores?

Review Exercises

a. Solve for y in terms of x. **b. Find solutions for $x = 0$ and $x = 2$.**

1. $x - 2y = 3$ **2.** $2x + 3y = 6$ **3.** $x + y = -3$ **4.** $x - y = -1$

5. $x + 2y = 4$ **6.** $3x + 2y = 6$ **7.** $2x - y = 4$ **8.** $4y - 5x = -10$

12-5 Histograms and Frequency Polygons

Graphs are often used to provide a visual display of the data in a frequency distribution. A bar graph that is used for this purpose is called a **histogram.** A line graph that is used for this purpose is called a **frequency polygon.**

For example, the frequency distribution at the right lists a set of scores on a ten-point quiz. The graph below at the left is a histogram that pictures these data. To the right of the histogram is a frequency polygon for the same data.

Score	Frequency
3	1
4	1
5	3
6	5
7	10
8	9
9	4
10	2

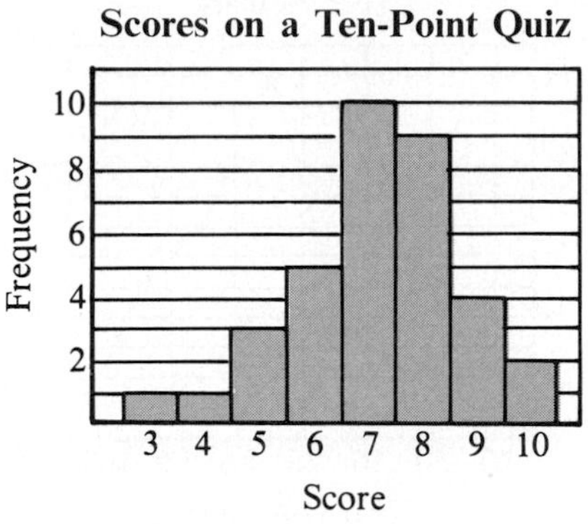

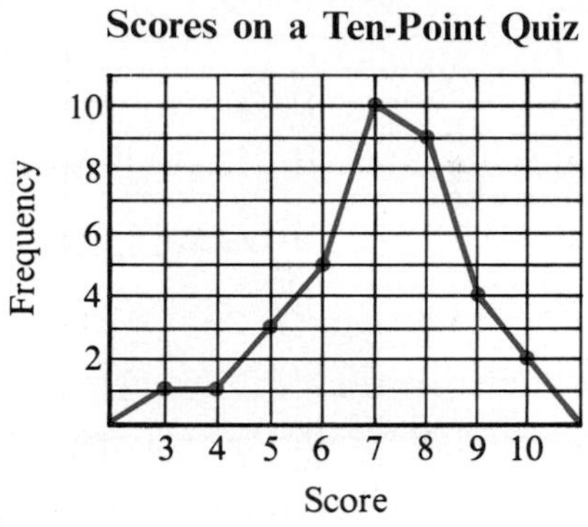

Notice that the histogram is different from the bar graphs that we made previously in that no space is left between the bars. Also note that, in the frequency polygon, the graph is connected to the horizontal axis at both ends.

EXAMPLE Use the histogram and the frequency polygon just given to find the range, mean, median, and mode of the set of quiz scores.

Solution The *range* is the difference between the least and the greatest numbers along the horizontal axis. Thus, the range is $10 - 3 = 7$.

To find the *mean,* multiply each item of data by its frequency, add the results, then divide by the sum of the frequencies.

$$\frac{3(1) + 4(1) + 5(3) + 6(5) + 7(10) + 8(9) + 9(4) + 10(2)}{1 + 1 + 3 + 5 + 10 + 9 + 4 + 2} \approx 7.1$$

The mean is 7.1.

Since there are 35 items, the *median* is the 18th item, which is 7.

The *mode* is represented by the tallest bar of the histogram and the highest point of the frequency polygon. Thus the mode is 7.

When the data in a frequency distribution are listed by intervals, the bars of a histogram for the data are drawn between the endpoints of the intervals. In making a frequency polygon for such data, the points are located at the *midpoints* of the intervals.

Test Scores (Percent)	Frequency
40–49	1
50–59	2
60–69	4
70–79	12
80–89	7
90–100	5

As an example, the frequency distribution above lists a set of test scores. Below are a histogram and a frequency polygon for these data.

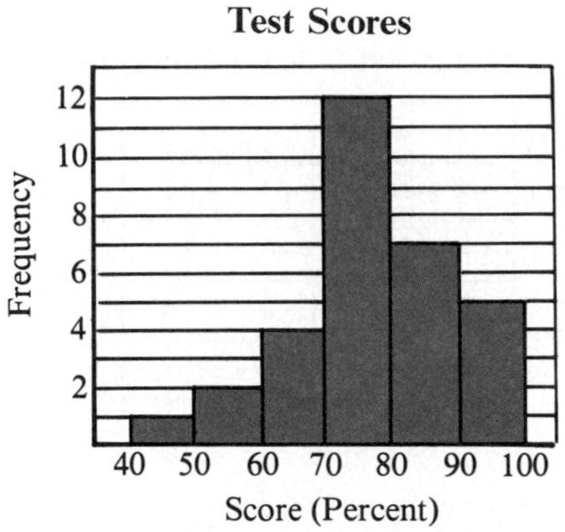

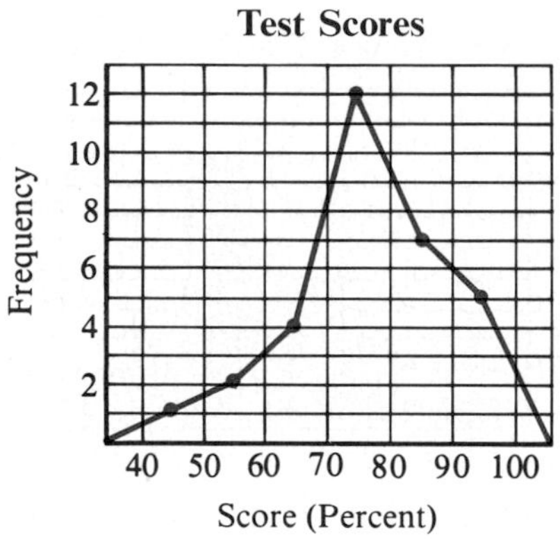

Class Exercises

Exercises 1-9 refer to the histogram at the right.

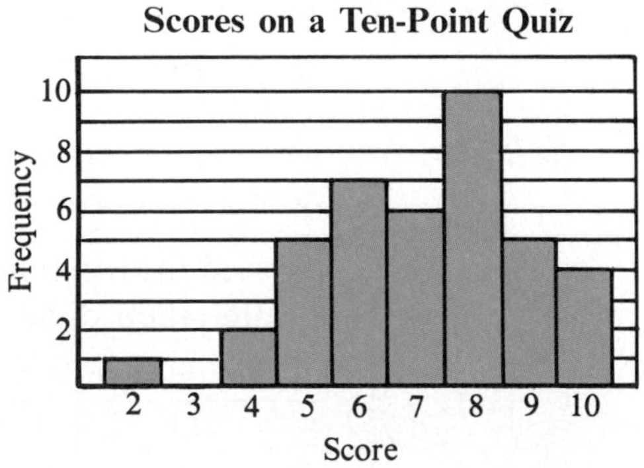

1. What is the range of the scores?

2. What is the mode of the scores?

3. How many students received scores of 8? 10? 3? 5?

4. How many students received scores less than 7?

5. How many students took the quiz?

6. What is the sum of all the scores?

7. What is the mean of the scores?

8. What is the median of the scores?

9. Make a frequency polygon for the data.

Written Exercises

Exercises 1-10 refer to the frequency polygon at the right.

A 1. How many people surveyed receive exactly 2 magazines?

2. How many people surveyed receive 4 or more magazines?

3. How many people were surveyed?

4. What is the median of the data?

5. What is the greatest number of magazines received?

6. What is the range of the data?

Magazine Subscriber Survey

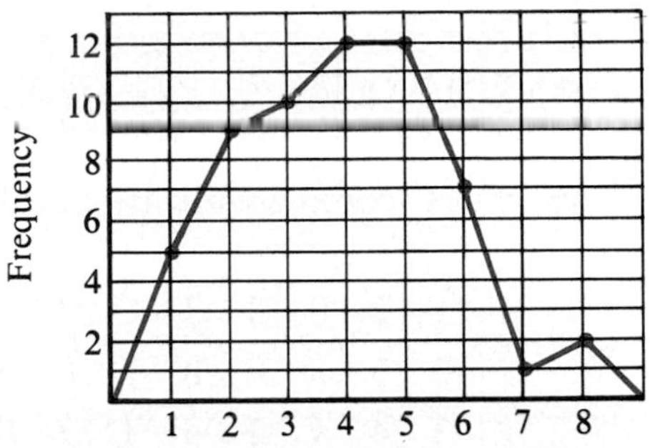

7. What is the number of magazines received by the fewest people?

8. What is the mode of the data?

9. What is the total number of magazines received regularly?

10. To the nearest tenth, what is the mean number of magazines received?

For Exercises 11-14, x represents an item of data and f represents the frequency of the item. Make the following.
a. a histogram **b. a frequency polygon**

11.

x	f
5	1
6	3
7	4
8	9
9	7
10	2

12.

x	f
20	2
21	8
22	12
23	6
24	0
25	1

B 13.

x	f
30-39	1
40-49	0
50-59	2
60-69	6
70-79	12
80-89	8
90-99	4

14.

x	f
0-25	5
26-50	9
51-75	16
76-100	22
101-125	25
126-150	11
151-175	3

Make a histogram and a frequency polygon for each set of data.

15. Students in the homerooms at Valley Junior High:

24 23 20 25 25 24 25
24 25 24 25 28 23 22
26 25 26 25 25 24

16. Runs scored by the Bluebirds in this season's games:

1 1 2 0 3 3 0 2 4 3
2 0 5 3 0 8 2 0 3 5
2 3 4 1 2 4 1 3 0 3

C 17. Visitors to the aquarium in the last two weeks:

946 518 402 473 553 672 850
979 436 541 622 705 814 902

18. Daily high temperatures in April (°C):

2 4 2 6 5 1 0 −3 −7 −5
−9 −5 0 3 1 6 6 9 12 14
17 19 18 15 12 9 6 4 5 2

19. The figure at the right shows a histogram and a frequency polygon for the same data drawn on a single set of coordinate axes. Explain why the area under the frequency polygon is equal to the area of the bars of the histogram. (*Hint:* Compare the area of the red triangles with the area of the blue triangles.)

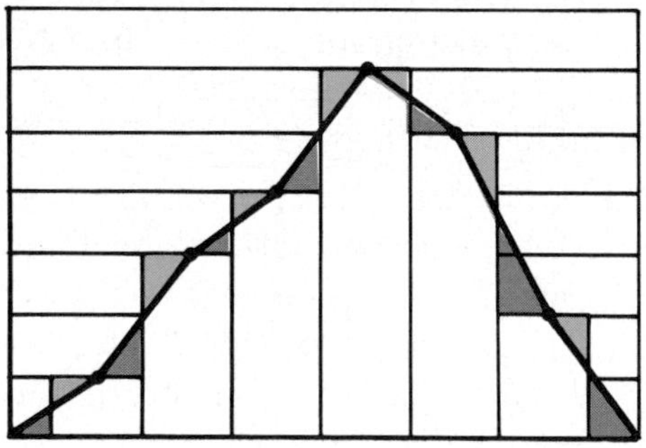

Review Exercises

Two game cubes, each labeled with the numbers 1–6, are rolled. Find the probability of each.

1. A 5 shows. **2.** A 6 shows. **3.** An odd number shows.

4. The sum is 5. **5.** The sum is 11. **6.** The sum is even.

7. The sum is less than 4. **8.** The sum is 3 or a 3 shows.

12-6 Expected Value of a Random Variable

Suppose that you play a game by spinning the spinner shown at the right, and you win as a prize the amount of money indicated by the pointer. Assume that the pointer never stops on a line between two sections of the spinner. What amount might you expect to win?

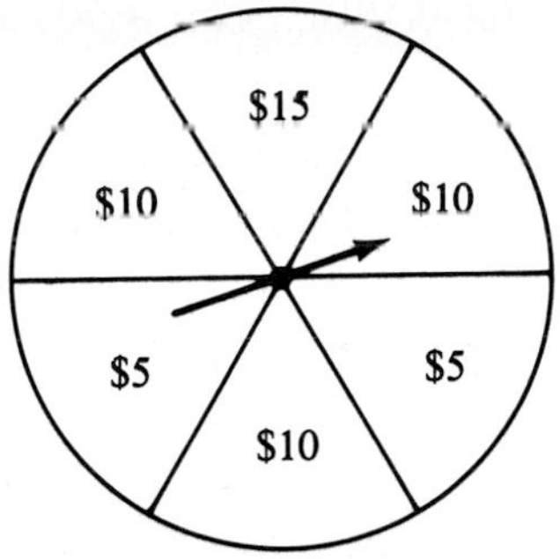

One way to estimate this amount is to make a large number of trial spins in order to collect some data and then find the mean of these data. For example, suppose that you make 80 trial spins: $5 comes up 27 times, $10 comes up 39 times, and $15 comes up 14 times. By recording the data in a frequency distribution such as the one at the right, you can readily calculate the mean of your trial spins.

Amount (Dollars) x	Frequency f	$x \times f$
5	27	135
10	39	390
15	14	210
Total	80	735

$$\text{mean} = \frac{735}{80} \approx 9.19$$

Thus you have determined experimentally that the expected value of your prize is about $9.19. Although you cannot win $9.19 *exactly,* it is the average amount you would win if you played many times.

Let's consider another way to find this expected value. Choose a variable such as X to represent the amount indicated by the pointer. Since the value of X is determined randomly, X is called a **random variable.** We can now construct a table of all possible values of X and their probabilities of occurrence.

X	5	10	15
$P(X)$	$\frac{2}{6}$	$\frac{3}{6}$	$\frac{1}{6}$

There is no way to know in advance what the *exact* value of a random variable will be in a single trial. However, it is possible to compute the *mean* value of a random variable over a large number of trials. By computing the mean value of our random variable X, we can find the expected value of the prize after spinning the spinner. To understand how this can be done, let's take another look at the data from the 80 trials above. Note that the mean could be represented by the following calculation.

$$\text{mean} = \frac{5(27) + 10(39) + 15(14)}{80}$$

$$= 5 \times \frac{27}{80} + 10 \times \frac{39}{80} + 15 \times \frac{14}{80}$$

Consider the 80 trial spins as a random sample of the type discussed in Chapter 11. If we assume that this is a representative sample of the results of spinning the spinner, we can conclude the following.

$$\frac{27}{80} = \frac{\text{number of fives in sample}}{\text{number in sample}} = P(5) \qquad \frac{39}{80} = \frac{\text{number of tens in sample}}{\text{number in sample}} = P(10)$$

$$\frac{14}{80} = \frac{\text{number of fifteens in sample}}{\text{number in sample}} = P(15)$$

We can then make the following substitutions.

$$\begin{aligned} \text{mean} &= 5 \times \frac{27}{80} + 10 \times \frac{39}{80} + 15 \times \frac{14}{80} \\ &= 5 \times P(5) + 10 \times P(10) + 15 \times P(15) \\ &= 5 \times \frac{2}{6} + 10 \times \frac{3}{6} + 15 \times \frac{1}{6} = 9\frac{1}{6}, \text{ or } 9.17 \end{aligned}$$

Therefore, the expected value of the random variable is about 9.17, and the expected value of your prize is about \$9.17. Notice that this is only slightly different from the expected value of \$9.19 that we computed experimentally. Since both expected values are approximations, this difference is not significant.

To find the expected value of a random variable, multiply each possible value by its probability and add the results.

EXAMPLE A box contains 4 nickels, 6 dimes, and 2 quarters. You are allowed to select one coin without looking. If V = the value in cents of the coin you select, what is the expected value of V?

Solution List all the possible values of V and their probabilities of occurrence. Multiply each value by its probability, then add.

V	5	10	25
$P(V)$	$\frac{4}{12}$	$\frac{6}{12}$	$\frac{2}{12}$

$$5 \times \frac{4}{12} + 10 \times \frac{6}{12} + 25 \times \frac{2}{12} = \frac{130}{12}$$

$$\approx 10.8$$

The expected value of V is 10.8 cents.

Class Exercises

V = the value of a coin to be selected at random.

V	1	5	10	25
$P(V)$	$\frac{1}{4}$	$\frac{1}{8}$	$\frac{3}{8}$	$\frac{1}{4}$

1. What types of coins are there?

2. If there are 8 coins in all, how many are nickels?

3. What is the expected value of V?

Written Exercises

X represents the possible values of a random variable and $P(X)$ represents their probabilities of occurrence. Find the expected value of X.

A 1.

X	10	20	30	40
$P(X)$	$\frac{1}{4}$	$\frac{1}{8}$	$\frac{3}{8}$	$\frac{1}{4}$

2.

X	15	30	45	60	75
$P(X)$	$\frac{1}{6}$	$\frac{1}{4}$	$\frac{1}{3}$	$\frac{1}{12}$	$\frac{1}{6}$

3.

X	2	5	10
$P(X)$	0.3	0.5	0.2

4.

X	−20	−40	0	20
$P(X)$	0.1	0.2	0.3	0.4

Find the expected value of the random variable X.

B 5. The faces of a cube are numbered 0 through 5. X is the number on the face that comes up when the cube is thrown.

6. In a set of envelopes, 2 are empty, 4 contain \$1, 3 contain \$5, and 1 contains \$10. X is the amount in an envelope selected at random.

C 7. Karen throws a cube with faces numbered from 1 through 6. If it comes up an odd number, she loses that number of points. If it comes up an even number, she wins that number of points. About how many points is she likely to have after 100 throws?

Self-Test B

Exercises 1–3 refer to the following set of data.
13, 10, 10, 11, 12, 12, 13, 14, 11, 13, 11, 14, 12, 12, 12

1. Make a frequency distribution for the data and use it to compute the range, mean, median, and mode of the data. **[12–4]**

2. Make a histogram for the data. **[12–5]**

3. Make a frequency polygon for the data.

4. In the table at the right, X represents the possible values of a random variable and $P(X)$ represents their probabilities of occurrence. Find the expected value of X. **[12–6]**

X	4	8	12	16
$P(X)$	$\frac{1}{6}$	$\frac{5}{9}$	$\frac{1}{6}$	$\frac{1}{9}$

Self-Test answers and Extra Practice are at the back of the book.

Standard Deviation

For many purposes the *range* of a set of data is a poor measure of its spread. Consider, for example, the frequency distributions and histograms below for the mass in kilograms of various rocks found by three groups of rock collectors.

Group A

Mass (kg)	Frequency
1	4
3	1
7	1
9	4

Group B

Mass (kg)	Frequency
1	1
3	3
5	2
7	3
9	1

Group C

Mass (kg)	Frequency
1	1
3	2
5	4
7	2
9	1

Group A

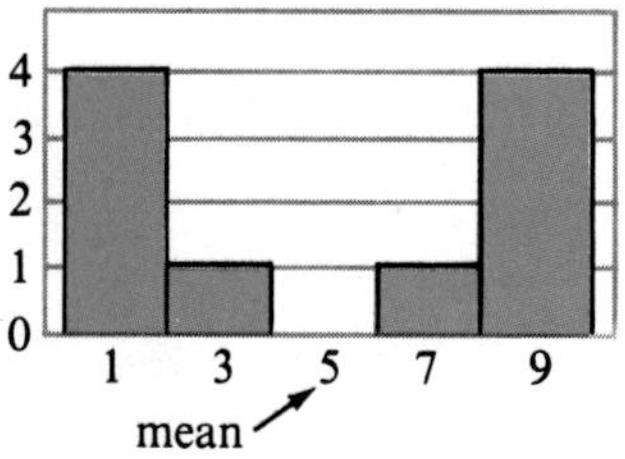

Group B

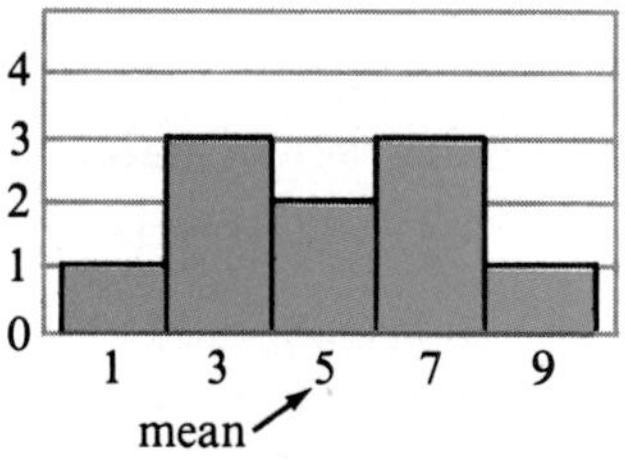

Group C

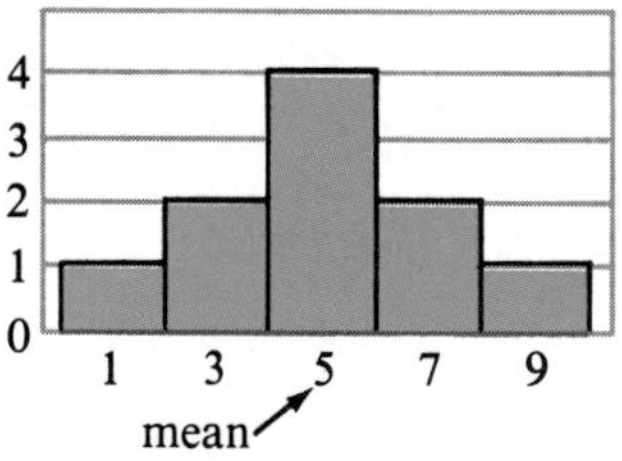

Each distribution has a range of 8. But a glance at each histogram reveals that distribution A is more spread out around its center, or mean, than are distributions B and C.

A more useful measure of the spread of a distribution is the **deviation** from the mean. Suppose a bowler has scores of 198, 210, and 156. The mean score is 188. The table at the right shows how much each score varies, or *deviates,* from the mean.

Score	Deviation
198	+10
210	+22
156	−32

The **variance** and **standard deviation** are two commonly used measures of how data are scattered around the mean. The variance is computed by squaring each deviation from the mean, adding these squares, and dividing the sum by the number of entries in the distribution. The standard deviation is found by computing the positive square root of the variance. The standard deviation is a more useful statistic than the variance because comparisons are being made of common units. For example, when data are given in meters, the variance will be in square meters, but the standard deviation will be in meters.

The table below shows the calculation of the variance and standard deviation for each frequency distribution on the preceding page. In each case, x is the mass and m is the mean, which is 5. Notice that the more a distribution is spread out from its mean, the larger its standard deviation.

Group A			Group B			Group C		
x	deviation $(x - m)$	$(x - m)^2$	x	deviation $(x - m)$	$(x - m)^2$	x	deviation $(x - m)$	$(x - m)^2$
1	−4	16	1	−4	16	1	−4	16
1	−4	16	3	−2	4	3	−2	4
1	−4	16	3	−2	4	3	−2	4
1	−4	16	3	−2	4	5	0	0
3	−2	4	5	0	0	5	0	0
7	2	4	5	0	0	5	0	0
9	4	16	7	2	4	5	0	0
9	4	16	7	2	4	7	2	4
9	4	16	7	2	4	7	2	4
9	4	16	9	4	16	9	4	16
		136 kg^2			56 kg^2			48 kg^2
variance $= \frac{136}{10} = 13.6$ kg^2			variance $= \frac{56}{10} = 5.6$ kg^2			variance $= \frac{48}{10} = 4.8$ kg^2		
standard deviation $= \sqrt{13.6} \approx 3.7$ kg			standard deviation $= \sqrt{5.6} \approx 2.4$ kg			standard deviation $= \sqrt{4.8} \approx 2.2$ kg		

Find (a) the mean, (b) the deviation, (c) the variance, and (d) the standard deviation of the given data. Use the table on page 498, or approximate the square root to the nearest hundredth by interpolation.

1. From a sample of four dairy cows, a farmer recorded the following yields for one day: 11 gal, 13 gal, 9 gal, and 15 gal.

2. In a survey of local stores, the following prices were quoted for a World watch: \$34, \$27, \$41, and \$38.

3. The fuel efficiency ratings of five new cars were 20, 19, 20, 22, and 33 mi/gal.

Chapter Review

Supermarket Spending

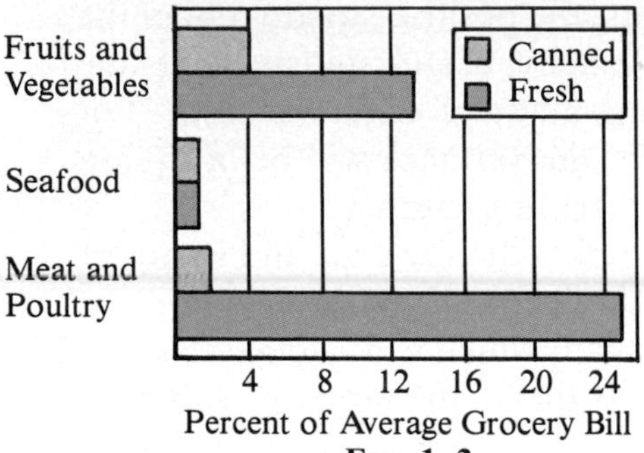

Exs. 1, 2

U.S. Occupations

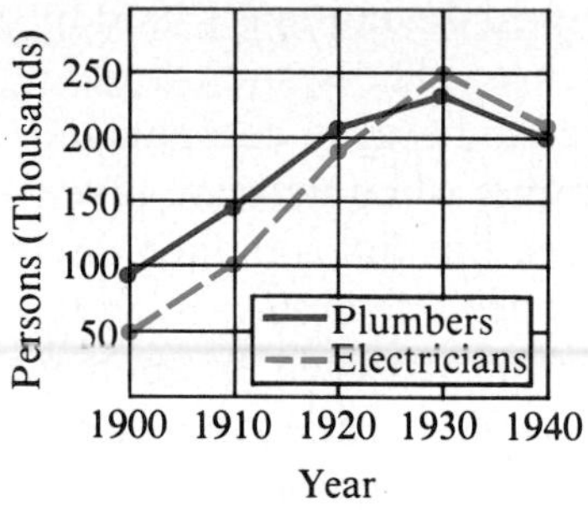

Exs. 3, 4

Exercises 1 and 2 refer to the double bar graph above. True or false?

1. More money is spent on fresh meat and poultry than on canned and fresh fruits and vegetables together. **[12-1]**

2. Approximately 5% is spent on fresh seafood.

Exercises 3 and 4 refer to the double line graph above. Complete.

3. There was approximately the same number of plumbers and electricians in the year __?__. **[12-2]**

4. In 1910 the number of electricians was approximately __?__.

Exercises 5-11 refer to the following set of data.

14, 18, 12, 10, 12, 16, 15, 20, 17, 12,
13, 19, 17, 14, 11, 18, 16, 15, 12, 14

Compute the following for the given data.

5. range **6.** mean **7.** median **8.** mode **[12-3]**

Make the following for the given data.

9. a frequency distribution **[12-4]**

10. a histogram **11.** a frequency polygon **[12-5]**

The table shows all possible values of a random variable X and their probabilities of occurrence. Compute the following.

X	2	4	6	8
$P(X)$	$\frac{1}{12}$	$\frac{1}{3}$	?	$\frac{1}{4}$

12. $P(6)$ **13.** the expected value of X **[12-6]**

Chapter Test

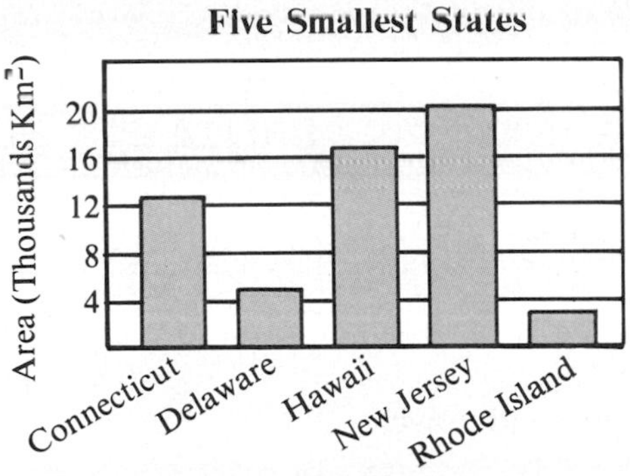

Exs. 1, 2

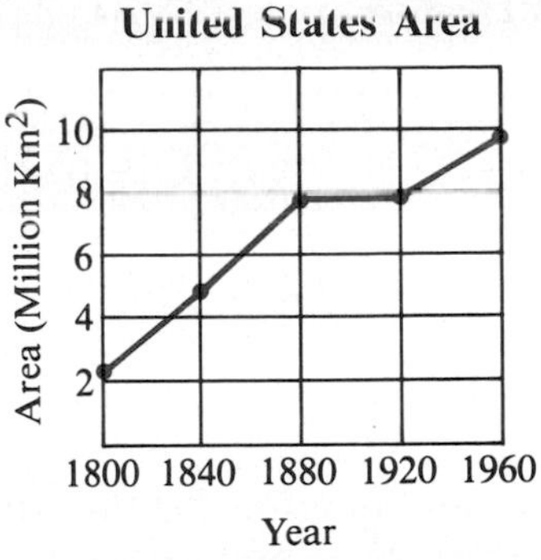

Exs. 3–5

Exercises 1 and 2 refer to the bar graph above.

1. What is the approximate area of Delaware? **[12–1]**
2. About how much smaller than New Jersey is Rhode Island?

Exercises 3–5 refer to the line graph above.

3. During which time period was there no increase in area? **[12–2]**
4. During which 80 years was there the greatest increase?
5. What was the approximate area of the United States in 1840?

Exercises 6 and 7 refer to the following set of data.

8, 5, 7, 6, 10, 9, 8, 7, 6, 7, 9, 8

6. Find the range, mean, median, and mode of the given data. **[12–3]**
7. Make a frequency distribution for the given data. **[12–4]**

Exercises 8 and 9 refer to the histogram at the right.

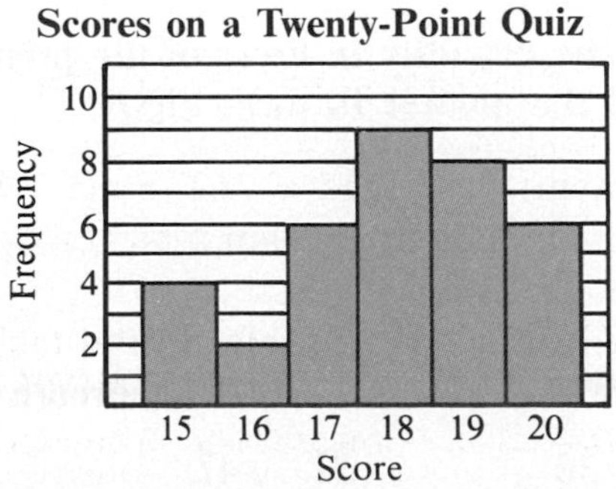

8. What is the range of the quiz scores? **[12–5]**
9. Make a frequency polygon for this same set of quiz scores.
10. A set of 10 cards is numbered 1 through 10, one number per card. X is the number on a card drawn at random. Find the expected value of the random variable X. **[12–6]**

Cumulative Review (Chapters 1–12)

Exercises

Write the decimal number that is equal to each of the following.

1. $|-3.79|$ **2.** $|-65.8|$ **3.** $|1.301|$ **4.** $|0.123|$ **5.** $|-100.01|$

Write as a proper fraction in lowest terms.

6. 0.666 . . . **7.** $0.58\overline{3}$ **8.** 0.2777 . . . **9.** $0.\overline{18}$

Write an equation for the word sentence and solve.

10. Eight less than the product of a number and three is seven.

11. The sum of one half a number and twelve is negative six.

12. The quotient of a number divided by eight is two.

13. A number minus nine equals five minus the number.

14. The product of the sum of a number and eight, times five, is twenty.

Find the measure of the third angle of a triangle having the following measures for the other two angles.

15. 77°, 41° **16.** 85.5°, 40.5° **17.** 110°, 35° **18.** 22.5°, 135°

Express as a percent.

19. $\frac{2}{5}$ **20.** $\frac{1}{8}$ **21.** $\frac{3}{500}$ **22.** $\frac{1}{12}$ **23.** $\frac{5}{4}$ **24.** $\frac{1}{3}$

Use a graph to solve the system. Do the lines intersect or coincide, or are they parallel?

25. $x - y = 7$
$x + y = 7$

26. $2x + 3y = 5$
$4x + 6y = 10$

27. $y = -2x + 1$
$y + 8 = -2x$

Find the capacity in liters of the prism or cylinder. Use $\pi \approx 3.14$ and round the answer to three digits.

28. Prism: base area = 1627.5 m^2
height = 50 m

29. Cylinder: base radius = 3.75 cm
height = 5.50 cm

For Exercises 31-35, refer to the table on page 498. Approximate the square root to the nearest hundredth.

30. $\sqrt{38}$ **31.** $\sqrt{47}$ **32.** $\sqrt{7}$ **33.** $\sqrt{11.1}$ **34.** $4\sqrt{18}$

If you choose a letter at random from the word EXCELLENT, what is the probability of the following outcomes?

35. a vowel **36.** a consonant **37.** the letter B **38.** the letter L

Find the range, mean, median, and mode of the set of numbers. Round to the nearest tenth if necessary.

39. 67, 85, 26, 26, 38 **40.** 0.5, 1.7, 0.8, 2.6, 1.4 **41.** 100, 101, 110, 90, 99, 99

Problems

Problem Solving Reminders
Here are some problem solving reminders that may help you solve some of the problems on this page.

- Sometimes more than one method can be used to solve a problem.
- Consider whether drawing a sketch will help.
- When rounding an answer to division, consider whether it is reasonable to round up or round down.

Solve.

1. J-Stores sells exercise bicycles for $169.95. This month the bicycles are offered at a 15% discount, followed by a rebate of $15.00. What is the total price to customers after the discount and rebate?
2. The price of Stuffed Shirt Starch Company stock went down $\frac{5}{8}$ on Monday, down $1\frac{1}{8}$ on Tuesday, and down $1\frac{3}{4}$ on Wednesday before going up $2\frac{7}{8}$ on Thursday. The stock went up $1\frac{1}{4}$ on Friday. What was the total loss or gain for the week?
3. A ferryboat travels from Eric's Island to Pearltown to Bonneville and back to Eric's Island. The course forms a right triangle with the route from Pearltown to Bonneville forming the hypotenuse. If the distance from Bonneville to Eric's Island is 45 km and the distance from Eric's Island to Pearltown is 80 km, what is the approximate distance from Pearltown to Bonneville? Use the table on page 498.
4. Christopher is required to take a history course and a language course. He can choose from American, European, or ancient history, and French, Spanish, or Italian language. How many combinations of two courses does Christopher have?
5. Zachary scored 83, 82, 75, 70, and 88 on biology quizzes. What is the least he can score on his next quiz if he wants to maintain an 80 average?

Skill Review

Addition

$\begin{array}{r} 46.7 \\ +\ \ 8.31 \\ \hline 55.01 \end{array}$

$\begin{array}{r} 14.71 \\ 3.009 \\ +\ 291.681 \\ \hline 309.400 \end{array}$

Add.

1. $\begin{array}{r} 34.3 \\ +\ 23.5 \\ \hline \end{array}$ **2.** $\begin{array}{r} 2.536 \\ +\ 7.019 \\ \hline \end{array}$ **3.** $\begin{array}{r} 8.7 \\ +\ 0.5 \\ \hline \end{array}$ **4.** $\begin{array}{r} 48.37 \\ +\ 12.6 \\ \hline \end{array}$

5. $\begin{array}{r} 83.55 \\ +\ \ 8.617 \\ \hline \end{array}$ **6.** $\begin{array}{r} 299.1 \\ +\ \ 68.33 \\ \hline \end{array}$ **7.** $\begin{array}{r} 24.6251 \\ +\ \ 9.88 \\ \hline \end{array}$ **8.** $\begin{array}{r} 933.068 \\ +\ 724.3997 \\ \hline \end{array}$

9. $\begin{array}{r} 19.6 \\ 2.71 \\ +\ 33.5 \\ \hline \end{array}$ **10.** $\begin{array}{r} 58.71 \\ 6.8 \\ +\ \ 3.59 \\ \hline \end{array}$ **11.** $\begin{array}{r} 118.7 \\ 4.91 \\ +\ \ 30.08 \\ \hline \end{array}$ **12.** $\begin{array}{r} 90.71 \\ 219.65 \\ +\ \ \ 3.34 \\ \hline \end{array}$

13. $\begin{array}{r} 5.4 \\ 12.137 \\ 1.25 \\ +\ 306.49 \\ \hline \end{array}$ **14.** $\begin{array}{r} 1.6256 \\ 6.006 \\ 9.36 \\ +\ 1.49 \\ \hline \end{array}$ **15.** $\begin{array}{r} 24.603 \\ 18.4 \\ 2.9 \\ +\ \ 0.216 \\ \hline \end{array}$ **16.** $\begin{array}{r} 911.34 \\ 0.52 \\ 26.1 \\ +\ \ 83.192 \\ \hline \end{array}$

17. 899.08 + 3.7 **18.** 14.6 + 5.99

19. 11.87 + 49.3 **20.** 38.75 + 116.6

21. 0.051 + 16.88 **22.** 578.57 + 12.1

23. 73.6 + 18.07 **24.** 63.583 + 8.09

25. 27.0564 + 281.4 **26.** 3.51032 + 14.99

27. 11.2 + 0.9013 **28.** 84.1 + 0.062

29. 6.8 + 37.51 + 108.2 **30.** 89.71 + 5.5 + 0.62

31. 43.6 + 12.1 + 0.008 **32.** 2.4 + 3.183 + 9

33. 4 + 0.463 + 43.4 **34.** 116.04 + 2.57 + 12.38

35. 7 + 112.4 + 0.06 **36.** 121.2 + 18 + 0.12

37. 16.24 + 5.6 + 18.09 + 6.7 **38.** 2.55 + 0.34 + 0.42 + 3.57

39. 61.476 + 14.1 + 0.59 + 366 **40.** 90.072 + 32.4 + 24 + 8.6

41. 193.7 + 4.08 + 11.5 + 1.9026 **42.** 0.428 + 83.7 + 6.999 + 7.06

43. 37.7 + 0.6 + 6.834 + 16 **44.** 1165 + 0.08 + 17.1 + 94.028

45. 570.2 + 74.4 + 6.553 + 9.2 **46.** 7.8118 + 27.6 + 5.302 + 14

Skill Review

Subtraction

$$\begin{array}{r} 983.210 \\ -\ \ 86.541 \\ \hline 896.669 \end{array}$$

$$\begin{array}{r} 300.710 \\ -\ \ 46.008 \\ \hline 254.702 \end{array}$$

Subtract.

1. 18.636 − 13.435	**2.** 234.86 − 9.25	**3.** 27.954 − 16.21	**4.** 326.5822 − 14.001
5. 71.5 − 16.3	**6.** 46.53 − 21.46	**7.** 8.434 − 6.297	**8.** 35.061 − 9.875
9. 6.952 − 5.06	**10.** 583.86 − 279.9	**11.** 214.005 − 63.26	**12.** 83.56 − 31.235
13. 453 − 17.46	**14.** 55.7 − 3.9	**15.** 206.771 − 160.48	**16.** 126.328 − 9.4078
17. 0.081 − 0.007	**18.** 80.09 − 12.763	**19.** 2.0056 − 0.918	**20.** 219.33 − 184.925

21. 55.7 − 3.9

22. 48.08 − 7.95

23. 279.5 − 33.7

24. 46.08 − 7.05

25. 605.01 − 31.23

26. 0.065 − 0.009

27. 22.916 − 17.4

28. 25.006 − 3.98

29. 175.6 − 28.51

30. 88.71 − 13.9

31. 518.2 − 327.41

32. 2.7736 − 0.1531

33. 800.6 − 315

34. 0.9001 − 0.035

35. 207.001 − 44.62

36. 91.003 − 17.6

37. 388.5 − 29.62

38. 56 − 7.88

39. 68 − 51.3

40. 276.1 − 8.39

41. 584.32 − 16.9056

42. 104.6 − 27.83

43. 9.8 − 6.88

44. 53.405 − 27.3

45. 212 − 0.511

46. 106.8 − 36.47

47. 11.92 − 4.6679

48. 137.05 − 8.6

49. 307.85 − 26.138

50. 6007.2 − 27.158

Skill Review

Multiplication

371.6	1 place
$\times$ 0.27	2 places
26012	
7432	
100.332	3 places

Multiply.

1. 785×1.2
2. 6.61×3
3. 808×17.2
4. 22.5×8.9
5. 89.06×0.5
6. 37.5×0.28
7. 212.8×0.67
8. 93.65×4.11
9. 0.16×8.34
10. 37.44×5.9
11. 5.37×0.012
12. 4.806×7.03
13. 54.72×0.9
14. 812.77×514
15. 0.462×0.93
16. 0.653×207
17. 61.437×5.82
18. 9148.2×6.35
19. 0.0025×0.602
20. 0.0007×0.923
21. 11.6×38.51
22. 47.3×6.05
23. 86.9×121.75
24. 36.91×0.57
25. 874.6×1.1
26. 27.5×40.1
27. 0.05×0.003
28. 20.35×3.7
29. 3.807×6.9
30. 13.405×21.3
31. 24.4×0.61
32. 643.21×1.626
33. 52.303×0.96
34. 0.837×25
35. 10.01×45.33
36. 71.7×3.02
37. 854.6×2.19
38. 41.6×212.5
39. 0.75×436
40. 362.008×24.7
41. 573×7.62
42. 11.3×6.4372
43. 66.7×5.329
44. 16.3×85.004
45. 5129.36×0.008
46. 814×93.11
47. 9.8413×16.55
48. 6.8×3.7592
49. 87.51×98.663
50. 251×0.0783

Skill Review

Division

$$\begin{array}{r} 12.51 \\ 6.8\overline{)85.068} \\ \underline{68} \\ 170 \\ \underline{136} \\ 346 \\ \underline{340} \\ 68 \\ \underline{68} \\ 0 \end{array}$$

To round a quotient to a particular place, divide to one place beyond the place specified and then round.

$$\begin{array}{r} 22.988 \\ 2.71\overline{)62.30000} \\ \underline{54\ 2} \\ 8\ 10 \\ \underline{5\ 42} \\ 2\ 680 \\ \underline{2\ 439} \\ 2410 \\ \underline{2168} \\ 2420 \\ \underline{2168} \\ 252 \end{array}$$

Rounded to the nearest hundredth, the quotient is 22.99.

Divide.

1. $4\overline{)140.8}$ **2.** $7\overline{)160.3}$ **3.** $1.8\overline{)13.68}$

4. $5.06\overline{)48.192}$ **5.** $3.8\overline{)59.66}$ **6.** $8.1\overline{)423.63}$

7. $0.25\overline{)22.175}$ **8.** $0.9\overline{)131.04}$ **9.** $11.42\overline{)41.112}$

10. $21.73\overline{)52.152}$ **11.** $0.8\overline{)200}$ **12.** $6.4\overline{)1152}$

Divide. Round to the nearest tenth.

13. $7.3\overline{)4001}$ **14.** $6.9\overline{)117}$ **15.** $0.56\overline{)27.8}$

16. $3775 \div 15.6$ **17.** $6.3 \div 2.4$

18. $11.9 \div 4.6$ **19.** $0.86 \div 1.5$

20. $27.69 \div 37.5$ **21.** $88.01 \div 0.6$

22. $47.611 \div 0.4$ **23.** $78.9 \div 41.3$

24. $44.7 \div 22.1$ **25.** $3.96 \div 1.57$

26. $54 \div 3.07$ **27.** $2.61 \div 39$

28. $260.13 \div 19.1$ **29.** $565.29 \div 11.8$

30. $1.0472 \div 0.66$ **31.** $247.863 \div 7.04$

32. $36.15 \div 1.09$ **33.** $2.8927 \div 2.8$

Divide. Round to the nearest hundredth.

34. $8.7553 \div 0.28$ **35.** $96.14 \div 2.6$

36. $0.0361 \div 0.46$ **37.** $88.92 \div 1.91$

38. $1.4357 \div 0.047$ **39.** $3.5156 \div 0.028$

40. $90.068 \div 1.73$ **41.** $361.57 \div 20.7$

42. $0.92 \div 6.03$ **43.** $0.054 \div 1.86$

44. $26.923 \div 1.001$ **45.** $560 \div 74.73$

46. $270 \div 269.5$ **47.** $11.99 \div 12.1$

Extra Practice: Chapter 1

Simplify the numerical expression.

1. $44.23 - 1.6$ **2.** 83×6 **3.** $4.80 \div 30$ **4.** $74 + 116$

Evaluate the expression when $d = 6$ and $y = 4$.

5. $y - 3$ **6.** $d + d$ **7.** $2y \times 3$ **8.** $y + d + 2$

Simplify the numerical expression.

9. $18 \div (2 \times 3) + 6$ **10.** $5 \times (5 - 2) \div 3$ **11.** $\frac{8 - 2 \times 3}{(6 - 4)(5 + 1)}$

Evaluate the expression when $x = 4.2$ and $y = 9$.

12. $4(x + y)$ **13.** $5y - x$ **14.** $(y - x)(x + y)$

Evaluate the expression when $a = 5$ and $b = 10$.

15. $3a - \frac{a}{5}$ **16.** $a(b - 2) \div 3$ **17.** $\frac{ab - 20}{a + b}$

Find the solution of the equation for the given replacement set.

18. $q + 9 = 17;\ \{8, 9, 10\}$ **19.** $b - 12 = 35;\ \{45, 46, 47\}$

20. $x \div 14 = 8;\ \{110, 112, 114\}$ **21.** $53 + m = 66;\ \{13, 15, 17\}$

22. $8f = 56;\ \{5, 6, 7\}$ **23.** $17t = 102;\ \{7, 8, 9\}$

24. $2g - 8 = 14;\ \{10, 11, 12\}$ **25.** $4(a + 6) = 36;\ \{1, 2, 3\}$

Replace _?_ with =, >, or < to make a true statement.

26. 31 _?_ 61 **27.** 18×4 _?_ 82 **28.** 47 _?_ $49 - 9$

Use > or < to write a true statement with the given numbers.

29. 35, 18, 6 **30.** 59, 41, 95 **31.** 208, 802, 280

Graph the solutions of the inequality. The replacement set for a is {0, 1, 2, 3, 4, 5, 6, 7, 8, 9, 10}.

32. $a < 14$ **33.** $a \geq 8$ **34.** $a + 6 > 9$ **35.** $10 - a \leq 5$

Find the solutions of the inequality. The replacement set for x is the set of whole numbers.

36. $x < 11$ **37.** $7 > x$ **38.** $x \geq 9$ **39.** $4 \geq x \geq 1$

Use inverse operations to solve.

40. $k + 16 = 28$ **41.** $n \div 6 = 122$ **42.** $7p = 217$ **43.** $p - 11 = 41$

44. $m \div 12 = 204$ **45.** $17 + z = 53$ **46.** $6m = 240$ **47.** $a - 35 = 41$

48. $b \div 7 \leq 14$ **49.** $f - 18 \geq 92$ **50.** $5a < 35$ **51.** $d + 9 > 27$

52. $3x - 7 = 31$ **53.** $2b + 19 = 37$ **54.** $(y \div 4) + 8 = 12$

Write a variable expression for the word phrase.

55. The difference when a number t is subtracted from eighteen

56. Five added to the product of a number x and nine

57. Forty divided by a number m, decreased by sixteen

58. The remainder when a number q is subtracted from two hundred

59. Eleven more than three times a number y

60. The sum of a number r and six, divided by twelve

Write an equation or inequality for the word sentence.

61. Twenty less than a number k is thirty-six.

62. The quotient when a number t is divided by thirteen is greater than nine.

63. The sum of a number y and the product of eight and six is less than or equal to fifty.

64. Fifteen more than the quotient of a number divided by two is sixty.

65. The remainder when the product of six and a number is subtracted from twenty is less than twelve.

Solve, using the five-step plan.

66. Recently, Ken ran a 400 m race in 52.3 s. This was 0.2 s slower than the school record. What is the school record?

67. On July 1, Kay had \$542.07 in her savings account. On September 1, she had \$671.82 in her account. How much did she save between July 1 and September 1?

68. A machine produces 3 plastic parts each minute that it runs. If the machine runs for 7 h, how many parts will it produce?

69. Exercise World is buying 4 new exercise bicycles for \$129.95 each and 6 exercise mats for \$47.85 each. What is the total cost?

Extra Practice: Chapter 2

Simplify the expression.

1. 3^4 **2.** 4^3 **3.** $5^2 + 8^2$ **4.** $2^3 + 3^3$

5. $(8 + 17)^0$ **6.** $(4 \times 6)^2$ **7.** $6^2 \times 18^0$ **8.** $4^2 \times 4^2$

Write as a single power of the given base.

9. $3^8 \times 3^4$ **10.** $7^2 \times 7$ **11.** $k^5 \times k^{13}$ **12.** $m^2 \times m^0$

Evaluate the expression if $a = 4$, $b = 2$, and $c = 6$.

13. $5c^3$ **14.** $(4b)^3$ **15.** $2ab^4$ **16.** $2a^3$

17. $3(ab)^2$ **18.** $(3c)^b$ **19.** $a^2 - b^4$ **20.** c^2a

21. ac^b **22.** $(ab)^0$ **23.** a^3b^2c **24.** $b^3 \times b^4$

Write the decimal in expanded form.

25. 734 **26.** 516.21 **27.** 0.024 **28.** 25.2

29. 2138 **30.** 91.9 **31.** 0.38 **32.** 307.009

Write as a decimal.

33. 18 and 21 hundredths **34.** 5 and 4 thousandths **35.** 242 and 6 tenths

36. 9 and 9 ten-thousandths **37.** 85 thousandths **38.** 6 ten-thousandths

Replace __?__ with the symbols $=$, $<$, or $>$ to make a true statement.

39. 48.2 __?__ 4.82 **40.** 0.03 __?__ 0.031 **41.** 1.452 __?__ 1.425

42. 0.008 __?__ 0.06 **43.** 21.74 __?__ 217.4 **44.** 7.44 __?__ 7.444

Round to the place specified.

45. hundreds; 871.21 **46.** tenths; 113.93 **47.** thousandths; 1.00414

48. hundredths; 0.0577 **49.** tens; 382.45 **50.** hundredths; 45.552

51. thousandths; 3.4279 **52.** hundreds; 84 **53.** tenths; 74.991

Use the properties to simplify the expression. Name the property or properties used.

54. $3(0 + 4.1)$ **55.** $5.4 + 3.8 + 1.6$ **56.** $9 \times 4.3 + 9 \times 0.7$

57. $8.51 \times 0 \times 712$ **58.** $1.625 \times 1.3 \times 8$ **59.** $4(32.5 + 2.8)$

What value of the variable makes the statement true?

60. $7.4 \times n = 1.84 \times 7.4$

61. $6.81 = r + 6.81$

62. $8.726z = z$

63. $3.4(5.12 + 9.4) = (5.12 + 9.4)p$

64. $(79 \times k) + (79 \times 4) = 79 \times 12$

65. $a \times 24.5 = 24.5$

66. $(6.4 \times h)12 = (12 \times 5.1) \times 6.4$

67. $(5.3 + 8) + y = 5.3 + 8$

Simplify the expression.

68. $(6^2 + 34) \div 7$

69. $8 + 6 \times 5^2$

70. $4 + (2.7 \div 0.3^2)$

71. $4.2 \times 7 - 1.1 \times 2^3$

72. $\dfrac{8.2 + 7.3 - 3.1 \times 2}{(7.9 + 4.5) \div 2^2}$

73. $\dfrac{(3.89 + 1.6)}{(14 \div 7)(5^2 - 4^2)}$

74. $3a^2 + (12 - 3^2)a^2$

75. $10k(k + 50) + 5[k^2 - (2 \times 5)^2k + 6]$

Evaluate the expression when $a = 2.5$, $b = 3$, and $c = 1.6$.

76. $3c + b^2$

77. $a^2 + bc$

78. $(a^3 + b - 3c)^0$

79. $a + 2b^3 - c$

80. $3a + 0.5b^2$

81. $b(a - c)^2$

82. $[4a + 2(b - c)^2] \div 8$

83. $(2b)^2 \times [(a + b) \div 11]$

Solve. Check your answer.

84. In a track meet, points are distributed in the following way: first place, 5 points; second place, 3 points; third place, one point. If the Centerville High track team received 4 first-place awards, 6 second-place awards, and 4 third-place awards in a recent meet, how many points did the team score?

85. Three hundred fifty people attended the drama club's Friday evening performance. On Saturday evening, 20 fewer people attended the performance. If the cost of each ticket was \$4.75, how much money did the club take in?

86. At the beginning of the week, the odometer on Tom's bike read 321 km. If he rides his bike 68 km this week and twice that amount next week, what will the odometer on his bike then read?

87. Cindy bought a camera for \$125.60, a zoom lens for \$75.50 and two rolls of film for \$8.35 each. How much money did she spend?

88. Last week Pearl and Amy drove from their home to Seattle. In going to Seattle, Pearl drove 185 km and Amy drove 35 km more than Pearl. For the return trip, they decided to divide the driving evenly. How much did each person drive on the entire trip?

Extra Practice: Chapter 3

Express as an integer.

1. $|{}^-3|$ **2.** $|5|$ **3.** $|1|$ **4.** $|0|$ **5.** $|{}^-6|$

6. $|4|$ **7.** $|{}^-2|$ **8.** $|{}^-7|$ **9.** $|9|$ **10.** $|{}^-8|$

Graph the number and its opposite on the same number line.

11. 6 **12.** $^-9$ **13.** 8 **14.** 5 **15.** $^-1$

Write the integers in order from least to greatest.

16. 0, 4, $^-4$, 3, $^-3$ **17.** 5, 0, $^-2$, $^-8$, 6 **18.** 7, $^-3$, $^-2$, 1, 9

19. $^-1$, 3, $^-7$, 5, $^-4$ **20.** $^-6$, $^-7$, 0, $^-5$, $^-2$ **21.** $^-4$, 5, 4, $^-5$, 0

List the integers that can replace *x* to make the statement true.

22. $|x| = 5$ **23.** $|x| = 2$ **24.** $|x| = 0$

25. $|x| = 4$ **26.** $|x| \leq 6$ **27.** $|x| \leq 3$

Graph the numbers in each exercise on the same number line.

28. 1, $^-1.5$, 0, $^-2$ **29.** $^-2$, $^-4$, 2.5, $^-3.5$ **30.** 3, 1.2, $^-2.4$, $^-5$

31. 7.6, $^-6.7$, 6, $^-7$ **32.** 1, 1.5, $^-2$, 2.5 **33.** 2, $^-1.8$, $^-2.1$, 0

Write the numbers in order from least to greatest.

34. $^-4.74$, $^-4$, $^-5$, 4.74, 4 **35.** 8.3, $^-8.3$, 8.03, $^-8.83$, $^-8$

36. 26.5, $^-26$, $^-2.65$, 2.6, $^-0.26$ **37.** $^-0.5$, 0.05, $^-5.5$, $^-5.05$, 5

38. 11.9, $^-12$, $^-11.9$, 11.09, 11 **39.** $^-42.6$, 42.06, $^-4.26$, 4.206, $^-0.42$

Draw an arrow to represent the decimal number described.

40. The number 5, with starting point $^-4$

41. The number $^-8$, with starting point 6

42. The number 6, with starting point $^-5$

43. The number $^-6$, with starting point 3

Find the sum.

44. $2.7 + 7.2$ **45.** $^-4.9 + {}^-7.6$ **46.** $^-2.25 + 2.25$

47. $^-3.8 + {}^-3.8$ **48.** $^-148 + {}^-256$ **49.** $6.1 + {}^-2.3$

50. $^{-}0.6 + ^{-}2.3$ **51.** $18.12 + 1.66$ **52.** $^{-}5.2 + 2.9$

53. $^{-}2.8 + ^{-}3.9$ **54.** $1.9 + 19$ **55.** $^{-}14.75 + 9.94$

56. $^{-}3.7 + ^{-}1.3$ **57.** $0.31 + 19.14$ **58.** $4.038 + ^{-}6$

Find the difference.

59. $30.5 - 18$ **60.** $16 - 24.3$ **61.** $10.6 - 11.2$

62. $16.2 - (-7)$ **63.** $5 - (-15.3)$ **64.** $18 - (-9.7)$

65. $-8.3 - 5.2$ **66.** $-7 - 14.6$ **67.** $-12.3 - 8$

68. $43.4 - (-136)$ **69.** $-3 - (-8.2)$ **70.** $-12.9 - (-4.5)$

Evaluate when $x = -3.2$ and $y = -5.7$.

71. $-y$ **72.** $-x$ **73.** $-|x|$

74. $-|y|$ **75.** $y - x$ **76.** $-x - y$

77. $x - (-y)$ **78.** $-x - (-y)$ **79.** $-y - (-x)$

Find the product.

80. $2.4(-1.2)$ **81.** $-1.4(3.4)$ **82.** $4.5(-1.7)$

83. $-8.2(-6.1)$ **84.** $-4.3(-3.4)$ **85.** $-6.2(-5.3)$

86. $-2.15(1.15)$ **87.** $3.14(-8.1)$ **88.** $-5.22(8.11)$

89. $4.25(-3.14)$ **90.** $1.11(-1.11)$ **91.** $-6.75(2.32)$

92. $-4.6(2.8)(-5.4)$ **93.** $7.85(-15)(0)$ **94.** $-8(9.2)(-20)$

Find the quotient.

95. $-15.5 \div 0.5$ **96.** $-16.4 \div 4$ **97.** $-150 \div 7.5$

98. $36.6 \div -0.06$ **99.** $38 \div -0.4$ **100.** $8.19 \div -9$

101. $-3.038 \div (-7)$ **102.** $-63.7 \div (-0.007)$ **103.** $-246 \div (-0.6)$

104. $-0.003 \div (1)$ **105.** $0 \div (-0.85)$ **106.** $-0.9 \div (-1.8)$

Write the expression without exponents.

107. 7^{-3} **108.** $(-4)^{-2}$ **109.** 2^{-5} **110.** $(-6)^{-4}$ **111.** 8^{-1}

112. $(-9)^{-2}$ **113.** 5^{-4} **114.** $(-1)^{-7}$ **115.** 3^{-6} **116.** $(-5)^{-3}$

117. $8^5 \times 8^{-7}$ **118.** $10^4 \times 10^{-3}$ **119.** $5^9 \times 5^{-9}$ **120.** $4^{-2} \times 4^0$

121. $9^{17} \times 9^{-17}$ **122.** $3^{-6} \times 3^4$ **123.** $6^{-2} \times 6^5$ **124.** $2^{10} \times 2^{-8}$

Extra Practice: Chapter 4

Express in two other ways.

1. $-\frac{3}{5}$ **2.** $\frac{-4}{13}$ **3.** $-\frac{8}{7}$ **4.** $\frac{6}{-11}$ **5.** $\frac{-9}{14}$ **6.** $-\frac{7}{10}$

Complete.

7. $\frac{1}{4} + \frac{1}{4} + \frac{1}{4} + \frac{1}{4} = \underline{\ ?\ }$

8. $\underline{\ ?\ } \times \frac{1}{3} = -\frac{2}{3}$

9. $5 \times \underline{\ ?\ } = -1$

10. $\frac{3}{10} = 3 \div \underline{\ ?\ }$

11. $\left(-\frac{1}{7}\right) + \left(-\frac{1}{7}\right) = \underline{\ ?\ }$

12. $4 \times \underline{\ ?\ } = \frac{4}{9}$

Complete.

13. $\frac{2}{5} = \frac{?}{20}$ **14.** $\frac{-8}{9} = \frac{?}{27}$ **15.** $-\frac{12}{30} = -\frac{2}{?}$

16. $\frac{20}{-36} = \frac{?}{-9}$ **17.** $3 = \frac{12}{?}$ **18.** $-4 = \frac{-28}{?}$

Write as a proper fraction in lowest terms or as a mixed number in simple form.

19. $\frac{15}{45}$ **20.** $-\frac{22}{64}$ **21.** $\frac{7}{5}$ **22.** $\frac{180}{240}$

23. $-\frac{144}{96}$ **24.** $-\frac{58}{12}$ **25.** $\frac{75}{125}$ **26.** $\frac{-145}{95}$

27. $\frac{14}{-8}$ **28.** $\frac{32}{28}$ **29.** $\frac{-63}{81}$ **30.** $-\frac{48}{54}$

Write as an improper fraction.

31. $5\frac{2}{3}$ **32.** $3\frac{4}{5}$ **33.** $-4\frac{3}{10}$ **34.** $-15\frac{1}{6}$

35. $-7\frac{1}{8}$ **36.** $9\frac{3}{25}$ **37.** $6\frac{1}{4}$ **38.** $-5\frac{11}{12}$

Write the set of fractions as equivalent fractions with the least common denominator (LCD).

39. $\frac{5}{6}, \frac{3}{8}$ **40.** $\frac{4}{5}, -\frac{3}{10}$ **41.** $\frac{4}{8}, \frac{5}{12}$

42. $-\frac{8}{15}, -\frac{7}{20}$ **43.** $-\frac{11}{28}, \frac{17}{42}$ **44.** $\frac{7}{30}, \frac{19}{70}$

45. $\frac{1}{4}, \frac{7}{12}, \frac{5}{18}$ **46.** $-\frac{5}{18}, -\frac{7}{75}, -\frac{7}{10}$ **47.** $\frac{4}{15}, \frac{8}{35}, \frac{1}{10}$

Add or subtract. Write the answer as a proper fraction in lowest terms or as a mixed number in simple form.

48. $\frac{5}{13} + \frac{4}{13}$ **49.** $-\frac{7}{8} - \frac{5}{8}$ **50.** $\frac{5}{12} - \frac{1}{12}$

51. $-\frac{4}{15} + \frac{1}{5}$ **52.** $-\frac{6}{14} - \frac{12}{21}$ **53.** $\frac{3}{16} - \frac{5}{8}$

54. $\frac{5}{9} + \left(-\frac{1}{4}\right)$ **55.** $-\frac{9}{14} - \frac{5}{32}$ **56.** $\frac{3}{7} - \left(-\frac{4}{5}\right)$

57. $-4\frac{1}{12} + 2\frac{4}{5}$ **58.** $5\frac{2}{3} - 2\frac{5}{8}$ **59.** $-3\frac{7}{12} + 7\frac{5}{16}$

60. $2\frac{3}{7} - \left(-4\frac{5}{6}\right)$ **61.** $-1\frac{3}{28} + \left(-4\frac{10}{21}\right)$ **62.** $-15\frac{1}{2} - \left(-8\frac{3}{4}\right)$

63. $\frac{3}{25} + \frac{2}{15} + \frac{7}{10}$ **64.** $2\frac{7}{12} + \frac{1}{5} + 1\frac{1}{6}$ **65.** $\frac{9}{11} - \frac{3}{5} - 1\frac{1}{2}$

Multiply or divide. Write the answer as a proper fraction in lowest terms or as a mixed number in simple form.

66. $-\frac{3}{4} \times \frac{4}{5}$ **67.** $\frac{21}{56} \times \frac{20}{25}$ **68.** $\frac{7}{8} \times \left(-\frac{4}{7}\right)$

69. $-\frac{9}{14} \times \frac{18}{45}$ **70.** $-\frac{15}{16} \times \left(-\frac{56}{25}\right)$ **71.** $-\frac{21}{52} \times \left(-\frac{13}{15}\right)$

72. $6\frac{3}{4} \times -1\frac{1}{3}$ **73.** $-2\frac{5}{8} \times \left(-\frac{16}{19}\right)$ **74.** $-4\frac{2}{7} \times 2\frac{1}{4}$

75. $\frac{4}{9} \div \frac{2}{9}$ **76.** $-\frac{3}{8} \div \left(-\frac{5}{16}\right)$ **77.** $-\frac{8}{15} \div \left(-2\frac{2}{7}\right)$

78. $-3\frac{3}{5} \div \left(2\frac{4}{15}\right)$ **79.** $-\frac{5}{6} \div 4\frac{1}{2}$ **80.** $3\frac{5}{9} \div (-32)$

81. $-16 \div 2\frac{10}{11}$ **82.** $\frac{3}{7} \div \frac{9}{20}$ **83.** $-\frac{11}{13} \div \left(-\frac{23}{52}\right)$

Write as a terminating or repeating decimal. Use a bar to show a repeating decimal.

84. $\frac{3}{8}$ **85.** $\frac{3}{5}$ **86.** $\frac{21}{22}$ **87.** $-\frac{5}{16}$

88. $\frac{1}{6}$ **89.** $-\frac{5}{9}$ **90.** $-\frac{8}{15}$ **91.** $-\frac{161}{189}$

92. $\frac{287}{385}$ **93.** $3\frac{5}{12}$ **94.** $-2\frac{3}{11}$ **95.** $4\frac{1}{18}$

Write as a proper fraction in lowest terms or as a mixed number in simple form.

96. 0.6 **97.** -0.04 **98.** 1.34 **99.** -4.22 **100.** -3.025

101. $0.\overline{6}$ **102.** $-2.\overline{09}$ **103.** $1.\overline{7}$ **104.** 8.2121 . . . **105.** $-2.1666\ldots$

Extra Practice: Chapter 5

Use one of the properties of equality to form a true sentence.

1. If $r + 8 = 15$, then $r = \underline{\ ?\ }$.

2. If $13 = w + 5$, then $\underline{\ ?\ } = w$.

3. If $-8e = -32$, then $e = \underline{\ ?\ }$.

4. If $6f = -54$, then $f = \underline{\ ?\ }$.

5. If $14 = -9 + u$, then $\underline{\ ?\ } = u$.

6. If $c + 13 = 10$, then $c = \underline{\ ?\ }$.

Simplify the expressions on both sides of the equation to obtain an equivalent equation.

7. $n - 7 + 4 + 10 = 42 \div 6$

8. $3 \times 18 \div 9 = 14 + k - 2$

9. $47 = 6v + 7 + 2v$

10. $5y - 4 + 2y - 3y = 32$

11. $3(h + 8) = 39$

12. $-28 = -7(g - 2)$

Use transformations to solve the equation. Write down all the steps.

13. $d + 9 = 24$

14. $-22 = t + 10$

15. $j - 7 = 13$

16. $-14 = r - 3$

17. $-5 + b + 11 = 26$

18. $-8 + g - 12 = -16$

19. $-6 = 7 + 13 + t$

20. $18 = q + 4 - 15$

21. $s + 8\frac{2}{3} = 12$

22. $-4\frac{2}{5} + w = 6$

23. $9 = u - 7.6$

24. $3.4 + e = -5$

25. $56 = 8t$

26. $-4m = 36$

27. $-55 = 11x$

28. $-7k = -42$

29. $\frac{a}{4.2} = -13$

30. $5 = \frac{y}{23.1}$

31. $\frac{c}{-0.6} = -14$

32. $3 = \frac{n}{-412}$

33. $16 = \frac{1}{3}g$

34. $\frac{7}{8}f = -21$

35. $12 = \frac{4}{-5}a$

36. $\frac{-9}{2}h = -27$

37. $-3.7 = 0.01z$

38. $8.5m = 25.5$

39. $\frac{-2}{3}b = \frac{4}{-5}$

40. $\frac{5}{14} = \frac{-3}{7}d$

41. $8 - 6x = 37 - 3$

42. $5e + 9 = -33 + 7$

43. $14 + \frac{w}{3} = 26$

44. $15 = \frac{-1}{4}m - 7$

45. $4a = a + 25$

46. $22 - 2c = 9c$

47. $\frac{4}{3}u + 8 = u$

48. $v = 6 - \frac{5}{4}v$

49. $-10 = \frac{2}{7}(s - 21)$

50. $\frac{5}{6}(n + 24) = 13$

51. $0.5(k + 18) = 14$

52. $-44 = (m - 10)2.2$

Use transformations to solve the inequality. Write down all the steps.

53. $y + 5 \leq -17$

54. $q - 8 > 24$

55. $5\frac{1}{6} - \frac{1}{3} < k$

56. $7.8 + 4.3 \geq m$

57. $f < (17 - 3)0.5$

58. $z \leq \frac{1}{2}(25 - 7)$

59. $6e > 42$

60. $-5a \leq 45$

61. $28 < -7u$

62. $52 \geq 4x$

63. $\frac{w}{-3} > 21$

64. $\frac{c}{4} \geq 17$

65. $-11 \leq \frac{a}{5}$

66. $\frac{e}{-2} < -23$

67. $10 > \frac{v}{7}$

68. $-5x + 7 + 2x - 13 < 9$

69. $-22 \geq 10d - 4 - 3d + 12$

70. $2 > \frac{4}{5}n + 3 - \frac{1}{5}n + 6$

71. $5 + \frac{3}{7}u - 8 + \frac{2}{7}u \leq 5$

72. $-w + 8 \leq 4w - 17$

73. $-6s - 4 < s + 31$

74. $10 + \frac{2}{3}h > -\frac{5}{3}h + 6$

75. $8 - \frac{1}{6}p \geq 4 - \frac{1}{3}p$

76. $4(m + 3) \geq 48$

77. $35 < -5(x + 2)$

78. $34 < (18t - 6)\frac{1}{3}$

79. $\frac{-1}{7}(14 + 21u) \geq 7$

Write a problem that the equation could represent.

80. $67 + x = 75$

81. $x - 9 = 32$

82. $45 - x = 38$

83. $x + 17 = 22$

84. $7x = 93$

85. $5x = 135$

86. $\frac{x}{12} = 5$

87. $\frac{1}{9}x = 7$

Follow the five-step plan for using an equation to solve.

88. Leroy's homeroom has sold \$262.50 worth of tickets to the school play. If each ticket costs \$3.50, how many more tickets must be sold to take in a total of \$651?

89. The dining hall staff is setting up tables for a new group of campers. There is room for 12 people at each table. If 75 girls, 69 boys, and 19 counselors must be fed, how many tables are needed?

90. It took Alfredo $3\frac{3}{4}$ h to ride his bicycle to and from the beach. The return trip was uphill and took him twice as long as the ride to the beach. How long will he spend riding in each direction?

91. On a visit to Sacramento, Cornelia saw \$4.55 worth of 35¢ picture postcards that she liked. If she could spend only \$2.80, how many of the postcards was she unable to buy?

92. Brightwood High sponsored a cheerleading contest in which 53 teams competed. If each team had five students, and 185 of the students were from within the state, how many teams were from other states?

Extra Practice: Chapter 6

1. Draw any segment AB and construct $\overline{CD}$ congruent to $\overline{AB}$.

Draw a labeled diagram to illustrate each description.

2. $\overrightarrow{XY}$ and point A on $\overrightarrow{XY}$ but not on $\overline{XY}$

3. $\overleftrightarrow{AB}$ and point R on $\overleftrightarrow{AB}$ but not on $\overrightarrow{AB}$

4. A circle with center A, radii $\overline{AM}$ and $\overline{AN}$, and chord $\overline{PQ}$

5. A circle with center G, diameter $\overline{KL}$, and radius $\overline{GN}$

Find the circumference of the circle with the given radius or diameter. Use $\pi \approx 3.14$.

6. $r = 57$ cm **7.** $r = 14.5$ m **8.** $d = 23$ km **9.** $d = 7.03$ m

10. Draw any acute angle J. Construct an angle congruent to $\angle J$.

11. Draw any obtuse angle A. Construct a bisector of $\angle A$.

The measures of two angles in the diagram are given. Find the measure of the third angle.

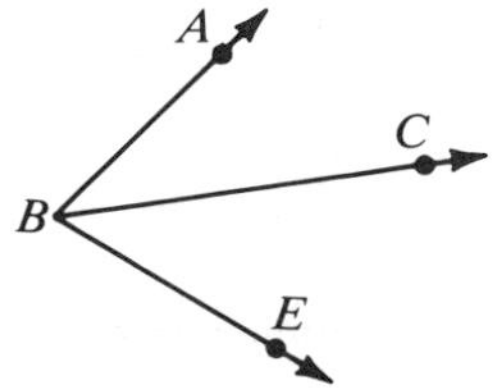

12. $\angle ABC = 56°$, $\angle CBE = 41°$, $\angle ABE =$ ___?___ °

13. $\angle ABC = 17°$, $\angle ABE = 83°$, $\angle CBE =$ ___?___ °

14. $\angle CBE = 24°$, $\angle ABE = 72°$, $\angle ABC =$ ___?___ °

Find the measure of each angle in the diagram at the right.

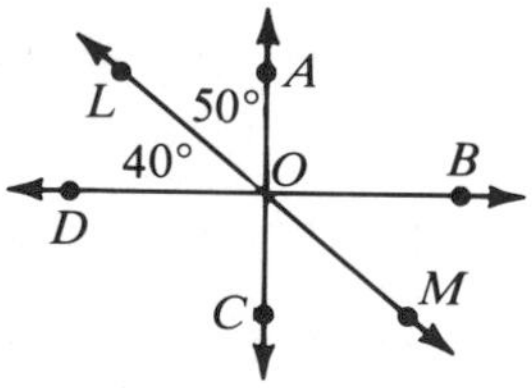

15. $\angle COM$ **16.** $\angle MOB$

17. $\angle AOB$ **18.** $\angle DOC$

19. Two angles are complementary. The measure of one is 4 times the measure of the other. What are the measures of the angles?

20. Two angles are supplementary. The measure of one is 16° greater than the measure of the other. What are the measures of the angles?

In the diagram at the right, $l \parallel n$.

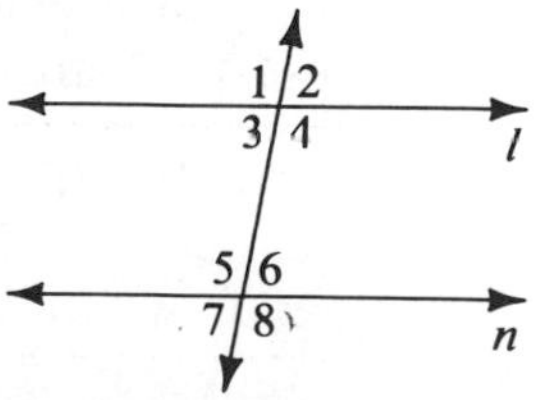

21. Name two pairs of alternate interior angles.

22. Name four pairs of corresponding angles.

23. $\angle 8 = 100°$. Find the measures of the other angles.

24. If the measure of one angle of a right triangle is 30°, what are the measures of the other angles?

25. An isosceles triangle has one angle that measures 110°. What are the measures of the other angles?

26. What is a triangle with three sides that are not congruent called?

27. The angles of a triangle measure 75°, 65°, and 40°. Is the triangle an obtuse triangle or an acute triangle?

28. How many acute angles does a right triangle have?

True or false?

29. A square is also a rhombus.

30. Every quadrilateral has at least two parallel sides.

31. An isosceles trapezoid has two sides that are congruent.

32. Opposite angles of a parallelogram are congruent.

33. A trapezoid is a special type of parallelogram.

34. A segment that connects opposite vertices of a quadrilateral is called a diameter.

35. What is the perimeter of a square with one side 65 mm?

36. One side of a regular decagon is 7.8 cm. What is the perimeter?

37. A triangle has sides of length 64.3 mm, 28.7 mm, and 56.2 mm. What is the perimeter?

38. One side of a rectangle is 2.8 m. The perimeter of the rectangle is 17.2 m. What are the lengths of the other sides?

39. A regular pentagon has perimeter 14.5 cm. What is the length of each side?

Are the triangles in each pair congruent? If so, name the triangles that are congruent and explain why they are congruent.

40.

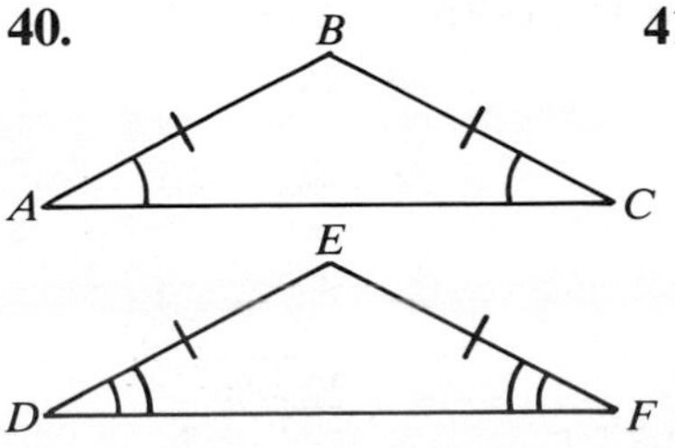

41.

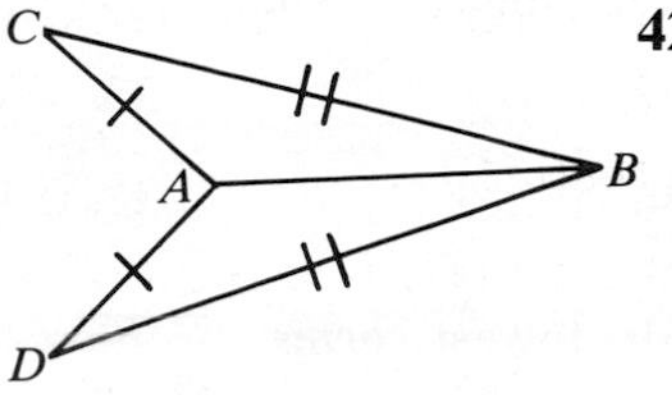

42.

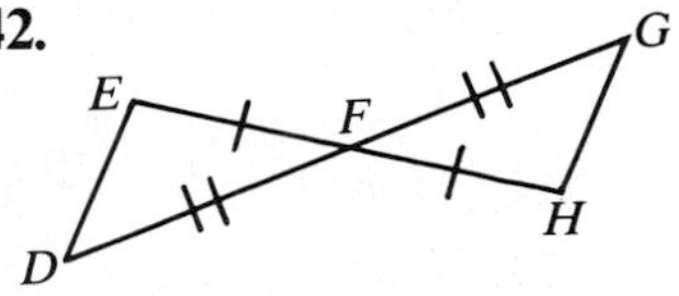

Extra Practice: Chapter 7

Write the ratio as a fraction in lowest terms.

1. $\frac{9}{36}$ **2.** 17 to 7 **3.** 15:35 **4.** 56 to 63 **5.** $\frac{1}{2}:\frac{2}{3}$

Solve the proportion.

6. $\frac{8}{16} = \frac{x}{78}$ **7.** $\frac{27}{x} = \frac{6}{2}$ **8.** $\frac{125}{25} = \frac{60}{x}$ **9.** $\frac{x}{18} = \frac{17}{51}$

Solve.

10. In order to make 4 servings, a recipe calls for 3 eggs to be used. How many eggs will be needed to make 32 servings?

11. Charlie runs 5 mi in 37 min. If he could maintain the same speed, how long would it take him to run 15 mi?

12. A dozen apples cost $1.80. What is the unit price?

13. A car travels 234 km in 4.5 h. What is the car's average speed?

14. A floor plan with the scale 1 cm = 2 m shows a room as 2 cm wide and 5 cm long. What are the actual width and length?

15. A certain map uses a scale of 1 cm = 6 km. If the distance from Hopeville to Breda is 150 m, how far apart are they on the map?

Express as a percent.

16. $\frac{7}{8}$ **17.** 1.73 **18.** $\frac{1}{4}$ **19.** 0.05 **20.** 0.375

21. $\frac{3}{5}$ **22.** $\frac{1}{10}$ **23.** $\frac{7}{28}$ **24.** 0.57 **25.** $\frac{2}{3}$

Express as a percent to the nearest tenth of a percent.

26. $\frac{1}{6}$ **27.** $\frac{5}{9}$ **28.** $\frac{6}{17}$ **29.** $\frac{7}{15}$ **30.** $\frac{21}{33}$

Express as (a) a proper fraction in lowest terms or as a mixed number in simple form and (b) a decimal.

31. 0.7% **32.** 27% **33.** 1.3% **34.** 44%

35. 135% **36.** 15.5% **37.** 0.3% **38.** 1%

Express as a fraction in lowest terms.

39. $\frac{1}{8}\%$ **40.** $\frac{5}{6}\%$ **41.** $83\frac{1}{3}\%$ **42.** $22\frac{1}{6}\%$

Solve. Round to the nearest tenth if necessary.

43. What is 40% of 75?

44. What is 20% of 81?

45. What is 17% of 108?

46. 5 is what percent of 50?

47. 12 is what percent of 30?

48. 56 is 112% of what number?

49. 27 is $33\frac{1}{3}$% of what number?

50. What is $11\frac{1}{9}$% of 1000?

51. 36 is what percent of 28?

52. 325 is 1.3% of what number?

53. 19 is 190% of what number?

54. 47 is what percent of 70?

Solve.

55. Carol has 60 boxes of light bulbs. If she sells 15% of the boxes today, how many will be left?

56. A calculator costs $6.25 plus $.25 sales tax. What is the sales tax rate?

57. At a pet store, fish that usually cost $1.25 each are on sale for $.75 each. What is the percent of decrease?

58. A restaurant raises its price for the salad bar 20% to $1.50. What did the salad bar cost before?

59. The band concert drew an audience of 270 on Thursday. On Friday, attendance increased 30%. How many people attended on Friday?

60. The discount rate at an appliance store sale is 15%. What is the sale price of a dishwasher if the original price was $600?

61. Nancy Allen earns a 12% commission on her sales. Last month she earned $4800. What was the total value of her sales?

62. Last Friday, 720 people at Data Tech drove cars to work. Of these, 585 bought gas on the way home. What percent of the drivers bought gas on the way home? Use a proportion to solve.

63. How much does a $53.00 iron cost if it is taxed at 5%? Use a proportion to solve.

64. Jill has $525 in a savings account that pays 6% simple interest. How much will she have in the account after 1 year, if she makes no deposits or withdrawals?

65. Holly has a savings account that pays 6.5% interest, compounded monthly. If she started the account with $750 and makes no deposits or withdrawals, how much will be in the account after 3 months?

Extra Practice: Chapter 8

For Exercises 1-6, give the coordinates of the point.

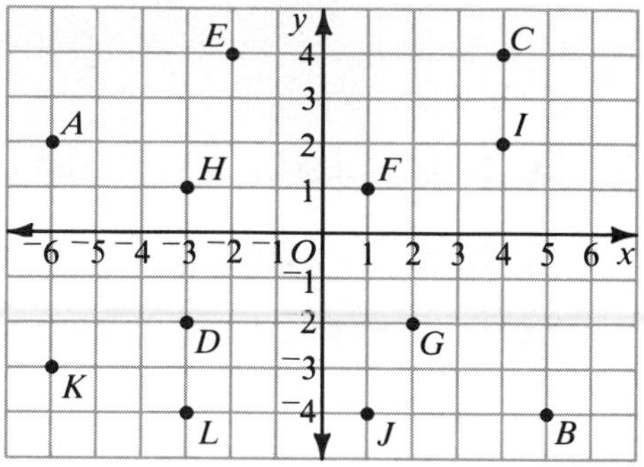

1. *A* **2.** *B* **3.** *C*

4. *D* **5.** *E* **6.** *F*

Name the point for the ordered pair.

7. $(2, -2)$ **8.** $(-3, -4)$

9. $(4, 2)$ **10.** $(-6, -3)$

11. $(1, -4)$ **12.** $(-3, 1)$

a. Graph the given ordered pairs on a coordinate plane.
b. Connect all the points in the order listed by means of line segments to produce a closed figure.
c. Name the figure as specifically as you can.

13. $(3, 3), (3, 0), (-2, 0), (-5, 0), (-5, 3), (3, 3)$

14. $(2, -2), (2, -6), (-2, -6), (-2, -2), (0, -2), (2, -2)$

15. $(1, 5), (-2, 2), (-5, -1), (0, -1), (6, -1), (1, 5)$

16. $(0, 7), (3, 5), (2, 2), (-2, 2), (-3, 5), (0, 7)$

17. $(7, -4), (4, -1), (2, 1), (1, 2), (1, -4), (7, -4)$

Tell whether the ordered pair is a solution of the given equation.

$-x + 2y = 4$

18. $(4, 0)$ **19.** $(-4, 0)$ **20.** $(2, 3)$ **21.** $(-2, 3)$

$x + 3y = 6$

22. $(0, 2)$ **23.** $(6, 0)$ **24.** $(2, 1)$ **25.** $(3, 1)$

$2x + y = 5$

26. $(3, 1)$ **27.** $(2, 1)$ **28.** $(1, 3)$ **29.** $(0, 5)$

a. Solve the equation for *y* in terms of *x*.
b. Find the solutions of the equation for the given values of *x*.

30. $2x + y = 8$
values of x: $-1, 0, 1$

31. $y - 3x = 4$
values of x: $-5, 0, 5$

32. $-x + y = 1$
values of x: $-1, \frac{1}{2}, 2$

33. $3x - 2y = -6$
values of x: $-2, 0, 2$

34. $2x + y = 6$
values of x: 0, 3, 1

35. $x - y = 3$
values of x: 6, -1, -3

Graph the equation on a coordinate plane. Use a separate set of axes for each equation.

36. $2x + y = 4$

37. $x - 3y = -3$

38. $x + 2y = -4$

39. $3x + 4y = 12$

40. $2x + 5y = 10$

41. $-x + y = -1$

42. $x + y = 2$

43. $3x - y = 3$

44. $4x - 2y = 3$

45. $2x = y - 2$

46. $y = x - 3$

47. $-3x + 4y = 12$

Use a graph to solve the system. Do the lines intersect, coincide, or are they parallel?

48. $x - y = -2$
$2x + y = 5$

49. $x - y = 6$
$2x + y = 0$

50. $2x + y = -2$
$x - y = -4$

51. $2x + y = 2$
$2x + y = -3$

52. $6x + 3y = 6$
$2x + y = 2$

53. $3x + y = -6$
$2x - y = 1$

54. A parking lot attendant charges \$3 for the first hour and \$1 for each extra hour after that. Write an equation that relates the total cost of parking (y) to the number of extra hours a car is parked (x). Graph the equation. What is the slope of the graph? From your graph determine how much it would cost to park a car for 5 h after the initial hour.

55. The initial charge for a phone call to Jonesboro is 25¢ for the first 3 min. After that the charge is 5¢ for every additional minute. Write an equation that relates the total cost of a phone call (y) to the number of additional minutes on the phone (x). Graph the equation. What is the slope of the graph? From the graph determine the cost of a call requiring 7 min beyond the initial 3.

56. The temperature in a town rose at a constant rate from 5 A.M. to 12 noon. At 9 A.M. the temperature was 17°C. At 11 A.M. the temperature was 21°C. Use this information to draw a graph and determine what the temperature was at 5 A.M. and at 12 noon.

Graph the inequality.

57. $x + 2y < 4$

58. $2x - y < 1$

59. $6x + y \geq 7$

60. $-x + 3y < 0$

61. $2x + y \geq 1$

62. $3x + y \leq -2$

Extra Practice: Chapter 9

Use $\pi \approx 3.14$ when needed.

1. What is the area of a square with a side that is 16 cm long?
2. What is the area of a triangle with base 72 mm and height 53 mm?
3. A square has a perimeter of 88 m. What is its area?
4. The legs of a right triangle are 28 cm and 35 cm. What is the area of the triangle?
5. Find the length of a rectangle with area 9720 m^2 and width 67.5 m.
6. Find the height of a triangle with area 4122.5 mm^2 and base 85 mm.
7. A parallelogram has base 60 mm and height 40 mm. Find its area.
8. Find the area of a parallelogram with height 15 cm and base 24 cm.
9. A trapezoid has height 18 cm and bases 113 cm and 121 cm. Find its area.
10. A parallelogram with area 1176 m^2 has height 56 m. Find its base.
11. A trapezoid with bases 51 m and 33 m has area 630 m^2. Find its height.
12. A parallelogram with base 45 cm has area 1440 cm^2. Find its height.
13. What is the area of a circle whose diameter is 140 cm?
14. A circle has radius 12 m. Find its area.
15. What is the radius of a circle whose area is 803.84 mm^2?
16. The circumference of a circle is 43.96 m. Find the area.
17. Find the diameter of a circle with an area of 379.94 m^2.
18. Find the area of a circle whose diameter is 36 cm.

Tell whether the figure is symmetric with respect to a point, to a line, or to both. Use the fact that the figure has symmetry to find the area.

19.

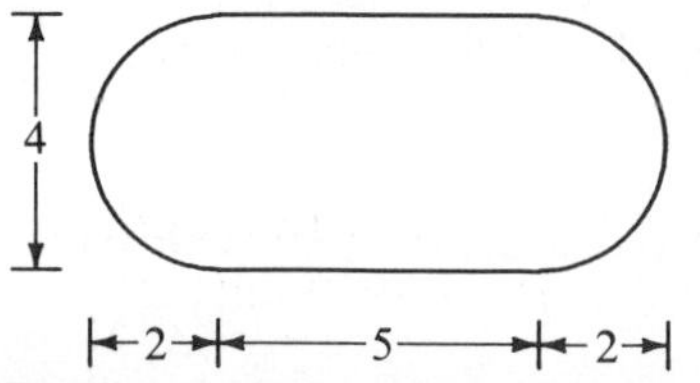

20.

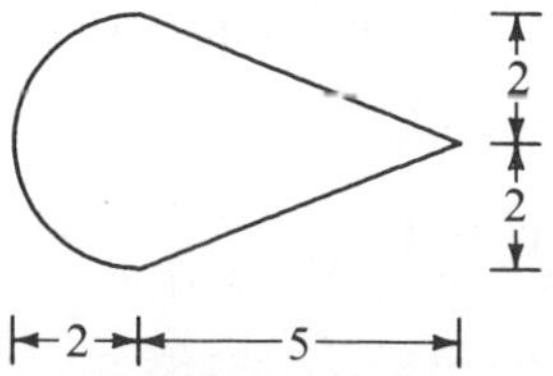

21. A prism with height 5 m has base area 173 m^2. Find the volume.

22. Find the volume of a cylinder with height 82 cm and base area 50 cm^2.

23. A right triangle with legs 15 mm and 7 mm is the base of a prism with height 24 mm. Find the volume of the prism.

24. Find the volume of a cylinder with height 300 cm and diameter 15 cm.

25. The volume of a triangular prism is 2340 cm^3. Find the height of the prism if the base area is 78 cm^2.

26. A cone with base area 234 mm^2 is 82 mm high. Find its volume and its capacity in liters.

27. A pyramid with height 52 cm has a rectangular base measuring 12 cm by 17 cm. Find the volume.

28. The base of a cone has diameter 70 cm. If the height of the cone is 120 cm, what is the volume?

For Exercises 29–32, find (a) the lateral surface area and (b) the total surface area of the figure described.

29. A prism of height 15 cm whose bases are right triangles with sides 15 cm, 36 cm, and 39 cm

30. A cylinder with radius 4 cm and height 11 cm

31. A cube with edges that are 15 cm

32. A rectangular prism of height 27 cm and base 15 cm by 12 cm

For Exercises 33–36, leave your answers in terms of π.

33. Find the surface area of a sphere with radius 18 cm.

34. Find the volume of a sphere with diameter 30 cm.

35. Find the radius of a sphere whose surface area is 576π m^2.

36. Find the volume of a sphere whose radius is 16 cm.

37. If the mass of 1 L of gasoline is 0.66 kg, what is the mass of 4 L?

38. Each edge of a cube of steel measures 12 cm. Find the mass of the cube if the mass of 1 cm^3 of steel is 7.82 g.

39. A rectangular prism of aluminum is 15 cm long, 7 cm wide, and 30 cm high. Find the mass of the prism if the mass of 1 cm^3 of aluminum is 2.708 g.

Extra Practice: Chapter 10

If the given symbol names an integer, state the integer. If not, name the two consecutive integers between which the number lies.

1. $\sqrt{9}$ **2.** $\sqrt{39}$ **3.** $-\sqrt{27}$ **4.** $\sqrt{10}$

5. $\sqrt{17}$ **6.** $\sqrt{5}$ **7.** $\sqrt{81}$ **8.** $-\sqrt{12}$

9. $\sqrt{60}$ **10.** $-\sqrt{78}$ **11.** $\sqrt{25}$ **12.** $\sqrt{19}$

13. $\sqrt{16}$ **14.** $\sqrt{43}$ **15.** $\sqrt{84}$ **16.** $\sqrt{64}$

Approximate to the tenths' place, using the divide-and-average method.

17. $\sqrt{24}$ **18.** $\sqrt{30}$ **19.** $\sqrt{92}$ **20.** $\sqrt{74}$

21. $\sqrt{51}$ **22.** $\sqrt{29}$ **23.** $\sqrt{10}$ **24.** $\sqrt{86}$

25. $\sqrt{37}$ **26.** $\sqrt{80}$ **27.** $\sqrt{5.6}$ **28.** $\sqrt{9.8}$

For Exercises 29–53, refer to the table on page 498. Approximate the square root to the nearest hundredth.

29. $\sqrt{8}$ **30.** $\sqrt{19}$ **31.** $\sqrt{5}$ **32.** $\sqrt{11}$

33. $\sqrt{24}$ **34.** $\sqrt{52}$ **35.** $\sqrt{39}$ **36.** $\sqrt{2}$

37. $\sqrt{31}$ **38.** $2\sqrt{18}$ **39.** $\sqrt{58}$ **40.** $5\sqrt{45}$

Approximate the square root to the nearest hundredth by interpolation.

41. $\sqrt{15.8}$ **42.** $\sqrt{6.3}$ **43.** $\sqrt{21.4}$ **44.** $\sqrt{83.6}$

State whether or not a triangle with sides of the given lengths is a right triangle.

45. 2, 3, 4 **46.** 3, 4, 5 **47.** 10, 20, 24

48. 8, 15, 17 **49.** 10, 12, 15 **50.** 6, 8, 10

51. 30, 40, 50 **52.** 7, 9, 12 **53.** 12, 16, 20

A right triangle has sides of lengths *a*, *b*, and *c*, with *c* the length of the hypotenuse. Find the length of the missing side. If necessary, use the table on page 498 for the square root values and round answers to the nearest hundredth.

54. $a = 5$, $b = 8$ **55.** $a = 4$, $b = 5$ **56.** $a = 3$, $c = 5$

57. $b = 12$, $c = 15$ **58.** $b = 15$, $c = 17$ **59.** $a = 7$, $b = 7$

60. $a = 6$, $c = 10$ **61.** $b = 8$, $c = 17$ **62.** $a = 13$, $c = 14$

Find the lengths marked x and y. In each exercise, the triangles are similar.

63.

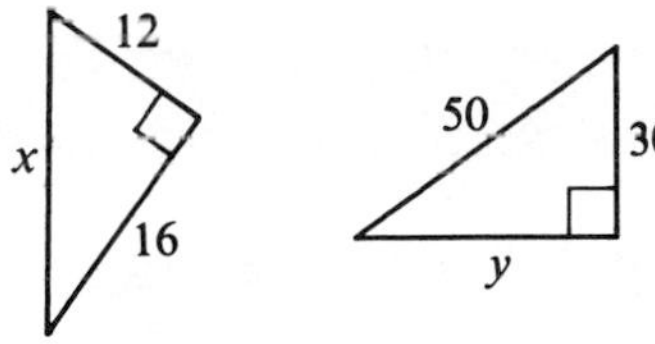

64.

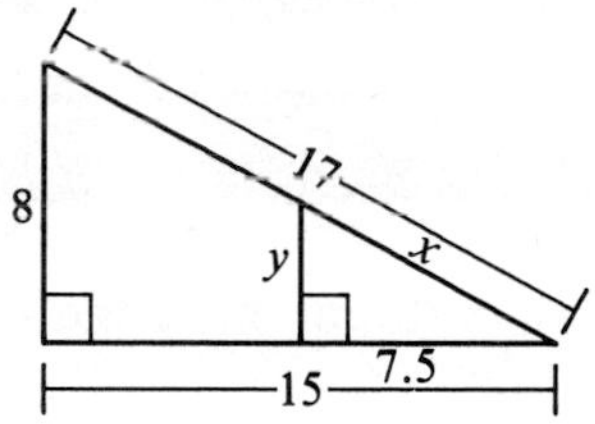

Find the lengths marked x and y in the triangle. Give your answer in terms of radicals when radicals occur.

65.

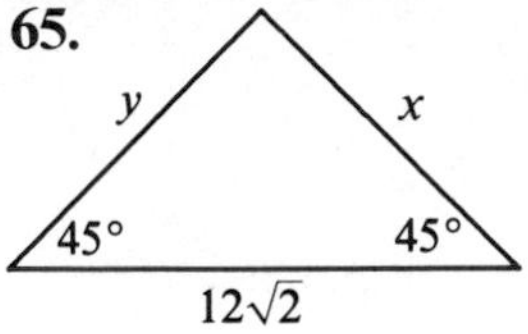

66.

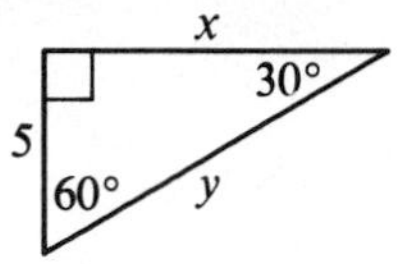

67.

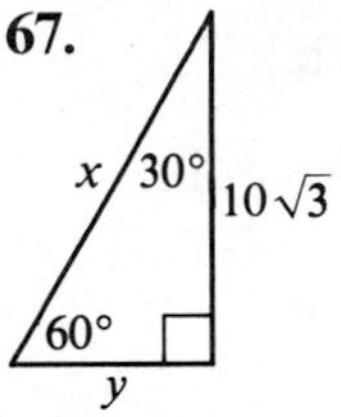

68.

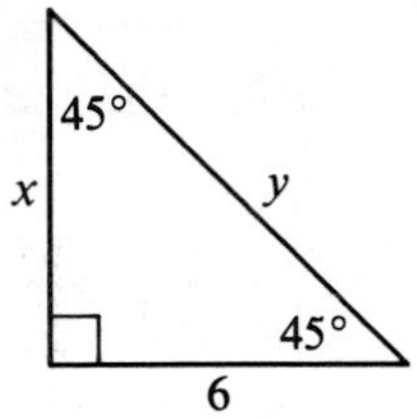

Rewrite the expression in lowest terms with the radical in the numerator.

69. $\frac{2}{\sqrt{3}}$ **70.** $\frac{5}{\sqrt{x}}$ **71.** $\frac{x}{\sqrt{2a}}$ **72.** $\frac{7}{\sqrt{4}}$

Use the diagram to name each ratio.

73. tan A **74.** sin A

75. cos A **76.** tan B

77. cos B **78.** sin B

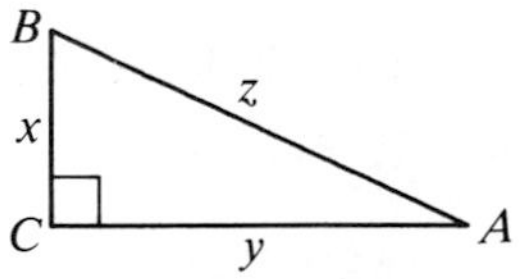

For Exercises 79–88, use the tables on pages 498 and 499. Find sin A, cos A, and tan A for the given measure of $\angle A$.

79. 27° **80.** 68° **81.** 89° **82.** 5°

Find the measure of $\angle A$ to the nearest degree.

83. $\sin A = 0.436$ **84.** $\cos A = 0.224$ **85.** $\tan A = 1.35$

Refer to the diagram at the right.

86. Find the value of x.

87. Find $\angle D$ to the nearest degree.

88. Find $\angle E$ to the nearest degree.

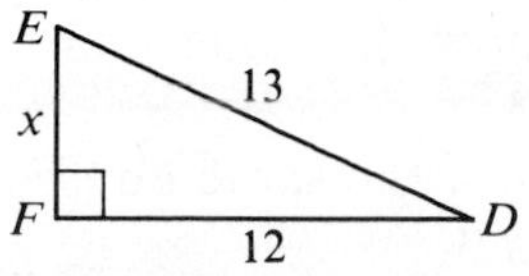

Extra Practice: Chapter 11

Find the value of each.

1. 6! **2.** 3! **3.** 10! **4.** 2! **5.** 5!

6. ${}_2P_2$ **7.** ${}_4P_4$ **8.** ${}_9P_3$ **9.** ${}_{15}P_2$ **10.** ${}_{28}P_4$

11. An auto dealer has 3 models on sale. Each is available in 5 colors, with or without air-conditioning. How many different cars are available?

12. In how many different ways can you arrange the letters in the word DIRECT if you take the letters 3 at a time?

Find the value of each.

13. ${}_4C_2$ **14.** ${}_{10}C_3$ **15.** ${}_6C_3$ **16.** ${}_{12}C_2$ **17.** ${}_{10}C_5$

18. How many combinations of 3 fish can you choose from 7 fish?

19. There are 52 basketball teams entered in a tournament. How many combinations can make it to the final game?

A bag contains 3 green, 2 blue, 1 red, and 1 white marble. Find the probability for a marble chosen at random.

20. *P*(red) **21.** *P*(white) **22.** *P*(not red)

23. *P*(green) **24.** *P*(not green) **25.** *P*(yellow)

26. *P*(not yellow) **27.** *P*(green or red) **28.** *P*(red, white, or green)

Kate has 24 albums: 4 by the Deltas, 6 by the Squares, 6 by the Tuscon Band, 3 by Eliot Smith, 3 by the Marks, and 2 by the Deep River Quartet. She selects one at random.

29. Find the odds in favor of selecting a record by the following.
a. the Marks **b.** the Deep River Quartet **c.** the Squares

30. Find the odds against selecting a record by the following.
a. Eliot Smith **b.** the Tuscon Band **c.** the Squares

Two game cubes are rolled. Find the probability of each.

31. a. The cubes show the same number.
b. The sum is 3.
c. The cubes show the same number or the sum is 3.

32. a. The difference is 1.
b. The sum is 12.
c. The difference is 1 or the sum is 12.

33. $P(A) = 0.40$, $P(B) = 0.60$, $P(A \text{ and } B) = 0.24$. Find $P(A \text{ or } B)$.

34. Find the probability that a month, chosen at random, begins with the letter J or has 30 days.

35. $P(A) = 0.25$, $P(B) = 0.20$, $P(A \text{ and } B) = 0.05$. Find $P(A \text{ or } B)$.

36. Two game cubes are rolled. Find the probability of each event.
   a. The cubes show the same number.
   b. The sum is 8.
   c. The cubes show the same number and the sum is 8.
   d. The cubes show the same number or the sum is 8.

Are A and B independent events? If they are, find $P(A \text{ and } B)$.

37. A white game cube and a red game cube are rolled.
   A: An even number comes up on the white cube.
   B: A 2 comes up on the red cube.

38. A bag contains 4 green marbles and 3 white marbles. A marble is drawn at random and replaced. Then a marble is drawn again.
   A: The first marble is green.
   B: The second marble is white.

A bag contains 3 dimes, 4 nickels, and 5 pennies. One of the coins is drawn at random and is not replaced. Then a second coin is drawn. Find the probability of the events described.

39. Both coins are dimes.

40. The first coin is a nickel and the second is a penny.

41. The first coin is a nickel and the second is a dime.

42. Both coins are nickels.

A bag contains 26 cards, each with a different letter of the alphabet. One card is drawn and is not replaced. Then another card is drawn. Find the probability of the events. Assume y is a vowel.

43. Two vowels are drawn.

44. Two consonants are drawn.

45. George has had 52 hits in 125 times at bat. Estimate the probability that George will get a hit on his next time at bat.

46. An inspector on an assembly line chose 200 condensers at random out of 4000 condensers. Of the 200, 6 were defective.
   a. What is the probability that a condenser will be defective?
   b. About how many defective condensers would you expect to find in the 4000 condensers?

Extra Practice: Chapter 12

Construct a bar graph to illustrate the data in the table.

1. **Water Usage**

Activity	Liters
5 min shower	100
dishwasher load	50
bath	125
15 min lawn watering	275

2. **Electricity Usage**

Appliance	Watts
radio	75
electric shaver	15
knife sharpener	40
stereo	100

3. Using the double bar graph, determine the following.

a. The approximate amount of U.S. exports to Japan

b. The approximate amount of U.S. imports from Canada

c. The country with the greatest difference between imports and exports

d. The total amount of U.S. exports to Mexico and France

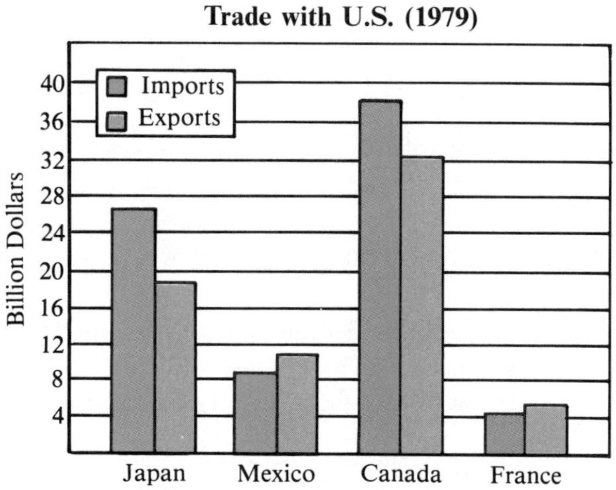

4. Construct a line graph to illustrate the data in the table.

Rollerskating Rink Association Membership

Year	1940	1945	1950	1955	1960	1965	1970	1975
Membership	147	200	287	328	610	522	555	963

5. Using the double line graph, determine the following.

a. In which year were the two league pennant winners closest in percent of games won? farthest apart?

b. In which year did the National League pennant winner win a larger percent of games?

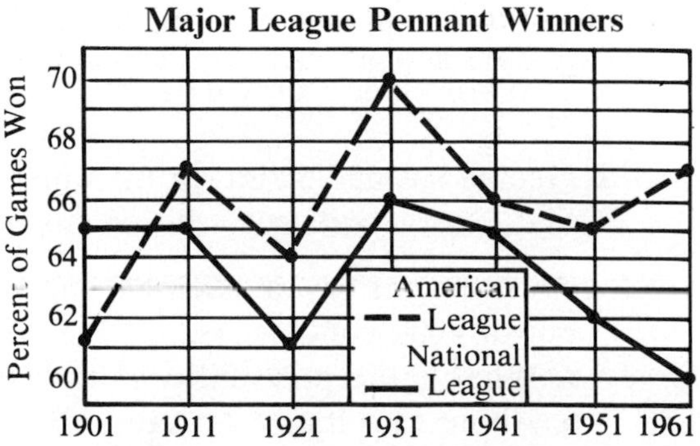

Find the range, mean, median, and mode of each set of data. Round to the nearest tenth if necessary.

6. 14, 9, 7, 5, 4, 4, 1

7. 40, 55, 37, 34, 30, 42

8. 106, 109, 84, 111, 95

9. 18.2, 11.6, 9.5, 12.3, 16.1, 12.5

Insert a new number into each set of data so that the mean of the resulting set is 13.

10. 10, 18, 22

11. 5, 8, 12

12. 6, 11, 15

Use the following data to make a frequency distribution. Then find the range, mean, median, and mode. Round to the nearest tenth if necessary.

13. 8, 7, 9, 9, 8, 10, 11, 12, 7, 7, 7, 10, 9, 10, 8, 10, 11, 9, 12, 9

14. 25, 35, 30, 25, 35, 35, 40, 25, 40, 45, 35, 45, 45

Exercises 15–18 refer to the histogram at the right.

15. How many kilograms of wool were produced in all?

16. How many shearings produced less than 10 kg of wool?

17. Find the range, mean, median, and mode of the data. Round to the nearest tenth if necessary.

18. Make a frequency polygon for the data.

Wool Production of Merino Sheep

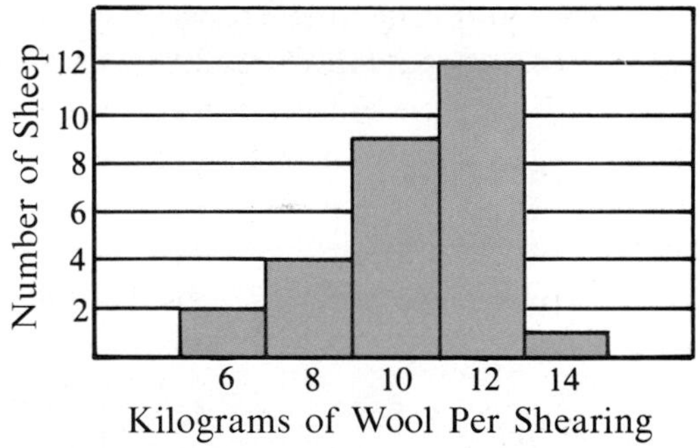

X represents the possible values of a random variable and $P(X)$ represents their probabilities of occurrence. Find the expected value of X.

19.

X	5	10	15	20
$P(X)$	$\frac{1}{8}$	$\frac{2}{8}$	$\frac{3}{8}$	$\frac{2}{8}$

20.

X	−2	1	3	5
$P(X)$	0.1	0.2	0.3	0.4

21. A set of cards is numbered 1 through 8, one number per card. X is the number on a card drawn at random.

Table of Square Roots of Integers from 1 to 100

Number	Positive Square Root	Number	Positive Square Root	Number	Positive Square Root	Number	Positive Square Root
N	$\sqrt{N}$	N	$\sqrt{N}$	N	$\sqrt{N}$	N	$\sqrt{N}$
1	1	**26**	5.099	**51**	7.141	**76**	8.718
2	1.414	**27**	5.196	**52**	7.211	**77**	8.775
3	1.732	**28**	5.292	**53**	7.280	**78**	8.832
4	2	**29**	5.385	**54**	7.348	**79**	8.888
5	2.236	**30**	5.477	**55**	7.416	**80**	8.944
6	2.449	**31**	5.568	**56**	7.483	**81**	9
7	2.646	**32**	5.657	**57**	7.550	**82**	9.055
8	2.828	**33**	5.745	**58**	7.616	**83**	9.110
9	3	**34**	5.831	**59**	7.681	**84**	9.165
10	3.162	**35**	5.916	**60**	7.746	**85**	9.220
11	3.317	**36**	6	**61**	7.810	**86**	9.274
12	3.464	**37**	6.083	**62**	7.874	**87**	9.327
13	3.606	**38**	6.164	**63**	7.937	**88**	9.381
14	3.742	**39**	6.245	**64**	8	**89**	9.434
15	3.873	**40**	6.325	**65**	8.062	**90**	9.487
16	4	**41**	6.403	**66**	8.124	**91**	9.539
17	4.123	**42**	6.481	**67**	8.185	**92**	9.592
18	4.243	**43**	6.557	**68**	8.246	**93**	9.644
19	4.359	**44**	6.633	**69**	8.307	**94**	9.695
20	4.472	**45**	6.708	**70**	8.367	**95**	9.747
21	4.583	**46**	6.782	**71**	8.426	**96**	9.798
22	4.690	**47**	6.856	**72**	8.485	**97**	9.849
23	4.796	**48**	6.928	**73**	8.544	**98**	9.899
24	4.899	**49**	7	**74**	8.602	**99**	9.950
25	5	**50**	7.071	**75**	8.660	**100**	10

Exact square roots are shown in red. For the others, rational approximations are given correct to three decimal places.

Table of Trigonometric Ratios

Angle	Sine	Cosine	Tangent	Angle	Sine	Cosine	Tangent
1°	.0175	.9998	.0175	**46°**	.7193	.6947	1.0355
2°	.0349	.9994	.0349	**47°**	.7314	.6820	1.0724
3°	.0523	.9986	.0524	**48°**	.7431	.6691	1.1106
4°	.0698	.9976	.0699	**49°**	.7547	.6561	1.1504
5°	.0872	.9962	.0875	**50°**	.7660	.6428	1.1918
6°	.1045	.9945	.1051	**51°**	.7771	.6293	1.2349
7°	.1219	.9925	.1228	**52°**	.7880	.6157	1.2799
8°	.1392	.9903	.1405	**53°**	.7986	.6018	1.3270
9°	.1564	.9877	.1584	**54°**	.8090	.5878	1.3764
10°	.1736	.9848	.1763	**55°**	.8192	.5736	1.4281
11°	.1908	.9816	.1944	**56°**	.8290	.5592	1.4826
12°	.2079	.9781	.2126	**57°**	.8387	.5446	1.5399
13°	.2250	.9744	.2309	**58°**	.8480	.5299	1.6003
14°	.2419	.9703	.2493	**59°**	.8572	.5150	1.6643
15°	.2588	.9659	.2679	**60°**	.8660	.5000	1.7321
16°	.2756	.9613	.2867	**61°**	.8746	.4848	1.8040
17°	.2924	.9563	.3057	**62°**	.8829	.4695	1.8807
18°	.3090	.9511	.3249	**63°**	.8910	.4540	1.9626
19°	.3256	.9455	.3443	**64°**	.8988	.4384	2.0503
20°	.3420	.9397	.3640	**65°**	.9063	.4226	2.1445
21°	.3584	.9336	.3839	**66°**	.9135	.4067	2.2460
22°	.3746	.9272	.4040	**67°**	.9205	.3907	2.3559
23°	.3907	.9205	.4245	**68°**	.9272	.3746	2.4751
24°	.4067	.9135	.4452	**69°**	.9336	.3584	2.6051
25°	.4226	.9063	.4663	**70°**	.9397	.3420	2.7475
26°	.4384	.8988	.4877	**71°**	.9455	.3256	2.9042
27°	.4540	.8910	.5095	**72°**	.9511	.3090	3.0777
28°	.4695	.8829	.5317	**73°**	.9563	.2924	3.2709
29°	.4848	.8746	.5543	**74°**	.9613	.2756	3.4874
30°	.5000	.8660	.5774	**75°**	.9659	.2588	3.7321
31°	.5150	.8572	.6009	**76°**	.9703	.2419	4.0108
32°	.5299	.8480	.6249	**77°**	.9744	.2250	4.3315
33°	.5446	.8387	.6494	**78°**	.9781	.2079	4.7046
34°	.5592	.8290	.6745	**79°**	.9816	.1908	5.1446
35°	.5736	.8192	.7002	**80°**	.9848	.1736	5.6713
36°	.5878	.8090	.7265	**81°**	.9877	.1564	6.3138
37°	.6018	.7986	.7536	**82°**	.9903	.1392	7.1154
38°	.6157	.7880	.7813	**83°**	.9925	.1219	8.1443
39°	.6293	.7771	.8098	**84°**	.9945	.1045	9.5144
40°	.6428	.7660	.8391	**85°**	.9962	.0872	11.4301
41°	.6561	.7547	.8693	**86°**	.9976	.0698	14.3007
42°	.6691	.7431	.9004	**87°**	.9986	.0523	19.0811
43°	.6820	.7314	.9325	**88°**	.9994	.0349	28.6363
44°	.6947	.7193	.9657	**89°**	.9998	.0175	57.2900
45°	.7071	.7071	1.0000	**90°**	1.0000	.0000	Undefined

Summary of Formulas

Circumference

$C = \pi d$

$C = 2\pi r$

Area

Rectangle: $A = lw$

Triangle: $A = \frac{1}{2}bh$

Parallelogram: $A = bh$

Trapezoid: $A = \frac{1}{2}(b_1 + b_2)h$

Circle: $A = \pi r^2$

Volume

Prism: $V = Bh$

Cylinder: $V = \pi r^2 h$

Pyramid: $V = \frac{1}{3}Bh$

Cone: $V = \frac{1}{3}\pi r^2 h$

Sphere: $V = \frac{4}{3}\pi r^3$

Lateral Area

Prism: lateral area = perimeter of base × height

Cylinder: lateral area = $2\pi rh$

Surface Area

Prism: total surface area = lateral area + area of bases

Cylinder: total surface area = $2\pi rh + 2\pi r^2$

Sphere: $A = 4\pi r^2$

Mass

Mass = Density × Volume

Distance

distance = rate × time

Percentage

percentage = rate × base

Interest

Interest = Principal × rate × time

Glossary

Absolute value (p. 72) The distance from 0 to the graph of a number on the number line.

Acute angle (p. 191) An angle with measure between 0° and 90°.

Acute triangle (p. 204) A triangle with three acute angles.

Adjacent angles (p. 192) Two angles with a common side and a common vertex, but with no common points in their interiors.

Alternate interior angles (p. 200) One of two pairs of angles formed when a transversal intersects two lines. In the diagram, ∠1 and ∠4 are one such pair, and ∠2 and ∠3 are the other.

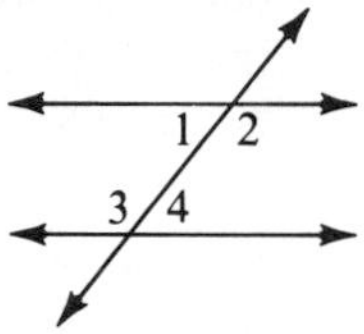

Angle (p. 191) A figure formed by two rays with a common endpoint.

Annual rate of interest (p. 260) A percent of the principal figured on a yearly basis.

Arc (p. 187) A part of a circle.

Area (p. 306) Amount of surface, measured in square units.

Base of a geometric figure (pp. 306, 312, 326, 331) A selected side or face.

Base, numerical (p. 40) A number that is raised to some power. In 5^3, 5 is the base.

Base, in percent relationship (p. 245) The number of which a percent is taken.

Bisect (p. 192) To divide a geometric figure into two congruent parts.

Capacity (p. 327) A measure of the volume of a container.

Center (pp. 187, 340) The point that lies equidistant from all points on a circle or a sphere.

Chord (p. 187) A segment that joins two points on a circle.

Circle (p. 187) A plane figure made up of all points that are the same distance from a given point in the plane.

Circumference (p. 188) The perimeter of a circle.

Collinear points (p. 182) Two or more points that lie on the same line.

Combination (p. 401) An arrangement of a group of things in which order does not matter.

Complementary angles (p. 195) Two angles whose measures have a sum of 90°.

Conditional probability (p. 424) The probability that an event *B* will occur given that an event *A* has occurred.

Cone (p. 331) A closed figure formed by a circular region and a curved surface that comes to a point.

Congruent figures (pp. 182, 191, 217) Figures that have the same size and shape.

Coordinate (p. 12) The number paired with a point on the number line.

Coordinate plane (p. 272) A plane marked with two perpendicular number lines, used to graph ordered pairs of numbers.

Coplanar (p. 183) Lying in the same plane.

Corresponding angles (p. 200) One of four pairs of angles formed when two lines are cut by a transversal, for example, ∠1 and ∠5, ∠2 and ∠6, ∠3 and ∠7, and ∠4 and ∠8.

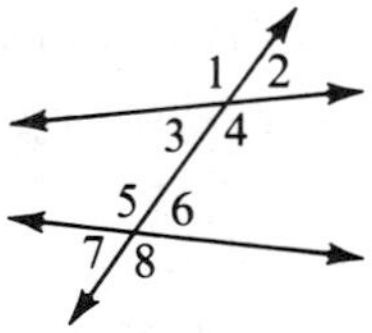

Cosine of an angle (p. 378) If ∠*A* is one of the acute angles in a right triangle, the cosine of ∠*A* (cos *A*) is the ratio of the length of the side adjacent to ∠*A* to the length of the hypotenuse.

Cylinder (p. 327) A geometric solid with two parallel bases that are congruent and one curved surface joining the bases.

Density (p. 344) The mass per unit volume of a substance.

Dependent events (p. 424) Two events in which the result of the first affects the result of the second.

Diagonal (p. 210) A segment that joins two nonconsecutive vertices of a polygon.

Diameter (pp. 187, 340) A chord that contains the center of a circle or a sphere. Also, the length of such a chord.

Endpoint (p. 182) The point at the end of a line segment or ray.

Equation (p. 9) A mathematical sentence with an equals sign to indicate that two expressions name the same number.

Equilateral triangle (p. 205) A triangle in which all sides are congruent.

Equivalent equations (p. 146) Equations that have the same solution.

Equivalent fractions (p. 110) Fractions that name the same number.

Equivalent inequalities (p. 159) Inequalities that have the same solutions.

Evaluate an expression (p. 3) To replace a variable in an expression with one of its values and then complete the indicated arithmetic.

Expanded form (p. 44) The method of representing a number as the sum of products of each digit and powers of 10.

Exponent (p. 40) A number indicating how many times the base is used as a factor.

Extremes of a proportion (p. 230) The first and last terms of a proportion.

Faces of a polyhedron (p. 326) The parts of planes that make up the sides and bases of a polyhedron.

Factor (p. 40) Any of two or more whole numbers that are multiplied to form a product.

Frequency (p. 453) The number of times that one item appears in a set of data.

Frequency distribution (p. 453) A table that pairs each item in a set of data with its frequency.

Frequency polygon (p. 457) A line graph of frequencies, connected to the horizontal axis at each end to form a polygon.

Function (p. 277) A set of ordered pairs in which no two different ordered pairs have the same x-coordinate.

Geometric construction (p. 184) A geometric drawing for which only a compass and a straightedge may be used.

Graph of an equation (p. 280) The line consisting of all points whose coordinates satisfy the equation.

Graph of a number (p. 12) The point on the number line paired with the number.

Grouping symbols (p. 5) Symbols such as parentheses, ( ), and brackets, [ ], that are used to group expressions.

Height (p. 306) The perpendicular distance between the bases of a geometric figure. In triangles, cones, and pyramids, the perpendicular distance from the base to the opposite vertex.

Histogram (p. 457) A bar graph that shows a frequency distribution.

Hypotenuse (p. 364) The side opposite the right angle in a right triangle.

Improper fraction (p. 111) A positive fraction whose numerator is greater than or equal to its denominator, or the opposite of such a fraction.

Independent events (p. 420) Events that have no effect on each other.

Inequality (p. 12) A mathematical sentence formed by placing an inequality sign between two expressions.

Integers (p. 72) The whole numbers and their opposites: . . . , $^-2$, $^-1$, 0, 1, 2, ...

Interest (p. 174) The amount of money paid for the use of money.

Interpolation (p. 361) A method of approximation.

Inverse operations (p. 16) Operations that undo each other, such as addition and subtraction or multiplication and division.

Irrational number (p. 133) All real numbers that are not rational.

Isosceles triangle (p. 205) A triangle with at least two sides congruent.

Lateral area (p. 335) The surface area of a solid, not including the bases.

Lateral surface (p. 335) The faces other than the bases of a solid.

Least common denominator (LCD) (p. 115) The least common multiple of two or more denominators.

Legs of a right triangle (p. 364) The two sides forming the right angle.

Like terms (p. 56) Terms in which only the numerical coefficients are different.

Line (p. 182) A figure determined by two points and extending in both directions without end.

Line segment (p. 182) Two points on a line and all the points between them.

Linear equation in two variables (p. 281) An equation with two variables that can be written in the form $ax + by = c$, where a and b are not both 0.

Lowest terms (p. 111) A fraction is in lowest terms when the numerator and the denominator have no common factor but 1.

Mass (p. 344) The measure of the amount of matter an object contains.

Mean (p. 449) The value found by dividing the sum of a group of numbers by the number of numbers in the group. Also called *average*.

Means of a proportion (p. 230) The second and third terms of a proportion.

Median (p. 449) The number that falls in the middle when data are listed from least to greatest. If the number of data is even, the median is the mean of the two middle items.

Midpoint (p. 182) The point of a segment that divides it into two congruent segments.

Mixed number (p. 111) A whole number plus a proper fraction.

Mode (p. 449) The number that occurs most often in a set of data.

Number sentence (p. 9) An equation or inequality indicating the relationship between two mathematical expressions.

Numerical coefficient (p. 3) In an expression such as $3ab$, the number 3 is the numerical coefficient of ab.

Numerical expression (p. 2) An expression that names a number, such as $2 + 3$.

Obtuse angle (p. 191) An angle with measure between 90° and 180°.

Obtuse triangle (p. 204) A triangle that has one obtuse angle.

Odds (p. 409) A ratio that compares the probability of an event occurring and the probability of the event not occurring.

Open sentence (p. 9) A mathematical sentence that contains one or more variables.

Opposites (p. 72) A pair of numbers such as $^-4$ and 4.

Ordered pair of numbers (p. 272) A pair of numbers whose order is important.

Origin (pp. 12, 272) The graph of zero on a number line or in a rectangular coordinate plane.

Outcome (p. 404) The result of an event.

Parallel lines (p. 200) Lines in the same plane that do not intersect.

Parallelogram (p. 209) A quadrilateral with both pairs of opposite sides parallel.

Percent (p. 241) A ratio of a number to 100, shown by the symbol %.

Percent of change (p. 249) The amount of change divided by the original amount.

Percentage (p. 245) The number that results from taking a percent of another number.

Perfect square (p. 356) A number whose square root is an integer.

Perimeter (p. 188) The distance around a plane figure.

Permutation (p. 396) An arrangement of a group of things in a particular order.

Perpendicular lines (p. 195) Two lines that intersect to form four right angles.

Plane (p. 183) A flat surface extending infinitely in all directions.

Point (p. 182) The simplest figure in geometry, representing an exact location.

Polygon (p. 213) A closed plane figure made up of line segments.

Polyhedron (p. 326) A three-dimensional figure formed of polygonal parts of planes.

Prime number (p. 111) A whole number greater than 1 that has only two whole-number factors, itself and 1.

Principal (p. 260) An amount of money on which interest is paid.

Prism (p. 326) A polyhedron that has two parallel, congruent faces called bases. The other faces are parallelograms.

Probability (p. 404) The ratio of the number of outcomes favoring an event to the total number of possible outcomes.

Proper fraction (p. 111) A positive fraction whose numerator is less than its denominator, or the opposite of such a fraction.

Proportion (p. 230) An equation stating that two ratios are equal.

Protractor (p. 191) A device used to measure angles.

Pyramid (p. 331) A polyhedron that has a polygonal base and three or more triangular faces.

Quadrilateral (p. 209) A polygon with four sides.

Radical (p. 373) An expression such as $\sqrt{5}$ or $\sqrt{a}$.

Radius (pp. 187, 340) A line segment joining any point on a circle or sphere to the center. Also the length of that segment.

Random variable (p. 461) A variable whose value is determined by the outcome of a random experiment.

Range (p. 449) The difference between the greatest and the least numbers in a set of data.

Rate (p. 234) A ratio that compares quantities of different kinds of units.

Ratio (p. 230) An indicated quotient of two numbers.

Ray (p. 182) A part of a line with one endpoint.

Real number (p. 133) Any number that is either a rational number or an irrational number.

Reciprocals (p. 126) Two numbers whose product is 1.

Rectangle (p. 209) A quadrilateral with four right angles.

Regular polygon (p. 213) A polygon in which all sides are congruent and all angles are congruent.

Relation (p. 294) A set of ordered pairs.

Relatively prime numbers (p. 111) Two or more numbers that have no other common factor but 1.

Rhombus (p. 209) A parallelogram in which all sides are congruent.

Right angle (p. 191) An angle with measure 90°.

Right triangle (p. 204) A triangle with a right angle.

Rigid motions (p. 217) Motions such as rotation, translation, and reflection, used to move a figure to a new position without changing its shape or size.

Sampling (p. 428) A method used to estimate probability by selecting a part of a larger group.

Scalene triangle (p. 205) A triangle with no two sides congruent.

Scientific notation (p. 98) A method of expressing a number as the product of a power of 10 and a number between 1 and 10.

Segment (p. 182) *See* line segment.

Semicircle (p. 187) Half of a circle.

Sides of an equation (p. 9) The mathematical expressions to the right and to the left of the equals sign.

Sides of a figure (pp. 191, 212) The rays that form an angle or the segments that form a polygon.

Similar figures (p. 368) Figures that have the same shape but not necessarily the same size.

Simple form (p. 111) A mixed number is in simple form if its fractional part is expressed in lowest terms.

Simplify an expression (p. 2) To replace an expression with its simplest name.

Sine of an angle (p. 378) If $\angle A$ is an acute angle of a right triangle, the sine of $\angle A$ ($\sin A$) is the ratio of the length of the side opposite $\angle A$ to the length of the hypotenuse.

Slope of a line (p. 288) The steepness of a line; that is, of the change in the *y*-coordinate to the change in the *x*-coordinate when moving from one point on a line to another point.

Solid (p. 326) An enclosed region of space bounded by planes.

Solution (p. 9) A value of a variable that makes an equation or inequality a true sentence.

Solving a right triangle (p. 382) The process of finding the measures of the sides and angles of a right triangle.

Sphere (p. 340) A figure in space made up of all points equidistant from a given point.

Square (p. 209) A rectangle with all four sides congruent.

Square root of a number (p. 356) One of the two equal factors of the number.

Statistical measures (p. 449) Measures including the range, mean, median, and mode used to analyze numerical data.

Supplementary angles (p. 196) Two angles whose measures have a sum of $180°$.

Surface area (p. 335) The total area of a solid.

Symmetric (pp. 321, 322) A figure is symmetric with respect to a line if it can be folded on that line so that every point on one side coincides exactly with a point on the other side. A figure is symmetric with respect to a point O if for each point A on the figure there is a point B on the figure for which O is the midpoint of $\overline{AB}$.

System of equations (p. 284) A set of two or more equations in the same variables.

Tangent of an angle (p. 378) If $\angle A$ is an acute angle of a right triangle, the tangent of $\angle A$ ($\tan A$) is the ratio of the length of the side opposite $\angle A$ to the length of the side adjacent to $\angle A$.

Terms of an expression (p. 3) The parts of a mathematical expression that are separated by a + sign.

Terms of a proportion (p. 230) The numbers in a proportion.

Transform an equation or inequality (pp. 146, 159) To rewrite an equation or inequality as an equivalent equation or inequality.

Transversal (p. 200) A line that intersects two other lines.

Trapezoid (p. 210) A quadrilateral with exactly one pair of parallel sides.

Triangle (p. 204) A polygon with three sides.

Trigonometric ratios (p. 378) Any of the sine, cosine, and tangent ratios.

Value of a variable (p. 2) Any number that a variable represents.

Variable (p. 2) A symbol used to represent one or more numbers.

Variable expression (p. 2) A mathematical expression that contains a variable.

Vertex of an angle (p. 191) The common endpoint of two intersecting rays.

Vertex of a polygon or polyhedron (pp. 204, 331) The point at which two sides of a polygon or three or more edges of a polyhedron intersect.

Vertical angles (p. 197) The angles opposite each other when two lines intersect to form four angles.

Volume (p. 326) A measure of the space occupied by a solid.

***x*-axis** (p. 272) The horizontal number line on a coordinate plane.

***x*-coordinate** (p. 272) The first number in an ordered pair of numbers that designates the location of a point on the coordinate plane. Also called the *abscissa.*

***y*-axis** (p. 272) The vertical number line on a coordinate plane.

***y*-coordinate** (p. 272) The second number in an ordered pair of numbers that designates the location of a point on the coordinate plane. Also called the *ordinate.*

Index

Credits

Mechanical art: ANCO. Cover concept: Kirchoff/Wohlberg, Inc., cover photograph: Balthazar Korab. Page 1, Gregory Heiser/Gamma-Liaison; 30, Milt & Joan Mann/The Marilyn Gartman Agency; 39, © Peter Menzel/Stock, Boston; 62, Ben Rose © 1982/The Image Bank; 71, W.K. Almond/Stock, Boston; 83, Clyde H. Smith/Peter Arnold Inc.; 87, Gary Milburn/Tom Stack & Associates; 98, NASA; 105, © Paulo Bonino 1982/ Photo Researchers, Inc.; 114, Judy Gibbs; 120, © Alvis Upitis/The Image Bank; 129, Greig Cranna; 136, Rainbow; 143, Courtesy of French National Railroads; 172, Miguel/The Image Bank; 174, Thomas Hovland/Grant Heilman Photography; 181, © Ted Kawalerski/The Image Bank; 190, 222, NASA; 229, Peter Arnold, Inc.; 237, Benn Mitchell © 1981/The Image Bank; 239, © 1980 Al Satterwhite/The Image Bank; 253, © John Lee/The Image Bank; 266, Greig Cranna; 271, Photo Courtesy of LEXIDATA; 292, © Lou Jones 1981/The Image Bank; 305, Runk/Schoenberger/Grant Heilman Photography; 310, © Joe Munroe/Photo Researchers, Inc.; 342, © Van Bucher 1982/Photo Researchers, Inc.; 348, © Dick Davis 1972/Photo Researchers, Inc.; 355, © Eunice Harris 1983/Photo Researchers, Inc.; 363, Milt & Joan Mann/The Marilyn Gartman Agency; 377, © 1979 Stuart Cohen/Stock, Boston; 388, © C.B. Jones 1982/Taurus Photos; 395, © David W. Hamilton/The Image Bank; 403, Mike Mazzaschi/Stock, Boston; 419, David Muench Photography; 430, © 1982 Arnold Zann/Black Star; 439, Animals Animals/Robert C. Fields; 448, © Werner H. Müller/Peter Arnold, Inc.; 455, © Gordon E. Smith 1980/Photo Researchers, Inc.; 460, © Tom McHugh 1979/Photo Researchers, Inc.; 464, Russ Kinne/Photo Researchers, Inc.

Answers to Selected Exercises

1 Introduction to Algebra

PAGE 4 WRITTEN EXERCISES **1.** 48 **3.** 105 **5.** 14.15 **7.** 4.5 **9.** 25 **11.** 4 **13.** 12 **15.** 27 **17.** 2 **19.** 47 **21.** 26 **23.** 512 **25.** 9 **27.** 24 **29.** 2.5 **31.** 112.5 **33.** 680.805 **35.** 3.15 **37.** 2

PAGE 4 REVIEW EXERCISES **1.** 51.87 **3.** 45.93 **5.** 0.27 **7.** 6.3

PAGES 7–8 WRITTEN EXERCISES **1.** 92 **3.** 51 **5.** 2 **7.** 126 **9.** 7 **11.** 36 **13.** 10 **15.** 70 **17.** 36 **19.** 196 **21.** 3 **23.** 1512 **25.** 91 **27.** 84 **29.** 0.5 **31.** 4.1 **33.** 5827.248 **35.** 14.6 **37.** $2x \times (y - 4) + 2x$ **39.** $x \times (y + z \div 3 + 1) - z$

PAGE 8 REVIEW EXERCISES **1.** 24 **3.** 13.2 **5.** 2040 **7.** 1.3 **9.** 0.63

PAGE 8 CALCULATOR KEY-IN **1.** 288 **3.** 16.5 **5.** 6048

PAGES 10–11 WRITTEN EXERCISES **1.** True **3.** False **5.** False **7.** True **9.** False **11.** 6 **13.** 85 **15.** 29 **17.** 8 **19.** No solution **21.** No solution **23.** 1518 **25.** 17 **27.** 11 **29.** 51 **31.** 12 **33.** 9 **35.** 2 **37.** No solution **39.** 4 For exercises 41 and 43, answers will vary. An example is given. **41.** $3x - 25 = 5$ **43.** $400 \div x + 16 = 20$ **45.** +, − **47.** +, ÷ **49.** −, −, +; or +, ÷, − **51.** −, +, ÷

PAGE 11 REVIEW EXERCISES **1.** 588 **3.** 8 **5.** 60 **7.** 172

PAGES 13–15 WRITTEN EXERCISES

1. 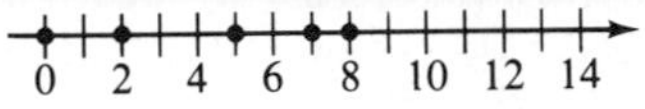

3. 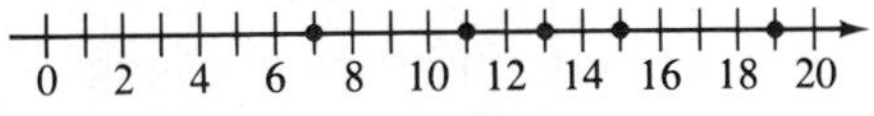

5. 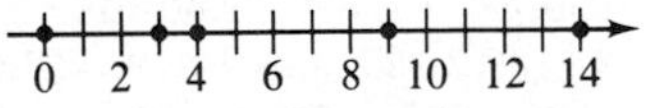

7. > **9.** > **11.** > **13.** > **15.** < **17.** > **19.** $18 < 32 < 46$, or $46 > 32 > 18$ **21.** $103 < 130 < 310$, or $310 > 130 > 103$ **23.** $689 < 698 < 986$, or $986 > 698 > 689$

25. 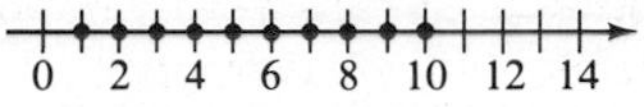

27. 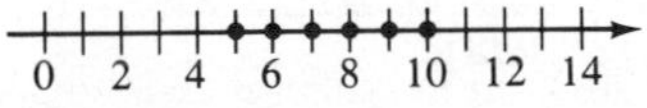

29. 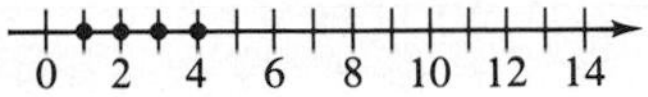

31. No solution

33. 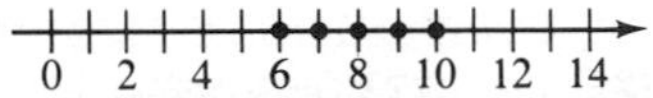

35. 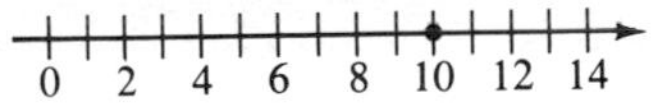

37. 0, 1, 2, 3, . . . , 11 **39.** 6, 7, 8, and so on **41.** 25, 26, 27, and so on **43.** 66, 67, 68, and so on **45.** 11, 12, 13, 14, 15, 16, 17, 18 **47.** 22, 23, 24, 25, 26, 27, 28 **49.** 104, 105, 106, 107, 108, 109, 110, 111, 112, 113, 114, 115, 116, 117 **51.** 5, 10 **53.** No solution **55.** 23 **57.** 4, 10 **59.** 14 **61.** No solution **63.** 5, 6, 7, 8, 9 **65.** 5, 6, 7, 8, 9, 10 **67.** 3, 4, 5, 6

PAGE 15 REVIEW EXERCISES **1.** 21.9 **3.** 6.17 **5.** 91.5 **7.** 0.9 **9.** 0.00644

PAGES 18–19 WRITTEN EXERCISES **1.** $x = 15 - 8$; 7 **3.** $f = 74 - 38$; 36 **5.** $y = 14 + 9$; 23 **7.** $b = 32 + 25$; 57 **9.** $c = 27 \div 3$; 9 **11.** $m = 108 \div 9$; 12 **13.** $n = 9 \times 6$; 54 **15.** $g = 7 \times 16$; 112 **17.** $a = 17 - 17$; 0 **19.** $n = 42 \div 14$; 3 **21.** $h = 297 \times 11$; 3267 **23.** $d = 110 + 87$; 197 **25.** $q = 465 \div 31$; 15 **27.** $p = 358 - 208$; 150 **29.** $c = 536 - 511$; 25 **31.** $g = 401 + 19$; 420 **33.** $r > 12 - 8$; all the numbers greater than 4 **35.** $p \geq 36 \div 4$; all the numbers greater than or equal to 9 **37.** $q \leq 59 + 24$; all the numbers less than or equal to 83 **39.** $a < 340 \times 17$; all the numbers less than 5780 **41.** $c \leq 177 - 113$; all the numbers less than or equal to 64 **43.** $t \geq 9 + 55$; all the numbers greater than or equal to 64 **45.** $y < 20 \times 80$; all the numbers less than 1600 **47.** $x > 86 \div 43$; all the numbers greater than 2 **49.** 5 **51.** 11 **53.** 46 **55.** 67.5 **57.** 56 **59.** 63 **61.** All the numbers less than or equal to 10.8 **63.** All the numbers greater than or equal to 8 **65.** All the numbers less than 32

PAGE 19 SELF-TEST A **1.** 25.8 **2.** 5.75 **3.** 2.46 **4.** 7.6 **5.** 46 **6.** 15 **7.** 168 **8.** 50 **9.** 6 **10.** 2 **11.** 9 **12.** 4 **13.** 6 **14.** 29 **15.** 8 **16.** No solution **17.** 3 **18.** > **19.** < **20.** = **21.** 0, 1, 2, 3, 4 **22.** 85, 86, 87, and so on **23.** 19, 20, 21, 22, 23, 24, 25, 26, 27 **24.** $g = 12 + 32$; 44 **25.** $d < 112 \div 7$; all the numbers less than 16 **26.** $5a = 49 - 4$; $a = 45 \div 5$; 9

PAGES 22–23 WRITTEN EXERCISES **1.** $8b$ **3.** $53 - d$ **5.** $30 + t$ **7.** $g + 9$ **9.** $78 - m$ **11.** $19 + n$ **13.** $d \div 11$ **15.** $12 - z$ **17.** $15 + 11t$ **19.** $(m + n) \times 91$ **21.** $r \div (83 - 10)$ **23.** $c(3 + 9 + 12)$ **25.** $(60 + 40 + 10) \div d$ **27.** $b + 3$ **29.** $x + 6$ **31.** $0.25q$ **33.** $x \div 60$ **35.** $x - 10$

PAGE 23 REVIEW EXERCISES **1.** 27 **3.** 576 **5.** All the numbers greater than 72 **7.** All the numbers less than or equal to 14

PAGES 25–26 WRITTEN EXERCISES **1.** $5d > 20$ **3.** $3w - 7 = 8$ **5.** $5 \div 6r < 42$ **7.** $n - 1 < 5$ **9.** $2n \div 3 = 15$ **11.** $(4 + x) \div 2 = 34$ **13.** $a(6 - 1) = a$ **15.** $59 - x > 2x + 3$ **17.** $(y + 12)5 = 100$ **19.** $(b \div 8) + 9 < 30$ **21.** $2n = (n + 4)8$ **23. a.** $2x = 32$ **b.** 16 **25. a.** $10y - 6 \geq 25$ **b.** 0, 5

PAGE 26 REVIEW EXERCISES **1.** 22 **3.** 108 **5.** 2 **7.** $\frac{23}{7}$, or $3\frac{2}{7}$ **9.** 33.66

PAGES 29–31 PROBLEMS **1.** 11.65 m **3.** \$2824.80 **5.** \$41,520 **7.** 936 people **9.** \$78.87 **11.** \$1596 **13.** \$89,336 **15.** \$23.29 **17.** \$12.75

PAGE 31 SELF-TEST B **1.** $12 \div y$ **2.** $x - 5$ **3.** $9g - 21$ **4.** $15 = 9 + 2x$ **5.** $25(b + 7) > 11 \div 4$ **6.** $24 - 4n \leq 12$ **7.** \$114.15 **8.** 49 passengers

PAGE 33 ENRICHMENT **1.** Answers vary.

PAGE 34 CHAPTER REVIEW **1.** B **3.** A **5.** True **7.** True **9.** True **11.** True **13.** True **15.** B **17.** D **19.** d

PAGES 36–37 CUMULATIVE REVIEW EXERCISES **1.** 809 **3.** 3.1 **5.** 351.9 **7.** 27 **9.** 25 **11.** 2 **13.** 55 **15.** 8.6 **17.** 28 **19.** 7 **21.** 3 **23.** 19 **25.** 13, 14, 15, and so on **27.** 0, 1, 2, 3, 4, 5, 6, 7, 8 **29.** 8, 9, 10, 11, 12 **31.** $g = 20 - 18$; 2 **33.** $z < 65 \div 5$; all the numbers less than 13 **35.** $7f \leq 13 + 1$; $f \leq 14 \div 7$; all the numbers less than or equal to 2 **37.** $t - 31$ **39.** $4 + 2k$ **41.** $n - 15 = 24$ **43.** $2n - 3 = 9$

PAGE 37 CUMULATIVE REVIEW PROBLEMS **1.** 6780 words **3.** 81 certificates **5.** 761 people **7.** 72 m

2 The Decimal System

PAGE 43 WRITTEN EXERCISES **1.** 64 **3.** 100 **5.** 14 **7.** 225 **9.** 1 **11.** 3^2 **13.** 9^2 **15.** $(16 \times 4)^2$ **17.** 2^7 **19.** 10^5 **21.** n^{11} **23.** 100 **25.** 81 **27.** 576 **29.** 1 **31.** 1875 **33.** 225 **35.** 1 **37.** 1000 **39.** 96 **41.** 52 **43.** 4 **45.** $\frac{1}{8}$ **47.** $n = 1$

PAGE 43 REVIEW EXERCISES **1.** $<, <$ **3.** $>, >$ **5.** $>, >$ **7.** $<, <$

PAGES 46–47 WRITTEN EXERCISES **1.** $(3 \times 10) + 8$ **3.** $(8 \times 1000) + (9 \times 10) + 1$ **5.** $(4 \times 0.1) + (7 \times 0.01)$ **7.** $(6 \times 0.01) + (3 \times 0.001)$ **9.** $(1 \times 0.1) + (8 \times 0.01) + (7 \times 0.001)$ **11.** 54.57 **13.** 9002.146 **15.** 7.43 **17.** 19.005 **19.** 0.0048 **21.** 6.025 **23.** $<$ **25.** $>$ **27.** $>$ **29.** $>$ **31.** $<$ **33.** $<$ **35.** $>$ **37.** $=$ **39.** $=$ **41.** $>$ **43.** $=$ **45.** $3.08 < 3.16 < 3.97$ **47.** $0.07 < 0.08 < 0.2$ **49.** $7.028 < 7.0862 < 7.11$ **51.** $0.406 + 0.215 < 0.27 + 0.81 < 1.62 + 0.09$ **53.** $(5 \times 10^3) + (2 \times 10^2) + (8 \times 10^1) + (0 \times 10^0)$ **55.** $(1 \times 10^2) + (8 \times 10^1) + (3 \times 10^0) + \left(0 \times \frac{1}{10^1}\right) + \left(8 \times \frac{1}{10^2}\right)$ **57.** $\left(0 \times \frac{1}{10^1}\right) + \left(9 \times \frac{1}{10^2}\right) + \left(1 \times \frac{1}{10^3}\right)$ **59.** $(7 \times 10^0) + \left(4 \times \frac{1}{10^1}\right) + \left(8 \times \frac{1}{10^2}\right) + \left(2 \times \frac{1}{10^3}\right)$ **61.** $(2 \times 10^2) + (0 \times 10^1) + (4 \times 10^0) + \left(5 \times \frac{1}{10^1}\right)$ **63.** $(3 \times 10^1) + (8 \times 10^0) + \left(0 \times \frac{1}{10^1}\right) + \left(0 \times \frac{1}{10^2}\right) + \left(3 \times \frac{1}{10^3}\right)$

PAGE 47 REVIEW EXERCISES **1.** 90 **3.** 5 **5.** 250 **7.** 27 **9.** $\frac{1}{5}$

PAGE 49 WRITTEN EXERCISES **1.** 30 **3.** 290 **5.** 650 **7.** 160 **9.** 72.46 **11.** 0.06 **13.** 0.01 **15.** 18.17 **17.** 0.001 **19.** 401.090 **21.** 250.341 **23.** 8.100 **25.** b **27.** a **29.** b **31.** c

PAGE 50 SELF-TEST A **1.** 16 **2.** 512 **3.** 9 **4.** 3125 **5.** a^{11} **6.** $>$ **7.** $>$ **8.** $<$ **9.** 80 **10.** 3.18 **11.** 300

PAGE 50 CALCULATOR KEY-IN **1.** 56, 56 **3.** 3243, 3243

PAGES 54–55 WRITTEN EXERCISES
1. 14.6; associative **3.** 14.24; distributive **5.** 18.97; commutative and associative **7.** 0.21; commutative and associative **9.** 0; associative and multiplication property of zero **11.** 72; distributive **13.** False **15.** True **17.** False **19.** $n = 0$ **21.** $t = 3.2$ **23.** $w = 0$ **25.** $c = 9$ **27.** $g = 15.9$ **29.** $n = 3$ **31.** $d = 1565$ **33.** $t = 0$ **35.** 3.88 **37.** 400 **39.** 900 For exercises 41 and 43, answers will vary. An example is given. **41.** $a = 1, b = 2, c = 3$; $(1 \times 2) + (2 \times 3) \neq 2(1 \times 3)$ **43.** $a = 4$, $b = 6, c = 10$; $(6 + 10)(4 + 10) \neq 10(6 \times 4)$

PAGE 55 REVIEW EXERCISES **1.** 31 **3.** 74 **5.** 13 **7.** 40

PAGES 57–58 WRITTEN EXERCISES
1. 54 **3.** 177 **5.** 247 **7.** 0.55 **9.** 73 **11.** $54m^6 + 7$ **13.** 29.9 **15.** $17x + 14y$ **17.** $36d$ **19.** $280m + 160$ **21.** 18.752 **23.** 1 **25.** 103.04 **27.** 128 **29.** 101.76
31. $(4^2 - 3) \times 5 - 2 = 63$
33. $12 - (10 \div 2) + (3 \times 8) = 31$
35. $4.2 + 3 \times [(3.6 \div 0.4) + 9.6] = 60$

PAGE 58 REVIEW EXERCISES **1.** 0.006 **3.** 200 **5.** 6 **7.** 30

PAGE 58 COMPUTER BYTE **1.** 800 **3.** 7000 **5.** 17 **7.** 0.0 **9.** 75

PAGES 62–63 PROBLEMS **1.** \$113.70 **3.** 22 bonus points **5.** 41 points **7.** \$488.75 **9.** 12,948 shares **11.** \$1.90

PAGE 63 SELF-TEST B **1.** 102 **2.** 93 **3.** 21 **4.** 67.96 **5.** 36 **6.** 189 **7.** $16a + 14$ **8.** 6.25 **9.** 13 **10.** $43b + 37$ **11.** \$182.24

PAGE 65 ENRICHMENT **1.** Answers will vary.

PAGE 66 CHAPTER REVIEW **1.** $=$ **3.** $<$ **5.** $=$ **7.** $<$ **9.** True **11.** True **13.** False **15.** B **17.** C **19.** E **21.** b

PAGE 68 CUMULATIVE REVIEW EXERCISES **1.** 7.5 **3.** 23 **5.** 124 **7.** 57.2 **9.** 0 **11.** 36.7 **13.** 101.38 **15.** 24.5 **17.** 5
19. $15 < 26 < 48$, or $48 > 26 > 15$
21. $115 < 125 < 225$, or $225 > 125 > 115$
23. $2^2 < 5^3 < 3^5$, or $3^5 > 5^3 > 2^2$ **25.** a **27.** a **29.** True **31.** True **33.** False **35.** False **37.** True

PAGE 69 CUMULATIVE REVIEW PROBLEMS **1.** \$3010 **3.** \$42.95 **5.** \$20 **7.** \$17

3 Positive and Negative Numbers

PAGES 73–74 WRITTEN EXERCISES

1.

3.

5.
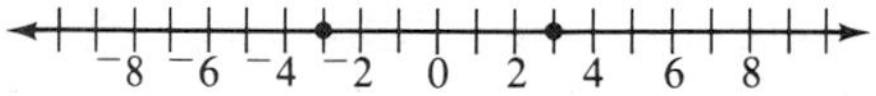

7.
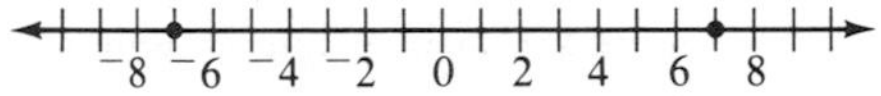

9.
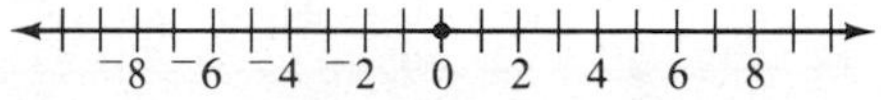

11. $>$ **13.** $>$ **15.** $<$ **17.** 3 **19.** 0 **21.** 9 **23.** 8 **25.** −15, −2, 0, 6 **27.** −12, −8, −1, 1, 7 **29.** −14, −10, 4, 8, 14 **31. a.** −6, 6 **33. a.** −4, 4 **35. a.** 0 **37. a.** −1, 0, 1 **39. a.** −4, −3, −2, −1, 0, 1, 2, 3, 4 **41. a.** −7, −6, −5, −4, −3, 3, 4, 5, 6, 7 **43.** positive **45.** $|n|$ represents the distance n from the origin.

PAGE 74 REVIEW EXERCISES **1.** $>$ **3.** $>$ **5.** $<$ **7.** $>$ **9.** $<$

PAGES 77–78 WRITTEN EXERCISES

1.
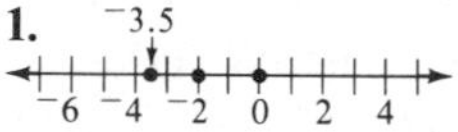

3.
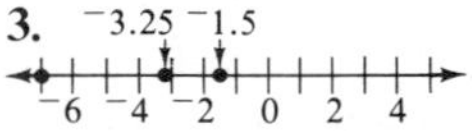

5.
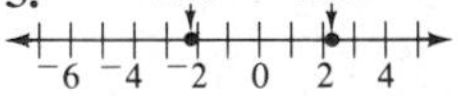

7.

9.
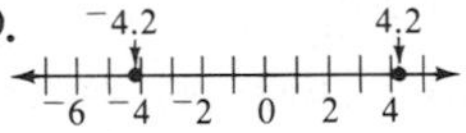

11.
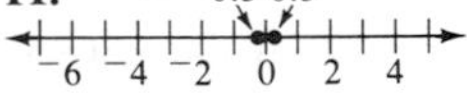

13. 2.36 **15.** 16 **17.** 3.03 **19.** $<$ **21.** $<$ **23.** $<$ **25.** $>$ **27.** $<$ **29.** −8, −7.6, −1.75, 6.03, 6.3 **31.** −100.5, −46.8, −2.1, −2, 3.11 **33.** −3.3, −0.33, −0.3, 30.3, 33

35.
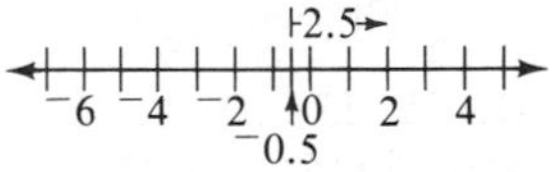

37.
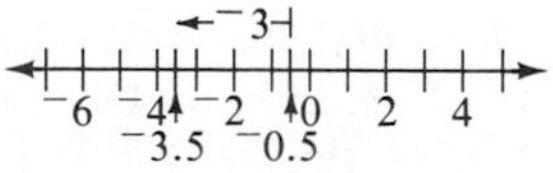

39.
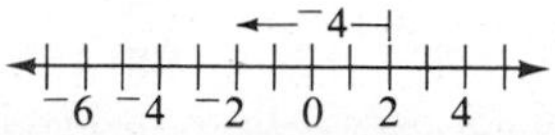

41. −4.1, 4.1 **43.** −26.3, 26.3 **45.** −1.19, 1.19 **47.** −4.5 **49.** −12 **51. a.** −4, −3, −2, −1, 0, 1, 2, 3, 4 **53. a.** −5, −4, −3, −2, −1, 0, 1, 2, 3, 4, 5

PAGE 78 REVIEW EXERCISES **1.** 11.14; distributive **3.** 27.18; multiplication property of one **5.** 132.3; distributive **7.** 1075; commutative and associative **9.** 0; associative property and multiplication property of zero

PAGE 82 WRITTEN EXERCISES

1.

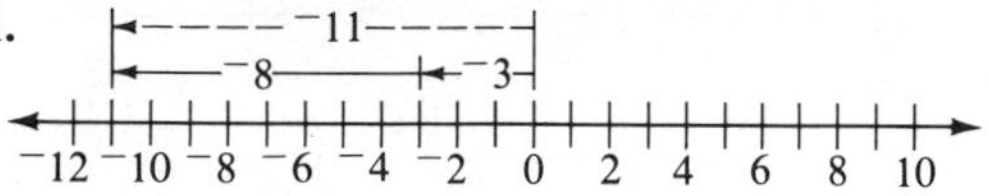

3.

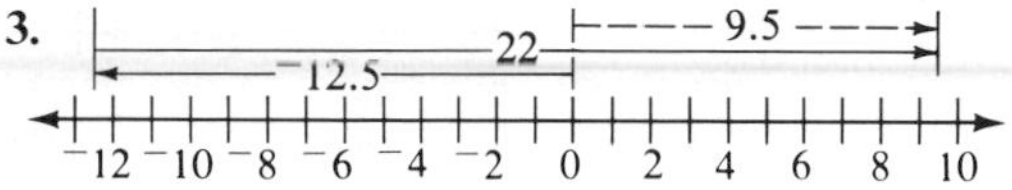

5. $^-19$ **7.** $^-13$ **9.** $^-0.3$ **11.** 0 **13.** 16.2 **15.** 4.17 **17.** $^-84$ **19.** 10.5 **21.** $^-18.72$ **23.** $^-26.1$ **25.** 0 **27.** $^-0.12$ **29.** 6.3 **31.** $^-10.8$ **33.** $^-7.25$ **35.** 12 **37.** $^-12$ **39.** $^-18.5$ **41.** $^-2.4$ **43.** $^-19.8$ **45.** $^-25.9$ **47. a.** $^-6.7$ **b.** $^-9$ **49.** $<$ **51.** $>$ **53. a.** $=$ **b.** $<$ **c.** $<$ **d.** $<$ **e.** $=$ **f.** $<$ **g.** $|x + y| \le |x| + |y|$

PAGE 83 PROBLEMS **1.** $^-7 + 13 + {}^-3$; 3°C **3.** $3.5 + {}^-11 + 2$; lost; 5.5 lost **5.** $^-4.30 + 2.50 + 2.60$; gain

PAGE 83 REVIEW EXERCISES **1.** 156.1 **3.** 64.9 **5.** 44.89 **7.** 4.2 **9.** 285

PAGES 85–86 WRITTEN EXERCISES **1.** $7 + (-19)$ **3.** $6.2 + 8.3$ **5.** -12 **7.** 14.5 **9.** -6 **11.** -27 **13.** 42 **15.** 15 **17.** -43 **19.** 20 **21.** 44 **23.** -1.1 **25.** 2.2 **27.** -24.6 **29.** -24.6 **31.** 3.37 **33.** 24.8 **35.** -41.3 **37.** 1.8 **39.** -5.9 **41.** 8 **43.** 6.2 **45.** -4.5 **47.** -1.7 **49.** 10.7 **51.** -10.7 **53.** -1.7 **55.** -8 **57.** -5 **59.** -13 **61.** 4 **63.** 9 **65.** 14

PAGES 86–87 PROBLEMS **1.** $-3 - (-11)$; 8°C **3.** $1226 - 1455$; -229 m **5.** $(1100 - 200) - 350$; 550 m **7.** \$10.25

PAGE 87 SELF-TEST A **1.** $>$ **2.** $>$ **3.** $<$ **4.** $=$ **5.** $=$ **6.** $^-54$, $^-4.52$, $^-0.25$, 0, 5.4 **7.** $^-7.3$, $^-3.79$, $^-0.37$, $^-0.09$, 37 **8.** 33 **9.** 0 **10.** $^-1.44$ **11.** 35 **12.** 0 **13.** $^-36$ **14.** 11.6 **15.** -11.6 **16.** -11.6

PAGES 90–91 WRITTEN EXERCISES **1.** 27 **3.** -56 **5.** 96 **7.** 0 **9.** -12 **11.** 5.1 **13.** -2.9 **15.** 15.4 **17.** -5 **19.** 459 **21.** -66.69 **23.** 0 **25.** 3.42 **27.** -111.24 **29.** 37.875 **31.** 61.38 **33.** -1.054 **35.** 0 **37.** 361.9 **39.** -40.81 **41.** -8.2 **43.** 66.0156 **45.** -100 **47.** $9m - 11$ **49.** 2 **51.** $-5a$ **53.** $5b$ **55.** -2 **57.** -2 **59.** 0 **61.** 2 **63.** -30 **65.** 0

PAGE 91 REVIEW EXERCISES **1.** 56 **3.** 154 **5.** 13 **7.** 26

PAGES 93–94 WRITTEN EXERCISES **1.** -6 **3.** 3 **5.** 0 **7.** -12 **9.** -7.5 **11.** 3.6 **13.** -35 **15.** -5.3 **17.** 8 **19.** 0 **21.** -0.5 **23.** -9.5 **25.** -2.2 **27.** 13.8 **29.** 0.1545 **31.** -6.3 **33.** 4.7 **35.** -1.85 **37.** -3.2 **39.** 0.625 **41.** -4.2 **43.** -1.2 **45.** -2 **47.** -72 **49.** -8

PAGE 94 REVIEW EXERCISES **1.** 49 **3.** 784 **5.** 112 **7.** 1 **9.** 37

PAGE 94 CALCULATOR KEY-IN **1.** 1.1 **3.** -28.201 **5.** 5101.015

PAGE 96 WRITTEN EXERCISES **1.** $-\frac{1}{32}$ **3.** $\frac{1}{1000}$ **5.** 1 **7.** $\frac{1}{25}$ **9.** $\frac{1}{64}$ **11.** $\frac{1}{49}$ **13.** 1 **15.** $\frac{1}{27}$ **17.** $\frac{1}{256}$ **19.** $-\frac{1}{8}$ **21.** 1 **23.** -3 **25.** 5 **27.** -2 **29.** -2 **31.** 8 **33.** 0 **35.** 1 **37.** -4 **39.** -3 **41.** $\frac{1}{x^5}$ **43.** $\frac{1}{a^5}$ **45.** $\frac{1}{w^8}$

PAGE 97 SELF-TEST B **1.** -47.46 **2.** -136.68 **3.** 378 **4.** -11 **5.** -31 **6.** 8 **7.** $\frac{1}{16}$ **8.** $-\frac{1}{216}$ **9.** $\frac{1}{343}$ **10.** $\frac{1}{81}$

PAGES 98–99 ENRICHMENT **1.** 5.798×10^3 **3.** 8.915673×10^6 **5.** 1.75 **7.** 5.01×10^{-2} **9.** 3790 **11.** 301,000 **13.** 0.056 **15.** 0.0000000399 **17.** 7.4×10^{-4} **19.** 1.5×10^{11}

PAGE 100 CHAPTER REVIEW **1.** $<$ **3.** $>$ **5.** $=$ **7.** $<$ **9.** $>$ **11.** $>$ **13.** False **15.** True **17.** True **19.** False **21.** True **23.** False **25.** False **27.** True **29.** True **31.** True **33.** True **35.** True **37.** c **39.** b

PAGES 102–103 CUMULATIVE REVIEW EXERCISES **1.** 6 **3.** All the numbers less than 180 **5.** 3 **7.** 17 **9.** $p + 42$ **11.** $w^3 + 17$ **13.** $59y^3$ **15.** $3m = 33$ **17.** $x - 77 \le x + 5$ **19.** 68.5 **21.** 190 **23.** 37.55 **25.** 175.8 **27.** 3248 **29.** $17n - 5m$ **31.** $8a^5b^2$ **33.** $4w^5 + 3w^3$ **35.** 6 **37.** 100 **39.** $-20, -7, 0, 6, 12, 15$ **41.** $-5, -3, 0, 1, 7, 9$

PAGE 103 CUMULATIVE REVIEW PROBLEMS **1.** \$59.46 **3.** 4 **5.** Deli Delights

4 Rational Numbers

PAGES 108–109 WRITTEN EXERCISES

1. 

3. 

5. 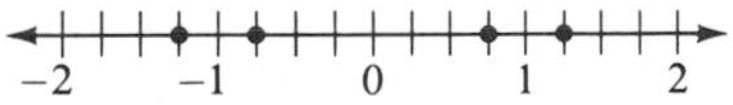

7. $\frac{-1}{2}, \frac{1}{-2}$ **9.** $-\frac{1}{11}, \frac{1}{-11}$ **11.** $-\frac{2}{9}, \frac{-2}{9}$ **13.** $\frac{-13}{6}, \frac{13}{-6}$ **15.** $\frac{-3}{4}, \frac{3}{-4}$ **17.** 6 **19.** $\frac{1}{4}$ **21.** 3 **23.** -3 **25.** $-\frac{7}{8}$ **27.** -1 **29.** $-\frac{1}{3}$ **31.** -3 **33.** -9 **35.** $\frac{7}{6}$ **37.** $\frac{3}{7}$ **39.** $-\frac{1}{9}$ **41.** $-\frac{2}{7}$ **43.** $-\frac{3}{8}$

PAGE 109 REVIEW EXERCISES **1.** 3, 4, 8, 18, 36 **3.** 1, 5, 6, 10, 15, 30, 45 **5.** 6, x

PAGES 112–113 WRITTEN EXERCISES **1.** 4 **3.** 5 **5.** 7 **7.** 3 **9.** 125 **11.** $\frac{3}{5}$ **13.** $2\frac{3}{4}$ **15.** $-\frac{1}{9}$ **17.** $-5\frac{2}{3}$ **19.** $\frac{-2}{5}$ **21.** $10\frac{5}{12}$ **23.** $-6\frac{1}{13}$ **25.** $-42\frac{6}{7}$ **27.** $1\frac{1}{2}$ **29.** $30\frac{11}{15}$ **31.** $\frac{13}{4}$ **33.** $\frac{38}{7}$ **35.** $\frac{43}{8}$ **37.** $-\frac{31}{8}$ **39.** $-\frac{65}{9}$ **41.** 2 **43.** 1 **45.** 4 **47.** -4 **49.** $\frac{1}{3}$ **51.** $\frac{1}{c}$ **53.** $\frac{x}{5y}$ **55.** $\frac{2}{3k}$

PAGES 113–114 PROBLEMS **1.** $\frac{1}{3}$ of the apartments **3.** Yes **5. a.** $\frac{1}{2}$ of the class **b.** $\frac{2}{5}$ of the class **c.** $\frac{30}{30}$, or $\frac{1}{1}$ of the class **d.** $\frac{9}{10}$ of the class **7. a.** $\frac{1}{6}$ of the bulbs **b.** $\frac{1}{2}$ of the total collection **9.** $\frac{1}{5}$ of the families

PAGE 114 REVIEW EXERCISES **1.** 49 **3.** 1296 **5.** 1 **7.** 5184 **9.** 243

PAGES 116–117 WRITTEN EXERCISES **1.** $\frac{4}{12}, \frac{1}{12}$ **3.** $\frac{6}{8}, \frac{5}{8}$ **5.** $\frac{6}{27}, -\frac{1}{27}$ **7.** $\frac{70}{147}, \frac{6}{147}$ **9.** $-\frac{20}{30}, \frac{7}{30}$ **11.** $\frac{16}{300}, \frac{21}{300}$ **13.** $-\frac{48}{112}, -\frac{7}{112}$ **15.** $\frac{35}{294}, \frac{30}{294}$ **17.** $\frac{70}{80}, \frac{25}{80}, \frac{42}{80}$ **19.** $\frac{108}{252}, \frac{441}{252}, \frac{112}{252}$ **21.** $\frac{2}{130}, \frac{78}{130}, \frac{45}{130}$ **23.** $-\frac{60}{72}, \frac{16}{72}, -\frac{63}{72}$ **25.** $\frac{2a}{6}, \frac{b}{6}$ **27.** $\frac{20h}{500}, \frac{5h}{500}, \frac{4h}{500}$ **29.** $\frac{3}{3c}, \frac{2}{3c}$ **31.** $\frac{3yz}{xyz}, \frac{xz}{xyz}, \frac{5xy}{xyz}$ **33.** $<$ **35.** $<$ **37.** $>$ **39.** $=$ **41.** $>$ **43.** $>$

PAGE 117 REVIEW EXERCISES **1.** 25.76 **3.** 4.87 **5.** -11.8 **7.** 23.4 **9.** 14.5

PAGE 117 CALCULATOR KEY-IN **1.** $<$ **3.** $>$

PAGES 119–120 WRITTEN EXERCISES **1.** $1\frac{1}{2}$ **3.** 0 **5.** $\frac{3}{8}$ **7.** $-\frac{11}{12}$ **9.** $1\frac{11}{12}$ **11.** $-\frac{41}{72}$ **13.** $3\frac{3}{8}$ **15.** $\frac{1}{4}$ **17.** $\frac{13}{24}$ **19.** $1\frac{1}{6}$ **21.** $-2\frac{1}{12}$ **23.** $-16\frac{23}{42}$ **25.** $\frac{19}{20}$ **27.** $1\frac{7}{12}$ **29.** $-6\frac{2}{3}$ **31.** $47\frac{11}{24}$ **33.** $-7\frac{29}{60}$ **35.** $\frac{b+5}{6}$ **37.** $\frac{2}{g}$ **39.** $\frac{6b+1}{2}$ **41.** $\frac{-5a-3}{a}$ **43.** $\frac{3t}{2}$ **45.** $-\frac{2n}{r}$ **47.** $\frac{7y}{4}$ **49.** $\frac{5x}{3}$

PAGES 120–121 PROBLEMS **1.** $2\frac{7}{24}$ cups **3.** $14\frac{11}{16}$ yd **5.** $\frac{5}{6}$ mi **7.** Right: $1\frac{5}{16}$ in.; bottom: $\frac{11}{16}$ in.

PAGE 121 SELF-TEST A **1.** $\frac{1}{8}$ **2.** $-\frac{1}{3}$ **3.** $\frac{7}{9}$ **4.** $\frac{2}{-3}$ **5.** $\frac{1}{4}$ **6.** $-2\frac{2}{5}$ **7.** $\frac{16}{21}$ **8.** $-1\frac{23}{48}$ **9.** $4\frac{1}{4}$ **10.** $\frac{11}{5}$ **11.** $-\frac{11}{3}$ **12.** $\frac{94}{15}$ **13.** $\frac{19}{12}$ **14.** $-\frac{69}{8}$ **15.** $\frac{56}{72}, \frac{63}{72}$ **16.** $-\frac{30}{147}, \frac{14}{147}$ **17.** $\frac{27}{450}, \frac{12}{450}$ **18.** $-\frac{16}{30}, -\frac{1}{30}$ **19.** $\frac{7}{12}$ **20.** $-\frac{2}{15}$ **21.** $-\frac{7}{10}$ **22.** $15\frac{7}{8}$ **23.** $22\frac{4}{9}$ **24.** $-4\frac{5}{24}$

PAGES 124–125 WRITTEN EXERCISES **1.** 7 **3.** -2 **5.** $\frac{1}{28}$ **7.** $-\frac{1}{60}$ **9.** $\frac{10}{27}$ **11.** $-\frac{1}{4}$ **13.** $-\frac{2}{27}$ **15.** $\frac{5}{8}$ **17.** 0 **19.** $\frac{15}{64}$ **21.** 1 **23.** $43\frac{11}{12}$ **25.** $-22\frac{1}{7}$ **27.** $3\frac{10}{27}$ **29.** $\frac{1}{24}$ **31.** $\frac{1}{72}$ **33.** $-4\frac{1}{2}$ **35.** $6n$ **37.** $-\frac{y}{2}$ **39.** $\frac{2}{5}$ **41.** 3

PAGE 125 REVIEW EXERCISES **1.** 60 **3.** -36 **5.** 8 **7.** $-3\frac{1}{9}$

PAGES 128–129 WRITTEN EXERCISES **1.** $\frac{2}{3}$ **3.** 25 **5.** $\frac{25}{72}$ **7.** $3\frac{8}{9}$ **9.** 6 **11.** $5\frac{1}{5}$ **13.** $-\frac{9}{16}$ **15.** 7 **17.** $5\frac{23}{64}$ **19.** -2 **21.** -9 **23.** $\frac{1}{3}$ **25.** $-\frac{1}{2}$ **27.** $-8y$ **29.** $1\frac{1}{7}$ **31.** $\frac{-2}{c^2}$ **33.** $\frac{3e}{4d}$ **35.** $\frac{4}{5}$ **37.** $\frac{5}{12}$ **39.** $\frac{2}{5}$

PAGES 129–130 PROBLEMS **1.** $9\frac{7}{9}$ packages **3.** 225 balloons **5.** $\frac{1}{19}$ **7.** \$7500 **9.** $40\frac{1}{6}$ ft; $12\frac{1}{4}$ ft by $8\frac{5}{6}$ ft **11.** $\frac{1}{6}$ of the class **13.** $\frac{3}{20}$ of the workers

PAGE 130 REVIEW EXERCISES **1.** $n = 240 - 135$; 105 **3.** $y = 156 \div 4$; 39 **5.** $x = 432 \div 12$; 36 **7.** $m = 418 \div 38$; 11

PAGES 134–135 WRITTEN EXERCISES **1.** 0.25 **3.** $0.\overline{2}$ **5.** 0.9 **7.** $-0.\overline{6}$ **9.** -0.375

11. -0.12 **13.** 1.1 **15.** $0.58\overline{3}$ **17.** $0.2\overline{6}$ **19.** $-1.3\overline{8}$ **21.** 0.15 **23.** $3.\overline{285714}$ **25.** $\frac{1}{20}$ **27.** $-\frac{3}{5}$ **29.** $2\frac{7}{100}$ **31.** $5\frac{1}{8}$ **33.** $-1\frac{3}{8}$ **35.** $12\frac{5}{8}$ **37.** $\frac{9}{40}$ **39.** $-1\frac{413}{500}$ **41.** $-\frac{5}{9}$ **43.** $-1\frac{1}{90}$ **45.** $\frac{5}{33}$ **47.** $\frac{35}{99}$ **49.** $-1\frac{4}{33}$ **51.** $2\frac{121}{900}$ **53.** $\frac{41}{333}$ **55.** Rational **57.** Rational **59.** 3.0, $3.00\overline{9}$, $3.0\overline{9}$, 3.1 **61.** 1, = **63.** $-\frac{5}{4}$, =

PAGE 135 SELF-TEST B **1.** $3\frac{3}{4}$ **2.** $-\frac{1}{24}$ **3.** $1\frac{1}{5}$ **4.** $1\frac{41}{64}$ **5.** 15 **6.** $-8\frac{1}{7}$ **7.** $1\frac{1}{2}$ **8.** $-\frac{1}{8}$ **9.** 14 **10.** $\frac{1}{20}$ **11.** $-4\frac{1}{2}$ **12.** $2\frac{2}{29}$ **13.** 0.625 **14.** $0.\overline{18}$ **15.** -0.0125 **16.** $1.1\overline{6}$ **17.** $\frac{7}{8}$ **18.** $1\frac{2}{3}$ **19.** $-2\frac{213}{1000}$ **20.** $\frac{7}{30}$

PAGE 135 COMPUTER BYTE **1.** $0.\overline{142857}$ **3.** $0.\overline{90}$ **5.** $0.\overline{76}$ **7.** $0.\overline{51}$

PAGE 138 CHAPTER REVIEW **1.** False **3.** True **5.** False **7.** False **9.** True **11.** False **13.** C **15.** K **17.** D **19.** H **21.** B **23.** E **25.** 0.3125 **27.** $-\frac{1}{8}$

PAGE 140 CUMULATIVE REVIEW EXERCISES **1.** 58 **3.** 7 **5.** 5 **7.** 0.12 **9.** 225 **11.** 0.08 **13.** 10.24 **15.** 750 **17.** $75.70 > 75.40 > 75.06$ **19.** $0.33 > 0.30 > 0.03$ **21.** -7, 7 **23.** -5, -6, -7, and so on; also 5, 6, 7, and so on **25.** -5, 5 **27.** -32, -33, -34, -35, -36, -37, -38, -39, 32, 33, 34, 35, 36, 37, 38, 39 **29.** $y = 18$ **31.** $b = 12$ **33.** $n = -4$ **35.** $-\frac{4}{5}$ **37.** $\frac{2}{5}$ **39.** $-1\frac{3}{7}$ **41.** $-\frac{2}{7}$ **43.** $\frac{2}{5}$ **45.** $-5\frac{5}{8}$ **47.** $8\frac{23}{136}$

PAGE 141 CUMULATIVE REVIEW PROBLEMS **1.** \$196.88 **3.** No **5.** \$787.50 **7.** \$444.75

5 Equations and Inequalities

PAGE 145 WRITTEN EXERCISES

1. Addition property of equality
3. Multiplication property of equality
5. Addition property of equality
7. Multiplication property of equality **9.** 11 **11.** -5 **13.** 21 **15.** 3 **17.** -3 **19.** 7 **21.** 1.2 **23.** -9 **25.** 12 **27.** 0

PAGE 145 REVIEW EXERCISES **1.** 103 **3.** 35 **5.** 1.5

PAGES 147–148 WRITTEN EXERCISES **1.** $b + 7 = 22$ **3.** $72 = 20 + u$ **5.** $2 = -12 + v$ **7.** $10 + f = 36$ **9.** $33 = 10n - 7$ **11.** $11q - 2 = 20$ **13.** $15 = 5z + 5$ **15.** $10x + 7 = -13$ **17.** $4j + 8 = 36$ **19.** $20 = 2e - 10$ **21.** $-18 - 6w = 48$ **23.** $14 = 16 + 2b$ **25.** $15n + 30 = 45$ **27.** $3.2 = 15.6 + c$ **29.** $24 = k + 2$ **31.** $20g + 4.3 = 24.3$ **33.** $-\frac{8}{7} = \frac{6}{7} - v$ **35.** $6.6 = 3.3 - 3x$ **37.** $2h - 5 = 17$ **39.** $-22m - 15 = 6$ **41.** $25n + 6.3 = 26.3$ **43.** $\frac{10}{3}d + \frac{3}{8} = 33$

PAGE 148 REVIEW EXERCISES **1.** -6 **3.** -17 **5.** -8 **7.** 8 **9.** 20

PAGE 151 WRITTEN EXERCISES **1.** 15 **3.** -26 **5.** 23 **7.** -24 **9.** 7 **11.** -16 **13.** -1 **15.** -38 **17.** 40 **19.** -38 **21.** 13 **23.** -22 **25.** $3\frac{5}{8}$ **27.** $9\frac{1}{4}$ **29.** 6.4 **31.** $10\frac{1}{7}$ **33.** -6 **35.** 16.2 **37.** -2 or 2 **39.** -11 or 11

PAGE 151 REVIEW EXERCISES **1.** $\frac{1}{3}$ **3.** $\frac{1}{8}$ **5.** $\frac{1}{12}$

PAGE 154 WRITTEN EXERCISES **1.** 6 **3.** -38 **5.** -49 **7.** 99 **9.** 128 **11.** -528 **13.** -17 **15.** -4131 **17.** 972 **19.** -4896 **21.** 84 **23.** 158.5 **25.** 15.2 **27.** -400 **29.** $\frac{35}{16}$, or $2\frac{3}{16}$ **31.** $-\frac{1}{6}$ **33.** 280 **35.** -1.4 **37.** -124 **39.** 3.15

PAGE 154 REVIEW EXERCISES **1.** 6, 5, 4, 3, 2, 1, 0 **3.** 22, 23, 24, and so on **5.** 9, 8, 7, 6, 5, 4, 3, 2, 1, 0 **7.** 4, 5, 6, 7, 8, 9, 10, 11

PAGES 157–158 WRITTEN EXERCISES
1. Simplify both sides; divide both sides by 6
3. Subtract 4 from both sides; divide both sides by -3 **5.** Simplify the right side; add 12 to both sides; divide both sides by 4 **7.** 2 **9.** 6 **11.** 3 **13.** 6 **15.** 56 **17.** -30 **19.** -180 **21.** -9 **23.** -6 **25.** $\frac{10}{9}$, or $1\frac{1}{9}$ **27.** -15 **29.** 3 **31.** $-\frac{12}{5}$, or $-2\frac{2}{5}$ **33.** 1 **35.** 4.7 **37.** 40 **39.** 1 **41.** 5 **43.** 1 **45.** $\frac{81}{2}$, or $40\frac{1}{2}$ **47.** -29 **49.** $\frac{9}{6} = 4(4 - y)$; $\frac{29}{8}$, or $3\frac{5}{8}$ **51.** $\frac{1}{3}y - \frac{5}{18} = 2y$; $-\frac{1}{6}$

PAGE 158 SELF-TEST A **1.** 12 **2.** -8 **3.** $17 = 8x - 17$ **4.** $8 = 5m - 45$ **5.** 5 **6.** 47 **7.** -26 **8.** -7 **9.** 162 **10.** 32 **11.** 20 **12.** $-\frac{33}{2}$, or $-16\frac{1}{2}$ **13.** -4

PAGES 161–162 WRITTEN EXERCISES
All the numbers: **1.** less than 12 **3.** greater than 42 **5.** less than 3 **7.** greater than or equal to 20 **9.** less than -18 **11.** less than 7 **13.** less than -7 **15.** less than or equal to 12 **17.** less than or equal to 15 **19.** less than -26

21. less than or equal to 60 **23.** less than or equal to -11 **25.** less than -168 **27.** greater than 21.3 **29.** less than $5\frac{3}{7}$ **31.** less than or equal to -3.87 **33.** less than or equal to 47 **35.** less than or equal to -10.8 **37.** greater than or equal to 3 **39.** greater than 21 **41.** greater than -4.1 **43.** less than or equal to -92.4 **45.** greater than $22\frac{13}{16}$ **47.** greater than or equal to -9 **49.** greater than $\frac{1}{5}$ **51.** less than -1.7

PAGE 162 REVIEW EXERCISES **1.** -2.6, -1.4, 1.2, 3.2 **3.** -12.2, -12.09, -11.2, 12, 112 **5.** -30.05, -5.3, -5.03, 0.35, 3.05 **7.** -2.89, -2.8, 2.089, 2.89, 28.9

PAGES 165–166 WRITTEN EXERCISES All the numbers: **1.** less than -6 **3.** greater than or equal to -9 **5.** less than -30 **7.** greater than or equal to -42 **9.** greater than $5\frac{2}{5}$ **11.** greater than or equal to -10 **13.** greater than 2 **15.** greater than or equal to 3 **17.** greater than -4 **19.** less than or equal to 5 **21.** less than 8 **23.** less than or equal to $-3\frac{1}{13}$ **25.** less than or equal to -3 **27.** greater than 1 **29.** less than or equal to -2 **31.** greater than 15 **33.** less than 2 **35.** greater than 24 **37.** less than -7.2 **39.** greater than or equal to -10.3

PAGE 166 REVIEW EXERCISES **1.** $n + 9$ **3.** $n - 16$ **5.** $n + 3$ **7.** $\frac{n}{5}$, or $n \div 5$

PAGE 166 CALCULATOR KEY-IN 852

PAGE 168 WRITTEN EXERCISES **1.–16.** Answers will vary. **17.** E **19.** D **21.** B

PAGE 168 REVIEW EXERCISES **1.** $\frac{9}{2}$, or $4\frac{1}{2}$ **3.** 44 **5.** -18 **7.** 6

PAGES 172–173 PROBLEMS **1.** Neon **3.** Osmium **5.** Osmium **7.** 11 plants **9.** \$45 **11.** Byrne: \$300,000; Chang: \$60,000; Weinstein: \$317,000 **13.** 12 nickels

PAGE 173 SELF-TEST B **1.–8.** All the numbers: **1.** greater than 46 **2.** greater than or equal to -98 **3.** greater than 71 **4.** greater than or equal to 5 **5.** less than or equal to $-25\frac{1}{2}$ **6.** less than -68 **7.** less than -1 **8.** less than or equal to 6 **9., 10.** Answers will vary. **11.** 15 min

PAGE 175 ENRICHMENT **1.** \$125.86; \$162.75; \$20.00 **3.** \$249.75; \$323.80; \$35.00 **5.** \$665.61; \$676.09; \$90.00

PAGE 176 CHAPTER REVIEW **1.** False **3.** True **5.** False **7.** False **9.** True **11.** False **13.** True **15.** D **17.** A **19.** C **21.** c **23.** c

PAGE 178 CUMULATIVE REVIEW EXERCISES **1.** True **3.** False **5.** False

7.
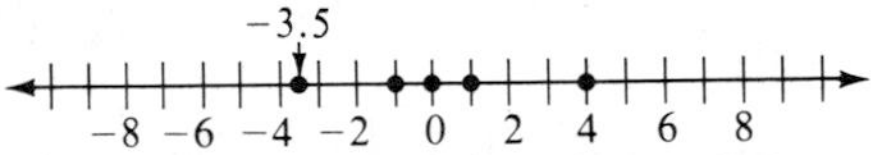

9.
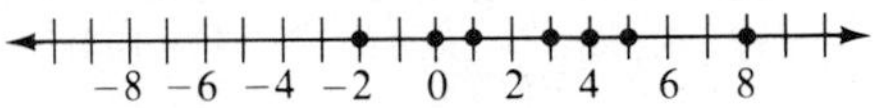

11. $\frac{5}{40}, \frac{16}{40}$ **13.** $\frac{4}{6}, \frac{1}{6}$ **15.** $-\frac{48}{88}, -\frac{33}{88}$ **17.** $\frac{20}{24}$, $-\frac{21}{24}$ **19.** -78.51 **21.** -120 **23.** -16.867 **25.** $\frac{3}{4}$ **27.** $46\frac{11}{20}$ **29.** $6\frac{22}{25}$ **31.** $4\frac{2}{25}$ **33.** $99\frac{11}{25}$ **35.** 6.09 **37.** 5.657 **39.** 4000 **41.** 12 **43.** All the numbers greater than $1\frac{1}{2}$ **45.** All the numbers less than or equal to $\frac{1}{4}$ **47.** 7 **49.** $\frac{14}{3}$, or $4\frac{2}{3}$

PAGE 179 CUMULATIVE REVIEW PROBLEMS **1.** \$2.97 **3.** 220,000 readers **5.** \$418.50 **7.** \$656.38 **9.** 100 inquiries

6 Geometry

PAGES 185–186 WRITTEN EXERCISES **1.** $\overrightarrow{AN}$, or $\overrightarrow{AK}$ **3.** $\overleftrightarrow{AN}$, $\overleftrightarrow{NK}$, $\overleftrightarrow{AK}$, $\overleftrightarrow{NA}$, $\overleftrightarrow{KN}$, $\overleftrightarrow{KA}$ Answers to 5–12 will vary.

5.

7.
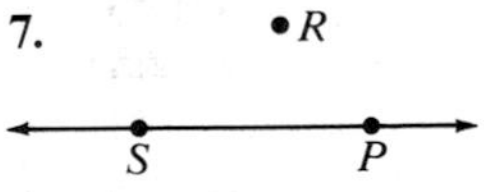

9.
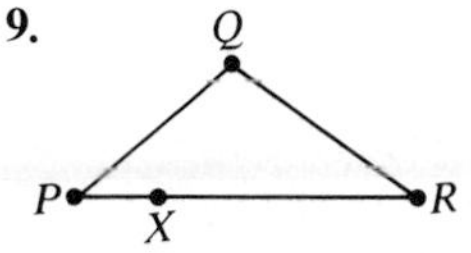

11.
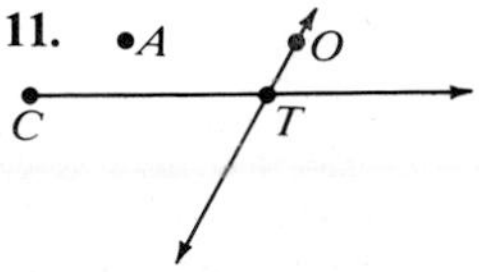

13. P, R, T; or P, Q, S **15.** Yes **19.** $\overline{EF}$, or $\overline{FE}$ **21.** $\overrightarrow{DG}$, or $\overrightarrow{DE}$, or $\overrightarrow{DF}$ **25.** 24 **27.** 10 **29.** 4 **31.** 7

PAGE 186 REVIEW EXERCISES **1.** 56.0 **3.** 1.201 **5.** 2842.35 **7.** 0.863 **9.** 7.455

PAGES 189–190 WRITTEN EXERCISES

1.
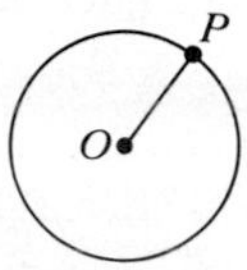

3.
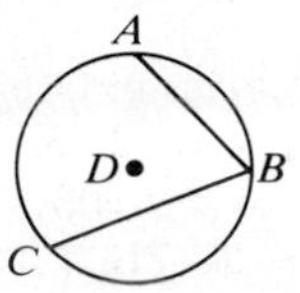

7. 2360 m **9.** 157 cm **11.** 4 **13.** 132 **15.** 17.5 **17.** 0.07 **19.** 18,800 km

PAGE 190 REVIEW EXERCISES **1.** $<$ **3.** $<$ **5.** $<$ **7.** $>$

PAGE 190 CALCULATOR KEY-IN 3.14084507; 3.14285714

PAGE 194 WRITTEN EXERCISES **1.** 50 **3.** 34 **9.** 45° **11.** 90° **15.** They form a right angle.

PAGE 194 REVIEW EXERCISES **1.** 114 **3.** 112 **5.** 84 **7.** 60 **9.** 72 **11.** 138

PAGES 198–199 WRITTEN EXERCISES **1.** 38° **3.** 67° **5.** 73° **7.** 52° **9.** 28° **11.** 152° **13.** 80° **15.** 128° **17.** 33°, 57° **19.** 60°, 30° **21.** 30°, 150° **23.** 72°, 108° **25.** 90°

PAGE 199 REVIEW EXERCISES **1.** 343 **3.** 6 **5.** 21.25 **7.** 10 **9.** 10.5

PAGES 202–203 WRITTEN EXERCISES **1.** $\angle 5$, $\angle 7$ **3.** $\angle DBC$, $\angle 9$ **5.** $\angle 2$, $\angle 7$ **7.** $\angle DBC$, $\angle 11$ **9.** 58° **11.** 32° **13.** 122° **15.** 90° **19.** Supplementary angles **21.** $\angle 2 \cong \angle 3$ **23. a.** Construct an angle congruent to $\angle 1$ with vertex *P*. **b.** $\angle 1$ and the constructed angle are congruent alternate interior angles. **25.** $\angle 2 \cong \angle 3$ because they are alternate interior angles. Therefore, $\angle 1 \cong \angle 3$. Because corresponding angles 1 and 3 are congruent, $\overline{AB} \parallel \overline{DC}$.

PAGE 203 SELF-TEST A

1. 

2. 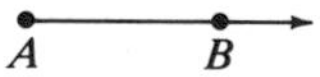

3. 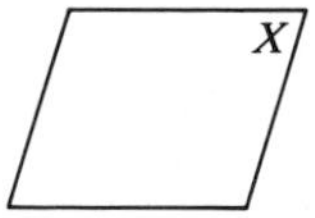

4. 

5. 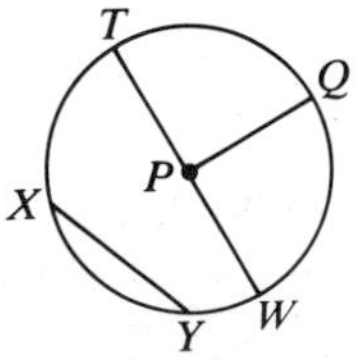

6. 154 **7.** 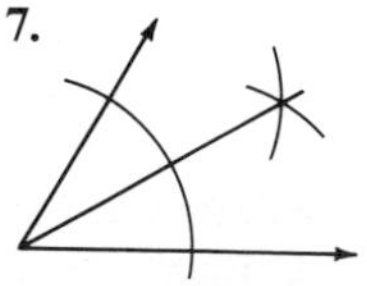

8. 82° **9.** m$\angle ARQ = 54°$, m$\angle QRT = 36°$ **10.** m$\angle ABC = 63°$, m$\angle XYZ = 117°$ **11.** *YQS* **12.** *TQR*

PAGES 206–208 WRITTEN EXERCISES **1.** 67° **3.** 112°; 34° **5.** 62°; 62° **11.** Yes **13.** 90°, 45°, 45° **15.** $x = 65$, $y = 25$ **17.** $x = 72$, $y = 36$ **19.** $x = 84$, $y = 126$ **21. d.** Each side appears to be three times as long as the corresponding side of $\triangle DEF$. **23.** A right triangle **25.** 125° **27.** 30°

PAGE 208 REVIEW EXERCISES **1.** $d - 9 = 5$ **3.** $-4 = x + 20$ **5.** $14z > 98$ **7.** $2m - 10 = 2$

PAGES 211–212 WRITTEN EXERCISES **1.** 115° **3.** 115° **5.** 12 **7.** $\overline{AB}$, $\overline{EC}$, $\overline{DC}$ **9.** $\angle BCE$, $\angle D$ **11.** True **13.** True **15.** True **23.** 44 **25. b.** The median is parallel to the parallel sides.

PAGE 212 REVIEW EXERCISES **1.** -9.175 **3.** 97.96 **5.** -35.36 **7.** 9 **9.** -6.24

PAGES 214–216 WRITTEN EXERCISES **1.** 16 cm **3.** 50 m **5.** 42.5 mm **7.** 71.2 mm **9.** 6.25 in. **11.** 45.1 m **17.** 135° **19.** 144° **21. a.** 360° **b.** 540° **c.** $n - 2$ **d.** $(n - 2)180°$

PAGE 216 REVIEW EXERCISES **1.** 3.81 **3.** -7.95 **5.** 49.82 **7.** -37.2

PAGES 219–221 WRITTEN EXERCISES **1.** ASA **3.** SSS **7.** SAS **9.** $\triangle ABC \cong \triangle DBE$; rotation; SAS **11.** $\triangle KLM \cong \triangle NML$; reflection, or reflection and translation; SAS **13.** $\triangle SXR \cong \triangle PXQ$, SAS; $\triangle SXP \cong \triangle QXR$, SAS **15.** $\triangle GHK \cong \triangle FHK$, SAS; $\triangle GDK \cong \triangle FEK$, SSS **17.** $\angle A \cong \angle D$, $AC = FD$; SAS **19.** $\angle X \cong \angle S$, $\angle ROS \cong \angle YOX$; ASA

PAGE 221 SELF-TEST B **1.** 90°; right **2.** 60°, 60°, 60°, acute **3.** 35°; obtuse **4.** 90° **5.** 54° **6.** $\overline{WT}$ **7.** $\overline{XR}$ **8.** 30 **9.** 22 **10.** 64.2 cm **11.** True **12.** True **13.** False

PAGE 223 ENRICHMENT **3.** *P* and the center of the circle

PAGE 224 CHAPTER REVIEW **1.** $\overrightarrow{OE}$ **3.** $\overleftrightarrow{AC}$, or $\overleftrightarrow{CA}$ **5.** Approximately 11.8 **7.** 0, 90 **9.** True **11.** False **13.** False **15.** True **17.** False **19.** False **21.** True

PAGE 226 CUMULATIVE REVIEW EXERCISES **1.** \$12.45 **3.** \$160.87 **5.** \$821.10 **7.** \$375.90 **9.** $54y$ **11.** $100r$ **13.** $24a$ **15.** $1.6n - 6.72$ **17.** -15.8 **19.** 5.218 **21.** 9.1 **23.** -14.805 **25.** 324

27. 2.5 **29.** $-\frac{21}{29}$ **31.** $-\frac{29}{41}$ **33.** $\frac{6}{37}$ **35.** $\frac{9}{250}$ **37.** $11\frac{21}{25}$ **39.** $0.\overline{6}$ **41.** $3.8\overline{3}$ **43.** $8.08\overline{3}$ **45.** $\frac{5}{6}$ **47.** $2\frac{14}{33}$ **49.** 22 **51.** 169 **53.** 19 **55.** 53.2

PAGE 227 CUMULATIVE REVIEW PROBLEMS **1.** 15 cm **3.** 4.4 km **5.** Up $4\frac{5}{8}$ points **7.** Adult \$4, student \$2 **9.** 20 cm, 15 m **11.** 15.2 m

7 Ratio, Proportion, and Percent

PAGE 232 WRITTEN EXERCISES **1.** $\frac{5}{4}$ **3.** $\frac{3}{7}$ **5.** $\frac{2}{1}$ **7.** $\frac{25}{8}$ **9.** No **11.** Yes **13.** 12 **15.** 6 **17.** $10\frac{1}{2}$ **19.** 3 **21.** $2\frac{4}{5}$ **23.** $1\frac{1}{2}$ **25.** $3\frac{1}{2}$ **27.** $6\frac{2}{5}$

PAGE 233 PROBLEMS **1.** 8 cans **3.** $11\frac{1}{4}$ oz; $10\frac{2}{3}$ servings **5.** 12 vests **7.** $1333\frac{1}{3}$ ft^2 **9.** 6955 votes for, 2782 votes against

PAGE 233 REVIEW EXERCISES **1.** $\frac{1}{3}$ **3.** $\frac{6}{7}$ **5.** $\frac{11}{14}$ **7.** $11\frac{2}{7}$

PAGES 236–237 PROBLEMS **1.** \$0.17 **3.** \$16 **5.** \$5.25 **7.** 195 km **9.** 240 km **11.** Best Brand **13.** Sparkle Window Cleaner **15.** 5 gal **17.** 62 km/h, 74 km/h

PAGE 237 REVIEW EXERCISES **1.** 20 cm **3.** 84 cm **5.** 142.4 m **7.** 57.4 m

PAGES 239–240 WRITTEN EXERCISES **1.** 40 in. **3.** 22.5 in. **5.** 2 in. **7.** 4 cm **9.** 30 cm **11.** 0.63 mm **13. b.** 15 cm, 14.5 cm **c.** 70 cm

PAGE 240 REVIEW EXERCISES **1.** 0.365 **3.** 46.775 **5.** 60.006 **7.** 99.901

PAGE 240 COMPUTER BYTE **1.** 2 **3.** 13.5

PAGES 243–244 WRITTEN EXERCISES **1.** 83% **3.** 0.52% **5.** 472% **7.** 0.3% **9.** 80% **11.** 37.5% **13.** 27.5% **15.** $83\frac{1}{3}$% **17.** 45.5% **19.** 21.4% **21.** 78.9% **23.** 46.2% **25. a.** $\frac{9}{25}$ **b.** 0.36 **27. a.** $2\frac{12}{25}$ **b.** 2.48 **29. a.** $\frac{9}{2000}$ **b.** 0.0045 **31. a.** $\frac{7}{250}$ **b.** 0.028 **33. a.** $\frac{23}{400}$ **b.** 0.0575 **35.** $\frac{3}{800}$ **37.** $\frac{1}{120}$ **39.** $\frac{4}{125}$ **41.** $\frac{1}{6}$ **43.** $\frac{1}{9}$ **45.** $>$ **47.** $<$ **49.** $>$ **51.** $=$ **53.** $=$

PAGE 244 PROBLEMS **1.** $\frac{7}{10}$, 70% **3.** $\frac{3}{5}$, 60% **5.** $\frac{1}{3}$, 33.3%

PAGE 244 REVIEW EXERCISES **1.** 15 **3.** 39.51 **5.** -10 **7.** 21.50

PAGES 246–247 WRITTEN EXERCISES **1.** 132 **3.** 7% **5.** 20 **7.** 40 **9.** $33\frac{1}{3}$% **11.** 162 **13.** $\frac{17}{900}$ **15.** $66\frac{2}{3}$% **17.** 175%

PAGES 247–248 PROBLEMS **1.** 52% **3.** 68.1 g **5.** \$375 million **7.** 150 customers **9.** \$18,200 **11. a.** 80 people **b.** 14 people

PAGE 248 SELF-TEST A **1.** $\frac{3}{5}$ **2.** $\frac{3}{1}$ **3.** $\frac{2}{25}$ **4.** 3 **5.** 2.4 **6.** 54 **7.** \$2.50 **8.** 110 km **9.** 570 km **10.** 1235 km **11.** 2660 km **12.** 66% **13.** 32.7% **14.** 250% **15.** $16\frac{2}{3}$% **16.** 4.44 **17.** 50 **18.** $33\frac{1}{3}$% **19.** 1.77

PAGES 250–251 PROBLEMS **1.** \$253 **3.** 12.5% **5.** 25 mi/gal **7.** 450 Calories **9.** 1352 people **11.** \$7000

PAGE 251 REVIEW EXERCISES **1.** 9.72 **3.** 17 **5.** 520 **7.** 220.5 **9.** 0.04

PAGES 253–254 PROBLEMS **1.** 16% **3.** \$3600 **5.** \$5.50 **7.** \$72 **9.** 3% **11.** \$79,800 **13.** \$89,400 **15.** \$9250

PAGE 254 CALCULATOR KEY-IN **1.** 1.05×25

PAGE 257 WRITTEN EXERCISES **1.** 5.12 **3.** 80% **5.** 40

PAGES 257–258 PROBLEMS **1.** 82.5% **3.** 49 books **5.** \$34.80; \$27.84 **7.** \$36.50 **9. a.** 108° **b.** \$3.6 million

PAGE 259 REVIEW EXERCISES **1.** 0.5 **3.** $0.1\overline{6}$ **5.** 2.25 **7.** 0.75

PAGE 259 COMPUTER BYTE

3. Delete lines 20, 30, 60, and 70.
Add: 5 INPUT "NUMERATOR: ";B
6 INPUT "DENOMINATOR: ";A
60 GOTO 5

PAGES 261–263 PROBLEMS **1.** \$600 **3.** 12.5% **5.** 5 years **7.** \$10,000 **9.** \$3650.33 **11.** \$4073.84 **13.** Steve **15.** \$7000 **17.** \$319.84 **19.** After 1 year: $1000 + 1000(0.05) = 1000(1 + 0.05) = 1000(1.05)$; after 2 years: $1000(1.05) + 1000(1.05)(0.05) = 1000(1.05)(1.05) = 1000(1.05)^2$; after 3 years: $1000(1.05)^2 + 1000(1.05)^2(0.05) = 1000(1.05)^3$, and so on

PAGE 263 SELF-TEST B **1.** 20% **2.** 930 books **3.** \$119.84 **4.** \$20.85 **5.** \$9.25 **6.** 42% **7.** \$2106 **8.** \$355.28

PAGE 265 ENRICHMENT **1.** 3; 21, 144, and 987 are divisible by 3; 5, 55, and 610 are divisible by 5. **3.** The new pattern is every other member of the Fibonacci sequence, beginning with 3. **5.** The new pattern is every other member of the Fibonacci sequence, beginning with 5.

PAGE 266 CHAPTER REVIEW **1.** 56 **3.** $\frac{13}{6}$, or $2\frac{1}{6}$, h **5.** 62.5 **7.** 77 **9.** 85 **11.** $16\frac{2}{3}$% **13.** 30% **15.** B **17.** False

PAGE 268 CUMULATIVE REVIEW EXERCISES **1.** 8 **3.** 7 **5.** 12 **7.** −19 **9.** 9 **11.** 45 **13.** −7, −2.5, −2.2, 0, 3, 6.4 **15.** −8.4, −3, −1.6, −1.0, 0.5 **17.** True **19.** True **21.** True **23.** $\frac{6}{9}, \frac{5}{9}$ **25.** $-\frac{88}{33}, \frac{27}{33}$ **27.** $\frac{28}{12}, \frac{9}{12}$ **29.** $\frac{68}{128}, -\frac{3}{128}$
31. All the numbers greater than or equal to 1

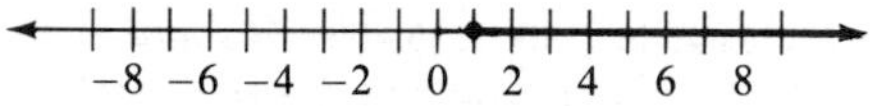

33. All the numbers less than −3

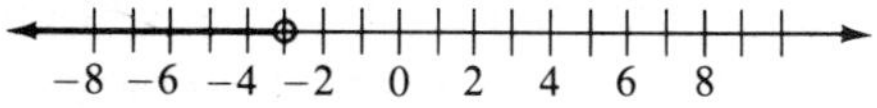

35. All the numbers greater than 3

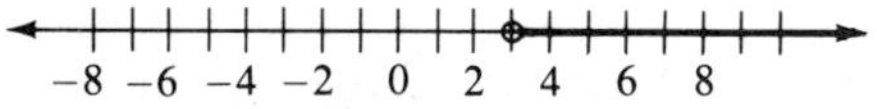

37. Rotation, ASA **39.** Rotation, SSS

PAGE 269 CUMULATIVE REVIEW PROBLEMS **1.** \$79.38 **3.** 23,500 ft **5.** 1230 lb **7.** 15 m, 5 m **9.** \$616.13

8 The Coordinate Plane

PAGES 274–275 WRITTEN EXERCISES
1. (−5, −5) **3.** (5, 1) **5.** (−3, −2) **7.** (−1, 4) **9.** *I* **11.** *V* **13.** *D* **15.** *W* **17.** *M* **19. c.** Rectangle **21. c.** Parallelogram **23. b.** (−5, 1), (−2, −2), (2, −2), (2, 1) **d.** Translation **25. b.** (−2, 3), (2, 3), (4, 1), (4, −1), (1, 1), (−1, 1), (−4, −1), (−4, 1) **d.** Translation **27. b.** (−6, −5), (−2, −1), (−9, −3) **d.** Reflection

PAGE 275 REVIEW EXERCISES **1.** 8 **3.** 27 **5.** −5 **7.** −15

PAGES 278–279 WRITTEN EXERCISES
1. Yes **3.** Yes **5.** No **7.** No **9.** No **11.** No **13.** Yes **15.** Yes **17.** $y = -2x + 7$ **19.** $y = 4x + 16$ **21.** $y = \frac{2}{3}x - 2$ **23. a.** $y = x + 7$ **b.** (2, 9), (−5, 2), (7, 14) **25. a.** $y = \frac{1}{2}x + 5$ **b.** (4, 7), (0, 5), (6, 8) **27. a.** $y = -\frac{1}{4}x + 5$ **b.** (4, 4), (−8, 7), (0, 5) **29. a.** $y = \frac{3}{2}x - 3$ **b.** (4, 3), (−2, −6), (−8, −15) **31. a.** $y = \frac{1}{2}x + \frac{5}{2}$ **b.** (3, 4), (5, 5), (−1, 2) **33. a.** $y = \frac{5}{2}x + 3$ **b.** (2, 8), $(1, 5\frac{1}{2})$, $(-3, -4\frac{1}{2})$ Answers to Exercises 35, 37, 39, 41, and 43 may vary. Examples are given. **35.** (0, −1), (−1, 0), (1, −2) **37.** (−1, 1), (1, −1), (0, 0) **39.** (−1, 0), (0, 5), (1, 10) **41.** (6, 0), (0, −4), (3, −2) **43.** (0, 6), (−3, 0), (1, 8) **45.** $x + y = 0$ **47.** $x + y = -3$

PAGE 279 REVIEW EXERCISES **1.** 3 **3.** 28 **5.** 3 **7.** −56 **9.** −4

PAGES 281–283 WRITTEN EXERCISES
1.–33. Each graph is a straight line through the points listed: **1.** (0, −7), (7, 0), (8, 1) **3.** (−8, 0), (−2, −3), (0, −4) **5.** (0, 10), (1, 8), (5, 0) **7.** (0, 0), (1, 1), (2, 2) **9.** (−2, −1), (0, 0), (2, 1) **11.** (0, −6), (6, 0) **13.** (−3, 0), (0, −3) **15.** (0, 4), (1, 0) **17.** (−2, 0), (0, 6) **19.** (−8, 0), (0, 2) **21.** (−4, 0), (0, 3) **23.** $(-\frac{5}{2}, 0)$, (0, 1) **25.** (0, 6), (6, 0) **27.** (0, −6), (2, 0) **29.** (−12, 0), (0, 6) **31.** $(0, -\frac{1}{2})$, $(\frac{1}{3}, 0)$ **33.** (0, −8), (6, 0)

35.

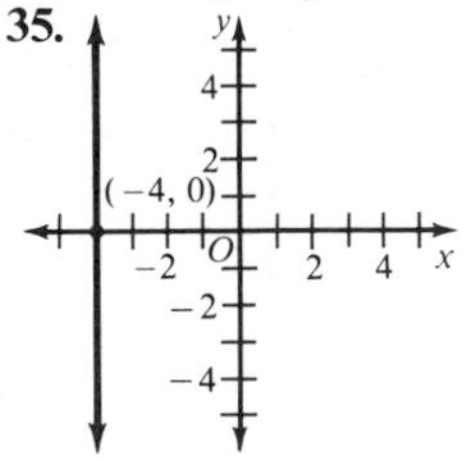

37.

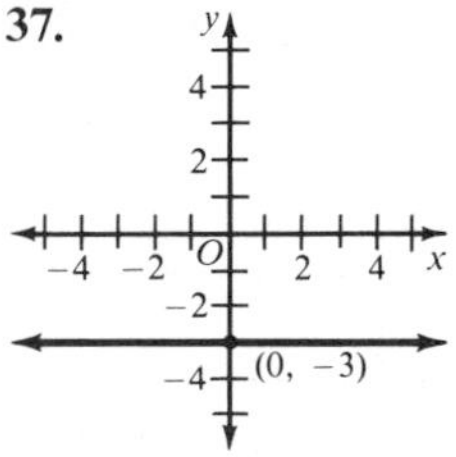

39.

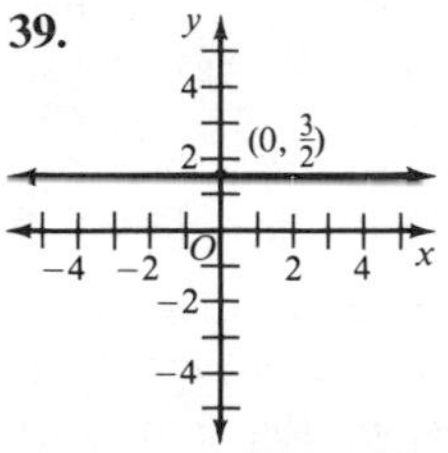

47. $-\frac{3}{4}$

PAGE 283 SELF-TEST A

1. $(-3, 6)$ **2.** $(4, -4)$ **3.** $(6, 6)$ **4.** C **5.** T **6.** P

7.-12.

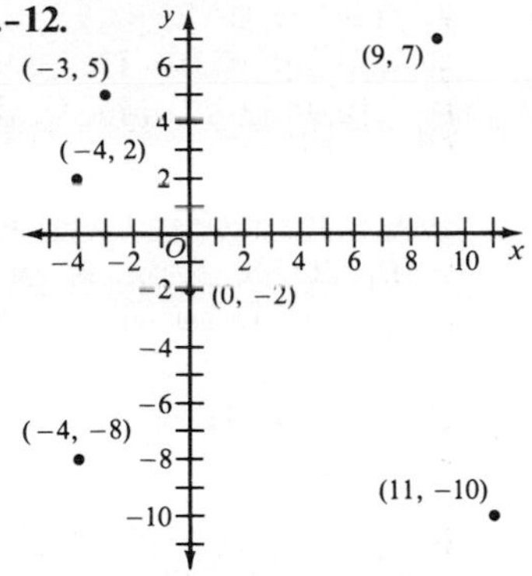

13. $(0, \frac{1}{2})$, $(-4, -\frac{1}{2})$, $(9, 2\frac{3}{4})$ **14.** $(-3, 12)$, $(\frac{1}{2}, 5)$, $(11, -16)$

15.

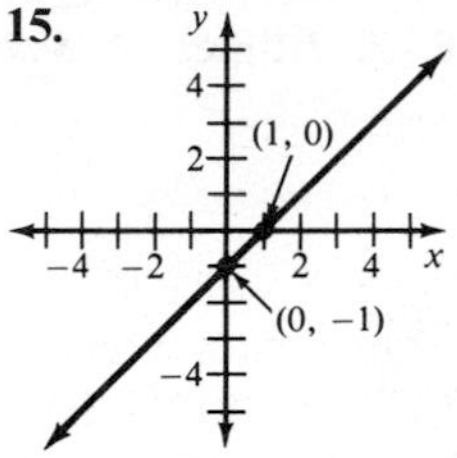

16.

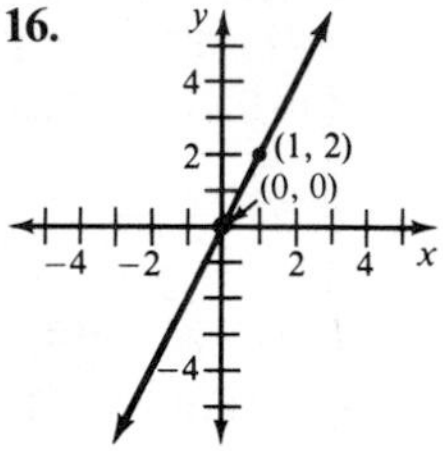

17.

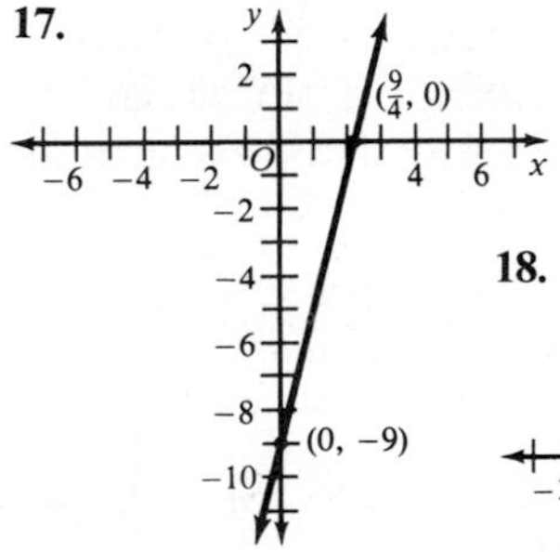

18.

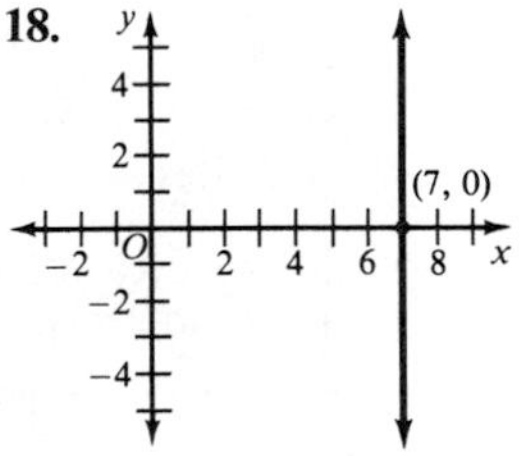

PAGES 286–287 WRITTEN EXERCISES

1. Intersect at $(3, 3)$ **3.** Parallel **5.** Coincide **7.** Parallel **9.** Intersect at $(0, 6)$ **11.** Coincide **13.** Intersect at $(-2, 4)$ **15.** Parallel **17.** Intersect at $(4, -1)$ **19.** 2

PAGE 287 REVIEW EXERCISES **1.** $\frac{9}{8}$, or $1\frac{1}{8}$ **3.** $\frac{7}{8}$ **5.** $\frac{4}{5}$ **7.** $\frac{1}{13}$

PAGE 287 CALCULATOR KEY-IN $13,107.20

PAGES 291–293 PROBLEMS **1.** Slope $= \frac{3}{2}$ **3.** 4°C **5.** 170 mi **7. a.** $y = 4.5x + 2$ **c.** 7 **9. a.** $y = \frac{7}{12}x + \frac{1}{6}$ **c.** $\frac{32}{3}$, or $10\frac{2}{3}$, min **11.** 5.5 s

PAGE 293 REVIEW EXERCISES All the numbers: **1.** greater than $1\frac{1}{3}$ **3.** greater than or equal to -1 **5.** less than or equal to 0 **7.** greater than or equal to 1 **9.** greater than 41

PAGE 293 CALCULATOR KEY-IN 1, 121, 12321, 1234321; 123454321, 12345654321, 1234567654321, 123456787654321, 12345678987654321

PAGES 296–297 WRITTEN EXERCISES

1. $y = -3x - 6$ **3.** $y = x - 2$ **5.** $y = 3 - x$ **7.** Solid line through $(0, 9)$ and $(9, 0)$, shaded region at right above line **9.** Solid line through $(-1, 0)$ and $(0, 2)$, shaded region at left above line **11.** Solid line through $(0, 4)$ and $(2, 0)$, shaded region at right above line **13.** Solid line through $(-\frac{5}{2}, 0)$ and $(0, 5)$, shaded region at left above line **15.** Dashed line through $(0, -\frac{1}{3})$ and $(\frac{1}{2}, 0)$, shaded region at left above line **17.** Solid line through $(0, 8)$ parallel to x-axis, shaded region below line **19.** Solid line through $(-1, 0)$ and $(0, -1)$, shaded region at left below line **21.** Solid line through $(-3, 0)$ parallel to y-axis, shaded region to left of line **23.** Dashed line through $(-\frac{5}{2}, 0)$ and $(0, 5)$, shaded region at right below line **25.** $x < 4$ **27.** $y \geq -3$

PAGE 297 SELF-TEST B

1. Intersect at $(4, 2)$

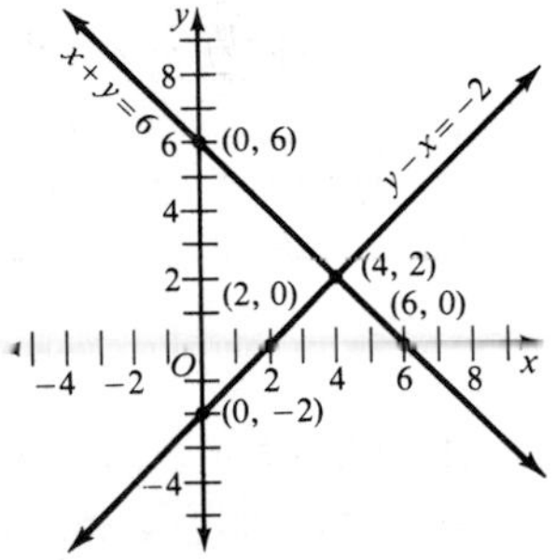

2. Coincide

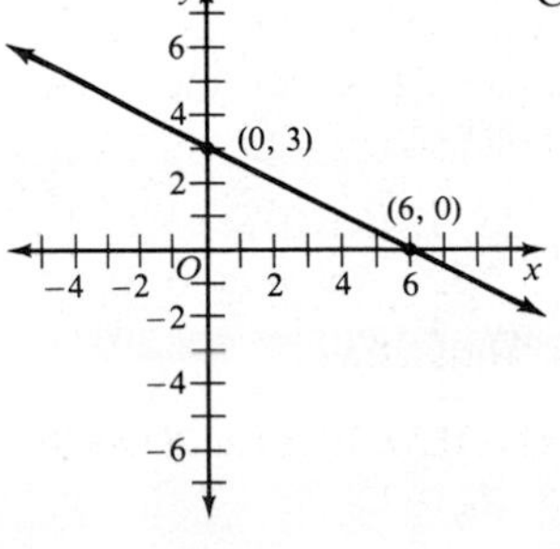

3. Parallel

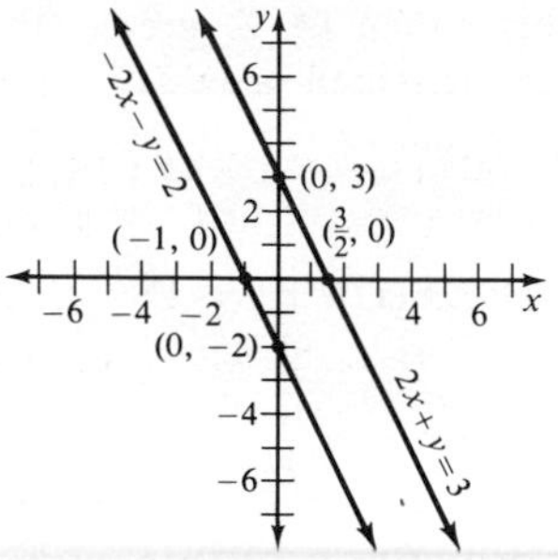

4. 4 weeks

5.

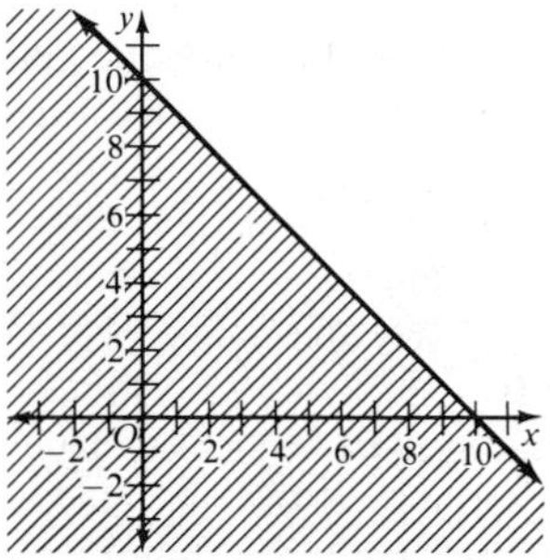

6.

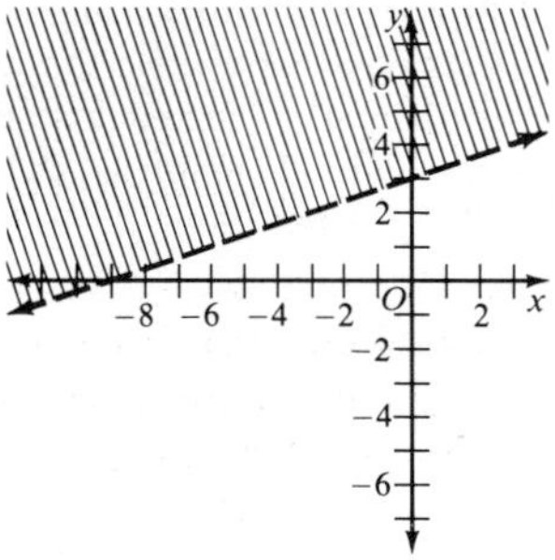

7.

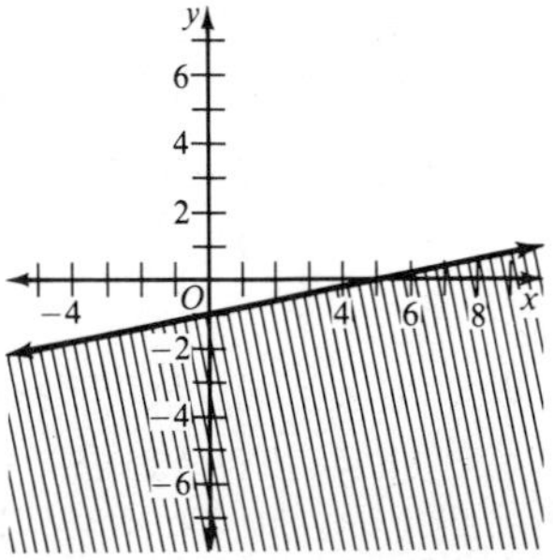

PAGES 298–299 ENRICHMENT
1. $y = 0.5x + 1.32$ Answers to Exercises 3, 5, and 7 may vary. Examples are given.
3. 2.97 kg **5.** $y = -3.3x + 20.8$ **a.** 15.85°C **b.** 6.3 h **7.** $y = 0.59x + 7.39$; \$10,930; \$11,520

PAGE 300 CHAPTER REVIEW **1.** False **3.** True **5.** C **7.** B **9.** Straight line through (−2, 2) and (0, 0) **11.** Straight line through (−1, 0) and (0, 2) **13.** C **15.** constant **17.** dashed

PAGE 302 CUMULATIVE REVIEW EXERCISES **1.** $5b$ **3.** $(y + z) - 12$ **5.** $3p + 7$ **7.** 288.01 **9.** 100.76 **11.** 4.8911 **13.** 554.09 **15.** 3.0088 **17.** −425.0612 **19.** −8.174 **21.** $-\frac{3}{14}$ **23.** $\frac{9}{8}$, or $1\frac{1}{8}$ **25.** $-\frac{247}{50}$, or $-4\frac{47}{50}$ **27.** $t = -\frac{3}{4} \times \frac{1}{5}$; $-\frac{3}{20}$ **29.** $x + 12 > 2x$; the solutions are all the numbers less than 12. **31.** 20.7 m **33.** 1.6 **35.** 42 **37.** No **39.** Yes

PAGE 303 CUMULATIVE REVIEW PROBLEMS **1.** \$84.88 **3.** 7 times **5.** \$9799; \$10,038 **7.** 44.1% **9.** 0.5 kW·h

9 Areas and Volumes

PAGES 308–310 WRITTEN EXERCISES **1.** $17\frac{1}{2}$ **3.** 30 **5.** 36 **7.** 1400 m; 105,600 m^2 **9.** 70 cm; 210 cm^2 **11.** 72,900 **13.** 8 km **15.** 4.8 **17.** 40, 100; 40, 96; 40, 36; 40, 19 **19.** area **21.** The greatest possible area for a rectangle with perimeter 20 is $(\frac{20}{4})^2 = 25$.

PAGES 310–311 PROBLEMS **1.** \$2268 **3.** 600 m **5.** 225 m^2 **7.** 39.6 m^2 **9.** 48 m^2 **11.** 448 tiles

PAGE 311 REVIEW EXERCISES **1.** 180 **3.** 88 **5.** 17 **7.** 60

PAGES 314–316 WRITTEN EXERCISES **1.** 88 **3.** 36 **5.** 120 m^2 **7.** 59.28 km^2 **9.** 14 cm **11.** 6 m **13.** 23.5 **15.** 16.5 **17.** 40 **19.** 80 cm^2 **21.** 54 **23. a.** 2 : 3 **b.** 2 : 3 **c.** 2 : 3 **d.** 2 : 3 **e.** 2 : 3 **f.** 4 : 9

PAGE 316 REVIEW EXERCISES **1.** 1 **3.** 64 **5.** 1.44 **7.** 7; −7 **9.** 0.6; −0.6

PAGES 318–319 WRITTEN EXERCISES **1.** 1386 km^2 **3.** 1.54 cm^2 **5.** 50.2 m^2 **7.** 78.5 cm^2 **9.** 707 cm^2 **11.** 10 cm **13.** 14; 14π; 49π **15.** 4; 8; 16π **17.** 5; 10; 10π **19.** 4 **21.** 18π **23.** $1050 + 50\pi$

PAGE 320 PROBLEMS **1.** 113 m^2; 141 m^2 **3.** 400 m **5.** 9540 m^2 **7.** 21.5%

PAGE 320 REVIEW EXERCISES
1. translation **3.** reflection **5.** rotation, or rotation and translation

PAGES 323–324 WRITTEN EXERCISES
1. 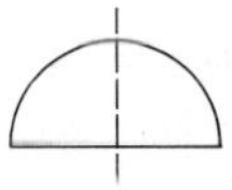 **3.** 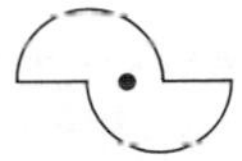 **5.** 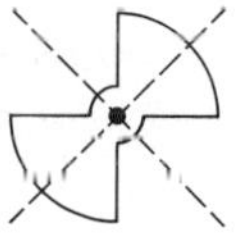

7. 452 **9.** 800 **11.** 103 **13.** 471 **15.** 12 **17.** 98.1

PAGE 325 SELF-TEST A **1.** 1344 **2.** 18 **3.** 124 **4.** 4000 m **5.** 7.5 cm **6.** 29 cm **7.** 180 **8.** 280 **9.** 19.6 cm^2 **10.** 254 m^2 **11.** 113 m^2 **12.** 106 **13.** 15 **14.** 71.5

PAGES 328–330 WRITTEN EXERCISES
1. 90 **3.** 108 **5.** 22,600 **7.** 514 **9.** 50 L **11.** 6330 L **13.** 4π; 3 **15.** 5; 4 **17.** 3; 9π **19.** 60 **21. a.** quadrupled **b.** halved **c.** doubled **23.** 3

PAGE 330 PROBLEMS **1.** 96 L **3.** 7070 cm^3 **5.** 1.62 cm

PAGE 330 REVIEW EXERCISES **1.** 32 **3.** 0.845 **5.** 1256 **7.** 10; -10

PAGES 333–334 WRITTEN EXERCISES
1. 72 **3.** 301 **5.** 56 **7.** 0.16 L **9.** 1000 L **11.** 10 **13.** 6 **15.** 3 **17.** 15 **19.** 3 **21.** 18

PAGE 334 PROBLEMS **1.** 2,590,000 m^3 **3.** 14,700 cm^3

PAGE 334 REVIEW EXERCISES **1.** 36 m **3.** 105 cm **5.** 51.2 km **7.** 580.8 km

PAGES 337–339 WRITTEN EXERCISES
1. 5700 cm^2 **3.** 14.56 m^2 **5.** 1660 cm^2; 2560 cm^2 **7.** 226; 283 **9.** 360; 468 **11. a.** 30 **b.** 72 **13.** 5 cm **15.** 6 **17.** 72 m^2; 120 m^2 **19.** $n - 2$ **20. a.** 298 **c.** 440

PAGE 339 REVIEW EXERCISES **1.** 6 **3.** 105 **5.** 35 **7.** 38

PAGES 341–343 WRITTEN EXERCISES
1. 36π; 36π **3.** 144π; 288π **5.** 400π; $\frac{4000}{3}\pi$ **7.** $\frac{16}{3}\pi$ **9.** 9.68π **11.** 51.84π; 62.208π **13.** 9; 324π **15.** 8; $\frac{2048}{3}\pi$ **17.** 324π **19.** Earth's volume is about 49.3 times that of the moon. **21. a.** 2 : 3 **b.** 2 : 3 **c.** $4r : 3h$, or 2 : 3

PAGE 343 REVIEW EXERCISES **1.** 2.1 **3.** 0.64 **5.** 3.5 **7.** 810

PAGE 343 CALCULATOR KEY-IN **1.** 126

PAGES 345–346 WRITTEN EXERCISES
1. 6300 **3.** 4300 **5.** 810 g **7.** 34 kg **9.** 460 t **11.** 180 g **13.** 33.12 g **15.** 72.7 g **17.** 7460 kg

PAGES 346–347 **1.** 13.28805 kg **3.** 81.12 g **5.** 3.91 t

PAGE 347 SELF-TEST B **1.** 41.8 **2.** 27,200 **3.** 9248; 9.248 **4.** 0.314 m^3 **5.** 1200 m^3 **6.** 10,816 cm^3 **7. a.** 98 **b.** 122 **8. a.** 94.2 **b.** 251 **9. a.** 3024 **b.** 3672 **10. a.** 1296π cm^2 **b.** 7776π cm^3 **11. a.** 144π m^2 **b.** 288π m^3 **12.** 8240 g **13.** 181.76 g

PAGE 349 ENRICHMENT **1.** New York **3.** Rio de Janeiro **5.** Moscow **7.** Casablanca **9.** 40°N, 105°W **11.** 55°N, 0° **13.** 15°N, 15°W **15.** 65°N, 165°W

PAGE 350 CHAPTER REVIEW **1.** False **3.** True **5.** False **7.** False **9.** 3864 cm^3 **11.** 45.2 **13.** 266 **15.** 2304; 18,432 **17.** 60.48 kg

PAGES 352–353 CUMULATIVE REVIEW EXERCISES **1.** 5 **3.** 10 **5.** 12.5 **7.** -22.5 **9.** $\frac{37}{12}$, or $3\frac{1}{12}$ **11.** $\frac{2}{5}$ **13.** $\frac{52}{3}$, or $17\frac{1}{3}$ **15.** $-\frac{37}{4}$, or $-9\frac{1}{4}$ **17.** All the numbers greater than 3 **19.** All the numbers less than or equal to 40 **21.** All the numbers greater than or equal to 9 **23.** 7 **25.** 21 **27.** 45°; 45° **29.** 8.1 **31.** 24% **33.** 63,200 **35.** $y = 18 - 4x$ **37.** $y = -8\frac{1}{3} + x$ **39.** $y = \frac{20}{x}$ **41.** 196π cm^2 **43.** $15{,}625\pi$ km^2 **45.** $3{,}258{,}025\pi$ cm^2 **47.** 256π; $\frac{2048}{3}\pi$ **49.** 5184π; $62{,}208\pi$

PAGE 353 CUMULATIVE REVIEW PROBLEMS **1.** 1929 stories **3.** 25 m **5.** $6075 **7.** 5%

10 Square Roots and Right Triangles

PAGE 357 WRITTEN EXERCISES **1.** 6 and 7 **3.** -4 **5.** 1 **7.** -6 **9.** 7 and 8 **11.** 5 and 6 **13.** 3 and 4 **15.** 1 and 2 **17.** 3 **19.** 4 and 5 **21.** 9 **23.** $>$ **25.** $<$ **27.** $=$ **29.** $>$ **31.** 81 **33.** 11

PAGE 357 REVIEW EXERCISES **1.** 6.57 **3.** 8.67 **5.** 11.95 **7.** 0.13

PAGE 360 WRITTEN EXERCISES **1.** 3.3

3. 5.7 **5.** 2.8 **7.** 5.1 **9.** 7.5 **11.** 9.5 **13.** 2.3 **15.** 3.0 **17.** 2.8 **19.** 1.8 **21.** 12.3 **23.** 26.5 **25.** 3.9 **27.** 8.4 **29.** 0.6 **31.** 0.2 **33.** 1.41 **35.** 2.23

PAGE 360 REVIEW EXERCISES **1.** 58 **3.** 6.72 **5.** 3.89 **7.** 93.57

PAGE 360 CALCULATOR KEY-IN
1. a. 1 **b.** 10 **c.** 100 **3. a.** 8.3666002 **b.** 83.666002 **c.** 836.66002 **5. a.** 0.7348469 **b.** 7.3484692 **c.** 73.484692

PAGES 362–363 WRITTEN EXERCISES
1. 8.06 **3.** 7.48 **5.** 9.85 **7.** 64.03 **9.** 0.87 **11.** 22.25 **13.** 26.15 **15.** 59.40 **17.** 12.57 **19.** 0.37 **21.** 0.43 **23.** 2.43 **25.** 9.03 **27.** 2.95 **29.** 7.13 **31.** 27.15 **33.** 22.36 **35.** 19.46 **37.** 58.91

PAGE 363 PROBLEMS **1.** 9.22 m **3.** $21 **5.** 3.87 cm **7.** 5.92 m

PAGE 363 REVIEW EXERCISES **1.** 0.81 **3.** 0.0036 **5.** 13.69 **7.** 590.49

PAGE 366 WRITTEN EXERCISES **1.** 289 **3.** 400 **5.** Yes **7.** Yes **9.** Yes **11.** Yes **13.** No **15.** $c = 10$ **17.** $a = 3.32$ **19.** $c = 11.24$ **21.** $b = 70$ **23.** $a = 27$, $b = 36$, $c = 45$

PAGES 366–367 PROBLEMS **1.** 108.2 km **3.** 55.7 m **5.** 7.1 cm **7.** 17.3

PAGE 367 SELF-TEST A **1.** 7 and 8 **2.** −9 **3.** 8 **4.** 7 **5.** 9.3 **6.** 4.2 **7.** 7.1 **8.** 3.1 **9.** 2.4 **10.** $c = 5$ **11.** $a = 28$ **12.** $b = 16$

PAGES 371–372 WRITTEN EXERCISES
1. RQ **3.** 9 **5.** 104° **7.** 25 **9.** 65 **11.** 5, 9 **13.** 25, 27 **15.** $46\frac{2}{7}$, 14 **17.** 180 cm **19. a.** 18 **b.** 18 **21.** $\angle CDA \cong \angle BCA$; $\angle A \cong \angle A$; so $\angle B \cong \angle DCA$ **23.** Yes; angles congruent, sides proportional **25.** No. The lengths of the sides may differ.

PAGE 372 REVIEW EXERCISES **1.** 519 **3.** 1562 **5.** 2.2454 **7.** 4.878 **9.** 3741.36

PAGES 375–376 WRITTEN EXERCISES
1. $\frac{3\sqrt{10}}{5}$ **3.** $\sqrt{3}$ **5.** $\frac{2\sqrt{x}}{x}$ **7.** $x = 3.2$, $y = 5.5$ **9.** $x = 7.4$, $y = 8.6$ **11.** $x = 3.2$, $y = 4.5$ **13.** $2\sqrt{2}$ **15.** $5\sqrt{3}$, $10\sqrt{3}$ **17.** $AB = 5.4$ **19.** $BC = 6$ **21.** $BC = 1.7y$ **23.** $x = 6$, $y = 3$

PAGES 376–377 PROBLEMS **1.** 8.7 m **3.** 20 m **5.** 56.6 cm **7.** 40; 28.3 **9. a.** $0.9r$ units **b.** $0.4r^2$ units^2 **11.** 5.2 m

PAGE 377 REVIEW EXERCISES **1.** 1.25 **3.** $0.\overline{2}$ **5.** 1.1 **7.** $0.1\overline{6}$

PAGES 380–381 WRITTEN EXERCISES
1. $\sin A = \frac{3}{5}$; $\cos A = \frac{4}{5}$; $\tan A = \frac{3}{4}$; $\sin B = \frac{4}{5}$; $\cos B = \frac{3}{5}$; $\tan B = \frac{4}{3}$ **3.** $\sin A = \frac{80}{89}$; $\cos A = \frac{39}{89}$; $\tan A = \frac{80}{39}$; $\sin B = \frac{39}{89}$; $\cos B = \frac{80}{89}$; $\tan B = \frac{39}{80}$ **5.** $\sin A = \frac{a}{c}$; $\cos A = \frac{b}{c}$; $\tan A = \frac{a}{b}$; $\sin B = \frac{b}{c}$; $\cos B = \frac{a}{c}$; $\tan B = \frac{b}{a}$ **7.** 5; $\tan A = \frac{5}{12}$ **9.** $\sqrt{21}$; $\sin A = \frac{\sqrt{21}}{11}$ **11.** 24; $\cos A = \frac{12}{13}$ **13. a.** $\frac{\sqrt{3}}{2}$; 0.866 **b.** $\frac{1}{2}$; 0.500 **c.** $\sqrt{3}$; 1.732 **15. a.** 6.4 **b.** 2.7 **c.** 0.4 **17. a.** 3.8 **b.** 8.2 **c.** 0.5

PAGE 381 REVIEW EXERCISES **1.** b **3.** a **5.** b **7.** b

PAGE 384 WRITTEN EXERCISES
1. 0.4226; 0.9063; 0.4663 **3.** 0.9994; 0.0349; 28.6363 **5.** 0.6293; 0.7771; 0.8098 **7.** 0.9613; 0.2756; 3.4874 **9.** 0.6428; 0.7660; 0.8391 **11.** 0.9063; 0.4226; 2.1445 **13.** 81° **15.** 1° **17.** 76° **19.** 30° **21.** 60° **23.** 6 **25.** 58° **27.** 25° **29.** 70° **31.** $c = 9.4$, $m\angle A = 32°$, $m\angle B = 58°$ **33.** $m\angle B = 18°$, $a = 9.5$, $b = 3.1$ **35.** $a = 8.1$, $m\angle A = 64°$, $m\angle B = 26°$ **37.** $m\angle A = 70°$, $c = 43.9$, $a = 41.2$ **39.** $m\angle B = 32°$, $a = 19.2$, $c = 22.6$

PAGES 385–386 PROBLEMS **1.** 42.0 m **3.** 11° **5. a.** 42.5 m **b.** 10.7 m **7.** 39° **9.** 67°

PAGE 386 SELF-TEST B **1.** ~ **2.** $\frac{TN}{TY}$ **3.** $7\frac{1}{2}$ **4.** = **5.** $3.1\sqrt{2}$ cm **6.** $4\sqrt{3}$, $8\sqrt{3}$ **7.** $\frac{p}{q}$ **8.** $\frac{r}{q}$ **9.** $\frac{p}{r}$ **10.** $m\angle P = 60°$, $p = 5.2$, $m\angle R = 30°$ **11.** $q = 24.1$, $p = 23.5$, $m\angle R = 12°$ **12.** $m\angle P = 67°$, $r = 3.4$, $q = 8.7$ **13.** $m\angle P = 33°$, $p = 13.1$, $r = 20.1$

PAGE 387 COMPUTER BYTE **1.** 3, 4, 5 **3.** 5, 12, 13 **5.** Output: THERE IS NO SUCH TRIPLE.

PAGE 389 ENRICHMENT **1.** 3 **3.** 2 **5.** 4 **7.** There is no square root because a is negative and n is even. **9.** -10 **11.** 5 **13.** 6 **15.** 4 **17.** 2 **19.** 3 Calculator Activity **1.** 2.1544347 **3.** 2.1867241 **5.** 1.4953488 **7.** About 9.4203395 ft

PAGE 390 CHAPTER REVIEW **1.** 2 **3.** 5.35 **5.** 4.899 and 5 **7.** False **9.** False **11.** F **13.** 45 **15.** $7\sqrt{2}$ **17.** A **19.** D **21.** F

PAGES 392–393 CUMULATIVE REVIEW EXERCISES **1.** $\frac{10}{27}$ **3.** 3300 **5.** $-3\frac{1}{3}$ **7.** Commutative **9.** Associative **11.** Distributive **13.** -100 **15.** 0 **17.** -200 **19.** 2.5 **21.** -1 **23.** $>$ **25.** $<$ **27.** $a = 38$ **29.** $m = 2.5$ **31.** $z = 7\frac{1}{3}$ **33.** 11.6 ft **35.** $n = 4$ **37.** $n = 10$ **39.** Straight line through $(0, \frac{7}{2})$ and $(7, 0)$ **41.** Straight line through $(0, 5)$ and $(1, 0)$ **43.** 55.545π **45.** $\frac{5\sqrt{2}}{2}$ **47.** $2\sqrt{n}$

PAGE 393 CUMULATIVE REVIEW PROBLEMS **1.** 40 dimes, 52 quarters, 49 nickels **3.** \$22.50 **5.** \$2.17 **7.** 52 in. $\times$ 52 in.

11 Probability

PAGE 398 WRITTEN EXERCISES **1.** 120 **3.** 5040 **5.** 720 **7.** 40,320 **9.** 360 **11.** 74,046

PAGES 398–400 PROBLEMS **1.** 6 **3.** 24 **5.** 42 **7.** 24 **9.** 12 **11.** 5040 **13.** 720 **15.** 216 **17.** 20 **19.** 6

PAGE 400 REVIEW EXERCISES **1.** 7 **3.** 3 **5.** 12 **7.** 165

PAGES 402–403 PROBLEMS **1.** 15 **3.** 15 **5.** 210 **7.** 252 **9. a.** 4 **b.** 6 **c.** 4 **d.** 1 **e.** 15 **11.** 10,192

PAGES 407–408 WRITTEN EXERCISES **1.** $\frac{1}{6}$ **3.** $\frac{2}{3}$ **5.** 0 **7.** $\frac{1}{4}$ **9.** $\frac{1}{5}$ **11.** $\frac{1}{2}$ **13.** $\frac{3}{4}$ **15.** $\frac{2}{5}$ **17.** $\frac{3}{5}$ **19.** $\frac{1}{3}$ **21.** $\frac{1}{2}$ **23.** $\frac{1}{3}$ **25.** $\frac{2}{3}$ **27.** $\frac{1}{12}$ **29.** $\frac{1}{6}$ **31.** $\frac{1}{18}$ **33.** $\frac{2}{9}$ **35.** $\frac{5}{12}$ **37. a.** $\frac{1}{9}$ **b.** $\frac{5}{9}$ **c.** $\frac{4}{9}$ **d.** $\frac{8}{9}$ **e.** $\frac{4}{9}$ **39.** $\frac{1}{2}$

PAGE 408 REVIEW EXERCISES **1.** 0 **3.** $\frac{1}{3}$ **5.** $\frac{1}{2}$ **7.** $\frac{3}{4}$

PAGES 411–412 WRITTEN EXERCISES **1.** 1 to 1 **3.** 1 to 2 **5.** 5 to 1 **7.** 2 to 3 **9.** 3 to 2 **11.** 3 to 1 **13.** 1 to 1 **15.** 2 to 3 **17.** 5 to 1 **19.** 7 to 2 **21.** 7 to 5 **23. a.** 1 to 1 **b.** 1 to 1 **25.** 5 to 13 **27.** 1 to 3 **29.** 2 to 7 **31.** $\frac{5}{8}$

PAGE 412 SELF-TEST A **1.** 24 **2.** 60 **3.** 10 **4.** 105 **5.** $\frac{1}{8}$ **6.** $\frac{1}{2}$ **7.** $\frac{1}{4}$ **8.** 1 **9.** 1 to 3 **10.** 3 to 1

PAGES 414–415 WRITTEN EXERCISES **1.** $\frac{13}{15}$ **3.** 0.3 **5. a.** $\frac{1}{3}$ **b.** $\frac{1}{2}$ **c.** $\frac{5}{6}$ **7. a.** $\frac{1}{6}$ **b.** $\frac{5}{6}$ **9. a.** $\frac{1}{2}$ **b.** $\frac{1}{3}$ **c.** $\frac{5}{6}$ **11. a.** $\frac{1}{5}$ **b.** $\frac{2}{5}$ **c.** $\frac{2}{5}$ **13. a.** $\frac{1}{4}$ **b.** $\frac{3}{10}$ **c.** $\frac{11}{20}$ **15. a.** $\frac{1}{9}$ **b.** $\frac{1}{6}$ **c.** $\frac{5}{18}$ **17.** 13 to 7 **19.** 1 to 4

PAGE 415 REVIEW EXERCISES **1.** $\frac{13}{15}$ **3.** $\frac{1}{2}$ **5.** $\frac{5}{8}$ **7.** 1.1 **9.** 0.3

PAGES 418–419 WRITTEN EXERCISES **1.** 0.7 **3.** $\frac{7}{12}$ **5.** 0.5 **7. a.** $\frac{1}{4}$ **b.** $\frac{1}{3}$ **c.** $\frac{1}{12}$ **d.** $\frac{1}{2}$ **9. a.** $\frac{1}{2}$ **b.** $\frac{1}{3}$ **c.** $\frac{1}{6}$ **d.** $\frac{2}{3}$ **11.** $\frac{11}{20}$ **13.** $\frac{7}{10}$ **15.** $\frac{5}{18}$; 13 to 5 **17.** $\frac{13}{36}$; 23 to 13

PAGE 419 PROBLEMS **1.** 90% **3.** 80% **5.** $\frac{3}{16}$

PAGE 419 REVIEW EXERCISES **1.** $\frac{5}{36}$ **3.** $\frac{1}{6}$ **5.** $\frac{6}{25}$ **7.** $\frac{12}{25}$

PAGES 422–423 WRITTEN EXERCISES **1.** A: $\frac{1}{4}$ B: $\frac{1}{4}$ C: $\frac{1}{2}$ **3.** A: $\frac{1}{16}$ B: $\frac{9}{16}$ C: $\frac{5}{8}$ D: $\frac{3}{8}$ **5.** A: $\frac{1}{9}$ B: $\frac{2}{9}$ C: $\frac{4}{9}$ **7.** A: $\frac{1}{16}$ B: $\frac{9}{16}$ C: $\frac{7}{16}$ D: $\frac{3}{8}$ **9.** A: $\frac{1}{16}$ B: $\frac{1}{16}$ **11.** A: 0.216 B: 0.064 **13.** A: $\frac{1}{2}$ **15.** A: $\frac{1}{64}$ B: $\frac{9}{64}$ C: $\frac{27}{64}$

PAGE 423 REVIEW EXERCISES **1.** 6 **3.** 10 **5.** 15 **7.** 56

PAGES 426–427 WRITTEN EXERCISES **1. a.** A: A red marble is drawn. B: A red marble is drawn. **b.** $\frac{1}{3}$ **3. a.** A: A blue marble is drawn. B: A red marble is drawn. **b.** $\frac{4}{9}$ **5.** $\frac{1}{15}$ **7.** $\frac{7}{30}$ **9.** $\frac{7}{15}$ **11.** $\frac{2}{11}$ **13.** $\frac{3}{10}$ **15.** $\frac{3}{5}$ **17.** $\frac{5}{14}$ **19.** $\frac{4}{91}$

PAGE 427 REVIEW EXERCISES **1.** 0.75 **3.** 0.875 **5.** 0.3125 **7.** 0.04 **9.** 0.054

PAGES 429–431 PROBLEMS **1.** 0.32 **3.** 0.22 **5.** 0.54 **7.** 460 **9. a.** 0.35 **b.** 14 hits **11.** no **13. a.** 5 to 7; 1 to 2; 1 to 3 **b.** about 13,333 cars **15.** 0.9965

PAGE 431 SELF-TEST B **1.** $\frac{7}{12}$ **2.** 0.2 **3.** 0.5 **4.** $\frac{4}{5}$ **5. a.** $\frac{1}{36}$ **b.** $\frac{5}{18}$ **c.** $\frac{11}{36}$ **d.** $\frac{25}{36}$ **6. a.** $\frac{5}{18}$ **b.** $\frac{1}{6}$ **7. a.** 0.04 **b.** 56 plants

PAGE 432 ENRICHMENT **1.** $P(\text{sum} = 2) = \frac{1}{36}$; $P(\text{sum} = 4) = \frac{1}{12}$;

$P(\text{sum} = 6) = \frac{5}{36}$; $P(\text{sum} = 7) = \frac{1}{6}$;
$P(\text{sum} = 8) = \frac{5}{36}$; $P(\text{sum} = 9) = \frac{1}{9}$;
$P(\text{sum} = 10) = \frac{1}{12}$; $P(\text{sum} = 11) = \frac{1}{18}$;
$P(\text{sum} = 12) = \frac{1}{36}$

PAGE 434 CHAPTER REVIEW **1.** false **3.** false **5.** false **7.** mutually exclusive **9.** $\frac{5}{6}$ **11.** $\frac{2}{9}$ **13. a.** $\frac{35}{132}$ **b.** $\frac{35}{66}$

PAGES 436–437 CUMULATIVE REVIEW EXERCISES **1.** 49.5 **3.** 7.475 **5.** $m + 3n$ **7.** $1\frac{6}{35}$ **9.** $\frac{21}{32}$ **11.** $-3\frac{2}{3}$ **13.** 20 **15.** all numbers greater than or equal to -2 **17.** 42 **19.** 13.3 **21.** 46.8 **23.** 20% **25.** 36 **27.** 4, -7; $-\frac{1}{2}$ **29.** 468 m; 13,308.75 m^2 **31.** 144 m; 756 m^2 **33.** no **35.** 2 **37.** 6 **39.** 1

PAGE 437 CUMULATIVE REVIEW PROBLEMS **1.** no **3.** 30% markup **5.** $\frac{41}{80}$ **7.** about 5.6 lb

12 Statistics

PAGES 442–444 WRITTEN EXERCISES
1. Percent of students employed
3. Babysitting; store sales **5.** Babysitting
7., 11. See graphs below.

PAGE 444 REVIEW EXERCISES **1. a.** 0.18 **b.** $\frac{9}{50}$ **3. a.** 0.09 **b.** $\frac{9}{100}$ **5. a.** 0.825 **b.** $\frac{33}{40}$ **7. a.** $0.\overline{3}$ **b.** $\frac{1}{3}$ **9. a.** 0.255 **b.** $\frac{51}{200}$

PAGES 447–448 WRITTEN EXERCISES
1. 5 P.M. **3.** 4 P.M.–5 P.M.

5.

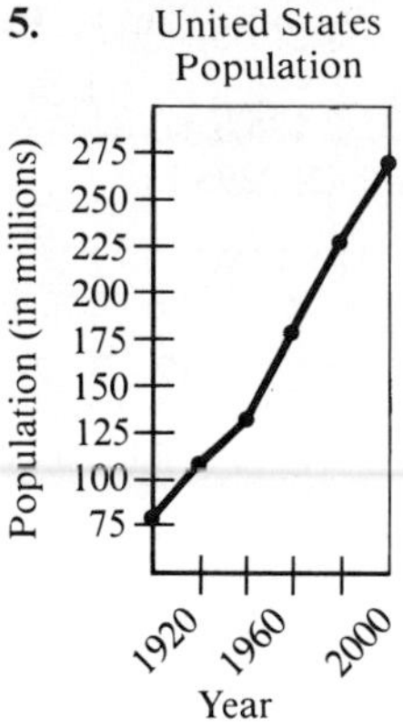

9.

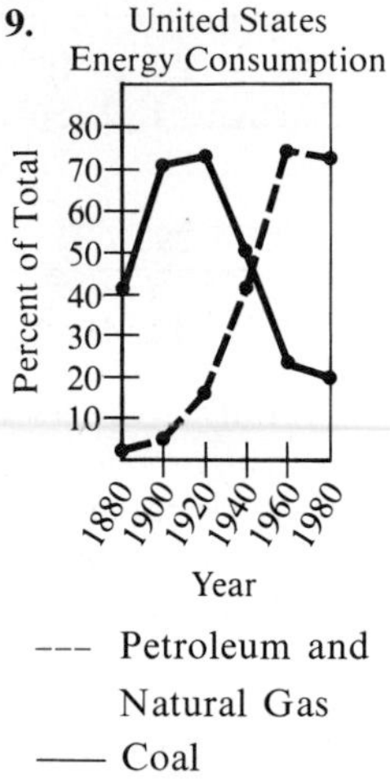

PAGE 448 REVIEW EXERCISES **1.** -18.2 **3.** 9.3 **5.** 50.96

PAGES 451–452 WRITTEN EXERCISES
1. 10, 6, 4, 3 **3.** 54, 88.2, 87, none **5.** 4.3, 10.1, 9.9, none **7.** 34, 1.4, 0, -9 **9.** 6, 99.6, 100, 101 **11.** 18 **13.** 10.5 **15.** 190 cm **17.** 15 **19.** It is decreased by 5.

PAGE 452 SELF-TEST A **1.** California **2.** \$4.5 billion **3.** See graph below. **4.** 5, 102.25, 102, 102 **5.** 16

PAGE 443
Ex. 7

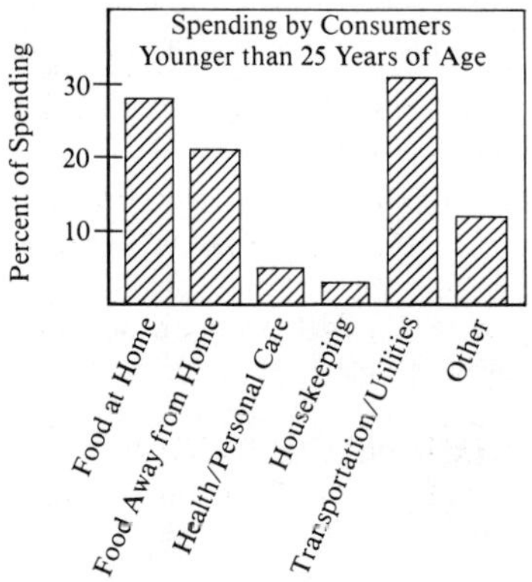

PAGE 443
Ex. 11

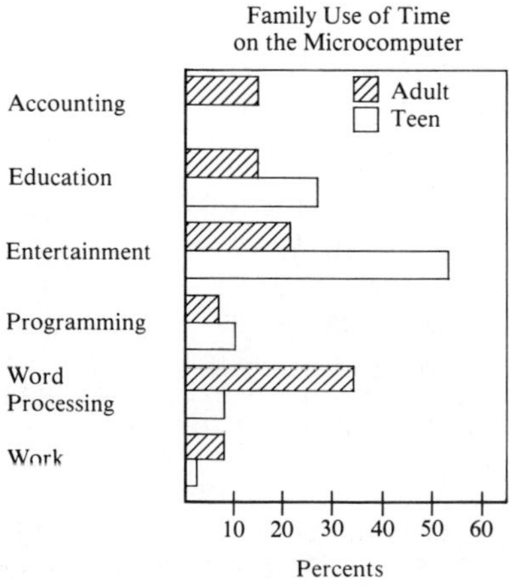

PAGE 452
Ex. 3

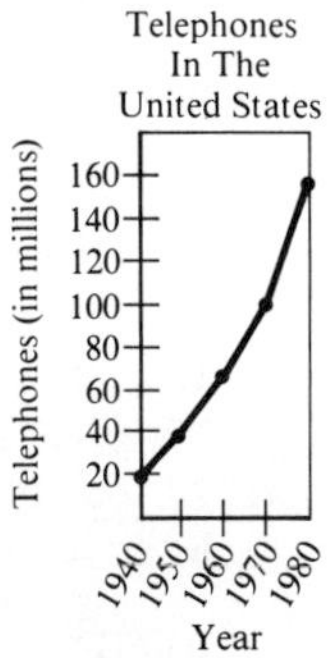

PAGES 455–456 WRITTEN EXERCISES

1.

x	f	$x \times f$
5	1	5
6	4	24
7	3	21
8	3	24
9	1	9
Total	12	83

7. a. 4 **b.** 7.8 **c.** 8 **d.** 8 **9. a.** 10 **b.** 7.12 **c.** 8 **d.** 4, 8 **11.** 6; 5; 4.5; 4 **13.** 5; 2.6; 2; 1, 2 **15.** 6, 7, 2, 3, 3, 3

17. Frequency distributions will vary depending on the intervals chosen. An example is given.

Scores	Frequency
51–60	1
61–70	4
71–80	8
81–90	6
91–100	5

19. 150 **21.** 73.75

PAGE 456 REVIEW EXERCISES

1. a. $y = \frac{1}{2}x - \frac{3}{2}$ **b.** $(0, -1\frac{1}{2})$, $(2, -\frac{1}{2})$

3. a. $y = -x - 3$ **b.** $(0, -3)$, $(2, -5)$

5. a. $y = -\frac{1}{2}x + 2$ **b.** $(0, 2)$, $(2, 1)$

7. a. $y = 2x - 4$ **b.** $(0, -4)$, $(2, 0)$

PAGES 459–460 WRITTEN EXERCISES

1. 9 **3.** 58 **5.** 8 **7.** 7 **9.** 226

11. a.

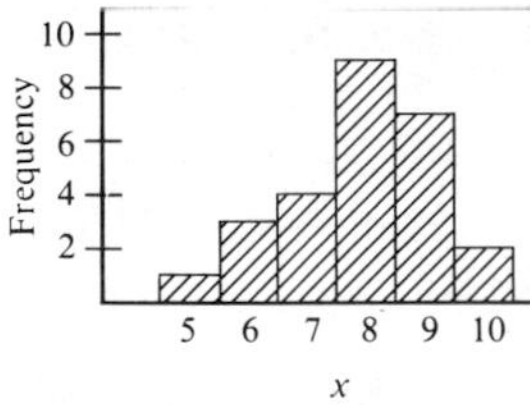

b.

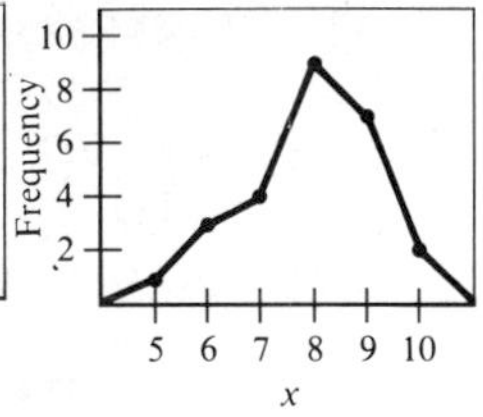

13. a.

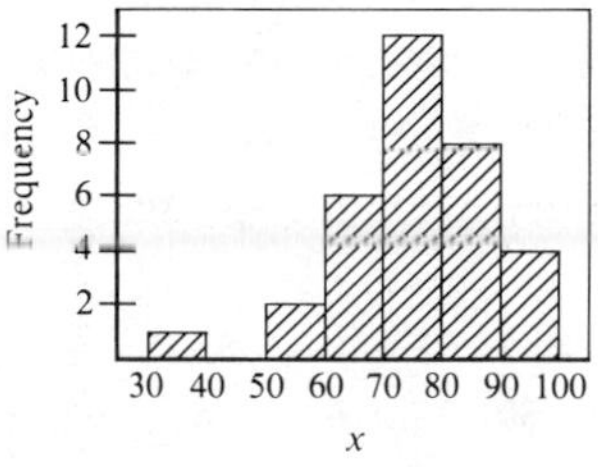

b.

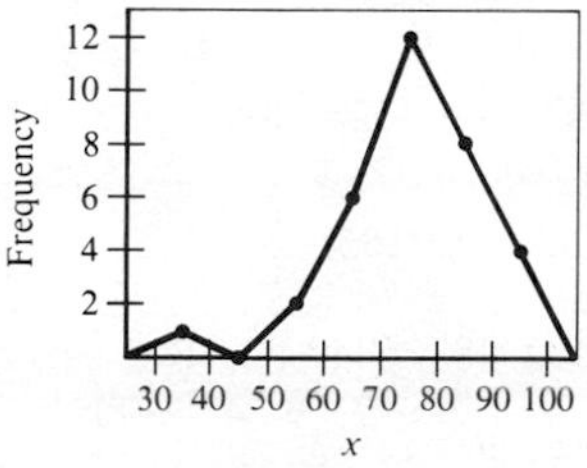

17. Graphs will vary depending on the intervals chosen. **19.** Each red triangle is congruent to a blue triangle.

PAGE 460 REVIEW EXERCISES **1.** $\frac{11}{36}$ **3.** $\frac{3}{4}$ **5.** $\frac{1}{18}$ **7.** $\frac{1}{12}$

PAGE 463 WRITTEN EXERCISES **1.** $26\frac{1}{4}$, or 26.25 **3.** 5.1 **5.** $2\frac{1}{2}$, or 2.5 **7.** 50 points

PAGE 463 SELF-TEST B

1.

x	f	$x \times f$
10	2	20
11	3	33
12	5	60
13	3	39
14	2	28
Total	15	180

range = 4
mean = 12
median = 12
mode = 12

2.

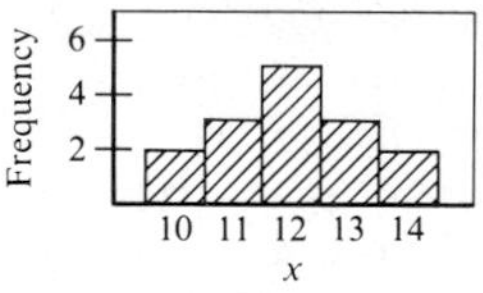

3.

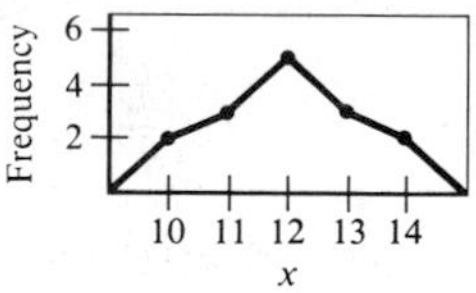

4. $8\frac{8}{9}$, or $8.\overline{8}$

PAGE 465 ENRICHMENT **1. a.** 12 gal **b.** −1, 1, −3, 3 **c.** 5 gal² **d.** 2.24 gal **3. a.** 22.8 mi/gal **b.** −2.8, −3.8, −2.8, −0.8, 10.2 **c.** 26.96 (mi/gal)² **d.** 5.19 mi/gal

PAGE 466 CHAPTER REVIEW

1. True **3.** 1924 **5.** 10 **7.** 14.5 **11.**

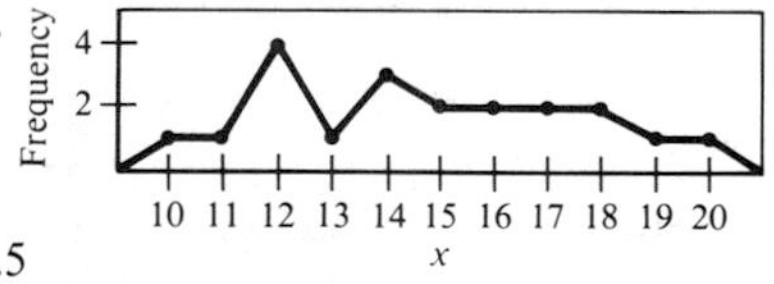

13. $5\frac{1}{2}$, or 5.5

PAGES 468–469 CUMULATIVE REVIEW EXERCISES **1.** 3.79 **3.** 1.301 **5.** 100.01 **7.** $\frac{7}{12}$ **9.** $\frac{2}{11}$ **11.** $\frac{x}{2} + 12 = -6$; -36 **13.** $x - 9 = 5 - x$; 7 **15.** 62° **17.** 35° **19.** 40% **21.** $\frac{3}{5}$% **23.** 125% **25.** Intersect at (7, 0) **27.** Parallel **29.** 0.243 L **31.** 6.86 **33.** 3.33 **35.** $\frac{1}{3}$ **37.** 0 **39.** 59, 48.4, 38, 26 **41.** 20, 99.8, 99.5, 99

PAGE 469 CUMULATIVE REVIEW PROBLEMS **1.** $129.46 **3.** 92 km **5.** 82

Skill Review

PAGE 470 ADDITION **1.** 57.8 **3.** 9.2 **5.** 92.167 **7.** 34.5051 **9.** 55.81 **11.** 153.69 **13.** 325.277 **15.** 46.119 **17.** 902.78 **19.** 61.17

21. 16.931 **23.** 91.67 **25.** 308.4564 **27.** 12.1013 **29.** 152.51 **31.** 55.708 **33.** 47.863 **35.** 119.46 **37.** 46.63 **39.** 442.166 **41.** 211.1826 **43.** 61.134 **45.** 660.353

PAGE 471 SUBTRACTION **1.** 5.201 **3.** 11.744 **5.** 55.2 **7.** 2.137 **9.** 1.892 **11.** 150.745 **13.** 435.54 **15.** 46.291 **17.** 0.074 **19.** 1.0876 **21.** 51.8 **23.** 245.8 **25.** 573.78 **27.** 5.516 **29.** 147.09 **31.** 190.79 **33.** 485.6 **35.** 162.381 **37.** 358.88 **39.** 16.7 **41.** 567.4144 **43.** 2.92 **45.** 211.489 **47.** 7.2521 **49.** 281.712

PAGE 472 MULTIPLICATION **1.** 942 **3.** 13,897.6 **5.** 44.53 **7.** 142.576 **9.** 1.3344 **11.** 0.06444 **13.** 49.248 **15.** 0.42966 **17.** 357.56334 **19.** 0.001505 **21.** 446.716 **23.** 10,580.075 **25.** 962.06 **27.** 0.00015 **29.** 26.2683 **31.** 14.884 **33.** 50.21088 **35.** 453.7533 **37.** 1871.574 **39.** 327 **41.** 4366.26 **43.** 355.4443 **45.** 41.03488 **47.** 162.873515 **49.** 8633.99913

PAGE 473 DIVISION **1.** 35.2 **3.** 7.6 **5.** 15.7 **7.** 88.7 **9.** 3.6 **11.** 250 **13.** 548.1 **15.** 49.6 **17.** 2.6 **19.** 0.6 **21.** 146.7 **23.** 1.9 **25.** 2.5 **27.** 0.1 **29.** 47.9 **31.** 35.2 **33.** 1.0 **35.** 36.98 **37.** 46.55 **39.** 125.56 **41.** 17.47 **43.** 0.03 **45.** 7.49 **47.** 0.99

Extra Practice

PAGES 474–475 CHAPTER 1 **1.** 42.63 **3.** 0.16 **5.** 1 **7.** 24 **9.** 9 **11.** $\frac{1}{6}$ **13.** 40.8 **15.** 14 **17.** 2 **19.** 47 **21.** 13 **23.** no solution **25.** 3 **27.** $<$ **29.** $6 < 18 < 35$, or $35 > 18 > 6$ **31.** $208 < 280 < 802$, or $802 > 280 > 208$

33.

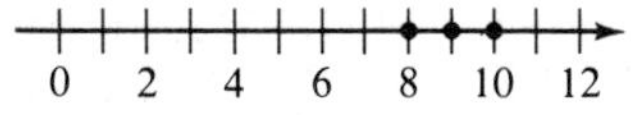

35.

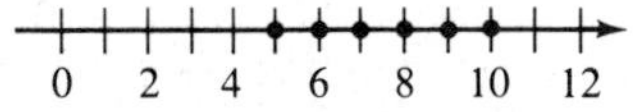

37. 0, 1, 2, 3, 4, 5, 6 **39.** 1, 2, 3, 4 **41.** 732 **43.** 52 **45.** 36 **47.** 76 **49.** All the numbers greater than or equal to 110 **51.** All the numbers greater than 18 **53.** 9 **55.** $18 - t$ **57.** $\frac{40}{m} - 16$ **59.** $3y + 11$ **61.** $k - 20 = 36$ **63.** $y + (8 \times 6) \leq 50$ **65.** $20 - 6x < 12$ **67.** \$129.75 **69.** \$806.90

PAGES 476–477 CHAPTER 2 **1.** 81 **3.** 89 **5.** 1 **7.** 36 **9.** 3^{12} **11.** k^{18} **13.** 1080 **15.** 128 **17.** 192 **19.** 0 **21.** 144 **23.** 1536 **25.** $(7 \times 100) + (3 \times 10) + 4$ **27.** $(2 \times 0.01) + (4 \times 0.001)$ **29.** $(2 \times 1000) + (1 \times 100) + (3 \times 10) + 8$ **31.** $(3 \times 0.1) + (8 \times 0.01)$ **33.** 18.21 **35.** 242.6 **37.** 0.085 **39.** $>$ **41.** $>$ **43.** $<$ **45.** 900 **47.** 1.004 **49.** 380 **51.** 3.428 **53.** 75.0 **55.** 10.8; commutative and associative properties **57.** 0; associative property and multiplication property of zero **59.** 141.2; distributive property **61.** 0 **63.** 3.4 **65.** 1 **67.** 0 **69.** 158 **71.** 20.6 **73.** 0.305 **75.** $15k^2 + 30$ **77.** 11.05 **79.** 54.9 **81.** 2.43 **83.** 18 **85.** \$3230 **87.** \$217.80

PAGES 478–479 CHAPTER 3 **1.** 3 **3.** 1 **5.** 6 **7.** 2 **9.** 9 **17.** $^{-}8$, $^{-}2$, 0, 5, 6 **19.** $^{-}7$, $^{-}4$, $^{-}1$, 3, 5 **21.** $^{-}5$, $^{-}4$, 0, 4, 5 **23.** $^{-}2$, 2 **25.** $^{-}4$, 4 **27.** $^{-}3$, $^{-}2$, $^{-}1$, 0, 1, 2, 3 **35.** $^{-}8.83$, $^{-}8.3$, $^{-}8$, 8.03, 8.3 **37.** $^{-}5.5$, $^{-}5.05$, $^{-}0.5$, 0.05, 5 **39.** $^{-}42.6$, $^{-}4.26$, $^{-}0.42$, 4.206, 42.06 **45.** $^{-}12.5$ **47.** $^{-}7.6$ **49.** 3.8 **51.** 19.78 **53.** $^{-}6.7$ **55.** $^{-}4.81$ **57.** 19.45 **59.** 12.5 **61.** -0.6 **63.** 20.3 **65.** -13.5 **67.** -20.3 **69.** 5.2 **71.** 5.7 **73.** -3.2 **75.** -2.5 **77.** -8.9 **79.** 2.5 **81.** -4.76 **83.** 50.02 **85.** 32.86 **87.** -25.434 **89.** -13.345 **91.** -15.66 **93.** 0 **95.** -31 **97.** -20 **99.** -95 **101.** 0.434 **103.** 410 **105.** 0 **107.** $\frac{1}{343}$ **109.** $\frac{1}{32}$ **111.** $\frac{1}{8}$ **113.** $\frac{1}{625}$ **115.** $\frac{1}{729}$ **117.** $\frac{1}{64}$ **119.** 1 **121.** 1 **123.** 216

PAGES 480–481 CHAPTER 4 **1.** $\frac{-3}{5}, \frac{3}{-5}$ **3.** $\frac{-8}{7}, \frac{8}{-7}$ **5.** $-\frac{9}{14}, \frac{9}{-14}$ **7.** 1 **9.** $-\frac{1}{5}$ **11.** $-\frac{2}{7}$ **13.** 8 **15.** 5 **17.** 4 **19.** $\frac{1}{3}$ **21.** $1\frac{2}{5}$ **23.** $-1\frac{1}{2}$ **25.** $\frac{3}{5}$ **27.** $-1\frac{3}{4}$ **29.** $\frac{-7}{9}$ **31.** $\frac{17}{3}$ **33.** $-\frac{43}{10}$ **35.** $-\frac{57}{8}$ **37.** $\frac{25}{4}$ **39.** $\frac{20}{24}, \frac{9}{24}$ **41.** $\frac{6}{12}$, $\frac{5}{12}$ **43.** $-\frac{33}{84}, \frac{34}{84}$ **45.** $\frac{9}{36}, \frac{21}{36}, \frac{10}{36}$ **47.** $\frac{56}{210}, \frac{48}{210}$, $\frac{21}{210}$ **49.** $-1\frac{1}{2}$ **51.** $-\frac{1}{15}$ **53.** $-\frac{7}{16}$ **55.** $-\frac{179}{224}$ **57.** $-1\frac{17}{60}$ **59.** $3\frac{35}{48}$ **61.** $-5\frac{7}{12}$ **63.** $\frac{143}{150}$ **65.** $-1\frac{31}{110}$ **67.** $\frac{3}{10}$ **69.** $-\frac{9}{35}$ **71.** $\frac{7}{20}$ **73.** $2\frac{4}{19}$ **75.** 2 **77.** $\frac{7}{30}$ **79.** $-\frac{5}{27}$ **81.** $-5\frac{1}{2}$ **83.** $1\frac{21}{23}$ **85.** 0.6 **87.** -0.3125 **89.** $-0.\overline{5}$ **91.** $-0.\overline{851}$ **93.** $3.41\overline{6}$ **95.** $4.0\overline{5}$ **97.** $-\frac{1}{25}$ **99.** $-4\frac{11}{50}$ **101.** $\frac{2}{3}$ **103.** $1\frac{7}{9}$ **105.** $-2\frac{1}{6}$

PAGES 482–483 CHAPTER 5 **1.** 7 **3.** 4 **5.** 23 **7.** $n + 7 = 7$ **9.** $47 = 8v + 7$ **11.** $3h + 24 = 39$ **13.** 15 **15.** 20 **17.** 20 **19.** -26 **21.** $3\frac{1}{3}$ **23.** 16.6 **25.** 7 **27.** -5 **29.** -54.6 **31.** 8.4 **33.** 48 **35.** -15

37. -370 **39.** $1\frac{1}{5}$ **41.** $-4\frac{1}{3}$ **43.** 36 **45.** $\frac{25}{3}$, or $8\frac{1}{3}$ **47.** -24 **49.** -14 **51.** 10 **53.-79.** All the numbers: **53.** less than or equal to -22 **55.** greater than $4\frac{5}{6}$ **57.** less than 7 **59.** greater than 7 **61.** less than -4 **63.** less than -63 **65.** greater than or equal to -55 **67.** less than 70 **69.** less than or equal to $-4\frac{2}{7}$ **71.** less than or equal to $11\frac{1}{5}$ **73.** greater than -5 **75.** greater than or equal to -24 **77.** less than -9 **79.** less than or equal to -3 **81.-87.** Answers will vary. **89.** 14 tables **91.** 5 postcards

PAGES 484–485 CHAPTER 6

3. 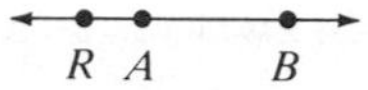

5. 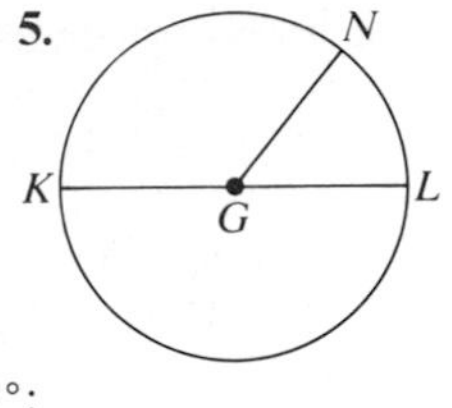

7. 91.1 m **9.** 22.1 m **13.** 66 **15.** 50° **17.** 90° **19.** 18°, 72° **21.** $\angle 3$, $\angle 6$; $\angle 4$, $\angle 5$ **23.** $\angle 1 = \angle 4 = \angle 5 = 100°$; $\angle 2 = \angle 3 = \angle 6 = \angle 7 = 80°$ **25.** 35°, 35° **27.** Acute triangle **29.** True **31.** True **33.** False **35.** 260 mm **37.** 149.2 mm **39.** 2.9 cm **41.** $\triangle ABC \cong \triangle ABD$; SSS

PAGES 486–487 CHAPTER 7 **1.** $\frac{1}{4}$ **3.** $\frac{3}{7}$ **5.** $\frac{3}{4}$ **7.** 9 **9.** 6 **11.** 1 h 51 min **13.** 52 km/h **15.** 0.025 cm **17.** 173% **19.** 5% **21.** 60% **23.** 25% **25.** $66\frac{2}{3}$% **27.** 55.6% **29.** 46.7% **31. a.** $\frac{7}{1000}$ **b.** 0.007 **33. a.** $\frac{13}{1000}$ **b.** 0.013 **35. a.** $1\frac{7}{20}$ **b.** 1.35 **37. a.** $\frac{3}{1000}$ **b.** 0.003 **39.** $\frac{1}{800}$ **41.** $\frac{5}{6}$ **43.** 30 **45.** 18.4 **47.** 40% **49.** 81 **51.** 128.6% **53.** 10 **55.** 51 boxes **57.** 40% **59.** 351 people **61.** \$40,000 **63.** \$55.65 **65.** \$762.25

PAGES 488–489 CHAPTER 8 **1.** $(-6, 2)$ **3.** $(4, 4)$ **5.** $(-2, 4)$ **7.** G **9.** I **11.** J **13. c.** Rectangle **15. c.** Triangle **17. c.** Right triangle **19.** Yes **21.** No **23.** Yes **25.** Yes **27.** Yes **29.** Yes **31. a.** $y = 3x + 4$ **b.** $(-5, -11)$, $(0, 4)$, $(5, 19)$ **33. a.** $y = \frac{3}{2}x + 3$ **b.** $(-2, 0)$, $(0, 3)$, $(2, 6)$ **35. a.** $y = x - 3$ **b.** $(6, 3)$, $(-1, -4)$, $(-3, -6)$ **37.-47.** Each graph is a straight line through the points listed: **37.** $(0, 1)$, $(-3, 0)$ **39.** $(0, 3)$, $(4, 0)$ **41.** $(0, -1)$, $(1, 0)$ **43.** $(0, -3)$, $(1, 0)$ **45.** $(0, 2)$, $(-1, 0)$ **47.** $(0, 3)$, $(-4, 0)$ **49.** Intersect at $(2, -4)$ **51.** Parallel **53.** Intersect at $(-1, -3)$ **55.** $y = 5x + 25$; Slope = 5; 60¢ **57.** Dashed line through (0, 2) and (4, 0), shaded region at left below line **59.** Solid line through (0, 7) and (1, 1), shaded region at right above line **61.** Solid line through (0, 1) and (1, -1), shaded region at right above line

PAGES 490–491 CHAPTER 9 **1.** 256 cm^2 **3.** 484 m^2 **5.** 144 m **7.** 2400 mm^2 **9.** 2106 cm^2 **11.** 15 m **13.** 15,400 cm^2 **15.** 16 mm **17.** 22 m **19.** Both; 32.6 **21.** 865 m^3 **23.** 1260 mm^3 **25.** 30 cm **27.** 3536 cm^3 **29. a.** 1350 cm^2 **b.** 1890 cm^2 **31. a.** 900 cm^2 **b.** 1350 cm^2 **33.** 1296π cm^2 **35.** 12 m **37.** 2.64 kg **39.** 8530.2 g

PAGES 492–493 CHAPTER 10 **1.** 3 **3.** -6, -5 **5.** 4, 5 **7.** 9 **9.** 7, 8 **11.** 5 **13.** 4 **15.** 9, 10 **17.** 4.8 **19.** 9.5 **21.** 7.1 **23.** 3.1 **25.** 6.0 **27.** 2.3 **29.** 2.83 **31.** 2.24 **33.** 4.90 **35.** 6.25 **37.** 5.57 **39.** 7.62 **41.** 3.97 **43.** 4.63 **45.** No **47.** No **49.** No **51.** Yes **53.** Yes **55.** 6.40 **57.** 9 **59.** 9.90 **61.** 15 **63.** $x = 20$, $y = 40$ **65.** $x = 12$, $y = 12$ **67.** $x = 20$, $y = 10$ **69.** $\frac{2\sqrt{3}}{3}$ **71.** $\frac{x\sqrt{2a}}{2a}$ **73.** $\frac{x}{y}$ **75.** $\frac{y}{z}$ **77.** $\frac{x}{z}$ **79.** 0.4540, 0.8910, 0.5095 **81.** 0.9998, 0.0175, 57.2900 **83.** 26° **85.** 53° **87.** 23°

PAGES 494–495 CHAPTER 11 **1.** 720 **3.** 3,628,800 **5.** 120 **7.** 24 **9.** 210 **11.** 30 **13.** 6 **15.** 20 **17.** 252 **19.** 1326 **21.** $\frac{1}{7}$ **23.** $\frac{3}{7}$ **25.** 0 **27.** $\frac{4}{7}$ **29. a.** $\frac{1}{7}$ **b.** $\frac{1}{11}$ **c.** $\frac{1}{3}$ **31. a.** $\frac{1}{6}$ **b.** $\frac{1}{18}$ **c.** $\frac{2}{9}$ **33.** 0.76 **35.** 0.40 **37.** Yes, $\frac{1}{12}$ **39.** $\frac{1}{22}$ **41.** $\frac{1}{11}$ **43.** $\frac{3}{65}$ **45.** 0.416

PAGES 496–497 CHAPTER 12 **3. a.** \$19 billion **b.** \$38 billion **c.** Japan **d.** \$16 billion **5. a.** 1941; 1961 **b.** 1901 **7.** 25; 39.7; 38.5; none **9.** 8.7; 13.4; 12.4; none **11.** 27 **13.** 5; 9.2; 9; 9 **15.** 292 kg **17.** 8; 10.4; 10; 12 **19.** $13\frac{3}{4}$, or 13.75 **21.** $4\frac{1}{2}$, or 4.5